The New Shopper's Guide to Organic Food

Also by Lynda Brown

Fresh Thoughts on Food
The Cook's Garden
Gardeners' World, Vegetables for Small Gardens
The Modern Cook's Manual
The Shopper's Guide to Organic Food
Organic Living

The New Shopper's Guide to Organic Food

Lynda Brown

FOURTH ESTATE · *London*

First published in Great Britain by
Fourth Estate
A Division of HarperCollins*Publishers*
77–85 Fulham Palace Road
London W6 8JB
www.4thestate.com

10 9 8 7 6 5 4 3 2 1

A catalogue record for this book is available from the British Library

ISBN 1-84115-425-3

Typeset by Rowland Phototypesetting Ltd,
Bury St Edmunds, Suffolk
Printed in Great Britain by
Clays Ltd, St Ives plc

The organic food sector is developing at a rapid pace, and though every endeavour has been made to provide accurate information, no responsibility can be taken by the author or the publishers for any changes occurring after the book has gone to press.

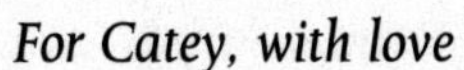

For Catey, with love

CONTENTS

FOREWORD

We live collectively on one twelfth of the Earth and raise our food on a quarter of the surface we occupy. During the last forty years, nearly a third of the world's arable land has been lost through erosion and continues to be lost at a rate of ten million hectares a year. Organic agriculture signposts the way back, and Lynda Brown has provided us with a road map for the future of organic.

Combining farming, the environment, and organic food, with the issues that count, and the how and why of organic, she has sought to explain the ins and outs of the organic system and given us a concise analysis of current thinking. It is a call for change: we need to begin with the biodiversity around us and understand that it is necessary to preserve what is being lost, so that one day we do not wake up and realise that everything that we once loved has disappeared.

Conservation of natural resources lies at the heart of organic farming. If it takes 500 years to replace one inch of topsoil, we must start to work together to save the soil that is left, and to reclaim that which is being lost to erosion, as quickly as possible. No one knows how long it will take to clean up the polluted water wells of the world. As a first step, preserving the quality of our water and reducing its use through the best conservation and agricultural practices that organic farming demands, we can start to tackle the problem.

Do we have all of the answers today? No, but by explaining the true value of organic food and agricultural practices, Lynda Brown has raised the flag. Often, we assume that we have whatever knowledge is needed to solve any problem, when in reality we don't. We search and seek information to enlighten us. Only through books like the *New Shopper's Guide* will we begin the process of improving the very fabric of life.

Howard-Yana Shapiro, Ph.D.
Vice-President Agriculture, Seeds of Change

PREFACE

Welcome to the *New Shopper's Guide to Organic Food*. In it you will find everything you need to know about organic food and farming, what to buy, and for the first time, an extensive directory of where to buy organic food and a taste of Organic Britain as it is today. I have also included some new sections – one on superfoods, for example, and a separate section dealing with organic websites.

Organics has now come of age. My first hope, therefore, is that this book will enable you to understand more about what organic food and farming really means, and why it is so important for all of us – and especially our children – that it flourishes more and more. My second hope is that it fills you with the same kind of missionary zeal and sheer gratitude as I have that we now have the choice of a better, more caring, more responsible and more visionary way forward – not just for how our food is produced, but one that extends to every aspect of our lives. For going organic is as much a lifestyle change as it is switching to organic milk or organic bread, a holistic philosophy, where nurture and respect for mankind and nature go hand in hand.

My third hope is that as many people as possible who are sceptical about organic food and farming, especially in government, academic and farming institutions, also read this book and understand that muck it may be, but magic it certainly isn't. The organic way is about finding new, creative, viable and sustainable solutions. In this sense organics is at the cutting edge of where the twenty-first century needs to be. As a consumer, the benefits of organic food and farming are blatantly obvious. The blueprint it offers brings hope for us all.

In the three years since the first edition was published, much has changed but one thing remains certain. The organic revolution continues to belong to consumers and its continued success depends on us. My favourite slogan (coined by organic apple growers in the USA) is 'changing the world one fruit at a time'. Not a bad thought, and so easy to do. Happy organic shopping!

1: What is Organic Farming?

'A true conservationist is a person who knows that the world is not given by our fathers, but borrowed from our children.'
John J. Audubon (American naturalist) 1785–1851

Organic farming is a system of agriculture that works in partnership with nature rather than against it. Unlike modern, industrialised agriculture, it does not seek to dominate or abuse natural systems, but to work in harmony with them to produce healthy, nutritious food in a manner that is beneficial to man and planet alike – for all time. As one Swiss expert has put it, organic farming is 'practising ecology'. This is why when you buy organic food you are buying much more than food grown 'naturally', 'without artificial fertilisers' and 'not sprayed with harmful synthetic pesticides'. In organic farming systems, food production is viewed not as supplying a commodity, but as a holistic enterprise where sustainability and health, each as important as the other, are interlinked.

Health and respect for natural systems are the twin cornerstones of organic farming, but there is a third all-embracing key which sets organic farming apart from the rest: soil. Soils are the lifeblood and heart of organic agriculture and, more than anything else, organic farming is based on the principle that healthy soils are the foundation for healthy crops, healthy animals and hence healthy people.

Organic farming has always recognised that the soil is a living entity, that our success must come from nurturing and protecting the hand that ultimately feeds us, and that if you take something out of the soil, you must return it. Ironically, although this notion has been dismissed as cranky for so many years, recent floods and soil erosion have at last brought home to everyone the importance of soil (to see just how important soils are and the critical role that composting plays, see p. 15. The twenty-first century has already been described as the 'make or break' century. My personal belief is that organic farming's role in protecting our soils and halting the asset-stripping of soils and of the environment generally, that has been the hallmark of modern agriculture for the last fifty years, will become increasingly crucial in the debate about how agriculture should move forward, and that the future science of agriculture lies not in what happens above the ground but in what happens beneath it.

The organic view of sustainability

First, organic farming is about agricultural sustainability. Modern organic farming is thus the science of sustainability in practice. The principles of sustainable production and consumption underpin everything that organic farming is trying to achieve, and make organic agriculture the foundation of a philosophy that seeks a sustainable future for life on earth – one that stretches far beyond the field and garden. It is, in short, a philosophy for living and well-being in the best sense of the word: namely, the ability to be well, and live well, with ourselves and with our planet.

The current state of play

The latest annual Organic Food and Farming report, published by the Soil Association in autumn 2001, reveals that the UK organic market continues to grow unabashed: in the year 2000–2001 it grew at a rate of 33%. The latest retail value is put at £802 million per year, with local and direct sales rising to over £70 million. We now have over 550,000 hectares of land under organic management, representing some 3.2% of total land farmed, compared to just under 3% in the EU as a whole. Numbers of licensed or in conversion producers have risen to over 3,500, tripling in three years, and the value of primary organic foods rose by 45% from 2000 to £97 million.

Government support

In April 2001, a new government funding programme for conversion to organic agriculture of £20 million per year for seven years was introduced. Though a significant increase from previously (£1 million per year), it is very little compared to that spent on agriculture in general. Out of the available £3 billion from the CAP for UK agriculture, only 0.7% is specially allocated for organic farming conversion schemes. Similarly, the budget for organic research and development (£2.1 million) is just over 2% of that spent on agricultural research generally (£104 million) – yet by 2007, 6% of farmland will be organic. In contrast, the government is spending double that (£5 million) on GM food research, and around £24 million for research into biotechnology in general.

Organic farmers are eligible for the same subsidies as conventional farmers, but because of the way they manage their land and livestock – for example, less livestock on a given area of land – the Soil Association estimates that organic farmers qualify for 15–30% less CAP subsidy support than non-organic farmers. As subsidies account for a very large part of all farm income, this means current agricultural policies discriminate against all farmers who farm less intensively.

The Organic Targets Bill

The Organic Targets Bill is a Private Members' bill, initiated in 1999 by Sustain (The Alliance for Better Food and Farming), and has two main objectives: to have an agreed action plan for organic farming; and that 30% of agricultural land in England and Wales should be organic by 2010. The majority of back-bench MPs have signed up to the bill and have pledged their support, as have over 100 organisations – including six supermarkets: ASDA, The Co-op, Iceland, Marks & Spencer, Sainsbury and Waitrose. The Welsh Assembly has set their target of 10% of farmland in Wales to be organic by 2005, but until recently the government refused to do likewise. In November 2001 it finally agreed that an Action Plan was needed for organic farming, which is an important first step. The benefits of the bill for consumers would be considerable, and if implemented could change the face of British food and agriculture. To find out more and how you can give your support, contact Sustain, tel: 0207 837 1228, or visit their website: **www.sustainweb.org** and click on to their organic apple icon.

The rest of Europe

Other European countries, notably Sweden, Denmark, Germany and increasingly, Italy, have taken a different, much more pro-active and supportive approach than successive British governments, and is one of the main reasons why organic farming is more advanced in these countries. Europe's three female agricultural ministers (Germany, Sweden and Denmark) have all set organic targets for the amount of land they want to see farmed organically, and have joined forces to persuade their colleagues to develop an action plan for organic farming for Europe.

The Danish way

Denmark provides an illuminating role model of what can be achieved. Organic farming has been a high priority for the Danish government since it introduced its first law to promote the development of organic agriculture in 1987. Shortly afterwards, it established its own Organic Food Council, to promote and evaluate the development and possibilities for Danish organic agriculture, and from the early days recognised the necessity for an adequate conversion package which included ongoing payments, post-conversion. In 1996, the government established the Danish Research Centre of Organic Farming (DARCOF). This 'centre without walls' involves 15 institutes, around 100 scientists and 40–50 ongoing research projects, and has an annual budget of €5 million. At the opening of the Danish Parliament in October 2000, their prime minister reiterated their commitment that 'the organic way of thinking shall be introduced in all relevant policy-areas'.

The result is that today organic food represents over 20% of food sales of staple products such as milk, carrots and oats, they have a healthy export market, and a single organic logo, owned and run by the government, recognised by most Danish consumers. Recently, they have introduced the idea of an European organic logo, run the first ever government conference on organic farming, and established a Council For Higher Food Quality, responsible for objective quality criteria for organic and conventional foods. They have also achieved a voluntary agreement to phase out pesticides in public parks, and have introduced a pesticides tax. The money collected is used to fund environmental activities.

THE BENEFITS OF ORGANIC FARMING

Every time you buy organic food you are choosing the most effective and direct way of supporting and saying 'yes' to the following benefits of organic farming:

- protects the soil and helps prevent soil erosion
- promotes health
- protects the environment
- brings with it improved animal welfare
- minimises use of pesticides and uses no artificial fertilisers

- uses no growth promoters or routine antibiotics
- uses no genetically modified organisms (GMOs)
- protects bio-diversity
- promotes sustainability
- causes less pollution
- uses less energy
- supports local communities and respects local systems and growing conditions
- ensures safer and healthier working conditions for developing countries
- brings with it more rural employment
- ensures complete farm-to-table traceability and accountability.

▲▲

What organic farming is not

Just as it is important that we all understand what organic farming is, it is also important to be clear about what organic farming is not. Organic farming is sometimes portrayed as being backward in some way, but the fact is that it is neither a return to outdated methods of farming, nor is it subsistence farming, or just 'muck and magic'. Old-fashioned methods of farming can be just as unsustainable as modern industrial farming. As one expert pointed out to me, anyone can clear land, grow crops until the land is exhausted and move on, and any agricultural system based on the non-sustainable use of natural resources can be ultimately just as harmful to the environment as the use of chemical fertilisers and pesticides. That is *not* the organic way. Indeed, some of the most spectacular successes with organic farming are achieved when traditional subsistence farmers adopt organic methods, and productivity, soil quality, economic and social well-being, and the environment in general, all improve substantially. Similarly, no farmer trying to make his living in the modern world would ever expect to farm using 'muck and magic': it would be economic suicide.

Converting to an organic system

In the UK, conversion from a conventional to an organic farming system generally takes a minimum of two to three years, and could take longer, depending on individual circumstances or on the crop, the prime objective being to 'clean' the land and build natural fertility. During this time, produce from the farm may not be sold as organic. Every year, during the conversion period, the farm will be inspected by an independent certifying body. If it has met the necessary standards, it will then be registered and, after the first harvest, its produce may be sold as organic. Thereafter it will continue to be inspected annually.

Generally, for livestock, the land needs to be converted first, though simultaneous conversion – whereby land and livestock can be converted at the same time – is allowed under certain circumstances. The initial conversion, in a sense, is just the beginning. As any established organic farmer (or gardener) will tell you, organic farms get better and better as time goes by, eventually achieving full health and the desired balanced ecosystem.

EU regulations

EU regulations allow for shorter conversion periods according to the previous status of the land; for example, this may happen if the land has already been part of an environmental scheme that prohibits the use of non-allowed fertilisers and pesticides. But these provisions are used sparingly in the UK. EU regulations also allow for the conversion period to be reduced to one year for land used by non-herbivores such as poultry and pigs. Farms do not have to convert all at once, and most are converted piecemeal. Parallel cropping, however – that is, the growing of conventional and organic crops together – is not allowed.

ORGANIC V. CONVENTIONAL FARMING: THE DIFFERENCES THAT COUNT

'The difference between conventional farming and organic farming is the difference between war and peace. Conventional farmers wage war on nature, winning from her what they can, using their armoury of chemicals to keep her at bay while they take as much as they can get. Organic farmers attempt to apply a creative process of conflict resolution whereby nature volunteers her bounty in return for a balancing contribution towards her well-being. E. M. Schumacher wrote, "We speak of the battle with Nature, but we would do well to remember that if we win that battle, we are on the losing side."'

Craig Sams, founder and president, Whole Earth Foods

Organic and conventional farming systems differ in approach in several respects, and it is these differences that explain why you cannot convert a chemical farm into an organic one merely by not using chemicals. The first objective of an organic farm is to be able to sustain itself; in other words, to buy in as little as possible. Organic farms aim to provide their own fertility, raise their own animals and grow their own feed. This makes for a fundamentally cost-effective, low-energy system. The second objective is to be sustainable in the wider context; that is, to use farming practices that encourage the balance of nature and that nurture and sustain the environment. In practice, the differences look something like this:

The environment

Protection Caring for the environment, maintaining biodiversity and providing for and protecting ecological habitats are fundamental to organic farming and are built into its standards. Everything possible is done to promote ecological balance, including maintaining hedgerows, walls and existing habitats, planting trees and allowing for greater field margins. Removing hedges and exploiting peat bogs are both prohibited.

Pollution Minimising pollution is a top priority. Organic farming systems are designed to cause as little pollution as possible to the land, the atmosphere and watercourses, and are embodied in standards (more on this later); this involves everything from manure management to the prohibition of polluting practices such as the burning of plastic waste.

Genetic engineering Genetically modified (GM) crops and animals have no place in organic farming, and the use of GM seeds, crops, feedstuffs, animals and any genetically modified organism, including all forms of GM derivatives and yeasts, is prohibited in organic farming systems. Though individual farmers may not share this view, conventional agriculture believes on the whole that GM technology will be a huge benefit to agriculture. It places no such restrictions on the use of GMOs, and much conventional livestock is currently fed GM feedstuffs. (see p. 171)

General husbandry

Soil Nothing is more important to an organic farmer or grower than the soil. It is the foundation on which the organic farming system is built. The prime objective of an organic farmer is to build healthy, 'living' soils that are enriched with organic matter to provide natural fertility, and that are high in microbial activity and other soil life and provide a mine of complex nutrients that plants can tap into and animals can thus feed off. In conventional agriculture, the soil plays a far less important role and soil improvement is not a priority. The artificial fertilisers used do not improve the soil, which gradually becomes impoverished, and the extensive use of insecticides, fungicides and fumigants severely depletes soil life. For more on soils, see p. 15.

Growth A guiding principle of organic farming systems is that neither produce nor animals should be forced beyond their natural capabilities. Since no artificial fertilisers are allowed on crops, and no growth-promoting agents, including antibiotics, are used for livestock, both grow and develop more slowly, thus maximising the potential to develop more flavour.

Extensive vs Intensive As well as aiming to be self-sustaining, organic farming systems operate extensive farming practices, and are relatively low energy-users. Conventional farming systems are mainly intensive, usually highly specialised and high energy-users, dependent on external inputs. They are thus incapable of being self-sustaining.

Rotations Rotations form the basis of ongoing soil fertility and are at the core of organic crop production and good farm management, breaking pest cycles, and helping to support a more diverse and stable agri-ecosystem. A five- or seven-year rotation cycle is common. Crops and animals are rotated to prevent soil imbalance and pest and disease build-up. 'Green manures' form an essential part of the fertility-building programme; here clover leys are fundamental – they contain a wide variety of species that help build up soil fertility and structure and provide first-class grazing for animals.

Scale Though there are exceptions, herd and field sizes are smaller, the excesses of monoculture are avoided and most farmers operate mixed farms.

Varieties Organic growers favour and promote biodiversity. Though modern varieties and breeds play an integral role, those suited to organic growing, rather than those bred only for high yields and intensive monoculture, are of particular importance. Traditional breeds best suited to local climates are a feature of organic livestock husbandry.

Fertilisers Organic farmers employ crop rotations and use composted animal manures and home-made compost, green manures and plant debris in order to build up soil fertility, to provide a humus-rich base for soil life to flourish, and to supply plants with a balanced diet comprising all the essential nutrients that they require for health. Supplementary feeds such as calcified seaweed (a general plant tonic), bio-dynamic soil preparations and natural minerals may also be applied if necessary. Non-organic sources of manure are restricted and sources documented; manures from intensive or factory farming and sewage sludge are prohibited. By contrast, conventional farming systems primarily use artificial fertilisers to provide plants with the main elements needed for growth; their crop rotation is more limited, or non-existent; and with such systems compost is rarely made or used, generally there are no restrictions on manures and so on.

Pest and disease management Organic farmers try to use as few sprays as possible, and almost all harmful synthetic pesticides, including OPs, (organophosphates), are banned. The minimal use of pesticides, along with conservation practices and a biodiverse approach means that natural predators can flourish; indeed, pests and diseases are generally far less of a problem on organic farms than on conventional ones. Total control is impossible, even with pesticides, and the objective on organic farms is to keep pests and their natural enemy populations in balance. Growing healthy crops is the best defence. Observing crops, timing sowings to avoid major pest attacks, choosing resistant varieties, using protective agri-fleece as a physical barrier, appropriate rotations and good crop hygiene, are the standard preventative measures. In addition, organic growers encourage natural predators in both the micro and macro environment through the use of hedges, ponds and other natural features, and through scientific measures such as biological control whereby predator species are introduced to control pest populations. Low doses of permitted sprays such as soft soap are used as a last resort. By contrast, in conventional agriculture a wide range of pesticides are used extensively and routinely. For the handful of pesticides that are currently allowed in UK organic agriculture, see p. 40.

Records and traceability Organic food guarantees full farm-to-table traceability. As well as complying with all conventional health and safety and the former Ministry of Agriculture, Fisheries and Food (MAFF) regulations, in order to qualify for certification as an organic farm of holding, detailed records of every aspect of the farm – its practices, goods bought in and sold out, crops, feedstuff, bedding and manures used and livestock kept – must be held for inspection purposes, and may be examined at any time by the certifying body concerned. As well as being inspected annually, every farm may also receive unannounced visits to check that standards are being upheld and enforced. No such comprehensive regulatory procedures are in place in conventional farming systems, nor are such systems subject to the same legal enforcement procedures.

Crops

Green manures An essential part of organic production. Up to 25% of organic land is taken out of cash production every year to grow nitrogen-fixing legumes such as clover, which are turned back into the soil to break down and enhance its fertility.

Weed management Organic growers use no herbicides, but employ a combination of physical means to control weeds. Hand weeding, hoeing, machine weeding, machine mowing, mulching and flame-gunning are most common. In tropical countries canopy crops are grown to provide shade and suppress weeds. But weeds are not necessarily treated as an enemy: in some vineyards and orchards, for example, they provide habitats for natural predators and protective cover for the soil, as well as providing food and shelter for wildlife generally.

Post-harvest treatment Organic produce receives no post-harvest chemical treatment, such as insecticides, fungicides, ripening-inhibitors or sprout suppressants, all of which are routinely used in conventional food crop production.

Livestock

Animal welfare It is the aim of organic farming to provide conditions for livestock that prevent disease and promote optimum health. Stocking densities are lower on organic farms, as is the total number of animals on holdings. The factors that reduce the risk of disease and stress, and make for happy, healthy animals, are numerous: appropriate housing, with enough space to fulfil all of their behavioural needs (stretching, turning, running about, flapping wings), clean bedding, a healthy diet and, above all, good stockmanship, which includes more time spent monitoring the animals' welfare and well-being. Intensive farming practices, including those to do with housing and feeding, are banned. In addition the purchase of animals for slaughter, through livestock markets, is forbidden. The Soil Association also forbids the export of livestock for slaughter.

Breeding and rearing Livestock form an integral part of most organic farms. Though it is permitted to buy in up to 10% of stock per year, the aim is to maintain closed flocks and herds by breeding and rearing all replacements, to provide as much home-grown feed as possible, and to use farm manure as part of the ongoing fertility-building of the soil.

Calving and weaning A fundamental aspect of organic livestock management is that newborn stock are suckled naturally for as long as possible to enable them to develop natural immunity and to give them the healthiest start in life. The weaning process is twice as long as in conventional systems, and may be considerably longer. Organic calves are not allowed to be sold for veal export, and may not be sold at less than one month old.

Diet Organic livestock are fed a natural diet suitable to their species, and which mainly comprises organic feedstuffs, most of which are usually grown on the farm. The feeding of animal proteins to herbivores for organic stock was banned in 1984.

Medication The prime concern of organic farming systems is to raise animals that are naturally healthy and robust. This is achieved by raising them in non-intensive ways, giving them high-quality feedstuffs and ensuring that they lead stress-free lives. Illness is rarely a problem, and vet bills are minimal. Homoeopathic treatment is preferred.

Routine use of antibiotics Routine antibiotics are banned, though antibiotics must be, and are, used when necessary to prevent suffering or where there is no other effective treatment. Antibiotics are used extensively and routinely in conventional agriculture. For more on this, see p. 172.

BIODYNAMIC FARMING

Biodynamic farming is a specialised form of organic farming and gardening that operates world wide in over thirty countries. Based on a series of lectures about agriculture given by the Austrian philosopher Rudolf Steiner, it was established in 1924. Often described as 'organic-plus', biodynamic farming is a uniquely holistic system that has a spiritual dimension and recognises that the influence of planetary rhythms on the growth of plants and animals is profoundly important for their health and vitality.

Interest in, and appreciation of, biodynamic farming principles are increasing; the methods of promoting soil and crop vitality, for example, are consistent with the emerging view of the importance of the soil foodweb (p. 15) and the critical role it plays in the overall effort to produce healthy crops. Many fine wine-makers are now converting to biodynamic methods; biodynamic tea plantations such as those that provide the Hampstead Tea & Coffee Company and Robert Wilson's teas (p. 237) show how the biodynamic way can benefit a whole community. Biodynamic farming is, in essence, the ultimate expression of sustainable farming; and though large-scale biodynamic farms do exist – in Australia, for example – it expresses the 'small is beautiful (and healthy)' principle writ large. Any biodynamic farm is very special – and the food it produces is probably of the highest quality on earth. Appropriately enough, the Bio-Dynamic Agricultural Association's (BDAA) Demeter logo, which you will find on certified biodynamic products, represents the Greek goddess of agriculture and protector of all the fruits of the earth.

Biodynamic foods are becoming more popular, and even fashionable. Cook's Delight organic store in Berkhamsted (p. 462), a long-time enthusiast for biodynamic foods, now sells around 25% biodynamic products, including some fresh produce. And the organic superstore Planet Organic in London has just opened the first dedicated biodynamic section.

Finally, the BDAA is both an organisation that anyone who is interested in biodynamic farming and gardening can join, and the official certification body in the UK for Demeter products. To find out more, contact them at the Painswick Inn Project, Gloucester Street, Stroud, Glos, GL5 1QG, tel/fax 01453 759501, email: bdaa@biodynamic.freeserve.co.uk, or visit their excellent website (one of the best) at **www.anth.org.uk/biodynamic**, which includes a list of biodynamic farms selling to the public.

Camphill Communities

The now international Camphill movement was founded sixty years ago by Dr Karl König; it consists of community villages that farm biodynamically, where people with special needs live and work alongside co-workers, and where every member of the community is valued equally. Camphill's are among the best-known biodynamic farms. Altogether there are 90 communities spread over 20 countries, with 47 in the UK and Ireland; to find out about those in the UK and Ireland, consult the BDAA website given above, which includes maps and information about all of them.

Some, such as the Loch Arthur Creamery in Beeswing, Dumfries and Galloway, and Botton Village Food Centre in North Yorkshire, which have both won food awards for their excellent products, sell direct from the farm, or locally. Let my colleague, food writer Joanna Blythman, explain:

> ***'Camphill communities produce some really impressive foods and other goods and are an inspiration for us all. The herb workshop at Grangemockler Community, County Tipperary, makes tinctures, creams and herbal remedies from its organic herbs. Botton Village in North Yorkshire makes wonderful jams and juices, and breeds organic seeds from its seed workshop. Breads and pizzas are the speciality of Grange Village in Gloucestershire. Camphill Holywood in County Down is an organic bakery, coffee shop and trading centre for biodynamic produce. Newton Dee Village, Aberdeen, has a food store and café selling produce from its two farms and market gardens. Camphill Milton Keynes Community has a bakery, small café and a 'tools for self-reliance' workshop. Larchfield Community in Cleveland supplies bread and meat to local shops and restaurants. Camphill Communities, East Anglia, sells vegetables, grains, breads and honey to their local community.***

Ruskin Mill in Nailsworth, Gloucestershire, and Sturts Farm, Wimborne Minster in Dorset are two others. If it's inspiration you are seeking, make a point of visiting them when you can.

For more information on biodynamic farming, see Appendix.

PRINCIPLES OF ORGANIC FARMING AND WHERE ORGANIC STANDARDS FIT IN

Organic farming is as varied as nature itself, and no two organic farms are ever the same. Organic practices vary from farm to farm and from country to country, depending on local climatic and geographical conditions. In conventional agriculture, dependency on regular inputs of chemicals largely dictates how the farm is managed, and enables this kind of farming to become customised and highly specialised. To a certain extent chemicals also provide a cushion against climatic conditions. In organic farming, the opposite is true. Organic farms are constantly changing and evolving. Each farmer 'listens' to his or her farm and strives to work in harmony with it, finding new solutions to problems and adapting each year to the seasons, the soil and the overall dynamics of the farm. Nature is constantly throwing up new challenges, so organic farmers also need to be creative and innovative, and thus they build up considerable expertise and agriculture in the broadest sense.

As already mentioned, organic farming is a holistic system incorporating crop rotations and maintaining biodiversity, as well as ensuring optimum crop health by building up soil fertility, its natural driver. Whereas in conventional farming, chemicals provide many of the answers, in organic farming it is the farm itself and the combined effort of all its practices that collectively overcome problems and enable the farm to work as an integrated ecosystem.

Organic standards are a very recent development. They provide the legal framework that enables farmers who farm organically to sell their products as 'organic'; and have been developed in response to the growing numbers of consumers who want to buy food produced by farmers using organic methods. Organic standards protect both consumers and genuine farmers from bogus claims. The Soil Association, who were the first to introduce an inspection and certification scheme in 1973, published its first standards (which you can see on their website: **www.soilassociation.org**) in 1967. With standards, of course, came mounting bureaucracy and constant changes and additions, the most recent of which are the new European organic livestock standards, introduced in August 2000. For more on standards, see p. 30.

THE HEART OF THE MATTER: THE SOIL

'If we destroy the soil – and it is not indestructible – Mankind will vanish from the earth as surely as the dinosaurs.'

Lady Eve Balfour, *The Living Soil*, 1943

'Soil erosion is one of the world's greatest disasters. It takes five hundred years to form one inch of topsoil, yet world wide we are losing 71 billion tons of soil each year (13 tons of soil per person/year). The statistics are frightening. Mismanagement of soils due to poor agricultural practice costs the US alone $27 billion each year. If we want to grow food to feed the world, we need to radically rethink agriculture's abuse of natural resources and to start to care for our soils again. This is especially true when there are more than 3 billion malnourished people in the world today.'

David Pimentel, Professor of Ecology and Agricultural Sciences, Cornell University, New York

Our soils are the most precious environmental asset that we have, and although we are hardly aware of it, the amount of life in our soils – known as the soil foodweb – far exceeds the life that we see above them. Indeed, it is impossible to underestimate either their importance or, as Professor Pimentel graphically describes, the folly of the systematic abuse of soils that has taken place over the last fifty years in the name of agricultural progress.

Organic farmers have long understood that a healthy soil is fundamental to sustainable agriculture. If organic agriculture has a mantra it is this: healthy soil equals healthy plants and animals, equals healthy people. Almost all of the world's food is produced in soils. As Sir Albert Howard prophesied in his book, *The Soil and Health*, written in 1947, the fertility of the soil is the future of civilisation. If you take a peek at this remarkable stuff it is easy to see why and how organic farming, which is based on maintaining soils, is so important to the future of the world; and why conventional agriculture cannot do this.

The soil foodweb

The soil foodweb is a complex ecosystem of animals, plants, insects, nematodes, protozoa and microbes. In one gram of healthy soil there can be over 10,000 species and a billion or more living organisms, most of which are microbes. Micro-organisms were present in soils a billion or so years before plants came along and it is their presence that enabled plants to develop in the first place. The millions of soil bacteria and especially fungi – or threads, whose hyphae create living bridges between the plants' roots and minerals and other nutrients – that we can't see, are important in breaking down nutrients into forms that the roots can absorb, and in protecting plants against diseases – which, in turn, leads to improved crop vigour and pest and disease resistance.

Bacteria and fungi amount to the workhouse of the soil; the richer and more complex the soil, the more millions of beneficial microbes present – and the more life they can support. Conversely, the poorer the soil, the fewer the microbes. A desert soil, for example, has only around 1 million bacteria per gram; a healthy soil, around 600 million.

Artificial fertilisers and pesticides impact adversely on the soil foodweb, leading to reduced nutrient cycling and diminished crop vigour. In fact, they do much more damage than this: they kill beneficial organisms but allow pathogens to thrive, locking the farmer into a chemical dependency that forces the whole soil ecosystem into a spiral of decline. This happens because when nitrate levels are high and the soil is lacking in oxygen – which is common in soils with poor structure and little organic matter – pathogens thrive. Feed a soil with artificial nitrates instead of organic matter, and you select for pathogens, which then require pesticides in order to kill them, which in turn kill beneficial bacteria – and so the cycle is perpetuated. Because of the 'boom and bust' life-cycle of pathogens, they increase much more rapidly than the beneficial organisms, which have slower life-cycles and fewer offspring and longer reproductive times – another reason why pesticides begin to be ineffective as time goes on. Eventually the complexity of soil life is lost. Ultimately, it deteriorates until it becomes 'dirt' and the only organisms that thrive in dirt are pathogens.

Making a meal of it

In order to make protein, plants require nitrogen, usually in the form of nitrates or ammonia (giving a plant artificial nitrogen is a bit like giving it a blood transfusion). But unless 'banked' in some way, nitrates, which are highly soluble, will leach with the water flow into deeper soil and thus into places where plants can't reach them. Excess leaching, as we know, then goes on to cause pollution elsewhere.

This is where another critical role of bacteria and fungi comes in. They are both extremely rich in protein, which is organic nitrogen; in fact, bacteria are the most concentrated form of nitrogen on earth. When they multiply – which they do constantly if they have enough food – they gather up inorganic nitrogen from the soil and convert it into protein in their bodies, forming a 'bank account' of nitrogen that will not leach away or be lost as a gas, since bacteria attach themselves to soil and organic matter with their own 'superglue'. Thus the more bacteria and fungi there are in soils, the bigger the bank balance and the more nutrients are retained.

The cycle doesn't stop there. Once nutrients have been retained, other kinds of soil organisms, such as beneficial nematodes, protozoa and soil mites, feed on the bacteria and fungi. Soil invertebrates such as mites, spiders and beetles wake up in the spring, feed on a winter's worth of decomposing bacteria and fungi, releasing the immobilised nitrogen held in the bank account back into the soil as ammonium. This is quickly converted into nitrate in crop and vegetable soils, along with phosphorus and other nutrients. The result is a regular drip feed where it matters – at the root systems – supplying crops with a steady diet of nitrates and other essential nutrients all season long, as and when they need them.

Cultural practices such as the application of composts containing high numbers of bacteria and fungi and the foods to feed these organisms kick-start the process outlined above. The net result – and a most important economic benefit – is that once a soil foodweb is working in this way, farmers need to apply fewer fertilisers but often achieve the same yields as if they had used inorganic ones.

Root cause

Though it is what we see that we call a plant, this is only half of the story: its roots are where most of the action takes place, and the relationship between the roots of a plant and soil bacteria and fungi is critical to plant health. This is another reason why good soil structure is so important: the better the soil, the more easily roots can develop. Plant roots do not make enzymes that can break down organic matter into a form from which to derive nutrients (hence the view that plants perform just as well being fed using readily absorbable artificial nutrients). What happens is that roots exude food molecules to feed beneficial bacteria and fungi, and these in turn serve both to provide the roots with essential nutrients and to form a protective bio-shield around the roots, which wards off pathogens and protects the plant from disease. In this way, roots effectively 'farm' bacteria and fungi, to their mutual advantage. It's rather like having nature's underground defence corps on twenty-four-hour standby. It's been estimated that to do the job properly – to prevent and suppress disease effectively – a healthy soil needs around 15–20,000 different species. An organic farmer's role is to ensure that there is a sufficient quantity and variety of species throughout the growing season to do their work for him. One of the reasons why conventional agriculture has never yet managed to curb disease is that the crucial role that soil micro-organisms play has been discarded.

What else do soil micro-organisms do?

Rather like worker ants or bees, soil micro-organisms are responsible for just about everything that keeps a soil ticking over, from the species of bacteria and fungi that bring about the decomposition of crop residues, manure and other organic material – which will only occur in soils if they are present – to the micro-organisms that live in the root zones of plants that produce various hormones and other chemical 'signals' that stimulate plant growth and development.

Soil structure and tilth depend on what are known as 'soil crumbs', or the way soil particles collect together to form an aggregate mass. These will not form unless the many sand, silt and clay particles are 'glued' together by the gums and gels that only certain species of soil bacteria can produce; and these crumbs are further strengthened against disintegration by beneficial fungi that grow throughout the aggregate and physically bind it. Soil organisms also act as nature's pollutant-removers. Most herbicide and other pesticide molecules can be 'eaten' or degraded by certain kinds of soil microbes, if those species are present. But to guarantee their presence you need a soil rich in biological activity; so, ironically, organically managed soils are better able to rid themselves of chemical pollutants than are poor soils.

Compost: the cure-all

Not too many people reading this book, I guess, unless they are serious gardeners, have ever given a second thought to the art and science of compost, let alone know exactly what it does. Compost, decomposed organic matter, is a rich brown, crumbly sweet-smelling substance, rich in humus (the soil equivalent of bone marrow) and trace elements, and teeming with a huge diversity of beneficial micro-organisms in much greater quantities than are typically present in agricultural soil. All organic farms make and use it; and all organic materials, including farmyard manures, have usually composted before they can be spread on the land. This is because the act of composting breaks down organic matter and recycles nutrients, eventually turning them into forms that plants can absorb; equally importantly, the process of thermal composting generates high temperatures that kill pathogens.

Though compost-making has been carried out for thousands of years, the modern science of composting is only just beginning to be developed. What is becoming clear is that compost provides the key to generating healthy soils and healthy crops, and that it could play a formidable role in the future development of sustainable agricultural practices. The reason is simple. Well-made composts inoculate the soil with every possible type of beneficial micro-organism, enhancing and improving the soil foodweb while providing a feast of nutrients for it to thrive on. Composts thus revitalise and re-energise soils. If intensive agriculture systems adopted the wholesale use of composts instead of pinning their hopes on GM crops, our soils would be saved and the health of our crops could be transformed. It's as simple as that.

ORGANIC V. CONVENTIONAL SOILS: THE DIFFERENCES THAT COUNT

Poor soil structure, a feature of soils farmed intensively or signalling the absence of organic matter or of rotation, leads to devitalised crops, increased soil erosion and panning, which in turn lead to the contamination of surface waters with agrochemicals that have been washed off with the soil during heavy rains. This happened most recently in Gloucestershire, where, because of the crisis in beef farming, farmers have ploughed up their pastures to grow potatoes. As a result, as one National Trust executive put it, the River Wye now runs red all the time; soil erosion has become a major problem, and river life, because of the run-off of artificial nutrients and chemicals that the mud brings with it, a major casualty.

In soils rich in organic matter, such as those farmed organically, this does not happen to anything like the same extent. Water retention is better, the soils are less prone to erosion and therefore less likely to contribute to water pollution. Also, in organic systems more land is managed as grassland or covered with fertility-building crops, so there are far fewer exposed soils.

A very visible example of what organic soils can achieve and of the differences that count can be found at the Rodale Institute in America. This has one of the longest cropping-systems trials in the world, the Farming Systems Trial™, which systematically compares organic and conventional agriculture. Their research shows that organic soils have a better physical structure, hold water better, use nitrogen more efficiently and leach up to 50% less, and are biologically more active, having more and better-balanced organic matter. Further, improvements in the quality of organic soils lead to better yields, especially in drought years. To find out more, visit their website: **www.rodaleinstitute.org**.

The soil foodweb, and its importance, does not relate only to crops: the organisms that make up the foodweb in turn supply food for many insects and animals above the ground. This is another reason why maintaining a healthy, diverse and rich soil foodweb is so important for total ecological balance.

Soils worldwide . . . and global warming

Over the last forty years around 30% of the world's total crop land has been lost through soil erosion by wind and water. We've all seen pictures of America's dust bowls: soils that once contained a healthy supply of organic matter, now reduced to lifeless dirt. Mechanised modern farming especially strip-mines the soil. Ecology Action in the USA has calculated that for every pound of food produced this way, up to six pounds of soil in the USA and eighteen pounds in China are lost for ever through the soil being eroded by wind and water. If we continue in this way, there will come a day when no matter what high-tech fix is applied, what is left of the earth's soils will fail to sustain the earth's population.

Eroded soils, then, cause ecological havoc – and with far-reaching consequences. Local pollutants, for example, end up in rivers and oceans far away. Agricultural practices also affect the global cycling of carbon and nitrogen. The important point here, which affects all our lives, is that both of these elements are facilitators of global warming. The difference between conventional and organic farming systems in this respect is that conventional systems cause greater losses of both to the atmosphere, whereas organic soils not only retain more of both, but release less carbon dioxide. Carbon sinks and the carbon and nitrogen cycles are the stuff of soil biology rather than of the food we eat, yet this elementary difference between the effects of the organic and conventional systems is profound. Organic farming systems offer a new means, if only partial, of reducing global warming; conventional farming systems do not.

BIODIVERSITY – AND WHY IT MATTERS SO MUCH

'There is no question that organic farming is good for biodiversity, good for the natural countryside, and good for the whole web of life.'

Minister for the Environment, Michael Meacher, 25 May 2000

As I wrote in *Organic Living*, biodiversity – literally 'living' diversity, from the Greek word *bio*, or life – is our natural inheritance that belongs to no one in particular and everyone in general. It is the earth's natural bank of sustainability and the means by which our earth adapts, evolves and regenerates itself. This rich reservoir operates at the local level and until recently provided all of mankind's basic necessities – food, water, shelter and clothing – as well as enriching his soul and imagination with the sheer wonder of it all. It is vital to preserve it, for without it we are, quite literally, dead.

Whereas modern large-scale agriculture relies on uniformity and standardisation, the central aim of organic farming is to co-exist with natural systems and create healthy and diverse ecosystems, to protect biodiversity in all its forms, whether this be by growing varieties suited to local conditions, raising traditional breeds of livestock, or nurturing as varied an agricultural landscape as possible and a wide variety of habitats for wildlife to thrive in. As farmland covers 76% of the UK, the most important factor in the conservation of the country's national biodiversity is the type of agriculture that predominates, especially given the widespread decline of common farmland species and the general abandonment of mixed farming. The decline in bird populations – skylarks have declined by 75%, song-thrushes by 66% and grey partridges by 80% – is particularly worrying, and even the former MAFF has established targets for reversing the decline by 2020.

Everyone now recognises that wildlife should not be confined like rare species in the protective cocoon furnished by sites of scientific interest (SSIs) but should be seen as crucial to all farmers; indeed, the 'whole farm system' approach pioneered by organic farmers, that has now been taken up by schemes such as LEAF (Linking Environment and Farming) is essential to delivering wildlife benefits. Furthermore, the biodiversity benefits of organic farming have been more or less proven, and have been recognised by just about every environmental organisation, including the RSPB, English Nature, the Wildlife Trust and the National Trust. For example, English Nature, who have begun converting some of their national nature reserves to organic grazing, conducted its own studies and concluded that not only was there a greater number and diversity of wildlife on organic farms, but that those species that have suffered the most decline on farmland over the last 50 years thrive better under organic farming systems. They also believe that their results probably underestimate the wildlife benefits and that if, instead of being surrounded by conventional farms, organic farms reached critical mass, covering a wide area, the benefits of an organic landscape would accelerate.

The Soil Association conducted its own review of nine studies comparing the biodiversity of organic lowland farming with similar conventional farms, and found that on the organic farms there were, overall, 40% more birds, double the number of butterflies and a staggering 500% more arable plants than on the conventional farms studied. The specific findings were:

Plants Five times as many wild plants in arable fields, 57% more species, and several rare and declining wild arable species found only on the organic farms, including some Biodiversity Action Plan species.

Birds 25% more birds at the field edge, 44% more in the field in autumn/winter; 2.2 times as many breeding skylarks and higher skylark breeding rates.

Invertebrates 1.6 times as many of the arthropods that comprise birdfood, 3 times as many non-pest butterflies in the crop areas, up to 5 times as many spiders and up to twice as many spider species.

Crop pests Significant decrease in aphid numbers; no change in numbers of pest butterflies.

Distribution of biodiversity benefits Though the field boundaries had the highest levels of wildlife, the highest increases were found in the cropped areas of the fields.

Quality of habitats Both the field-boundary and crop-area habitats were more favourable on the organic farms. The field boundaries had more trees and larger hedges, and suffered no spray drift; the crops were sparser, with no herbicides, allowing more weeds; there was also more grassland and a greater variety of crop types.

Overall, through its altogether more eco-friendly practices, organic farming was found to be reversing the trends in conventional farming that have caused the decline in biodiversity. In addition, organic farming practices offer all-important biodiversity benefits for the soil and for aquatic ecosystems.

As a recent news article in the *New Scientist* explained, biodiversity is not just good for the soul, it could help save the planet from global warming too. Ecosystems that contain more species are better at soaking up the greenhouse gas carbon dioxide – and a species-poor planet is likely to be a hotter one.

Biodiversity in action

On organic farms, measures to protect and improve biodiversity and conservation go hand in hand, both forming an integral part of organic standards. The main measures adopted are:

- operating mixed farms with the widest diversity of crops (and animals) wherever possible
- creating new habitat by planting native trees and hedges, building beetle banks and ponds, creating wild-flower banks, and protecting sites of scientific interest
- providing maximum shelter using wide field margins, and creating wildlife corridors to allow weeds and wild-flowers to flourish and provide refuge for predatory insect populations
- adapting agricultural practices so as to minimise the adverse effects on wildlife such as timed sowings, not cutting hedges every year, and leaving arable stubble to provide food and shelter for birds and other wildlife.

HOW YOU CAN HELP

The protection of biodiversity is an issue for everyone – in our own backyards, on a national scale, and worldwide. At the global level, the wholesale destruction of biodiversity and the dramatic loss of traditional varieties of crops like rice are becoming critical. The threat posted by GM crops and the impact they would have on the world's natural genetic pool are yet to be calculated. Organic farmers, gardeners and environmental and conservation organisations are leading the fight back. Join them. Meanwhile, to protect biodiversity, other simple actions you can take are:

1 Support organic farming
2 Buy organic food
3 If you get the chance, choose traditional and local varieties of fruits and vegetables to eat and of plants to grow
4 Say No to genetically engineered food and crops
5 Support local initiatives and conservation groups.

ORGANIC RESEARCH AND DEVELOPMENT

The key to the future development of modern organic farming lies as much in research and development as it does in consumer demand: as one organic researcher has pointed out – give organic farming the investment and the time that conventional farming has had, and the consumer will see a very different food-supply system.

Conventional farming has seen over 150 years of research and development, but organic R&D is still in its infancy and has been significantly hampered by a lack of funding (see p. 2). In addition, most agricultural R&D is financed by large agrochemical companies, who are unwilling to fund a farming system that strives to work without agrochemicals – even though sustainable and environmentally friendly solutions will benefit all farmers. Most organic R&D funding, therefore, has come from private sources in the UK. One company that deserves special credit is Organic Farm Foods in Lampeter.It is only recently, as a result of environmental concerns, that organic farming has seen any public investment in organic R&D, and it is still minimal compared with that allotted to conventional agriculture.

The other difficulty that organic R&D has had to contend with is that modern organic farming is about developing the 'whole farm system' approach, and through research, development and education reducing even further the need for inputs. Organic scientists adopt a holistic approach to solving problems. Unfortunately, most modern scientific research does not work that way, preferring the narrower, reductionist approach to solving problems. But despite the lack of adequate funding, progress is being made. Research organisations conducting research into sustainable, organic food production systems include the Elm Farm Research Centre (EFRC), the Henry Doubleday Research Centre (HDRC), the Welsh Institute for Rural Studies (WIRS), the Organic Centre for Wales at Aberystwyth University, the Scottish Agricultural Colleges (SAC), and Aberdeen and Newcastle Universities. Tesco and their suppliers have invested substantial sums at the two universities just mentioned. Sainsbury's and Waitrose have given financial support to various projects, as well as supporting the organic industry generally. ASDA, Iceland, Marks & Spencer have also funded the development of organic farming, while the Co-op, one of the country's largest landowners, is the only UK supermarket to have its own organic farmland.

Projects being undertaken by these organisations include the search for alternatives to copper-based sprays and for seed dressings to replace fungicide and pesticide dressings; cereal variety trials that look at the benefits for pest, disease and weed control that might be achieved by growing a mixture of species and varieties; variety trials and integrated pest and disease management for organic apple production; integrated control of slug damage; new ways to control weeds, pests and diseases in organically grown field vegetables; breeding programmes for livestock, and the investigation into the shelf life of organic vegetables.

Though the financial help that the various UK supermarket chains have given is welcome, and shows confidence in the market, ultimately funding should come from the public purse. The role of the consumer, who will ultimately reap the benefits, is simple. Buying organic food, and thus stimulating demand, is the surest way to ensure that funding for our new agriculture will increase.

The future for our soils

Some soil scientists are discovering that the future of sustainable crop management lies in the science of enhancing the good guys in the soil (the beneficial microbes) and getting rid of the bad guys (the pathogens) and of partnering the right soil foodweb to the right crop. Management of these 'micro-herds' could be our salvation. The prize will be a system of agriculture that needs no pesticides or fertilisers, in which soil foodwebs, aided by scientifically made organic composts, can be tailor-made to produce optimum crops. In short, in future farmers will be able to engineer (in the natural sense) designer-made soil foodwebs for particular crops.

This is not new: biodynamic farmers have been using specific compost preparations for the last fifty years – see Appendix 1 – and know better than anyone the value of soil foodwebs and what they can achieve: wine-makers are one group of growers who will readily attest to this. The scientific application and the inherent possibilities, however, have only just begun to be explored. Dr Elaine Ingham, Associate Professor of Soil Ecology at Oregon University, is the world's foremost expert on the soil foodweb. Much of the information on soils is taken from a speech she gave at the Cirencester Organic Conference in 2001, and her own website: **www.soilfoodweb.com** is a mine of both scientific and general information on soils and composts.

Dr Ingham has been studying and researching soil foodwebs for 20 years, on over 150 different crops, with some startling results. For example, every single time she and her team established a soil life appropriate for the plant they were trying to grow, the result was yields at least equal to those of conventional high-intensity chemical fields, and usually higher. In addition, when the plant material was tested it was quite often higher in protein (for which, incidentally, read more flavour); in some cases such as grape juice, protein levels rose by 300 per cent. In their scientific trials on strawberries, the soil life which had been destroyed by methyl bromide, was transformed and revitalised simply by adding composts, and yields increased substantially – to levels greater than those in conventional systems. There is much talk these days about making the desert bloom through GM crops, or of feeding the world hydroponically. Dr Ingham has a better solution. The conclusion that she and her team have come to is that if you grow crops in 100 per cent compost, you can grow just about anything, anywhere.

Organic landscapes

Up to now emphasis has been placed on individual farms converting to organic husbandry, which means that, rather like sites of scientific interest, organic farms are isolated oddities often surrounded by a sea of conventional farms. A new view, promoted by Professor Tim O'Riordan and his colleagues Andrew Lovett and Paul Dolman at the University of East Anglia, is emerging, that looks at a future scenario of 'joined-up' organic farms producing an organic landscape along with the many exponential benefits for the country as a whole that this would bring. Everyone agrees, for example, that if it is to flourish, biodiversity cannot just remain in protected isolated spots, but needs the rich reservoirs of an interlinked ecology between one part of a farm and another and between one farm and the next, where landscape management becomes a collective rather than an individual responsibility. This is not happening at the present – but it *could* happen if the notion of long-term organic stewardship were developed, for both organic and non-organic farms, in which environmental management and protection using organic methods would be the linchpin, instead of the piecemeal subsidy for this or that approach that is currently the case. Such a scheme could change our landscape for the better for ever, as well as bringing such benefits as long-term flood management, resulting in less flooding, considerably fewer pesticides in our watercourses, and more wildlife.

Organics worldwide

The organic sector worldwide is booming, just as it is in the UK. Keeping up with the latest statistics is a gargantuan task. Every week, it seems, they need to be revised – and always upward. How long the global love affair with all things organic will continue at this rapid pace is impossible to predict: what we do know is that conversion to organic farming and the worldwide production of organic food, both for home consumption and for export, are spiralling. For consumers this brings with it many more feel-good stories of sustainable-farming initiatives, big and small, an ever-increasing range of organic foods and products, more organic logos to grapple with – and just more to know and to be aware of.

Over a hundred countries are producing organic foods, from Japan to Zambia, from the Falkland Islands to the tiny Cook Islands in the South Pacific, on course to be the first totally organic nation. Even China is undergoing its conversion (export sales have just tipped $140 million and they have set up ten organic food research centres across the country), while Madagascar produces a range of organic foods such as coffee, cocoa, pineapples, honey, vegetables, vanilla, herbs, coconuts and palm oil.

In all, there are currently over 675,000 organic producers worldwide, and over 8 million hectares of land are farmed organically. By the year 2005, global sales are expected to reach $150 billion plus growth in organic foods is expected to exceed 20% in the next decade or so, and organic foods to account for 1–2% of total food sales. In Europe they already account for 3% of all food sales and Europe now has almost 3.5 million hectares of land managed organically and over 120,000 organic enterprises. As in the UK, the stampede for organic foods is fuelled in substantial part by the continuing food disasters. Europe has had its own taste of BSE, with much the same reaction as here: falling confidence in how food is produced and a growing consumer realisation that there has to be another way.

The French call it *bio-attitude*. Sales of organic food in France have risen by 25% each year since 1994, and organic stores and chains – including Planet Bio, Canal Bio, Naturalia – have opened all around the country. As in the UK, its capital is the organic hotspot. Meanwhile, organic farmers in the Languedoc and Brittany are forming links with local schools to supply them with organic food. The Italians, in top position with about one million hectares farmed organically (double the figure of three years ago), started their first organic schools meals scheme in 1987; today there are over a hundred initiatives across the country, involving parents, growers and local government. The agriculture minister, Alfonso Pecioraro, has announced that because of worries about GMOs and BSE schools should serve only organic food (he is also planning to impose a reduction in pesticides used on conventional crops). A law obliging schools to serve organic food has already been accepted in certain regions, and is now going before the national parliament. Many Italian supermarkets now reserve sections for organically farmed produce.

Germany is the largest organic market in Europe, and second only to the USA worldwide. Interestingly, most of its organic food is sold through health food stores rather than supermarkets. Berlin has opened its first organic ice-cream parlour: 1 Berliner Bio-Eisdiele, at 10 Liegnitzer Street. Germany also hosts one of the world's largest organic trade fairs, Bio Fach in Nuremberg. Europe's three female agriculture ministers – those of Germany, Sweden and Denmark – have joined forces to support organic agriculture as positively as they can. Sweden and Denmark have been at the forefront of sustainable farming methods, and Holland is a major organic player also, supplying in particular organic vegetables, dairy and pork products. In Eastern Europe, where many farmers have never used pesticides anyway, organic farming is expanding rapidly and playing a significant role in the revitalisation of the rural economies. Hungary, for example, has recently doubled its exports of organic food to over £8 million, and much of the organic soft fruit used for flavouring yoghurts, jam and other processed fruit products sold in Europe comes from Poland. Japan, Latin America, and most recently New Zealand, are experiencing rapid growth in this area. In Japan demand outstrips supply to the same extent as in the UK. Cuba adopted organic agriculture as part of its official policy in 1990, and by the middle of the decade was well on the way to becoming self-sufficient in basic fruit and vegetables, while over 80 per cent of crop pest control is biologically based.

Organic agriculture began in Egypt in 1978 when a biodynamic farm was established in the desert. There are now more than 180 organic farms there, and Egypt is a major exporter of medicinal herbs, vegetables and cotton and provides the UK's earliest new potatoes. In Africa, Tanzania exports organic honey, Burkina Faso produces 50,000 tons of organic mangoes, Zambia produces organic herbs and spices, and South Africa recently held its first organic trade show.

The country that grows the most GM crops, the USA, also grows more organic food than any other: it has some 1.4 million acres of certified organic farmland, and a market worth $6.6 billion, that is expected to rise to over $13 billion by 2003. In spring 2001, the United States Department of Agriculture (USDA) national organic standards took effect, decreeing that the standards of independent certifying bodies are not to be higher than the national ones. The same may be the case in Ireland (although its national standards are still being finalised). How this shakes down is an issue to watch carefully. In South America, Mexico is a major supplier of high-quality organic coffee, fruit, avocados and vegetables, Brazil is a major source of non-GM and organic soya. (In 1999 the state of Rio Grande do Sol made history by banning all field trials of GM soya and prohibiting any GMO releases.) Many organic orchards are being planted in Argentina, which also produces organic beef and crops such as sunflower seeds. The Chilean and Argentine governments have started subsidising land for organic farming.

Across the Pacific, New Zealand is stepping up its organic production (it has two organic farmers in parliament), and we have already seen more organic New Zealand apples, for example, as well as its delicious organic honeys. Its domestic organic sales increased by nearly 80% last year, and exports are expected to grow to over $100 million in the next five years, though government aid and initiatives, as yet, are minimal. Organic Australia has yet to happen big time but watch this space. Stop-press news: Sri Lanka has banned the import of all GM products, and Thailand has banned GM crop trials.

ORGANIC STANDARDS: WHAT YOU NEED TO KNOW

Organic standards fulfil two functions. First, they provide farmers with a working manual of how to farm organically, and processors and manufacturers with rules about processing it and protecting the integrity of organic food so as to avoid contamination with conventional produce. Secondly, they provide the legal stamp of authenticity and are, in effect, the consumer's organic guarantee. Enforcing and maintaining them is a costly but necessary business, and vital for consumer confidence and for the integrity of the organic movement.

The first thing to understand about standards is that they define methods of production, not the final product. As Francis Blake, standards director of the Soil Association and one of the world's leading experts on organic standards, points out, given the complexity of farming systems and the wide variation in the agro-ecological and social conditions that influence them, what is surprising is not that so many variations exist, but that a broad global agreement on what organic food and its processing comprise has been achieved in such a relatively short time.

Pore over any set of standards today and the first thing you will discover is how incredibly detailed, complex and stringent they are. They cover every aspect of registration and certification, of organic food production, of permitted and non-permitted ingredients, of the environment and conservation implications, of processing, packaging and distribution. There are rules governing all the agricultural practices that organic farmers employ, from the kinds of seeds that may be planted and the kinds and quantities of manures permitted and when they may be applied, to every conceivable aspect of animal welfare and all the minutiae of food processing. Standards also list practices that are prohibited, recommended or restricted, and give details of derogations (see p. 33).

In the early days, there were no written standards because none were needed – organic farming was never conceived as a marketing opportunity, and acceptance as an organic farmer was based simply on membership of a new organisation such as the Soil Association. This meant that any certification – like 'farm-assured schemes' today (see p. 84) – was a voluntary undertaking and carried little legal status. As the word spread and more and more people wanted to buy organic food, standards were introduced to safeguard genuine organic farmers and consumers from fraudulent claims.

As mentioned earlier, the first set of basic standards was drawn up by the Soil Association in 1967; Oregon state in America introduced them in 1974, and the newly formed International Federation of Organic Agricultural Movements (IFOAM) (see p. 36), in 1980. As organic products and organic trade developed, so government authorities became more interested, leading in the EU to the adoption in January 1991 of the first EU organic regulation 2092/91, known as 'the Regulation', which gave organic food the legal status it enjoys today.

Thus standards had to be drawn up from scratch, and as modern organic farming develops they are still in the process of being refined and adapted, both nationally and internationally. And as demand for organic food has risen, so standards have become the public face and cutting edge of organic farming. Those responsible for setting them have the impossible task of constantly trying to balance the founding principles of organic agriculture with modern organic food production, now that organic food is mainstream and so needs to be produced in large quantities. Although the collective benefits are immense – just think how many fewer pesticides are being used as a result of mass demand for organic food – we have to bear in mind that all food production is a compromise and that organic food is no exception. Standards are not perfect, and not everyone (myself included) agrees with every decision that standards committees take, but misgivings tend to be minor. The basic organic principles and practices remain, and as long as these are safeguarded then consumer guarantees concerning organic food are secure.

Why standards vary

Organic standards vary from one certification body to another – both in the UK and worldwide – from one set of official government standards to another, and even from farmer to farmer. There are three main reasons for this:

1. Although standards are the bible that organic farmers work from, they actually represent the minimum codes of practice necessary to qualify for organic status for that certification body. In reality, many organic farmers and food producers operate more stringent standards than are required – which is why buying local organic food is always best, simply because you can question the producer directly and decide for yourself.
2. Although all certification authorities must adhere to official standards where they exist, each may interpret them slightly differently and set its own higher standards in specific instances. The most obvious case here is the difference between the UK organic chicken standards set by the Soil Association and the UK Register of Organic Food Standards (the overall governing body which sets the standard to which the various organic bodies adhere) and other UK certification bodies outlined on pp. 79–80. Generally, however, there is far less variation between certification bodies than the impression often given. Indeed, certification bodies generally are beginning to work more closely with each other, and we can hope for more rather than less harmonisation in future.
3. Standards need to reflect the differences from country to country, because climate and geographical conditions vary so much.

Problems have arisen because the development of standards has been patchwork, and because government-set standards do not necessarily reflect a desire for improvement. Indeed, on occasion – when, for example, the US state legislators tried to impose the use of GM ingredients on their national organic standards – the authorities seem to actively want to lower existing standards. Why this should be so is anyone's guess. The best response to this is the kind of initiative being undertaken by the Soil Association and IFOAM to campaign both for the highest standards and for standards equivalence (see p. 35).

Derogation

This is the term applied when, because there is insufficient organic material to meet farmers' or manufacturers' needs, they are allowed to use the non-organic equivalent for the time being – be it straw for bedding, or a particular ingredient. This temporary measure ceases as soon as sufficient organic material can be sourced. Written request is required, and proof of the need given. Each request is considered on its own merits. The same system operates for permitted pesticides or practices classified as 'restricted'.

Fakes

No system is infallible, and though most people who produce organic food are dedicated to the practice and philosophy of organic farming, there are those who see organic food production merely as a way of making money by cheating consumers with conventional food sold as organic. This happens in a tiny minority of cases, and the way to prevent it from happening to you is very simple: *Ask to see the certification, or for confirmation of the audit trail* (the farm-to-table record). Anyone selling organic food must be able to provide proof, either direct or indirect, of its authenticity if required; and everyone selling genuine organic food can do this. If in any doubt, consult your local trading standards officer, who has responsibility to enact the Organic Products Regulations, drawn up in 1992 and amended in 1994.

Are standards under threat?

The answer to this is yes and no. Inevitably, the exponential growth in the demand and supply of organic food means that controlling and maintaining standards has become a Herculean task, and a huge learning curve for everyone involved. The pressure to drive prices down is another major threat, not least because it will result in more average-quality organic food. However, everyone – including supermarkets – is acutely aware that the integrity of organic food and the 'clear blue water' between it and the rest must be maintained if consumers are to continue to hold faith with, and be prepared to pay more for, organic food. That organic standards are constantly scrutinised and debated publicly – which does not happen in the conventional sector – is a thoroughly good thing, and brings results.

Standards are being tightened, harmonisation of standards is happening, and will continue to happen. Constant public debate will ensure that organic food quality and, just as important, the means of production of all our food remains at the top of the agenda. As long as this continues, and consumers continue to have their say and choose to buy organic foods that meet high standards, those standards will be upheld.

Working to the ideal

In an ideal world, all inputs into the organic system would be of organic origin. The only reason why they are not is because of a lack at the moment of some raw ingredients, or because certain aspects of the production cycle are insufficiently developed. To take a simple example, organic poultry producers have to buy in one-day-old chicks from conventional sources because no one is yet hatching organic chicks. Deadlines, however, have been set in key areas, and these give an idea of the progress that is being made:

- All chicks for poultry production are expected to be raised in organic hatchers by 2003.
- All fish must be raised in organic hatcheries by December 2002.
- 50% of organic feed for pigs and poultry must be grown on the holding or on other local holdings by 2010.
- All seeds used by organic farmers and growers must be organic by 2004, with derogations for particular species and varieties likely.

THE SOIL ASSOCIATION: A SPECIAL CASE

Unlike other certifying bodies, the Soil Association is both the country's leading campaigning organic charity organisation for sustainable farming, forestry and organic food and, through its subsidiary company, Soil Association Certification Ltd, the leading certification body, certifying around 70–80% of organic food on sale in the UK. As such it occupies a unique position. The organisation was founded in 1946 by a group of farmers, scientists and nutritionists who were concerned about the way food was being produced, and who believed that there was a direct connection between the health of the soil, plants and animals, and people. Producing healthy food from healthy soils was of paramount importance, they believed, and the principles of the organisation's founding fathers have guided their standards ever since. This has had a twofold outcome. First, there is no doubt that the Soil Association strives to set the highest standards at all times; it campaigns for high standards generally, and uses its influence wherever it can to see that organic standards retain their integrity. This means in effect that the Soil

Association is a major influence in driving standards forward. Second, because it is a membership organisation, members have their say in standards consultations, and any proposed changes are discussed openly. This is valuable because it means that consumers help to shape organic standards.

Soil Association Certification Ltd must, like all certification bodies, adhere to UKROFS (the overall UK authority) standards, and though their standards do differ in points of details, as has been mentioned already, if you sat down and compared them, you would find that apart from a few notable exceptions, there is not much difference. Whether, through its commitment to the highest standards, the Soil Association becomes the gold standard for organic food, or whether, as everyone hopes – including the Soil Association – the harmonisation of standards will mean that UKROFS moves closer to the Soil Association, remains to be seen. At the moment the main differences between the two are:

- Organic poultry standards (discussed fully in Appendix).
- Withdrawal times for medication: the SA requires three times the legal limit compared to twice that under the UKROFS ruling.
- Homogenisation: the SA requires that this and other processes be made clear on labels.
- Free-range pork: the SA requires that all pig production systems be based on free range.
- The environment: the SA sets additional standards for environmental conservation.
- Conventional manures: the SA requires all such manures to be adequately composted before being spread.
- GMOs: the SA has developed additional standards to safeguard against contamination from GM crops grown close to organic crops.
- The SA forbids the export of all livestock for slaughter.

Standards equivalence, and the role of the SA and IFOAM

'Standards equivalence' is becoming the new buzz term. It means ensuring that product produced in one country and certified organic by a certification body there has been grown or processed to standards equivalent to those of the body that certifies it in the importing country. This is all part of the new drive to ensure that standards are rigorously maintained, and to harmonise them worldwide. The two leading players are the Soil Association in the UK and the International Federation of Organic Agricultural Movements, IFOAM. This is an internationally renowned independent organic organisation with 700 member organisations worldwide in over 100 countries. It has its own accrediting body that approves and accredits those certification bodies who meet its own high standards, of which the Soil Association is one. The result is a simplification of the certification process for farmers wanting to export crops, plus reassurance for the consumer that imported crops certified by IFOAM-accredited organisations have been produced to the same high standards worldwide.

In a ground-breaking initiative in 2001, Sainsbury's announced that they would only buy imported organic products that met IFOAM's standards. Waitrose have joined them. The UK certification body, Organic Farmers and Growers, are also seeking IFOAM accreditation. Collectively this means a huge step forward in consumer confidence about imported organic goods. To reassure consumers further, the Soil Association has recently completed a massive equivalence review aimed at ensuring that all the certification bodies they deal with correspond exactly to their standards.

Demeter standards

The Bio-Dynamic Agricultural Association (BDAA, see p. 12) has its own additional standards, which are unique to biodynamic farming. It is mandatory to use their special preparations and to work with their lunar calendar; all holdings must be mixed, its own farm animals must be the primary source for a farm's manures; and home-made composts must form 25% of total manures used. Municipal composts are prohibited and irrigation water should be of suitable quality. Full Demeter status is granted only after the third harvest. For details of the labelling of Demeter products, see p. 77.

How standards work in practice

To be registered with a certification authority – which all producers, manufacturers and processors are required to do – each is required to pay an annual fee and to keep detailed records, ensuring a full audit trail from farm to table, any infringement of which results in the suspension and withdrawal of products from the market. The result is a unique system of checks and guarantees for the consumer, whereby every item of organic food can be traced back to the farm it was produced on. In addition, the organic food system complies with the same stringent regulations as does the conventional food sector.

Each certification agency is an organisation or company in its own right, with members or clients who pay a fee every year for its services, including their annual inspection. They may represent a particular sector of the organic market – for example, the Organic Food Federation (OFF) primarily certify processors and manufacturers, or have a specific philosophy – for example, Demeter, the BDAA's certification agency. As already noted, everyone's standards must, as a minimum requirement, conform to those laid down by the overall governing body UKROFS, which in turn conform to the EU organic regulations – these last are influenced at a global level by the International Committee on Food Labelling, Codex Alimentarius, and IFOAM. This inter-relation provides the structure for eventual harmonisation of organic standards. For more on this and EU regulations, and how you can view UKROFS standards for yourself, see Appendix.

What *is* organic

The following food and non-food crops have organic status:

- fresh foods, including meat and fish
- manufactured and processed foods
- fresh and dried herbs
- drinks and beverages
- cotton, Harris Tweed, linen, hemp
- wood
- seeds and plants
- fertilisers.

Coming next . . .

- healthcare and beauty products
- leather and hides
- wool
- wood products
- cut flowers.

For organic catering standards, see p. 108.

What *isn't* organic

No product of a producer growing to organic standards, but who has not been independently verified and certified, can be sold as organic.

Doing your bit

It's important for everyone that organic standards are upheld all the time. Use the checklist on p. 78 to check products when you shop, and you will be helping the organic movement to police standards.

2: Pesticides, Pollution and GMOs

The use of pesticides in organic farming has been the subject of recent media hype, much of it uninformed or grossly distorted. As anyone who has ever studied organic standards will have discovered, organic farming has never claimed to be entirely pesticide-free. Sometimes these are unavoidable – all farmers need some sort of help when adverse weather causes problems or pest populations build up to unacceptable numbers. The difference between organic and conventional farming lies in the approach to their use, the type and range of pesticides used, the frequency of usage, and the amount – in organic farming, a drop in the ocean compared with conventional farming. (For more on the use and abuse of synthetic pesticides and on pesticide residues in food, see Appendix 1.)

Many of the pesticides used in conventional farming are highly toxic, biodegrade slowly and can cause lasting harm. Collectively they have caused ecological damage on a grand scale, and many thousands of people worldwide have died from pesticide poisoning. The handful of sprays that organic farmers are allowed to use, on the other hand, are based almost exclusively on natural compounds which generally biodegrade quickly, leave no residues and have no known lasting harmful side-effects (the use of copper sprays is contentious, but they are being phased out). Systemic insecticides, organophosphates and organochlorines are prohibited. In exceptional circumstances selected synthetic compounds may be used, but the farmer has to establish the necessity and apply for a derogation of the usual rules (see p. 33). No such controls are in place for conventional farming.

In order for organic farming to work properly and successfully, farmers need to work hand in hand with nature at all times. All sprays have at least temporary undesirable side-effects and can upset the delicate ecobalance that the organic farmer spends his life creating and on which he depends for his livelihood. For this reason, the regulations state that their use is restricted to situations in which there is a direct threat to the crop, because organic farming recognises that no pesticide can ever be considered 'safe'. This is why all are under constant review, minimum doses are always used, maximum application rates are stipulated, and pesticides currently permitted are superseded when new methods of control are found. New insect sprays based on garlic, for example, are currently being developed.

Conventional farming takes a different approach. Pesticides are considered an essential part of successful modern farming and are used at every stage of the farming cycle from seed dressings to post-harvest spraying of storage crops. To give you an idea, over 300 active ingredients and some 3,500 pesticide products are approved for use in the UK. Conventional farming also believes that however harmful, as long as they are used responsibly and residues do not exceed the legal limits, pesticides are safe. This status quo is upheld until a particular pesticide may subsequently be withdrawn and becomes officially 'unsafe' – the most recent example of this being the organo chlorine lindane, which has only just been banned in the UK.

WHAT SPRAYS AND OTHER PEST CONTROLS *DO* UK ORGANIC FARMERS USE?

It is important to remember that organic farmers mainly use good farm husbandry based on a combination of natural methods, as described on pp. 7–10. Secondly, for use in the UK, as in conventional agriculture, all products used must be approved and confirmed as 'safe' under the PSD (Pesticide Safety Directorate). This is why certain pesticides, be they natural or otherwise, such as neem oil, quassia, pyrethins, and plant oils allowed in EU organic regulations, are not permitted for use in the UK. For a full list of pesticides allowed in EU organic agriculture, contact UKROFS. The Soil Association also produce their own fact sheet.

Seed treatment: all chemical seed dressings are forbidden. The only procedure allowed is hot water treatment to combat seed-borne diseases.

Weed control: all herbicides are forbidden (see p. 10).

Pest control:

- *Insecticides*: The main pesticides permitted are derris, derived from the roots of derris and other plants (rotonone) and soft soap (a fatty-acid potassium salt). Metaldehyde, used to control slugs and snails, and harmful to birds and hedgehogs, is permitted under UKROFS but not under SA standards. It can only be used in traps containing a repellent to higher animal species. It is currently under review and is likely to be banned in the near future.

- *Biological control agents*: Natural predators that include bacteria, viruses and fungi, are one of the most valuable pest control methods for organic agriculture. Only non-GM micro-organisms are permitted and some agents may only be used in traps. Two well-known examples are *Bacillus thuringiensis*, used to control caterpillar pests on fruit and vegetables, and the parasitic wasp, *Encarsia formosa*, used to control whitefly in glasshouses. Note that the use of *Bacillus thuringiensis* is currently under threat due to its use in GM crops, as resistance to it is already building up.
- *Pheromone traps*: These are hormonal attractants. In the UK they are permitted as a pest monitoring device only, and are mainly used in fruit orchards to monitor codling moths.

Fungicides: The two main compounds used are sulphur used to control blight in crops and scab in fruit orchards; and various copper compounds, used also to control blight (on potatoes), downy mildew on hops and grapes, and fungal diseases in orchards. Copper is a toxic metal that accumulates in soils, though not in the quantities used by organic farmers. Prior approval from the certification body is required and it is currently being phased out.

Sheep dips and warble fly: The use of organophosphates is banned. Should a farmer be required to use it, for example, to satisfy DEFRA requirements, the sheep automatically lose their organic status.

Post-harvest treatments: Although organic farming forbids the application of insecticides and fungicides to crops after harvesting, in exceptional circumstances the fumigation of storage buildings by, for example, methyl bromide is allowed (by derogation).

Miscellaneous: Beeswax (pruning agent) and ethylene, to de-green bananas.

POLLUTION: WHAT YOU NEED TO KNOW

The pollution of our land, our water and the air we breathe, whether through toxic chemicals or intensive agricultural practice, is a modern scourge that affects everyone worldwide. (For the damage that pesticides do, see Appendix.) To take one common example, every year intensive livestock farming produces huge quantities of nitrogen-rich manure, resulting in part from high-protein feeds. Because artificial nitrogen is used to fertilise the land, and livestock are not normally part of a rotational system but are often housed permanently inside, manure is regarded as a waste product disposal problem. To get rid of it, it is often spread very heavily on small areas of land, polluting rivers and drinking water. These 'manure mountains' are officially recognised as a major pollutant of waterways and a major threat to aquatic life.

Organic farming systems take a different approach. Because they are based on extensive management, which means fewer animals, and often combine livestock and crop management on the same farm, manure is a valuable resource, and it is responsibly managed. There are strict controls regarding the kind and quantity of farmyard manures, and when they can be used, and they must be returned to the land in ways that minimise any possible pollution.

Nitrogen – and the organic position

The artificial nitrates that greened the world, albeit superficially, and led to huge improvements in yields, now rank as a number one pollutant. Worldwide their use has increased nearly sevenfold since the 1960s to 80 million tonnes per year, even though in developed countries yields reached a plateau in the 1980s, and extra fertiliser applications have had no further effect. An estimated two-thirds of applied nitrogen fertilisers are not taken up by the crops, and invade non-agricultural systems. Meanwhile, the problems associated with them mount daily.

Artificial nitrogen forces plants and makes them grow lush. As a result, they are more prone to pest and disease attacks, necessitating repeated pesticide spraying. At the same time, artificial nitrogen destroys soil bacteria, depletes soil life generally and inhibits the natural biological process of nitrogen fixation. Conventionally grown plants have higher nitrate levels because they cannot convert all of the nitrates they receive into ripe proteins, and this depletes their overall health and vitality.

Excess nitrogen has many adverse environmental effects, too. Run-off into water systems causes 'eutrophication' (the formation of surface algal blooms), resulting in the death of aquatic life. It causes oxygen depletion in estuaries and coastal seas, and acidification in lakes and streams. The emission of ammonia gas causes acid rain, and nitrous oxide contributes to the greenhouse effect. Excess nitrates can also be harmful to human health and have been linked to allergies, and their breakdown products have been implicated in certain cancers.

Organic farming systems conserve both carbon and nitrogen better, and leach up to 60% less to the atmosphere. In addition, the new EU organic livestock regulations have further restricted the amount of nitrogen (which comes primarily from farmyard manures in organic systems) that can be used on organic farms to 170kg/hectare per annum. This equates to about 38 tonnes of farmyard manure or 25 tonnes of poultry manure; or, to put it another way, about two cows per hectare. (Except for nitrogen-sensitive areas, no such restrictions are imposed in conventional farming, despite the fact that the manure mountains produced as a result of intensive farming are a major pollutant.) As it is the livestock that produce the manures, this new requirement also means that the numbers of animals per holding are automatically restricted to what the land (or the surrounding local farms that the excess manures can be spread on) can sustain without causing significant pollution. This again is a major departure from the conventional approach, and points the way forward for the sustainable management of agricultural land.

GMOs – AND THE ORGANIC POSITION

Genetic engineering is the single most important issue of our lifetime. It has polarised scientists, doctors, farmers and consumers alike into two opposing camps, each side arguing the potential benefits, or the potential threats and damage, with equal passion. Governments have preferred, by and large, to sit on the fence – publicly – but privately most, including our own, are pro rather than anti. Consumers all over the world, meanwhile, have overwhelmingly said No to the notion of having genetically modified organisms in their food supply. This consumer backlash has led UK supermarkets to ban GM ingredients from their own brands; many are now banning GM animal feeds as well (see p. 171). The battle lines have been drawn, and the fight is set to continue for the foreseeable future.

I make no apologies for declaring which side of the fence I sit on. In 2000, with Joan Ruddock MP, we founded Women Say NO to GMOs. Our website, **www.gmno.org**, explains our position and tells you where, if you too are concerned, you can sign our petition.

As has been explained, organic farming is the only agricultural system to have rejected the use of genetic engineering in farming; and to declare unequivocally that genetically modified organisms have no place in organic farming systems (see p. 7). In the face of opposition, and the sheer might of the biotechnological industry, let alone global government enthusiasm for GM technology, this decision was a very brave one. If it hadn't been taken, I doubt that any of the controls we now have, however inadequate, would be in place. Nor would there have been the worldwide public debate that has raged non-stop over the last three years. By saying No to GMOs, the organic movement has provided consumers with CHOICE – and the world with a much-needed breathing space.

All this has not been achieved without considerable cost. Saying No to GMOs poses extra financial burdens, extra administration, yet more paperwork and more responsibilities, and incurs penalties. Organic crops found to be contaminated by GMOs cannot be sold as organic: in the USA a shipment of organic tortillas was recalled and destroyed because traces of GM sweetcorn were found, later attributed to contamination from adjacent GM sweetcorn crops.

Contamination is a very real threat to all farmers who do not want to grow GM crops. As beekeepers and farmers in Canada and the USA have found out – the hard way – distances between GM and non-GM crops are inadequate and contamination is sometimes inevitable. In the long term, whether organic farmers can remain 'pure' is impossible to predict; it will depend, quite simply, on who wins the battle.

What the fuss is about

There continues to be extensive coverage in the media of the GM debate. National organisations, including the Soil Association, Greenwatch Greenpeace, Friends of the Earth and the Five-Year Freeze, produce regular bulletins and give excellent information on their websites. For anyone interested in the cutting edge of the GM debate, in keeping up with the scientific papers, the legal wranglings and what's happening the world, the Natural Law Party (NLP) GM information email service nlpwessex@bigfoot.com is one of the most comprehensive. (Other GM websites and organisations can be found on p. 375).

Here, for those who would like to be reminded, is the nub of the issue, as I see it.

Genetic engineering allows scientists to take genes from the DNA of one organism and put them into the DNA of another, thus offering what seems, on the face of it, to be the ultimate prize: control of life itself, the ability to create new organisms, and an Aladdin's cave of endless scientific possibilities that could theoretically bring untold benefits to mankind. It's also the biggest gamble mankind has ever entered into, which, should it go wrong, could have devastating consequences for our health and for the environment and cause irreparable damage to the planet. The reason? Once released, GMOs can never be recalled – and that's the problem.

The advent of genetic engineering also raises huge moral, animal welfare, social and political issues. As seed supplies are replaced with GM seeds, for example, we face the prospect of shrinking natural gene pools and the consequent loss of biodiversity. And this at precisely the time when the need to maintain biodiversity is finally being realised, and the world's food and seed supplies are being monopolised by the major agrochemical and pharmaceutical companies that dominate biotechnology worldwide.

It's important for everyone to realise that the purported scientific advances (as yet still largely theoretical) are just the tip of the iceberg, almost a side issue. At its heart, the GM debate is about democracy and fundamental human rights, about who nature belongs to, and about whether, indeed, as the Prince of Wales has argued, to enter into the GM arena is a step too far and by tampering with nature in this way we are entering into realms that belong to God alone.

The genetic engineering genie is already out of the bottle. The question is, what do we use it for, and who should own and control it? For instance, the use of genetic engineering in medicines, by consenting individuals in properly controlled, closed positions, in order to cure hitherto incurable diseases, is very different from colonising the environment with crops that could never exist outside a laboratory and whose long-term effects haven't even been considered. Though consumers have said a resounding NO to GM foods, we and our children continue to be used as unwitting guinea-pigs, and our environment as an open-air laboratory. The question we all have to ask is, is this right? The outcome of this debate will not be clear for at least three generations, and will determine for evermore not just the food that we eat but the kind of world we shall inhabit – that we shall bequeath to our children.

Ultimately consumers will decide, and my own feeling is that GM foods, at least, are already a dead duck. But there is one positive effect of the GM debate perhaps worth mulling over. Because of the consumer backlash against GM crops, we are already beginning to see science turn its energies to developing ways of using GM technology without crossing species barriers, as well as more research being conducted into GM alternatives that organic farmers – and all the rest of us – can feel happier about. Which really would be progress.

Buying GM-free food

Despite repeated official announcements that consumers have the right to choose not to buy GM foods, to remain GM-free, laws have been introduced that allow up to 1% GM ingredients or derivatives to be included in foods without having to declare them on the label. This means that unless the product or supplier specifically says that they don't use them, if you want to avoid GM ingredients or derivatives for whatever reason, buying organic food (and own label supermarket products) is your best option.

GM CROPS: WHAT'S BEING ENGINEERED, AND WHERE

Over 99% of commercial GM crops currently planted are designed for weed and insect resistance, which benefits biotech companies and intensive farmers, and which leaves less than 1% that have been engineered for quality or other traits. Meanwhile, over 80% of GM acreage around the world is planted with just two crops, soya and corn (maize), both primarily commodity crops used in the processing industry and for animal feeds. Other GM crops being planted commercially are potatoes, canola (oil-seed rape), papaya in Hawaii, and cotton. America accounts for over 30% of all GM crops; Argentina, China (cotton) and Canada are the other major GM-crop-growing countries; others growing GM crops on smaller scales are Mexico, Spain, Australia, France, South Africa, India, Ukraine and Romania. This is what is being genetically engineered, drawn up by Greenpeace GM food expert, Jim Thomas:

- animals
- bacteria
- coffee
- cotton
- enzymes
- fish
- food crops and other plants
- grass
- trees
- vines
- vitamins

Also containing GM components:

- biological weapons
- cosmetics
- plastics, starches and industrial chemicals
- contraceptives
- drugs

▲▲

STATE OF PLAY

Latest estimates (from the International Acquisition Research Centre, based in the US) state land planted with GM crops has risen by almost 20% in 2001 to 52.6 million hectares; and that around 5.5 million farmers grew GM crops in 13 countries.

3: The Cost of Organic Food, and its True Value

In the last couple of years, organic food has become much more competitive – and in some areas, such as bread and other basics, is the same or nearly the same price as many conventional brands. It is primarily the huge numbers of farmers converting to organic production worldwide that has brought about the dramatic increase in the availability of organic food. This means greater security for the market, much greater economies of scale and, most importantly, more price stability. The industry is also much more professional, the supply chains and infrastructures necessary for success are now in place, and cost inefficiencies are being ironed out. The result for everyone is lower prices, and we can expect this trend to continue.

However, the cost of organic food remains a complex issue. The fact that much of it is still perceived as expensive continues to dog the industry; as does the fact that organic food is consistently compared with the cheapest rather than with conventional food produced with comparable care and dedication. At one end of the spectrum, the influx into the organic market of major food giants and supermarkets such as ASDA and Budgens, determined to offer organic food at affordable prices for all, has made the cost issue a major battleground.

The result is a certain amount of confusion for the consumer. But though there is no doubt that everyone would buy more organic food if it were cheaper, there is also a general consensus that organic food *should* cost more. The argument is about *how much more* it should cost, about the best way to increase the market, and whether artificially lowering prices is a sustainable option. Indeed, the EDLP (everyday low price) bubble has already begun to burst: Iceland have pulled out, and all responsible major manufacturers recognise that to artificially lower prices would devalue the market and send out mixed messages; they believe that, as Iceland has found out, such a strategy doesn't work.

Meanwhile, the central issues remain the same: the objective of organic farming is not, and never has been, to produce food as cheaply as possible, but to produce healthy food that we can all trust, using farming practices that nurture rather than harm the environment. It is more self-sufficient and inherently more self-sustaining than conventional agriculture and therefore a better bet in the long term. This, essentially, is what you pay for, and it is an investment in health and well-being in the broadest sense. Conversely, the fundamental problem with most conventional food production is that – as Professor Jules Pretty has noted – consumers are paying three times for their food: once at the till; once through taxes which are used mainly to prop up conventional farming; and once to clean up the pollution and environmental degradation that modern intensive farming in particular causes – not to mention the enormous cost imposed on all of us by catastrophes such as BSE and, most recently, the Foot and Mouth tragedy.

In short, we pay a more or less realistic price for organic food and an unrealistic price for all cheap food.

HOW HEALTHY IS FOOD PRODUCED BY CONVENTIONAL AGRICULTURE?

Most scientists maintain that, used responsibly, pesticides are perfectly safe, and that food produced using current methods deliver a high level of nutrition. Be that as it may, once you get away from the laboratory, things start to look rather different. The science of nutrition takes an essentially narrow view of health, concentrating on macronutrients – major vitamins and minerals – and tends to look at nutrition in terms of ill health rather than full health. *Both* approaches have huge implications for judging whether organic food is healthier or not. For example, established organic soils are teeming with beneficial microbes that play a vital role in the uptake of trace elements which are not normally measured, but which, it is now becoming clear, do have an important role in health. It is also becoming clear, as explained above, that it is the bioavailability and interaction of the whole mix of nutrients that are important.

Though not conclusive, epidemiological studies show that modern food production, in some respects, is failing to deliver health. Two examples illustrate the point:

- A widely reported study published in *Nature* magazine in 1997, looking at the effects of the so-called green revolution in South East Asia, where a huge change-over to artificial fertilisers and pesticides brought increased yields, found crops deficient in zinc and failing IQ levels in children.

- The dramatic decline in the sperm counts of Western males is another worrying instance of declining population health. In America, sperm count studies have shown a reduction from 120 million to just over 40 million per millilitre of semen; the World Health Organisation defines the minimum level that a man can reproduce at as approximately 20 million. Oestrogen-mimicking chemicals, which include several pesticides, have been linked to falling sperm counts. By contrast, though by no means conclusive, the only two studies of their kind conducted so far have shown that Danish organic farmers have high sperm counts.

A final point: cancers, hyperactivity, allergies and delinquent behaviour in children are all increasing fast. Time will tell whether lower nutrient intakes due to modern intensive agricultural practices are a major factor, but common sense says that a return to an organic diet has to offer a better, healthier way forward.

THE REAL PRICE WE PAY FOR CHEAP FOOD

Cheap food comes with a very high price tag in terms of animal welfare, the degradation of our countryside, our health, and the global pollution of our environment – all of these we pay heavily for, and not just at the till. The bill for BSE alone, for example, is well over £4 billion. Then there are the hidden, 'externalised' costs that have recently been calculated by Professor Jules Pretty and his team at Essex University, which work out at an average of over £2 billion per year. These are the costs we don't see but pay anyway, every time we buy cheap food. Water is a good example. UK farmers use 22 million kg of pesticides each year, some of which inevitably leach into our water supplies. Apart from the damage that pesticides cause to aquatic life, their removal costs water companies £120 million each year – and even then they are not removed completely, but to the legally acceptable limit. The cost of this is passed on to consumers in their water bills. As Jules Pretty comments, this represents a hidden subsidy for those who pollute. The non-polluter receives no such reward.

In fact, it's been calculated that every £1 worth of conventional food we buy actually costs another 25p at least in externalised costs. Conventional farmers also cost the tax-payer more in direct subsidies (40p compared with the 25p per £ that organic subsidies cost). If you started with a clean sheet, took away the subsidies and included the hidden costs in the price charged to consumers, organic food would work out at least 5% and possibly up to 20% cheaper than conventional food. Which is why, in buying organic food, you become part of the solution rather than propping up the problem.

THE COST OF PRODUCING ORGANIC FOOD

Farming extensively rather than intensively has various knock-on costs. Fewer animals and crops per hectare means lower yields. Organic farming is also more labour-intensive, and farmers employ up to twice as many people (sometimes more). They also bear the additional costs of the annual mandatory inspection, and of the need to remain GM-free and to source GM-free ingredients and feedstuffs. Organic feedstuffs can be up to four times as expensive as conventional feed. On the plus side, external inputs and vet bills are significantly less, and once an organic farm comes into its natural prime its yields match most conventional ones.

How much *should* organic food cost?

At the present time, this is impossible to say. The best guess is that food that we can really trust, grown using organic methods, should cost around 10–20% more than conventional food currently costs. This would apply to most primary foods, except meat, which should cost at least 50% more. But there are also certain economies to be made when organic food is processed, which can bring prices down. In reality, price depends on where, how and what you're buying. For more on this and tips on buying, see p. 72.

Does cheap organic food mean inferior organic food?

Not necessarily. All organic food has to be certified and so must meet UKROFS organic standards as a minimum. However, as organic food becomes a mass and therefore a 'mature' market, we will see more price differentiation and price competitiveness – and more variations in quality, depending, for example, on the kind of ingredients used, where they are sourced, how large- or small-scale the supplier is, and on the buying power of the retailer. Already the market is polarising into premium organic brands such as Pollen Organics and established names such as Green & Black's, and family organic brands and supermarket own-label products, each aiming at a different sector of the market.

Will the drive to bring down prices threaten organic standards?

It is everyone's worst nightmare that in the attempt to take organic food on board – be it out of a genuine desire that everyone should be able to afford it, whatever their budget, or for the obvious commercial benefit that comes from the fact that if the price is reduced more will be sold – organic farmers will be squeezed in the same way that conventional farmers have been squeezed, and that organic standards will be watered down. To date, all those producing or selling budget organic food have given public assurances that standards will not suffer. But there is evidence that this is already happening. For more on this see p. 33.

If standards *are* showing signs of falling, consumers cannot avoid shouldering some of the blame. With organic food as with conventional, aside from its organic credentials you generally get what you pay for, whether it be a salad dressing or a chicken. The market for organic food and its quality standards is determined not just by manufacturers and certification bodies, but also by what consumers will buy. So consumers need to stand firm, too, insist on proper safeguards, and support the organisations and manufacturers who uphold the highest organic standards. Then food producers who try to cut corners will fast lose credibility and find no outlet for their goods with those consumers who want genuine organic foods. See p. 55 for more discussion on quality.

One of the prime reasons why people buy and enjoy organic food is that they believe it tastes better, and, generally, that it is of a higher quality than most other food they buy. We now look at how well organic food stands up to these claims, and where we are today, now that organic food has become mainstream.

THE TASTE OF ORGANIC FOOD

Generally speaking, organic food tastes better – when Sainsbury's, for example, asked their online shoppers, 49% said so. This is because, though none of the following factors are themselves guarantees of extra flavour, they all bode well for it:

- Organic crops generally contain less water and more dry matter.
- Organic crops are not forced, so grow more slowly and have time to mature (main-crop carrots, for instance, will be left in the soil for 2–3 weeks longer than most conventional carrots).

- More traditional varieties are used.
- Research shows that biologically active soils that are nurtured with compost can produce plants with higher protein.
- Organic crops can contain more flavour-enhancing trace compounds.
- Organic animals live longer, grow at a more natural rate and graze on organic pastures rich in clover, herbs and other plants.
- Organic husbandry uses a wider variety of traditional breeds which often have more fat, which carries flavour. NB: marbled fat (the fat you find within the tissue) is not highly saturated, and is a sign of high-quality meat.
- Livestock are not pushed to give optimum yields.
- Organic full-cream milk is mainly whole milk – that is, milk that has not had its cream fraction reduced to the standard 3.5%.
- Organic processing standards aim to produce foods with the minimum of processing and outlaw all but a handful of the 7,000 processing aids used in food manufacture; this means a greater potential for 'cleaner' – and more 'natural' – tasting processed foods.

Thus organic foods clearly have the potential for maximising flavour; the best can be a taste revelation. But this is not to say that *every* organic carrot, loaf of bread, carton of milk, joint of beef, or soup, pasta sauce or breakfast cereal tastes better than any conventional version. As with conventional food, much depends on who produced or manufactured it, how fresh it was when you bought it, with processed organic foods, whether it's a premium product or a budget one – as well as your own personal preferences.

Remember, too, that:

- The flavour of any crop depends on a multitude of factors, including soil and climate, how long the land has been farmed organically, the maturity or 'ripeness' of the crop, and how and for how long it has been stored.
- Any crop grown out of season, whether organic or not – e.g. glasshouse tomatoes in winter – will have less flavour.
- How meat is handled during and after slaughter is as critical as how it is produced and is a major determinate of flavour. Also, taste and texture are closely linked, especially where meat is concerned, and because tenderness is prized most, added texture is not to everyone's taste.
- Supermarkets aim for a consistency of flavour that will appeal to a wide range of tastes, rather than individuality.

- Healthier alternative sweeteners such as organic apple juice, or wholewheat flour instead of white flour, have their own distinctive flavour notes that you may or may not find attractive.

For both taste and quality, size matters – and the rule that small is beautiful almost invariable holds true. It applies, in my experience, to all foods be they fresh or processed, but particularly to processed foods. Don't ask me why, but whether organic or not, food produced in small batches tastes better than food made in large batches.

Your taste buds

Overlying all of this is perhaps the most important variable of all: your taste buds. Taste is highly subjective, and much of what you like is conditioned by habit and, in many cases, a lack of tasting experience. Conventional food does little to enhance the situation: either food tastes the same – which usually means it has very little flavour – or it has so many added flavours (especially sugar and salt) that we lose any sense of what its natural flavour is, let alone the many ways it might express itself. It is rather sad that in order to get children to enjoy eating, so much effort is made to persuade them to cook, whereas if they were given more opportunity to taste different varieties of foods, feeding themselves good things to eat would follow on naturally.

Put simply, the kind of food you are used to eating will condition how you judge the taste of organic food. Taste seven different varieties of tomato grown in the same garden at the same time, and you will be amazed at how different they can be; the same is true of different brands of cornflakes.

The best way of proving to yourself that organic food tastes better is to eat a whole range of organic foods for a few weeks and then go back to the conventional kind. It is then that your taste buds will realise what you have been missing.

THE ORGANIC TASTE EXPERIENCE

As conventional manufacturers who attempt to make organic versions of the same recipe confirm, organic food has its own distinctive characteristics – though you may not be able to say exactly why or how it tastes different. It's the same with cheese: speak to cheese-makers who make organic and conventional versions of the same cheese, and they will tell you that they can tell the difference from day one. Look out for these differences:

- extra sweetness – not sugary, but a natural, more complex sweetness associated with ripe, healthy food
- earthier flavours
- cleaner flavours – organic milk is a good example
- fuller flavours
- a greater richness, especially in meat
- a longer-lasting flavour – in wine and cheese, for instance
- more background flavours, making food more multidimensional

plus:
- different textures – firmer and more fulfilling
- juiciness – as opposed to wateriness
- a 'vital' and appetising quality – the moreish factor, in other words.

QUALITY

In the early days of the organic movement, organic farmers were a secluded band of holistically orientated individuals operating traditional mixed farms and dedicated to the concept of promoting health. Mass-produced organic food was a twinkle in the eye of one of two equally dedicated manufacturers. Today, consumers still rightly want and expect something extra in the way of quality from their organic food; indeed, now more than ever there must be 'clear blue water' between organic and conventional food. The question is, first, how do you define quality? And second, where do you draw the line so as to maintain that 'clear blue water'?

Generally speaking, organic food has an image of high quality, which is largely justified. But the main reason why this image is not *totally* justified is simply that, as already noted, as the market has grown so has the variation in quality. This variation can be seen, for instance, in organic tomatoes grown under glass out of season, which have little flavour but which consumers like to have, or in the increasing range of manufactured organic foods that pay lip service to 'healthy' ingredients.

Unfortunately, too, the question of *how* food is produced has not until recently entered the public arena. Take a simple example. Everyone agrees that Parma ham is a superb high-quality product. And so it is – until you see the intensive conditions that the pigs are kept in. By contrast, what underpins all organic food is its method of production: it offers integrity and therefore quality of production – that is, food grown using methods that try to optimise health. How far this is achieved depends on such factors as the size of the farm, whether it is farmed to minimum standards or higher, and how long it has been organic – every organic farmer will tell you it takes years for a farm to reach balance and harmony and for soils to become truly healthy. During this time, crops become stronger and better, disease diminishes, yields and quality improve, and so on. Once the product leaves the farm, other factors come into play, and this is where the fun starts.

What exactly *is* quality?

We measure food quality primarily by its taste, texture and mouth feel; and, as a rule of thumb, the fresher, tenderer, more flavourful and more delicious it seems, the higher we rate its quality. In addition, the quality of manufactured food is judged by the percentage of 'real' ingredients and the absence of 'nasties' – additives, preservatives and flavourings – as well as by its nutritional profile – how much sugar, salt, cheap ingredients or fillers it has. The Food Standards Agency and environmental health officers measure food quality by absence of bugs; a butcher judges the quality of meat primarily by the conformation and colour of its fat; a grain merchant uses a machine to give him a detailed scientific breakdown of protein and water content, and so on. By these parameters, organic food generally scores as well as, and often better than, most conventionally produced foods.

How do you achieve the highest quality?

Producing food according to organic principles does not alone guarantee the highest all-round eating quality. To achieve this requires extra dedication and specialist knowledge and skills, including how it is handled or processed afterwards. This is where French and Italian food producers – and indeed all dedicated small producers, organic or not – have acquired their high reputation: they start with the eating quality they want to achieve and work back, making sure that every detail is taken care of. Though there are many honourable exceptions, organic farmers have not scored highly in this regard in the past simply because, just like conventional farmers, their skills have lain in growing the crops and raising the livestock rather than in tailoring the end product. It is the same with manufactured organic foods: pioneering companies such as Baby Organix, the Village Bakery and Green & Blacks have always led the way in their focus on quality and integrity, but manufacturing food is a skilled business and those skills have had to be learnt. Furthermore, in the past, being organic was good enough, but this is no longer the case. We have moved on and in future we can expect more premium organic foods that are not only produced according to the highest organic principles, but that offer us the best eating quality too. It is unrealistic, however, to expect all organic food to achieve the highest quality. That day could come, but would mean a return to food being mainly produced and consumed locally, and for us all to pay more for most of our food.

Organic convenience foods

This is one area where one can definitely say that organic foods are of higher quality: unlike conventional processed foods they contain no artificial preservatives, flavourings, phosphoric acid, hydrogenated fats, other additives or GMOs. (See chapter 14 for a full survey of organic convenience foods available.)

Should organic standards forbid organic 'junk' food?

The simple truth is that all manufactured and processed foods are devitalised foods, with more or less nutritional value. Organic or not, you may eat them for pleasure but you rarely eat them for health. There are now many organic brands that have just as much sugar, for example, as conventional brands. The health advantage that these organic processed foods have is the absence of the 'nasties' mentioned above. If it's healthy food you want, then stay with fresh organic food every time.

The answer to the question, *Should organic standards forbid organic junk food?*, is No, and for two reasons. First, because organic toffee, for example, made using organic sugar cane, as far as the farm production methods employed are concerned, is infinitely better for the health of the plantation workers who grow it and for the environment. Second, whether we like it or not, processed foods in all their forms – good and bad – constitute a bigger market than fresh food, and fulfilling this demand organically means substantially more organic holdings. And the more organic holdings there are, the sooner all farming will change to more sustainable methods of production. However, organic junk food should still be made with integrity, and there should be no junking of organic processing standards. This will ensure that organic junk food is of higher quality than the rest.

Is it OK to have organic lemonade with no lemons? Legally and technically it is perfectly feasible – and it has been done – to produce an organic lemonade that contains organic sugar, water and approved natural flavourings. But is this right? No, it's one example where standards should have been stricter and the manufacturers asked to produce a lemonade with more integrity.

MAINTAINING THE CLEAR BLUE WATER; SETTING OUR SIGHTS HIGH

This is the most difficult challenge that the organic food sector faces in the immediate future. There needs to be a clear dividing line between organic food and conventional food; a demonstrable difference at all times. The way to meet consumer expectations is for standards authorities to be vigilant and to drive standards ever upwards. Consumers can help enormously by making their voices heard and by understanding more about what organic food and farming really means – and how both should develop. The best place to start? Try the standards section on p. 30.

Post-BSE, any standard of food quality must take into account how food is produced, and put this criterion at the top of its list. Though there are many different 'farm-assured' schemes, those that guarantee organic are the *only* ones that have a holistic approach, that link growing methods with health and quality in the broadest sense, and that are mandatory and legally binding. Attend the bi-annual organic conference at Cirencester, for example, and you will find health always high on the agenda. All other food standards systems are voluntary, and while they are based on recommendations of best practice, the number of practices they prohibit is minimal.

Though the conventional parameters will always be important, Elm Farm Research Centre and various organic institutes in Europe have been working on a much broader approach to organic food quality, which may well pave the way for a definition of quality much better suited to the twenty-first century. Patrick Holden, director of the Soil Association, and Peter Segger, managing director of Organic Farm Foods, who fund research into health and vitality, have come up with a simple quality matrix for fresh foods that could fit the bill nicely – apply it to the food you eat and see how it shapes up. True food quality, according to them, can be summed up as follows:

- The absence of 'nasties': pesticide residues, GMOs, artificial preservatives, and so on.
- Life-building: to be as high as possible in essential life-building nutritional components such as vitamins and minerals.
- Life-protecting: to have the maximum amount of life-protecting substances such as cancer-preventing antioxidants.
- Vitality: the presence of that elusive but important factor, which is the best expression of a food's overall health, and tells you how near it is to the perfect archetype. A vitality index for fresh food has been worked out, and one or two pioneering Danish manufacturers are investigating how to apply this to processed foods also.

Why can't it be proved that organic food is nutritionally superior?

It is easy to see that organic food offers a safer haven than conventional food in terms of what it doesn't contain. *Proving* that it is better for you, however, is a more difficult proposition, and as hotly debated as how much it should cost.

Although well over a thousand studies on organic food have been completed, because funding for organic R&D is tiny compared with that for conventional food, not nearly enough comparative work has been done to prove, one way or another, whether organic food is nutritionally superior to conventional food. Not all the studies are of a high quality, and some are contradictory. Scientists who have surveyed the literature cannot agree, either: some say studies to date show categorically that organic food is better for you, while others declare avidly that they don't.

Such studies will always, in any event, be limited: to prove conclusively which system of agriculture, organic or otherwise, delivers the best health, you need to take a multidisciplinary approach, not one that merely looks at what happens in the laboratory. This has begun in more forward-looking European countries, but not yet in the UK.

Meanwhile, there is a considerable line-up of eminent bodies that feel moved, for no clear reason and on grounds unstated, to declare that there is no basis (the Royal Agricultural Society), or insufficient evidence (the Food Standards Agency), or no conclusive evidence (the House of Lords) for saying that organic food is better, or significantly different in nutritional content, or safer, than conventional food.

Given the many problems besetting modern food production, it is difficult to know why the Food Standards Agency felt it necessary to say that organic food is no better for you. But to be fair, though this is the impression that was widely reported, they actually hedged their bets. 'There is not sufficient information at present,' they said, to show that organic foods 'are significantly different in terms of their safety and nutritional content than those produced by conventional farming'. One factor underlying their conclusion is their belief that current levels of pesticide residues pose no threat to health.

Despite substantial disagreement on the subject, nevertheless, there is already plenty of evidence to show not only that organic farming has the potential to produce healthier food, but that it can often deliver it. For more on this, read the Soil Association's recent review, 'Organic farming, food quality and human health'.

WHY *IS* IT BETTER FOR YOU?

The potential health benefits of eating organic foods can be summarised in various ways but neatly divide into two halves: the absence or near-absence of some substances found in conventional food, and the presence – in some cases high levels – of others.

Absence: what you get none (or very little) of

Almost no residues See chapter 1 and Appendix for the details. To illustrate the point: unlike non-organic carrots, organic ones have never been subjected to a government health warning advising you to peel them and cut off the top inch or so before feeding them raw to children, in case pesticide residues in that particular carrot are higher than normal. As one friend said, wouldn't it be nicer not to have to deal with fresh food in such a defensive way?

No GMOs Organic standards prohibit the use of any kind of GMOs and at any stage of the organic farming cycle. I'm told that to date, only five tests on the safety of GMOs for human consumption have been carried out, and all have raised concerns.

Fewer nitrates The application of artificial nitrates increases water uptake (not good for flavour), leads to lush growth, which leaves the plants more susceptible to pests and disease, and inhibits the uptake of other nutrients. Organic crops, by contrast, often have significantly lower nitrate levels as well as a better balance of amino acids, which give a higher-quality protein.

Absence of BSE There has been no recorded case of BSE in cattle that have been exclusively bred and raised organically. The risk of Creutzfeldt-Jakob disease (CJD) is therefore greatly reduced, and if all farmers farmed organically it is unlikely that the BSE catastrophe would have happened. (The few cases that have been recorded were found in herds where conventional dairy cattle had been brought in as replacement stock.)

Fewer pathogens Pathogens such as E-coli, salmonella and listeria are much rarer in the organic food system, while remaining a growing health problem in the conventional system.

No artificial colourings, preservatives or flavourings In addition, only a very small number of processing aids (listed on p. 388) are permitted and minimal processing is used wherever possible. The one exception, recently allowed, is the use of sodium nitrite for curing bacon and hams (see p. 191).

No hydrogenated fats or oils These fats, which have been directly associated with increased rates of heart disease and skin cancer, are also prohibited in organic food processing; yet they are used widely in conventional processing and are found in many vegetable margarines.

No phosphoric acids This depletes calcium in bone reserves and brings the risk of osteoporosis, which can be caused by the consumption of drinks such as cola. Its presence is now of serious concern in the USA.

Thus, at a stroke, an organic diet excludes as far as humanly possible a considerable catalogue of proven and potential health risks, and halts the daily drip of residues regularly ingested as part of the average diet.

As far as antibiotics as growth promoters are concerned (see p. 172), the House of Lords Select Committee on Science and Technology recently concluded that there is a continuing threat to human health from their imprudent use. Artificial flavourings, preservatives and colourings are known causes of allergies and hyperactivity, especially in children, and many are concerned about the potential health risks of GM foods. BSE is still with us, and because of the long incubation period, no one yet knows how many people will have contracted CJD. How much more evidence do we need before the penny drops?

Presence: what you get more of

More vitamins and minerals Several studies confirm that organic foods have more dry matter, and often more minerals and more vitamin C – often as much as 10–20%. Other studies show that stored organic foods such as apples have more vitamin C than conventionally grown apples. Note, though, that this is *not* to say that every organic carrot will have a significantly higher nutritional content or that every apple will be rich in vitamin C. As already noted, much depends on the soil and the climate, the maturity of the crop, how it is stored and how long it is before you eat it. On the other hand, this does show farming methods can produce crops with more nutrients. Because nutrients don't work in isolation, but synergistically (as a paper by nutritional scientist Dr Virginia Worthington has explained), we also know that small increases in nutrients matter. For example, an increase in vitamin C increases the effect of vitamin E, folic acid and iron. An increase in vitamin E often increases the effect of selenium and vitamin A, which further increases the effect of iron, and so on. This means a farming system that can deliver more nutrients has to be better for you and the population as a whole.

Other kinds of evidence also point to the critical importance of how a crop is produced, as far as its ultimate nutritional quality is concerned. A recent detailed comparison of the most famous series of government reports analysing the nutritional content of foods, published by the Medical Research Council from the 1940s to 1991, McCance and Widdowson's *The Composition of Foods*, highlighted how the mineral content of crops grown over the last fifty years has plummeted. Plant pathologists in the USA also refer to the 'hidden hunger' of plants and believe that many crops suffer from poor diets, not getting sufficient micronutrients from the soil to fend off disease.

More life-protecting compounds Every plant is a living pharmacy full of thousands of chemical substances, present in minute quantities and christened 'secondary metabolites' – about which very little is known – which include phenols, flavonoids, tannins and alkaloids. Scientists in Denmark have found that one group, the phenols, are antioxidants (essential to good health in helping to mop up harmful free radicals, and used in cancer prevention) many times more powerful than vitamin C. Studies show that organic plants have a greater diversity and quantity of phenols; since nitrogen seems to suppress phenols, plants grown with chemical fertilisers tend to be lacking in this department. One study at the Swiss Research Institute of Organic Agriculture showed that organic apple samples had over 18% more phenolic compounds than conventionally grown samples. Another study found much higher levels of phenols in organic red wines than in their conventional equivalents. If confirmed, the consequences for global agriculture, relying as it does on nitrogen fertilisers, could be significant; and once again the potential for health that organic farming can deliver is evident. Note that soil type and plant variety also affect the quantity and diversity of secondary metabolites (in comparisons made thus far, traditional varieties have more than modern hybrids).

More PUFAs (polyunsaturated fatty acids) Studies on the fat composition of ruminants have shown that organically raised meat (in this case beef and veal) had a higher ratio of beneficial polyunsaturated fatty acids, while intensively raised meat had higher levels of saturated fats. This is largely due to the nature of the animals' feed. It is also well known that grass-fed animals develop higher levels of beneficial conjugated linoleic acid (CLA).

Better animal health The landmark Pottinger cat study conducted in the 1930s illustrated how important it is to feed animals a healthy diet. A range of studies comparing organically fed animals with those fed conventionally suggests that organic animals have better fertility (both male and female), less illness, better recovery from illness and better survival of the young. Biodynamically fed animals performed particular well. It was also found that they preferred organic feed, given the option. To date, no study of this type has shown that conventional animals outperformed organic ones. Another study, one that relates directly to the food we buy, concerned eggs. This showed that eggs produced by chickens that had grazed naturally on grass and had natural daylight, produced eggs that emitted more light energy (biophotones); also, this regime had a positive effect on their behaviour and health. Another study comparing biodynamically fed chickens with those fed conventional feed showed biodynamic eggs to be significantly heavier and to have heavier yolks.

More of the vital 'vitality factor' Like you and me, a plant needs good nutrition and the right environment to flourish, if it is to be healthy and radiate vitality. Such a plant is in harmony and balance with itself, and is *ipso facto* a healthy plant. Though self-evident to many organic farmers and gardeners, until recently this, and the consequences it may have for overall human health, have been difficult to illustrate. One of the techniques that scientists in Germany, Denmark and Switzerland, developing a holistic approach to crop health, are exploring is the use of 'crystallisation pictures' to see if they can detect differences between organic food samples and their conventional counterparts. These pictures look like snowflakes or frost on a windowpane, and what these scientists find is that biodynamic and organic food samples have a consistently more regular pattern and are more 'harmonious'. In short, they are more 'vital'. Again, the results are strongly affected by soil type variety, the way plants are fed, and their nitrogen levels, as well as by freshness and any processing involved. Furthermore, studies in Switzerland by Dr Ursula Balzer-Graf, involving the analysis of hundreds of crystallisation pictures, show that fresh organic foods produce a more regular and harmonious pattern than processed organic foods; similarly with crystallisation pictures of natural vitamin C, while those of synthetic vitamin C are extremely fractured.

If you combine the results of various health and vitality parameters for form a 'vitality index', organic crops consistently perform better than conventional crops. What this actually proves – if anything – is too early to judge. What is clear, however, is that measuring health in a narrow sense is no longer adequate; and that a holistic approach may reveal far more about the relationship between us, our soil and our health, and about the role that organic farming methods play in ensuring that our food is as healthy as possible.

For more on all these and related topics (such as, can organic farming feed the world), Sustain's report 'Organic food and farming: myth and reality' can be obtained from them direct or downloaded from their website **www.sustainweb.org** (click on to Organic Target Bill icon).

4: Shopping for Organic Food

THE MARKET

In the last two years organic food has moved from niche to market mainstream. Once again, in the year 2001, organic food sales rose – by 50%. 'Everyday organic' has become the new buzz term, and Tesco's claim of a couple of years ago that organic food was now part of the everyday shopping basket has come true.

Indeed, it has never been easier to shop for organic food, and there has never been so much choice. The biggest change is that supermarkets now dominate the organic food scene, so that around 75% of organic food is sold through major multiples and all of them now stock a core range of organic food. This includes the Co-op and Somerfield, who typically have smaller stores on the high street, and Budgens, who also sell organic food in their petrol station forecourt shops – unthinkable even a short while ago.

Elsewhere, led by Planet Organic and Fresh & Wild, London has seen the emergence of other organic one-stop stores – As Nature Intended and Here. All sell thousands of organic lines and are places where you can experience the whole organic lifestyle. Outside London, there are well-established organic shops and farm shops throughout the UK, and wholefood and healthfood shops have expanded their organic lines. The 'go local' food movement is flourishing – over 10% of people buy organic food locally – there are more farmers' markets, more box schemes, more organic cheese-makers, and more pubs, cafés and restaurants serving organic food.

There is also a new-found confidence and a new sense of pride in organic food generally. It has become fun, fashionable, and exciting. Packaging has become slick and chic, and the range of foods available, from artisan pastas to a basic loaf, is staggering. Sales of fresh produce, baby foods and dairy products continue to soar. The biggest growth market is convenience foods, especially ready meals and food-to-go. The only area that lags behind is that of meat, though availability here too has increased dramatically.

Two other major developments that have made an impact are the explosion of organic websites, where you can buy and source organic foods (see chapter

15 for full details); and the arrival on to the scene of conventional manufacturers, including food giants Mars, Unilever and RHM Foods (see p. 69 for others).

The organic consumer

Over half the population now buy some organic food, and regular organic shoppers are now spending over £20 a week. Whereas, too, the organic consumer was described until recently as predominantly female, middle-class, living in the South East, and either a new mum or over forty-five, things are moving so fast that the latest trend is to group organic shoppers not by class or where they live, or even by income, but as 'foodies', 'greenies', 'committed', or 'dabblers'.

Whichever category they come into, consumers are very clear about why they buy organic food. Health, taste and perceived nutritional benefits, plus a growing awareness of environmental issues, come top of the list. And there is no doubt that the mass exodus to organic food has been fuelled by food disasters, worries over pesticide residues, and a general disillusionment with conventional food. Post-BSE consumers want the kind of assurances and field-to-plate guarantees that organic food offers. There is also much more awareness, as we have seen, that what is good for us is good for the environment. Speak to anyone who buys organic food regularly, and he or she will say that the 'feel good' experience that buying organic food gives you is tremendously important. The recent foot-and-mouth tragedy has brought this home, and made it clear once and for all that we can treat the countryside as a food factory no longer.

The organic ideal and the organic brand

In coming of age, organic food has become a 'brand' in its own right and its emergence is probably the most significant development in the whole organic story. It means quite simply that organics are now seen by the conventional food industry as both highly desirable and necessary. The result is likely to be a massive takeover by that industry, most of which will come into organics for purely business reasons. This is not necessarily a bad thing, since it means more investment, additional expertise, better access to the latest food technology, and more variety.

For consumers, having more organic choice and the reassurance that they can buy an organic version of their favourite brand has to be a welcome development. But there is a price to pay. There will inevitably be a clashing of minds. The organic philosophy is a holistic philosophy embracing many ideals, and one that it is important to retain if organic food is to keep the trust and credibility it now enjoys, over and above its high-quality status. Conventional manufacturers who understand this and see that it represents a huge opportunity to take food production forward will gain everyone's respect. But consumers need to be aware that the organic dream could just as easily be hijacked by food producers who have no long-term commitment, who see organic food as offering not a better solution but just a different one that, for commercial reasons, they can no longer ignore; and that their perceived view of organic quality is often different from that espoused by dedicated organic companies.

Own brands

The emergence of supermarket own-brand organic labels has been another major development of growing confidence that organics are here to stay. It takes investment, time and energy to develop an own-brand label. Already, own-label organics account for 30% of Sainsbury's total organic sales, and we are likely to see more retailers developing their own-brand organics.

Own-brand labels have two characteristics: they reflect each supermarket's view of what its customers want in terms of quality and taste, and they are priced to give the best value for money. Generally, own-brand organic goods are made either by existing organic manufacturers working to the supermarket's own specifications, or by one of the supermarket's existing conventional suppliers who adapts his production facilities, undergoes the necessary certification procedures, and becomes a certified processor for that particular line or lines. Because of the volumes involved, suppliers are beginning to build dedicated organic plants. As a sign of things to come, Sainsbury's, for example, are supporting an initiative to create the first organic food-processing centre using locally produced foods in the West Midlands. In terms of such factors as authenticity, certification and traceability of ingredients there is no difference between own-brand and any other organic brand. Differences in quality or taste are due to normal quality factors: the grade of the organic produce used, for example, or the use of different recipes that have minor differences in ratios of ingredients but result in surprisingly different tastes.

ASDA, Tesco and Waitrose, too, have each developed own-brand organic ranges (Marks & Spencer are exclusively own-brand for all their food). Sainsbury's have the widest range – around 600.

Are organic own-brands a good thing?

As long as consumers continue to like them and buy them, supermarkets will make them. However, not everyone welcomes their development, and some see them as yet another encroachment by the conventional food sector on to organic territory. Patrick Holden, Director of the Soil Association, has described own-brands as one of the seven deadly threats to organic integrity. A bit extreme, perhaps, but his point is a valid one. As he says, the story of organic food production, and its visible links with the producer or the farm, help give it its integrity and are two of its great strengths. Giving consumers as much information as possible, and rekindling those links between consumer and producer, are vital for the maintenance of food quality. Own-brand signals a return to the 'faceless', depersonalised product and, it must be said, gives supermarkets more control. As he says, if own-brands reduce the bond between consumers and organic food, long-term trust in organics could be jeopardised. It could also signal less not more organic choice if own-brand products occupy shelf space previously allocated to independent brands.

How important are supermarkets, and will their own-brand labels force out smaller organic manufacturers?

It is impossible to overestimate the significance of supermarkets or the role they have played and continue to play in the development of organic food. Fired by customer demand, they have stepped in where the government has not. Led by Sainsbury's and Waitrose, who have supported organics consistently from the start, plus, increasingly, Tesco, they have worked enormously hard behind the scenes, encouraging their conventional producers and manufacturers to convert, providing the infrastructure necessary for them to do so, supporting organic initiatives and investing in organic R&D. Sainsbury's have gone so far as to use for their organic fresh produce a revolutionary new biodegradable packaging, made from potato starch and cellulose fibres. There is no doubt, therefore, that supermarkets will increasingly become custodians of the organic food sector. In the main, they have acted responsibly. How many continue to do so, or to stay with it, remains to be seen.

Until recently supermarkets had very little choice in the matter and in order to satisfy customer demand had to buy from small organic manufacturers. Many have benefited enormously from this exposure, now have strong brands in their own right, and/or have become own-label suppliers to a supermarket. But selling to a supermarket doesn't suit everyone; unless an organic manufacturer can gear up to its particular demands, selling to a major multiple is not necessarily a happy experience and carries high risks (if, for example, the supermarket decides to switch from one organic brand to another). Now that more organic brands are available, including those of conventional manufacturers, supermarkets have more choice and there have undoubtedly been some casualties. However, because multiples have expanded the market and have significantly raised the profile of organic food, there are many more outlets for it – organic shops and supermarkets, for example, all have a policy of supporting smaller, local organic manufacturers. And as long as the local or high-street organic supermarket food sector thrives, where small is beautiful and best, there will be room for everyone who is producing good organic products. For that to happen, though, consumers must support their small retailer as much as they already support their local supermarket.

GOING, GOING . . . GONE ORGANIC

Only some of the output of the following brands is organic, of course (Anchor still make most of their butter the conventional way, for instance). Take a look at this list – some of the names may surprise you.

- Anchor – organic butter
- Arla Foods – Harmonie milk, cheeses, fromage frais, baby desserts
- Ashbourne Biscuits – oatmeal, lemon, ginger
- Barts – herbs and spices
- Baxters – soups
- Brakspear – beers
- Bulmer's – cider
- Chesswood – tinned vegetable meals including vegetable chilli, curry and hotpot
- Cott – soft drinks
- Courtney's – water biscuits
- Cow & Gate – Olvarit baby foods

- Cranks – bread
- Epicure – dried fruit, honey
- Petty Wood & Co Ltd – Epicure dried fruit, jam, honey, oils, rice, cooking sauces, salad dressings, confectionery
- Express Dairies – milk, vegetable boxes, Yeo Valley yoghurts, delivered to your door
- Gordon's – mustards, chutneys, marmalade, mint sauce
- Granovita – Quick-Mix chocolate drink, vegetarian patés and burger mixes, mayonnaise, biscuits, snack bars, breakfast cereals, soya desserts
- Hartley's – jams, marmalade
- J. E. Hartley – frozen vegetables
- Harvestime – breads
- Haward's – silverskin and pickled onions
- Heinz – tomato ketchup, baked beans, baby food, spaghetti in tomato sauce, pasta, soya milk
- HP – spaghetti in tomato sauce
- Jackson's – teas
- Jordan's – cereals, muesli, yoghurt, porridge, cereal bars
- Kelloggs – cereals
- Kenco – instant coffee
- KP – nuts
- Libby's – fruit juices
- Linda McCartney – the Kitchen Garden burgers, pies and pasties
- Loseley – yoghurts, cream, soft cheese
- Mars – Seeds of Change pastas, pasta sauces
- Müller – yoghurts
- Nairn's – oatcakes
- Nescafé – instant coffee
- Prewitt – snacks, biscuits, cakes, hot chocolate, malted drink
- Quaker – oats
- Rank Hovis McDougal (RHM) – the Enjoy Organic Company cereals, sauces, frozen ready meals, pasta, pasta sauces, breads, frozen pizzas
- Rombout's – filter coffee
- Rowse Ltd – honey, Canadian maple syrup
- Ryvita – Allinson's wholemeal crispbread
- Shippam's – chicken and vegetable spread
- Silver Spoon – sugar

- Tate & Lyle – sugar
- Taylor's of Harrogate – teas, coffees
- Twining's – teas
- Unilever – Go Organic soups and sauces
- Walker's – shortbread
- Warburton's – breads and rolls
- Weetabix – Nature's Own Weetabix and malted wheat squares
- Whitworth's – sugar

What is the main threat to the organic food market?

The exponential rate of growth of the organic market, not just in the UK but worldwide, is unprecedented, but many people feel that its very success could also sow the seeds of its destruction. The pace of growth, they believe, is far too fast for organic food, and hence organic farming, to be sustainable in the long term, and it must be allowed to grow *organically* – that is to say, at a natural pace. In reality, market forces will run their course and there is little anyone can do to stem the demand for organic food. But where there is a will there is a way. If everyone – the organic movement, governments, producers, manufacturers and consumers – plays their part, the future of organic farming will be assured.

What about food miles?

The organic movement as a whole campaigns vigorously for the notion that fresh, local food is best. However, demand for organic food is so great that around 70% of fresh produce as well as much other organic food is imported. (In fact, 70% of conventional fresh produce is imported too, but this receives much less attention.) This isn't as bad as it sounds, though. Part of the problem with using chemicals is that it enables crops to grow virtually anywhere rather than where they grow best or where they can be grown successfully without using pesticides (for instance, with organic apples in South America or organic grapes in Egypt). Second, though clocking up food miles is not ideal, as with fairly traded crops but unlike most conventional produce, buying organic will always benefit the local community. Spearheaded by Peter Segger, who runs Organic Farm Foods, one of the largest organic fresh produce businesses in the UK, the organic movement is also currently working towards an organic trading code whereby a certain proportion of crops grown is always to be sold in the local community – an important first step in resolving some of the dilemmas posed by this issue.

SHOPPING: THE BASICS

Here we concentrate on basics to guide you through the aisles as you shop for organic food. For a comprehensive guide to where to buy see the directory.

Buying, storing and cooking

Buying organic food is just like buying any other food. The only real difference is that you may at first need to spend a little more time finding your local suppliers and then locating what you want in store. It always pays to be an opportunist: keep your eye open for promotional offers and always, always take advantage of seasonal organic produce. For advice on reading the labels, see p. 76.)

Advice and tips on storing individual foods are included in the relevant sections but generally there is very little difference in how you treat organic and non-organic food, as long as you remember a couple of important points:

1 *Fresh produce* No post-harvest sprays (to prevent moulds or sprouting, or to delay ripening) are used on fresh organic produce, so organic fruit and vegetables such as potatoes, avocados, citrus fruit and peaches do not last as long. On the other hand, because organic produce often contains more dry matter, it often lasts longer. As noted earlier, much depends on how long and how well the produce has been stored before it reaches you. The general rule here is always to store fresh produce properly (see the individual food sections for advice on this) and to eat it as fresh as you can.
2 *Processed foods* Because organic sausages, burgers, cooked ham and other chilled fresh foods do not contain artificial preservatives they should be eaten as soon as possible, or frozen. Dried, packet, tinned and frozen organic foods have a similar shelf life to conventional ones. In all cases, the label will state the best-before date quite clearly.

When it comes to cooking organic generally, you will find few differences compared with conventional food. What you most need to be aware of, as already mentioned, is that tastes can be deeper, stronger, sweeter, richer, and that the texture of organic food is often denser. Organic foods do not need complex recipes – indeed, the opposite applies. They are a celebration of the good and natural things in life, and the more simply you cook them, the more they will show their natural virtues – and the more you will appreciate the food you eat and enjoy the organic experience.

EASY STEPS TO EATING ORGANIC

Once you begin eating organic food regularly, you will quickly discover that you so much prefer it that, like most people, you will want to adapt your diet, shopping habits and budget to enable you to choose as much of it as you want. Here are a few suggestions.

- Buy at least one item each time you shop.
- As a good place to start, choose everyday staples like bread, milk, yoghurt, potatoes and mushrooms – they cost only a few pence extra.
- Bear in mind that the extra cost per serving of dried goods that store well like rice, pasta, dried beans, dried fruit, and tea and coffee is minimal.
- Try something new every week.
- Sample as many different organic foods and brands as you can – from organic tortilla chips to capers.
- Snap up promotional and seasonal offers.
- Remember that baked goods such as biscuits and cakes are usually good value. Whole Earth organic cola is worth every penny.
- If potential pesticide residues are a particular concern, choose organic wholewheat pasta and bread, carrots, main-crop potatoes, winter lettuces and celery, and go for organic apples, pears, strawberries and peaches when you can.
- If you want to use the peel, choose organic lemons and other citrus fruit.
- If fair trade, sustaining the environment and avoiding pesticides are high priorities, choose fair-traded and organic bananas, pineapple, tea, coffee, cocoa and chocolate, and organic rice.
- If you want to avoid GMOs, choose organic corn products – cornflakes, tortilla chips, sweetcorn, soya and soya products; and avoid processed conventional foods with soya or its derivatives on the ingredients list.
- For the best value, go local: join a local box scheme, visit a farmers' market or organic farm shop selling their own organic dairy products, fresh produce or meat.

- Visit a local farmers' market instead of the supermarket (for details, see p. 95).
- To find out how much choice there is, visit an organic supermarket or organic shop where they will be able to help you and answer your questions.
- Use holidays to go organic – use the directory as your local guide.
- Let your fingers do the walking, and cut down on petrol, pollution and waiting in supermarket queues – shop on-line and through mail order.
- Investigate a bulk-buying group, or start your own.
- Think about joining a subscription or community farm (see p. 99). Find out what's going on organically in your area.
- Don't assume that organic food is always more expensive – check out the prices, and you will always find something to suit your pocket.
- Make your organic priority those foods you eat a lot of.
- Include organic foods priced near to their conventional equivalents, or cheaper.
- Don't forget treats: judged per spoonful or per slice, the extra cost is very little.

▲▲▲

Where to start

With so much organic food around, so much choice and such a price range, the best way of deciding on your organic shopping basket is to apply the same sort of priorities as you would to your usual one, making the change gradually. Most people who start buying organic find that the more they buy the more they want to buy. Most start with fresh produce such as bread, milk and yoghurt, and basics such as flour, pasta and pasta sauces, breakfast cereals, soups, and, increasingly, tea and coffee. Inevitably the greatest choice can be found among those organic foods that are the most popular – an own-brand version of a particular organic food is always a good indication of what is most popular. Common sense is your best guide. If you normally buy the highest-quality conventional food and like pure natural tastes, then generally you should aim for the organic equivalent, whereas if you have a favourite mass-market brand you will probably like their organic equivalent better.

Organic food for mothers-to-be, babies and toddlers Mums-to-be, babies and toddlers are a special case, and the groups above all for whom an organic diet is most important (for more, see p. 303).

Organic meat Animal welfare costs make organic meat the one item in the shopping basket that usually costs significantly more than the conventional equivalent (for more details and tips on how to buy, see p. 178).

GOOD VALUE ORGANICS

Getting the best value from organic food means adopting a pick-and-mix approach to shopping. It also means adopting a broader notion of what good value means. For example, a freshly harvested lettuce from your local box-scheme producer that meets every criterion in terms of freshness, health and taste and costs less than many you will find in the supermarket is not *good* value – it's outstanding value. The same goes for the delicious neck of organic lamb that your butcher will let you have cheaply because few people can be bothered to cook it these days. Organic budget and family brands produced by organic and converted conventional manufacturers alike do not always pass the taste or nutritional tests that premium brands pass with ease, but they generally offer a sounder choice than their conventional equivalents, as well as an additive-and preservative-free one. Any organic version of a major cash crop such as rice, bananas, tea and coffee is worth every penny extra in social and environmental terms – and if you consider the real cost of producing them, they are positively cheap. And how do you quantify the feel-good factor and the part that organic food plays in enhancing the quality of your life overall?

From a cash-wise point of view, it's a bit easier – best bets are:

- Local box schemes
- Produce bought direct from producer
- Promotional offers
- Seasonal organic produce
- Organic watercress
- Organic yoghurts
- Bulk-buying of goods such as flour, grains, muesli, dried fruit, nuts, juicing fruit and vegetables
- Cheaper cuts of meat

- Own-label products.

▲▲

How can I be sure that the food I buy is genuinely organic?
The answer, of course, is to look for the certification logo or number on the packaging (see p. 78). As noted earlier, anyone selling genuine organic food can prove it.

Do organic manufacturers test for pesticide and GMO residues?
Some do, while others rely on the paperwork that accompanies all organic food and ingredients, certifying that they have been produced and processed according to organic standards.

If I'm not satisfied, what should I do?
Take the item back and complain nicely.

LABELS AND LOGOS

Labels and logos are a fact of life when shopping for food these days, and you need to know your way around them.

What organic labels contain

An organic label tells you all you need to know about an organic product, including all of its ingredients, and often it will give you extra information about its provenance as well.

Certification logo and number The certification logo and/or number is the consumer guarantee that the product is genuinely organic.

The word 'organic' in the title Only products that have been independently certified as organic can use this term.

Ingredients list All organic ingredients are clearly marked, as well as any permitted non-organic ingredients.

Nice to know Information about what organic farming is, how the product is produced or manufactured, or information about the producer or manufacturer.

Classes of organic food

Though most organic food on sale is 100% organic, as already mentioned there are two classes of certified organic produce.

1 If the word 'organic' appears in the food's title, as in 'Organic Baked Beans', the contents must be at least 95% organic in origin, and the remainder must come from a short list of non-organic ingredients, permissible because there is no organic equivalent available at present.
2 If the label says 'Baked Beans with 70/80/90% organic ingredients, the rest of the ingredients are from the short list mentioned above, phased out as more organic ingredients become available.

For an explanation of the two classes of organic foods, see p. 78.

Demeter labelling

Demeter products (see p. 12) have their own percentage system, and their products fall into three categories

Fully Demeter These products contain 95% or more organic ingredients, of which 90% must be Demeter-certified. The label will say 'Demeter'.

50–90% Demeter Must contain 95% or more organic ingredients, of which 50–90% must be Demeter-certified. The label must not say 'Demeter', but lists the Demeter ingredients followed by the other organic ingredients.

10–50% Demeter Must contain 95% or more organic ingredients, of which 10–50% must be Demeter-certified. The label must not say 'Demeter', but lists the organic ingredients first, and the Demeter logo figures alongside the Demeter ingredients.

Why are two classes of organic food allowed?

The lack of sufficient organic ingredients, especially the less common ones that are needed for processed foods, but also common ingredients like sugar and organic eggs, has severely hampered the development of manufactured organic foods. To overcome this, and to allow the market to grow, the 70%+ ruling was brought in (see p. 77) but it was always intended as a temporary measure; further, every manufacturer has to apply to use this concession, and permission is granted on a case-by-case basis. The 70%+ category will be phased out, and since we now have so many products that are made from 100% organic ingredients the sooner this happens the better. It causes confusion and is open to abuse: a manufacturer can formulate a recipe using more of a derogated conventional ingredient to bring costs down, for example. Occasionally, as in some of the Stamp Collection's excellent special dietary products (see p. 217), where an organic ingredient has not been developed or there is a temporary shortage, this can be justified, but otherwise not.

ORGANIC RIGHTS CHECKLIST

This is what you should know:

- Only food certified as organic can legally be sold as organic.
- All organic producers and manufacturers must be able to provide proof of authenticity if required.
- It is illegal for any retailer to repackage organic goods out of sight of the customer (including local home deliveries) unless the retailer has also been certified by an approved certification body.
- All manufacturers and processors producing organic foods must also be registered and inspected by an approved certification body.
- Organic foods are regulated under the organic-products regulation EU 2092/91 (see p. 31), and enforced by law. If you are in any doubt as to authenticity, contact your local Trading Standards Officer.

The organic logos

The organic logo (or number) appears on every packet of organic food, and on boxes of food sold loose. When buying from an organic producer direct or from a certified organic shop, you will usually see their certification symbol on show. These are the logos of the main UK certification bodies.

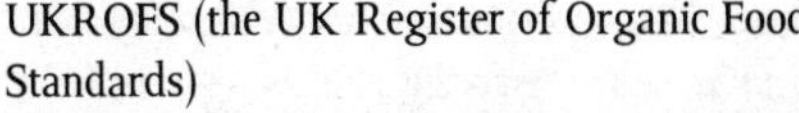

UKROFS (the UK Register of Organic Food Standards)

An independent body designated by the former Ministry of Agriculture, Fisheries and Food that administers the EU organic regulations, sets, maintains and oversees organic standards in the UK, and carries out inspections.
tel: 020 7238 6004

OF&G (Organic Farmers and Growers Ltd)
The UK's second-largest certifying organisation.
tel: 01743 440512

SOPA (Scottish Organic Producers' Association)
Certifies Scottish producers and works closely with the Soil Association.
tel: 01786 458090

OFF (Organic Food Federation)
Mainly certifies manufacturers and importers.
tel: 01760 720444

Soil Association Certification Ltd
The UK's leading certification body, and the best-known organic symbol.
tel: 0117 914 2400

Demeter/BDAA (Bio-Dynamic Agricultural Association
Certifies biodynamic farmers and their products worldwide.
tel: 01453 759501

IOFGA (Irish Organic Farmers' and Growers Association)
Certifies Irish producers and manufacturers.
tel: 00 353 506 32063

Food Certification (Scotland) Ltd
A recently accredited body which certifies organic farmed salmon only (no certification number allocated).
tel: 01463 222251

Organic Trust Ltd
An Irish certification body that certifies products in Ireland, and now authorised by UKROFS to certify UK products.
tel: 00 353 185 30271

Cmi Certification
Professional certification and inspection company for the agrifood business, the latest organisation to be accredited by UKROFS.
tel: 0131 317 2500

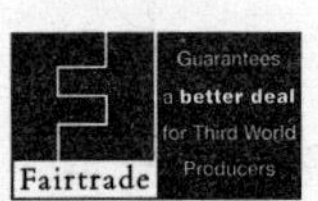

PLUS: The official Fairtrade mark of the Fairtrade Foundation, operating in the UK and guaranteeing that the product has been officially recognised as fair-traded. Look for it, for instance, on bananas, coffee, tea, chocolate, cocoa, orange juice and honey.
tel: 020 7405 5942

European certification bodies

These are some of the better-known ones that you may find on popular brands of imported manufactured foods such Allos, Biona, Bonvita, De Rit, Eunature, Lima, La Selva, Molen Aartje, Morgenland and Rapunzel: IFOAM (European-wide), KRAV (Sweden), Naturland (Germany), AIAB (Italy), CCPB (Italy), SKAL (Holland), Ecocert (European-wide)

WHAT IS FAIR TRADE?

There is some confusion about how fair-trade products fit into the organic scenario and vice versa. First introduced in the 1980s, fairly traded products aim to give a better deal to workers and small producers living in communities in less developed countries, particularly as regards prices paid, wages and living conditions. Companies that deal in fairly traded products also provide comprehensive social and welfare packages, including education and medical aid. In this way they offer consumers a more socially responsible product. Fairly traded products include handicrafts, jewellery, clothing, paper items, and a growing selection of food and drinks such as the commodity crops listed below, nuts, dried fruit, honey, dried herbs and spices, and preserves.

Fair-trade products come from a variety of companies. Some, such as Traidcraft and Oxfam (who have their own 'Fair Trade' logo), have for over twenty years been buying and selling products from poor or disadvantaged producers in the Third World in order to enable them to live more secure lives. Other fair-trade products come from more mainstream companies. Standards of fair trade can vary, which is why eighteen countries across Europe and North America now have a fair-trade consumer label, which appears on products as a guarantee that the producer has had a fair deal, for instance Max Havelaar in the Netherlands and TransFair in Germany. All share a common set of standards and are independently monitored through an international body, the Fairtrade Labelling Organisations International.

Tea, coffee, cocoa, chocolate, honey and bananas have all become successful fair-trade commodities. To date these are the only products, apart from oranges and sugar, to be covered by fair-trade labels. The UK's fair-trade label is the black and white Fairtrade mark, which you will see on these products on supermarket shelves and elsewhere. Like organic producers, manufacturers of Fairtrade-labelled products pay a monitoring fee and are inspected regularly. In addition, many companies operate their own voluntary 'fairly-traded' policies, but without the label they are not certified as Fair-traded.

What is the difference between organic and fair trade?

The essential difference between fair trade and organic is that organic logos guarantee a method of production, whereas fair-trade logos guarantee a particular method of trading, which includes a preset minimum price for crops irrespective of world prices. This means that organic products may or may not be fair-traded, and that fair-traded products may or may not be organic. Both sets of standards incorporate some of the other's ideals: for example, fair-trade standards discourage the use of chemicals and encourage environmentally friendly farming, and social and working practices are included in IFOAM's and other organic farming standards. The dream ticket is to have both. Because of the natural affinity of organic and fair-trade ideals, and of their organisations, increasingly this is beginning to happen.

Fair-trade organic products that you can buy

The following list, compiled by the Fairtrade Foundation, is a guide to Fairtrade organic products currently available, all endorsed with the Fairtrade mark. The list is constantly updated as new products are launched, and can be seen on their website at **www.fairtrade.org.uk/products.htm**. The Fairtrade Foundation also supply full details of product suppliers.

Chocolate and cocoa

- Equal Exchange organic cocoa is available from wholefood shops, delicatessens and by mail order.
- Green & Black's organic milk chocolate, Maya Gold chocolate and cocoa are available in most major supermarkets. Small 20g bars are sold in selected Sainsbury's and healthfood stores.
- Oxfam Masca organic cappuccino, milk, orange milk and plain chocolates are available in Oxfam shops.
- Traidcraft's organic chocolate bar range includes milk, plain, cappuccino and praline, available from Traidcraft and One World shops.

Coffee

- Organic Cafédirect and Machu Picchu ground coffees and decaffeinated freeze-dried instant coffees are sold in all major supermarkets, at Costa

Coffee, and are available from Oxfam, Tradecraft and Equal Exchange.

- Equal Exchange organic medium-roast, dark-roast and decaffeinated ground coffees and whole beans, as well as espresso fine-ground, Sumatran Takegon and Colombian Excelso ground coffees, are available from health- and wholefood shops, and by mail order.
- Percol Latin American organic ground coffee is available in all major supermarkets. Their organic Americano and espresso blends are stocked by Waitrose and Budgen.

Tea

- Equal Exchange organic Assam, Breakfast, Earl Grey, Darjeeling, Green Tea and Jasmine Green tea-bags and loose tea, and Earl Green, Lemon Green, Masala Chai and Mint Green tea-bags, are sold in health- and wholefood shops, delicatessens, and by mail order.
- Hampstead Tea & Coffee Company organic Biochai Masala, First Flush, Makaibari Darjeeling, Green and Oolong loose teas, and Wildwood and Earl Grey tea-bags, are sold in specialist shops and by mail order.
- Ridgways organically grown tea is available as tea-bags and loose tea, from most major supermarkets.
- Themis organic Memory, Vigour, Slimming and Vitality tea-bags are sold in healthfood shops.

Honey

- Equal Exchange set or clear organic honey is available from wholefood shops, delicatessens and by mail order.

Snacks and biscuits

- Equal Exchange plain-chocolate-covered Brazil nuts are available at selected Sainsbury's, wholefood shops and by mail order.
- Organic Brazil nut cookies are available from Traidcraft.

Sugar

- Equal Exchange organic raw cane sugar is available in health- and wholefood shops, and by mail order.
- Traidcraft organic raw cane sugar is stocked in One World shops, and sold by mail order.

Stockists

Fair-trade products are available at supermarkets, One World shops, wholefood shops and at Out of this World, and through Traidcraft and Oxfam. The following organisations offer a mail order service:

Equal Exchange	0131 220 3484
Hampstead Tea & Coffee	020 8731 9833
Oxfam Fair-trade Co	01392 429 428
Traidcraft	0191 491 0855
Fair-trade Foundation	020 7405 5942

Other food-quality logos

Schemes such as LEAF, Freedom Foods and the latest Red Truck food-assurance scheme all offer improved conventional standards of animal welfare or improved environmental practices, and usually represent quite large or large-scale farming enterprises rather than small producers. But none ban the use of pesticides, artificial nitrates or GM animal feeds for example, and they should not be confused with organic labels. The same applies to other green-sounding food-items found on labels such as 'traditional' and 'farmhouse', which also offer variations or improvements on intensive food-production systems.

5: Where to Buy and Eat Organic Food

It has never been easier to buy organic food (and drink), but don't just rely on what your regular supermarket has to offer – explore all the other possibilities too and gradually build up a list of organic suppliers and outlets that work for you. A visit to an organic supermarket or organic shop is a must. The other must is, whenever you can, to visit local organic farm shops and producers who sell direct. Buying direct from producers, especially meat, will help you to build up your personal organic 'taste bank'. The directory on pp. 405–535 has been specially designed with this in mind, and includes places to eat organic too.

The Organic Directory published by Green Books (tel: 01803 863260), and the various *Green Guides* published by Green Guide Publishing (tel: 0207 354 2709) are invaluable sources for where to buy organic food. The other really useful resource are organic websites that have lists of suppliers or that enable you to search for the ones in your areas; these are listed in chapter 15.

SUPERMARKETS

Conventional supermarkets

Supermarkets offer convenience and ready access to organic food. Their range has increased substantially. Organic food features and recipes appear regularly in their magazines, and most produce organic literature explaining the basics. At the last count Sainsbury's now stocks around 1,300, Waitrose 1,200 and Tesco around 1,000 organic lines. Other major multiples range from 200 to 700 or so.

The arrival of the complete supermarket organic Christmas dinner in 1999 was a landmark, and today at the best stores it is possible to do a complete organic shop. Remember, when comparing prices against non-organic items, to compare organic with the conventional *equivalent* and not the cheapest the supermarket has to offer. And check the prices per kilo rather than just looking at the price ticket, which might have been calculated differently.

Other points to bear in mind about conventional supermarkets are:

- The availability of organic goods varies considerably from store to store. Those in affluent areas and major cities, and large 'show-case' stores, contain the biggest range.
- All produce is sourced through accredited suppliers and organisations. In addition, Sainsbury's, Tesco, Marks & Spencer and Waitrose, for example, operate their own independent monitoring. The Soil Association symbol is the most commonly found, followed by OF&G.
- Supermarkets adopt the same standards of quality control for organic as for conventional vegetables and fruit, though they allow some relaxation over their size and their cosmetic appearance.
- Organic goods may be grouped together in the store, or found with conventional products, or occasionally, both.
- Conventional supermarkets have their own brands of 'green', environmentally friendly produce – for example, 'Nature's Choice', 'Heritage', 'Farm-Assured', 'Traditional', 'Naturally Reared' – and are committed to integrated crop-management schemes such as Linking Environment and Farming (LEAF). But although these offer improved standards, foods sold under these labels have been produced by conventional methods and should not be confused with organic foods.
- Leading multiples now offer own brand organic products.

Supermarket shopping tips

1. Ask a member of staff where you can find the organic food and drink, and take the time to get to know where it is. If you have a choice, check out other supermarket chains in your area to see if their organic options suit you better.
2. Stock up on organic promotional offers and keep an eye out for more, as they change regularly.
3. Supermarkets are still increasing their ranges – so keep an eye open too for new organic products.
4. Give your store feedback, and help them to help you. Tell them what you'd like to see, or aren't happy with. If there is something they don't stock, make a point of asking for it. As long as the chain stocks it, they will usually do their best to supply it for you.

Organic supermarkets

A visit to an organic supermarket can be a baptism of fire. They have gone from strength to strength and are the new movers and shakers of the retail food business: the new breed of lifestyle retail outlet, relatively small, customer-friendly, modern, spacious and stylish, where you can choose products that have an ethically clean bill of health, are good for you and good for the planet – and enjoy and pamper yourself at the same time.

All are dedicated to making shopping pleasurable again. Their commitment to the organic cause is total – and highly infectious. To step over the threshold is not just to taste the future, but to enter a different world; a special shopping experience that will keep you coming back time and time again. Nice-to-haves like juice bars, head massages, reflexology, and advice on natural beauty and healthcare are becoming a fixture in the larger stores – how have we managed without them all this time?

Pricewise, they vary. As Nature Intended and Here, for example, aim to be particularly price-conscious – though all, because of increased competition from the major multiples, are aware of the need to match conventional supermarket prices when they can. Generally speaking, you can expect to pay a bit more some or most of the time. The reason for this is obvious: their buying power compared with a major multiple's might is no competition. Location is another factor. As far as London is concerned, you will always pay more for your food, organic or otherwise, in Chelsea, for example, because of the huge rents that any central London site commands. In addition, because organic supermarkets provide a much better choice of brands and search out to support small, high-quality organic producers, their price range is wider than conventional supermarkets. However, you will find plenty of good deals, and many exceptions to the rule. Though each organic supermarket has its own distinctive style and ambience, they share many common characteristics:

- They are not always exclusively organic but sell a range of other natural/health/ethical (sometimes even conventional) goods as well; everything they sell, however, must satisfy their own codes of ethical shopping.
- The atmosphere is fun and personalised, and the staff are friendly and knowledgeable, keen to give you whatever organic advice and information you may need.
- They offer a high level of customer involvement, including events, regular

tastings and presentations. Fresh & Wild and As Nature Intended, for example, also produce a range of particularly informative leaflets.

- Other extras include organic juice bars, takeaways and occasionally, cafés, home deliveries and crèches.

At the moment all the major stores operate in London, though expansion into other cities is planned. The ethical co-operative chain, Out of This World, specialises in organic food and has stores in Newcastle and Nottingham. All those in London have organic fresh produce sections that the best greengrocers would be proud of. Planet Organic in Westbourne Grove has an impressive meat and butchery section; Planet Organic's deli in their Torrington Road branch is equally impressive. Planet Organic and Fresh & Wild have great food-to-go.

For addresses etc, see the directory.

INDEPENDENT SHOPS

With the move of organic food into the mainstream, it has become more commonplace for conventional food shop, greengrocers, bakers, cheesemongers and high-quality butchers to stock some organic produce, so it's always worth checking whether your local food shops have become part of the trend. General food shops concentrate on popular basic items, such as dairy products, organic chocolate, oats and organic flour. Good delis stock a wider variety, including some organic cheeses, pasta and pasta sauces, olive oil and so on. London is a special case. The capital has virtually gone organic – for a résumé, see the directory.

Organic shops

These are the next-best thing to shopping in an organic supermarket. The best, such as long-time stalwarts, the Cook's Delight in Berkhamsted, Hertfordshire, and Bumblebee in North London, have as wide a range as most organic supermarkets, and the total number of organic lines stocked can be over 2,000. All have the same dedication, are personally run, and offer the best of everything (or almost everything) an organic shopper could possibly want. To find your nearest, consult the directory and the websites offering local searches in chapter 15.

Although some are larger than others or have a more extensive range, all organic shops sell as wide a range of organic food and drink as possible, as well as non-food items such as organic and natural bodycare products and cosmetics, eco-friendly cleaning products and organic clothing.

Organic shops (and farm shops) are a critical element in the go-local movement. They support local organic producers and offer an organic focus for the community as well as a friendly, informative place to shop. Like all independents, they have to compete with supermarkets, so it is vital that we support them. Most customers, once they have found such a shop in their locality, are hooked.

A few other points:

- Some organic shops are 100% organic, while others sell mainly organic food plus other 'health' foods. The number of organic lines stocked ranges from around 500–700 to over 2,000. Special requests are catered for.
- Some have a very small range of organic meat, or only frozen, or fresh meat on certain days only.
- Some produce their own takeaway meals using organic ingredients or run a small 'organic' snackbar or café on the premises, while others sell organic sandwiches and tea and coffee.
- Many operate home delivery and/or box schemes, and sell the produce of local organic growers – which offers very good value.
- Generally, you can expect goods to be on sale at recommended retail prices, with discounts for buying loose or in bulk.
- Promotional offers, tasting and seasonal events, newsletters and an information board are regular features.
- Most organic shops are certified organic; note that not all of those who technically *should* be certified are, and that others not required by law to be certified elect to do so in order to give their customers added reassurance of their commitment.

NOTE: Although, apart from seasonal differences, you can expect stable prices for most products, prices for organic foods tend to vary from one shop to the next. This is because overheads vary considerably, depending on the kind of shop, its location, and so on. A small shop in a region well serviced by organic producers, such as Devon, Somerset and parts of Wales, can source organic food easily; those in areas where organic suppliers are scarce must work harder and transport the food further. Also since small shops do not have the buying power of multiples, they have to pay more for organic goods at wholesale. In addition, they support small producers, wastage may be higher, and staff costs are considerable.

Organic farm shops

The best, such as the award-winning Abbey Home Farm Shop in Cirencester – which has an excellent organic café and a wide range of home-made organic takeaways – and Scragoak Farm Shop in Kent and Growing Concern in Leicestershire, are inspirational cornucopias of organic everything. Biodynamic farm shops such as that belonging to the Camphill Communities at Loch Arthur in Beeswing, Dumfries, are very special too. All offer an opportunity not just to buy produce direct, but to meet the producers and see how organic fare is produced.

Produce that comes from the farm itself is generally excellent value. Fresh produce, in particular, can be 15–20% cheaper than organic produce from elsewhere; meat and dairy produce are also cheaper. Bought-in produce varies in price, depending on the supply chain – for instance, on whether the farm shop buys direct from another producer, via wholesale outlets or other intermediary sources. Discounts may be offered for bulk-buying.

Organic farm shops, of which several are exclusively organic, range from simple to impressively well stocked. And they need to be supported for exactly the same reasons that organic shops need to be supported. These are the basics that you need to know:

- All organic farm shops sell produce from their own farm; many also sell bought-in fresh organic produce.
- Many sell other products such as bread, flour, dried goods, oils, drinks, wines, beers, jams and confectionery. As with other outlets, produce sold as 'organic' will be certified.
- Organic farm shops may also sell conventional wholefoods and other items.
- Some may specialise in only meat or only fresh produce.
- Farm shops are open all year, opening times vary, so telephone first to check.
- They must conform to the same health-and-safety, labelling and trading standards as all retail shops.

In addition, many farms and smallholdings sell their organic produce direct – these are classified as 'farm-gate' outlets. Prices are usually lower than

those at a farm shop, but range and facilities are more limited. Phone first to check opening times and availability.
NOTE: Although reared or grown using organic methods, *not* everything produced on an organic farm is necessarily certified as organic; if this is the case, it will not be sold as organic. Some farm shops sell a selection of organic and high-animal-welfare, additive-free meat.

Organic butchers

The growing band of butchers specialising in organic meat, that have emerged over the last two years, is a cause for celebration. They offer consumers the best of both worlds: certified organic meat plus the advice, hanging facilities, expertise and pleasure that shopping from a real butcher's shop brings. If you have one in your area, try it out.

All those I have spoken to source their organic meat from well known and respected organic wholesalers such as Black Mountain Foods, the Welsh Organic Meat Centre and Pure Organic Foods (for details of these, see pp. 192–3). For advice on meat generally, see chapter 8.

Healthfood and wholefood shops

Both have increased their organic ranges considerably. Generally they stock store-cupboard basics such as dried foods, biscuits, canned soups and beans, breakfast cereals, soya products, juices and jams, oils, and often dairy products as well; some sell fresh produce too, plus eco-friendly household products. The two major healthfood chains, Health and Diet Centres (South East England) and Holland & Barrett, have increased their ranges.

Whereas healthfood shops focus as much on nutritional supplements as on food, wholefood shops specialise in natural and unrefined foods and, after organic shops and farm shops, increasingly offer the widest range of organic foods available (and usually with discounts for bulk-purchasing). Our research, which involved contacting and speaking to hundreds of shops up and down the country, has shown that many healthfood and wholefood shops now stock 15–40% organic foods, so it's always worth checking your local ones to see. *Wholefood co-operatives* are wholefood shops owned by their staff.

Oxfam and Traidcraft

As well as their own fair-traded foods, Oxfam sell organic Zambian honey, Café Latino and instant Mexicafé coffee, Maya Gold chocolate bars, cashew nuts, dried apricots and sultanas. The range varies from shop to shop. Traidcraft shops sell own-label organic coffee beans, dried apricots and honey.

London

The capital is spoilt for choice – see, for instance, the list of markets on pp. 93–4. Apart from the dedicated organic shops and supermarkets, Harvey Nichols and Selfridges Food Halls, and Terence Conran's Bluebird food complex, continue to stock an excellent range of organic foods, and Harrods and Fortnum & Mason now stock some. London also has its first organic delicatessen, Deli Organic. For addresses, see directory.

WORTH THE DETOUR . . .

The following list are examples of organic shops and farm shops that have won awards or commendations in the annual Soil Association Organic Food Awards, or that I have visited, or been inspired by. All can be located in the directory.

- Abbey Home Farm Shop, Cirencester, Glos.
- Beanies, Sheffield
- Brockhill Farm Organic Shop, Bracknell, Berks.
- Bumble Bee, North London
- Castletown Farm Shop, Carlisle, Cumbria
- Church Farm Organics, Wirral
- Cook's Delight, Berkhamsted, Herts
- Damhead, Edinburgh
- Phoenix Stores, Findhorn, Grampian
- Godshill Organics, Isle of Wight
- Gourmet Organix, Lynton, Devon
- Marshford Organic Farm Shop, Bideford, Devon
- Old Plaw Hatch, East Grinstead, E. Sussex
- Olivers Wholefood Store, Kew, Surrey
- Organic Health, Canterbury, Kent
- Owls Barn Organic Farm Shop, Christchurch, Dorset
- Pumpkin Organic, Gloucester
- Purely Organic Foods, Leamington Spa, Warks.
- Ravens Oak Dairy, Nantwich, Cheshire
- Riverford Farm Shop, Totnes, Devon

Grassroots, Glasgow
Growing Concern, Loughborough, Leics
Highfield Harvest, Topsham, Devon
Honeybrooks Organics Farm Shop, Burwash, E. Sussex
Infinity Foods, Brighton, E. Sussex
Loch Arthur Creamery, Beeswing, Dumfries
Longwood Farm, Bury St Edmunds, Suffolk
Lurgan Farm Shop, Aberfeldy, Perthshire
Marshford Organic Shop, Barnstaple, Devon
Ryton Organic Gardens Shop, Coventry
Seasons Forest Row, Forest Row, E. Sussex
Scragoak Farm Shop, Robertsbridge, E. Sussex
Sheffield Wholefoods, Sheffield
Standfield Hall Farm Shop, Pickering, N. Yorks.
The Organic Oasis, Haywards Heath, W. Sussex
The Organic Shop, Stow on the Wold, Glos
The Organic Stores, nr Chester
The Tree House, Aberystwyth

MARKETS

Traditional markets

Although you can find organic stalls in traditional and covered markets, the situation here has not changed in the last few years, and not much organic food is sold through them. The award-winning Global Organics stall in Stroud market (Wednesdays and Fridays) is one outstanding exception.

London's markets

In London, there are five markets specialising in organic food, where you can buy fruit and vegetables direct from the producers – meat, dairy produce, breads and, depending on the market, other goods such as organic tofu, pickles and relishes, wines and other beverages. As with all markets, it pays to get there early, to get the best choice. Prices vary, but are lower than retail outlets.

Borough Market Borough High Street, London Bridge SE1; website **www.boroughmarket.org.uk**.
Fridays, 12 am–6 pm, Saturdays, 9 am–4 pm.
Not exclusively organic, but a lovely market with some excellent organic produce, including Flour Power City's amazing bread stall. Neal's Yard

Dairy has a shop just outside. The market's excellent website lists current food providers.

Camden Organic Market Camden Lock Place, Camden, NW1 8AL
Saturdays, Sundays, 9 am–6 pm
Fruit, vegetables, herbs, breads, cheese.

Greenwich Organic Market off Stockwell Street, Greenwich, SE10
Saturday, 10 am–4 pm
Fruit, vegetables, meat, breads, cheese

Portobello Road Organic Market Portobello Road, N10
Thursday, 11 am–6 pm
A small market, with around half a dozen regular stalls. Fruit, vegetables, meat, breads, pickles and conserves.

Spitalfields Organic Food Market Old Spitalfields Market, Brushfield Street, E1 6AA
Tel: 01279 446663
Sunday, 10 am–5 pm
Established in 1992, this is London's largest organic market, part of Spitalfields' larger market, which is housed in a listed three-acre glass-covered Victorian building. Around a dozen organic stalls selling fruit, vegetables, meat, dairy produce, breads, cheese, tofu, tea and coffee, and wines. Raw Health (p. 287) demonstrate Oscar juicers there. Longwood Farm (p. 413) has a permanent shop for meat, and their shop next door, Unwin's Organic Provisions, sells dairy produce, groceries and dried goods.

Farmers' markets

In the last two years farmers' markets, where producers sell direct to the public, have enjoyed a spectacular success and become a shopping phenomenon in their own right. Many people assume that most of the stalls at farmers' markets are organic. In fact, though you will always find organic producers there – and farmers' markets are one of the best and most enjoyable ways of sourcing local organic food – this is not the case; most stallholders are caring conventional producers. Producers in conversion to organic systems often have stalls in farmers' markets too.

Whether organic or not, farmers' markets are special. They are at the forefront of the 'Go Local' movement and symbolise a return to how markets used to be. They benefit producers, the community and the environment, cut food miles to a minimum, and offer the ultimate local shopping experience. Over two hundred are now held, weekly or monthly, up and down the country, several in cities including London and its suburbs, with new ones starting up all the time.

Farmers' markets vary in size and in what they offer. Some come and go, some operate only in the summer, some are very small and very local, others attract huge crowds and offer family entertainment and craft stalls as well. All aim to create an atmosphere that is vibrant, upbeat and fun and make shopping a sociable and enjoyable experience.

FARMERS' MARKETS – THE ESSENTIALS

What can I buy?

Farmers' markets operate strict codes of practice. Apart from the codes that apply to all retail outlets:

- All products must be grown, bred, caught, pickled, brewed, baked, smoked, processed or made by the stallholders themselves. No middlemen or bought-in produce is permitted and the farmer/producer (or family member) must sell the wares themselves.
- Foods on sale typically include breads, vegetables, fruit, herbs, milk, cream, cheese, eggs, meat, fish, bacon, smoked and cooked meats, honey and other bee products, preserves, wine-cider, apple juice and cordials. Often the varieties of fruit and vegetables will be local, the meat will come from rare breeds, there will be seasonal delights such as turnip tops and treats such as unpasteurised Guernsey or Jersey cream that are a rarity anywhere else. Generally, home-made fare such as cakes or savouries contain one or more local ingredient.
- Though local foods are the major attraction, often there is a plant or herb stall, and some markets allow local crafts as well.

How are they organised?

- Each market is run independently and has its own set of rules that traders must adhere to. The National Association of Farmers' Markets (a partnership between the Farm Retail Association, the National Farmers' Union, the Soil Association and Envolve), to which the majority belong, has established common standards to protect the integrity of farmers' markets for consumers and traders.
- Traders are vetted by the organisers, and preference is given to organic producers and those committed to sustainable and environmentally friendly farming practices.
- Traders must farm within a given radius of the market venue, usually 30–40 miles, sometimes less. Major cities such as London seek traders from further afield, but no further, usually, than 100 miles.
- Quality control is strict, and traders are encouraged to sell only high-quality produce. Prices will be similar to those in local shops or at the farm gate.

Shopping tips and market know-how

- Markets operate within fixed hours, from around 9–10 am to 1–3 pm; check dates, details and opening times before you go. Traders cannot sell goods before the official opening time, and markets finish promptly.
- Check out public transport facilities, proximity to a car park and toilets, and whether the market is covered or not.
- For the best selection, go as early as you can.
- Take plenty of cash and small change, and a large stout shopping bag. In summer, a coolbox is useful.
- Have a good look around before you buy. Talk to traders, ask as many questions as you want about their wares and how they are produced, and accept tastings.

▲▲▲

How do I find out about my local farmers' markets, or markets elsewhere?

They are all advertised locally – or contact the following:

1 National Association of Farmers' Markets

South Vaults
Green Park Station
Green Park Road
Bath BA1 1JB
email: nafm@farmersmarkets.net
website: **www.farmersmarkets.net**
Send a large SAE for a full list of farmers' markets in the UK, and to find out how to start your own, or visit their website.

2 London Farmers' Markets
6 St Paul Street
London N1 7AB
tel: 020 7704 9659
email: infoelfm.demon.co.uk
website: **www.londonfarmersmarket.com**
Send a large SAE for a list of farmers' markets in London and the UK, or visit their website. For a list of London's main farmers' markets, see the London section of the directory.

LOCAL IS BEST

The phenomenal success of farmers' markets has brought home to many people that where food is concerned, organic or not, local is best. Increasingly, too, local authorities and other organisations, including the National Farmers' Union, and even the government, are coming round to the view that food produced and consumed locally offers a sustainable way forward for everyone. The recent foot-and-mouth outbreak, when the nonsense of trucking animals hundreds of miles around the country for slaughter, and the consequences that such practices can cause, horrified the nation and may have had something to do with this apparent change of heart.

Locally produced food is fresher, healthier and more economical; it cuts down on transport costs and packaging, helps communities to thrive, restores trust and reconnects the consumer to the farmer, and makes buying food a pleasurable and meaningful experience again. A grassroots movement that is flourishing worldwide, local buying initiatives extend to cities and include all kinds of community and farming projects, as well as national and local campaigns. Farmers' markets, for example, began in America in the 1970s, and there are now over 2,500 generating over $1 billion worth of income annually for growers. The Seikatsu Club, a consumer co-operative in Japan, was started by a group of Japanese women who wanted to buy fresh organic produce. It now has 153,000 members and is famous worldwide. The Bio Co-op consumer co-operatives in France, started in 1987, are run by and for local organic consumers; today over 160 branches operate all over France. Bio Co-op Lisbon has recently started in Portugal, and there are similar initiatives in India and elsewhere.

Wherever we live local buying is something we can all get involved in and help to nurture. The directory at the end of the book is designed, in part, with this in mind. Many tourist boards and the economic development departments of local authorities now produce a local food directory; if yours does not have one, ask it to provide one. Buying organic and fair-traded food (see p. 81) and goods, meanwhile, because these are predominantly produced on a small scale, helps local communities and cultures in other countries to flourish.

I am beginning to realise more and more – as the examples here show – the power for good that consumers have. A few years ago the idea of local food was anathema to many supermarkets, but now some are adapting their buying ethos to stock some local produce in regional stores. If consumers create the demand, they will respond – the task for them is to do so responsibly.

Going local can take many forms. Two kinds of initiative that we can expect to see more of in future are city farms and subscription and community farming.

City farms and community gardens

City farms and community gardens are run for and by local communities so as to bring the country to the city. Their motto, 'Plant a seed and grow a community', says it all. They range from nature gardens, allotments and ecological parks to working demonstration city farms. All provide a haven for wildlife and a green focus for local people, especially children. Many grow and sell food using organic methods and practise composting and recycling. The UK has 65 city farms and around 1,200 community gardens, attracting over 3 million visitors a year and benefiting 300,000 local people.

City farms are very varied, and no two are exactly the same. They range from, for instance, the small community orchard in the idyllic village of Lustleigh in Devon, owned by the parish council, where locals are free to take what they want for their own use and part of the crop is sold for cider to help with the upkeep, to the 220-acre farm and sustainable demonstration centre, Earth Balance, in Bomarsund, north of Newcastle in Northumberland, set up with funding from the county council and where North East Organic Growers grow their organic produce for their box scheme (see p. 440). To find out more about city farms and if there is one near you, visit their website (see the box below) or contact them directly on 0117 923 1800.

Subscription and community farms

In the past, farms have been mainly under private ownership. Now collective schemes are emerging that allow people to get more involved, to become social investors and to reap a share of the harvest. There are many models, but two broad types. Subscription farms, already well established in America and Japan, are a variation on box schemes, where you can pay in advance for a share of the harvest which is then divided up and supplied to you as a weekly box. Members also help with the growing, harvesting and packing. Perry Court Biodynamic Farm near Canterbury in Kent (p. 458) is one such example. Community-owned farms, on the other hand, enable you to part-own a local farm by buying a modest number of shares. Members help with the running of the farm, which is owned co-operatively by all. Tablehurst biodynamic farm in Forest Row, Sussex (p. 468) is one of these.

At the moment in the UK, ventures that offer an ongoing hands-on partnership between consumers and farmers are new, sporadic and very local, but we can expect more novel initiatives that will enable consumers to get involved at a practical level with the production of their food. As a first step, the Soil Association has published an excellent report with case studies, 'A Share in the Harvest', price £15. Order direct 0117 929 0661 or from their website: **www.soilassociation.org**.

Interested? A new venture, run by Richard Prince and Jill Ferguson, Organics at Cost Ltd, is a subscription farm scheme in the making. Anyone interested in joining their Family Farm Club and becoming a founder member of their subscription farm, which they hope to buy in the Bedford/ Buckinghamshire area, should ring them on 01278 741584 or visit their website at **www.organicsatcost.co.uk**.

East Anglian Food Link

One of the first organisations to develop the concept of local organic food for local people, the EAFL is a non-profit-making advice and consultancy co-operative and a useful contact point for what's happening locally in East Anglia. For their free booklet, listing organic producers, retail outlets and farmers' markets, send an A5 SAE with two extra first-class stamps for p&p to East Anglia Food Link, 49a High St, Watton, Thetford, Norfolk IP25 6AB. To find out more about them, visit their website: **www.eafl.org.uk** or phone 01953 889200.

▼▼

LOCAL FOOD LINKS: GETTING STARTED

These are some of the many ways you can access local food and become involved in the 'go local movement'. Relevant websites are included here for easy reference:

- Box schemes
- Farmers' markets: **www.farmersmarkets.net**
- London farmers' markets: **www.londonfarmersmarkets.com**
- WI markets: **www.wimarkets.co.uk**

- Farm shops
- Food co-ops and community buying groups
- City farms, community gardens and orchards: **www.farmgarden.org.uk**
- Local food directories
- Soil Association local food links: **www.soilassociation.org**

▲▲

BOX SCHEMES

Box schemes have revolutionised the buying of organic vegetables, and continue to be a phenomenal success. For many thousands of families their weekly box of organic products is an enduring delight, one of the highlights of their week. In the last couple of years many more local schemes have been set up, while regional and national box schemes have diversified effectively into mail order/online or home delivery services, offering an ever-widening range of organic food and drink as well as non-food items. Online organic supermarkets (see p. 361) all offer boxes of produce, and Waitrose have launched the first supermarket online box scheme, Waitrose Organics Direct.

Generally speaking, standards are high, in terms both of produce quality and of customer service.

Box schemes offer a different way of shopping and eating organically grown produce. Their appeal is twofold. The best (usually local) enable consumers to enjoy a weekly box or bag of the freshest and healthiest seasonal vegetables either grown or purchased direct from the grower, with a flavour that can be out of this world and a variety that can be stunning. Second, whether local or not, box schemes forge that valuable link with the land that modern lifestyles have lost.

Though the term 'box scheme' persists, because so many have diversified into home delivery services and there are so many variants on the theme, the term is beginning only really to apply to traditional local box schemes. Because they vary in scope and in the kind of services they offer, it is well worth checking those available in your area, to see which is likely to suit you best. The core idea, however, of offering customers a mixed box of seasonal certified organic produce, with as much coming from the UK as possible and for a fixed price, remains immutable. To find ones near to you see the directory.

Freshness and quality

The shelf life of vegetables and fruit naturally varies from one type to the next, and all produce requires delicate, professional and speedy handling at all times if it is to reach you in the best condition. This is an impossible task, but box-scheme operators do the best they can. Freshness also depends on the time of year. A lettuce that is cut on a hot day, unless kept cool, will wilt within half an hour – yet is still far fresher than one you will buy in a shop.

Thanks to supermarkets, whatever we may say about it, consumers have come to associate quality not only with freshness and taste but with all the extras such as trimming, washing, grading and appropriate packaging. And whereas you will get the most alive vegetables from a local box scheme, you will sometimes find better quality control, including trimming and packaging, in regional and national box schemes. The reason is not far to seek: these will have better packing facilities, and many operate state-of-the-art temperature-controlled storage conditions. All operators, whether local, regional or national, aim to get produce to you as fast as possible.

Ultimately, 'freshness' depends on the supply chain – how many times produce has been passed on or how far it has travelled before reaching you.

Ask your box-scheme operator where they source their produce and what precautions they take to keep it in optimum condition. Finally, no one these days should expect to pay for third-rate organic vegetables. If, for any reason, this is your experience, write a letter to the certification body and change to another box scheme.

Value for money

The majority of box schemes offer very good value for money. Prices for fixed boxes depend on the type of scheme and the size of the box, and are fixed for the year, irrespective of what the box contains.

Local: A traditional local box scheme may offer produce up to 30–40% cheaper than retail prices. Indeed, if the truth be known, they are too cheap, and customers who have access to them are very lucky people. Boxes still start from £5 and rarely exceed £15–£20, with £7–£12 the average price you can expect to pay. Many offer bulk-buying of surpluses, making prices even more economical. Delivery charges other than to named drop-off points usually incur a small extra charge.

Regional and national: These box schemes incur more direct costs: they employ more people, give more customer option, and transport and packing costs are much higher. In effect they offer a personalised home delivery service, and what you get usually represents very good value, though some schemes are more expensive than others. Their prices, which include delivery, range from around £12–£15 for basic starter boxes to up to around £25–£30 for large family boxes.

Imported produce

Many people are shocked to learn that most box schemes contain imported produce. The main reason for this, as noted earlier, is that the amount of UK organic produce available, including basics such as carrots and potatoes, is still nowhere sufficient to satisfy demand (though much as I dislike reporting it, I have heard accounts of organic wholesalers turning away UK produce in favour of cheaper imported produce when supplying box schemes and organic shops). Also, customers now want not just avocados in their box but a wide variety – including organic tomatoes and organic apples – all year round, which can only be achieved using imported produce. It's worth remembering, though, that should there be an unexpected severe frost or catastrophic floods, imported produce can be a lifeline for everyone.

In practice, the amount of imported produce used by local box schemes is minimal. In regional and national schemes it averages out at about 30%, but in the 'hungry gap' – late spring – it may reach up to 70%. Though imported produce is sourced on the open market, many operators develop their own links and form partnerships with organic growers all over the world – things may even out after all. Anyway, your box-scheme operator will be happy to tell you which produce has been imported, so you can always ask not to have it, if you prefer. In Denmark, for example, their largest box scheme, Aarstiderne (website **www.aarstiderne.com**), which has 10,000 customers per week, offers a 'dogmatic box' for people who will eat only local or Danish-grown organic produce. An idea that could catch on here.

Do all box schemes have to be certified?

Any grower or company that either grows organic produce or packs organic produce out of sight of the customer must themselves be inspected and certified by one of the approved certification bodies. This means that virtually all box schemes must be certified. The only exception is where the box-scheme operator handles customer inquiries and takes the orders but the boxes themselves are made up and sent out to customers from a certified packer. In reality, however, to avoid any confusion and to give their customers added assurance, box-scheme operators in this position usually undergo certification.

Are box schemes for me?

Most people who subscribe to organic box schemes of whatever kind become devotees. Research has shown that those who join local schemes don't just rediscover how good vegetables are and how much flavour they have – they rediscover also the joy of eating in season. And knowing the producer adds a human dimension that a supermarket never can. People find that they eat and cook more vegetables, and that their children eat more too. Many are surprised to discover that the lack of choice is not a drawback but a bonus – there is an excitement in what this week will bring, and you find yourself cooking vegetables that you may not usually cook, such as beetroot or Swiss chard. Similarly, many of those who join regional or national box schemes speak enthusiastically of the flavour of the vegetables and the convenience they offer.

However, getting the best out of a box scheme is a two-way process, one that requires a change of attitude in the customer. A box scheme does not offer you a year-round supply of anything you want, the produce will not be perfect, and delivery in cities can be erratic. Furthermore, eating in season has its low points too. While summer boxes are universally a delight, most winter boxes inevitably focus on roots and greens. If your vegetable consumption is very low, or you don't relish the thought of eating parsnip (or swede), however fresh, every week for two months, if you are wedded to your weekly supermarket shop or don't particularly value the less tangible benefits that box schemes offer, they are probably not for you.

The small print

Joining up with a box scheme is easy.

- There is no subscription and no conditions are attached, nor do you need to commit yourself to buying for any fixed period of time, though some company-operated box schemes ask for a week's cancellation notice. Unless the scheme operates a door-to-door delivery, you may be asked to join the rota for pick-up and delivery points.
- Inevitably, not everything is perfect all of the time. If for any reason you are dissatisfied with a particular item, or the delivery goes astray, a refund or substitution is usually offered.

HOW THE DIFFERENT TYPES OF BOX SCHEMES OPERATE

Local

Are rural, predominantly – though not exclusively – seasonal, and run by the growers themselves who, in the main, operate within a radius of twenty miles or less and for part of the year only, from early summer onwards. Each week the grower harvests whatever crops are in season, makes up the bags or boxes and then takes them to central delivery points for customers to collect. Customers acting as distributors from pick-up points or as co-ordinators receive a discount, or a free box from time to time.

- Crops are harvested, bagged and ready for collection within 24–36 hours. Usually the grower determines what goes into the box – the customer does not find out what it contains until it arrives. These days, most growers also buy in a few extras such as mushrooms, lemons or avocados as optional extras. Many offer customised choice as well as fixed boxes, most produce customer leaflets, and hold open days, and some produce regular newsletters and recipe sheets as well.

- Those operating all the year round will import some produce. Larger ones often buy in from other UK organic growers. Box-scheme growers generally take personal pride in growing their produce – some grow over 80 different varieties of vegetables and fruit, including many unusual or heritage varieties – and are immensely skilled. Quite simply, they offer the best produce you will ever eat.

Regional and national

Though there are exceptions such as Riverford Farm in Devon and Scragoak Farm in Kent, which are grower-owned and run, generally these box schemes are run by small, committed organic companies. They cater for the ever-growing demand in towns and cities, and operate all year round. They usually buy direct from selected growers or well-known wholesale companies dealing exclusively with organic produce. Some use some 'grade-out' produce – that is, produce that does not meet the cosmetic standards required by large retailers.

- They operate from a central depot where bought-in produce is immediately bagged and boxed and delivered to the customer's home rather than to a central pick-up point. Some have an arrangement whereby the produce is bagged for them, on the spot, by the grower, or form partnerships with growers' co-operatives who provide the packing facilities and who act as wholesalers as well.
- They operate like any other mail order service. All offer customer choice with a wide range of other foods, drink and non-drink items. Most offer a seven-day ordering system and online ordering. Some national operators charge extra to deliver to outlying areas such as the north of Scotland. They often have a catalogue and produce regular newsletters, and include recipes.
- They offer a range of boxes including fruit and dairy; or special boxes, such as a Mediterranean box that includes pasta and pasta sauces. A few offer meat boxes.
- The produce is well packed in sturdy, recyclable boxes.

What will the box contain?

Depending on the type of box scheme, the season and the size, boxes contain six to twelve or more different vegetables. Basics – potatoes, roots, onions – will always be included. You can also expect at least one green vegetable and seasonal salad stuff, plus unusual vegetables such as Chinese lettuce, chillis, mushrooms, and seasonal treats such as strawberries, squash and asparagus, either home-grown or imported.

- Local box schemes generally contain more variety and more unusual vegetables, though as already noted there will be less variety at certain times of the year. Also, because the growers produce such a diverse range of crops, though the customer may have very little say in what goes into the box the choice can be better than that found in retail outlets. The range and type of vegetables grown are governed by what grows best for each grower and what provisions each has made for protected cropping (polytunnels, glasshouses, and so on). Every grower's portfolio will be slightly different, varying also according to which part of the country he/she is growing in.
- Some regional and national operators offer almost as wide a range as the best local producers; others aim to give the best value for money and concentrate more on standard produce.
- Quality control for all box schemes is important, but vegetables usually arrive unwashed, and presented with a minimum of trimming (though this is now changing), salad stuff and highly perishable items will be packed separately, but most vegetables will be loose.
- As well as imperfections in size, and blemishes, you should expect the occasional insect.

Is there a future for box schemes?

The future of local box schemes remains assured. With the increased availability of organic produce from supermarkets and the advent of online organics, how regional and national box schemes develop remains to be seen, though the best will continue to prosper.

EAT OUT ORGANIC

The organic lifestyle is becoming fashionable and, more and more, restaurants, cafés, pubs and hotels throughout the UK are using organic ingredients in their menus. Organic wines, beers, teas and coffees are served regularly in many catering outlets, including department stores – Debenham's are the latest to introduce organic meals.

London, which is spearheading Europe's organic evolution, has over thirty organic eateries – the indispensable London Organic Food Directory website, **www.londonorganicfood.com**, lists them all. Pizza Piazzas have their own organic pizza chain, Pizza Organic, which has branches in the London area, with others planned for major cities elsewhere. The Savoy Hotel has been offering its own organic breakfast for some time now. You can buy organic soups on railway stations, at the Café Aroma chain and in London's latest fast-real-food-cum-juice bars, crussh (to see their sites, check out their website: **www.crussh.com**); plus organic sandwiches in supermarkets, organic Fairtrade espresso coffee from the UK's largest coffee chain, Costa, and bursting-with-health organic juices and wheat grass from juice bars. Planet Organic and Fresh & Wild in London both offer great organic food-to-go and have their own juice bars. Following on from the success of their organic snacks, drinks and baby food available in their restaurants, this year also saw the launch of Sainsbury's first certified organic eatery in the restaurant at their Sevenoaks store. The directory at the end of this book includes a selection of certified establishments, and of those that use organic ingredients regularly or feature organic dishes on their menu, or offer an organic breakfast. Outside London, the organic farm shop cum café, Abbey Farm near Cirencester, deserves a special mention: lovely atmosphere, friendly service, excellent home-made food using much of their own glorious organic produce, and all at very reasonable prices.

Organic catering is a specialised business, subject to the same strict regulations as organic processing; it poses extra demands and calls for commitment and energy from all concerned. Because supplies are seasonal and more fragmented and prices vary more, sourcing organic ingredients can take far more effort and time as well as more paperwork; restaurants need to be more flexible, changing dishes and menus frequently according to what actually arrives rather than always being able to stick with what they had planned for. At the moment there are very few places that are fully organic in the sense that they use only organic foods and ingredients, or that have elected to be certified and can therefore use the organic title in their name and in their dishes. Many prefer just to use organic ingredients – but this should be made clear on their menus, and usually is.

Eating out organically is that extra bit special – good fun, reviving and nourishing all in one. One of the most enjoyable ways to experience organic food, it's also another way of using your purse power to support organic farming and the wider organic ethos. How much extra a meal in an organic restaurant costs depends on the style and circumstance of each individual establishment. But generally, all you are paying for is the extra cost of the raw ingredients. Expect to be pleasantly surprised.

Eating out organically has other advantages, too. Catering food is largely anonymous. Except in restaurants that make a point of using local or organic produce, or that specify their suppliers, it is in the catering industry generally that most intensively produced, cheap food ends up, and where accountability for that food is not part of the menu. Organic eateries are different. All the food has a quality and an identity that can be traced, and is prepared by people who also care about how the food they are cooking is produced. Chefs who use organic ingredients tend to cook them in simple but imaginative ways; the restaurants and cafés are big on organic hospitality and you feel a positive buzz – which is not only infectious, but a great seasoning for your food.

Organic catering standards

These have been drawn up by the Soil Association and by Organic Farmers & Growers, and any organic catering establishment will be certified by one or the other. Their standards are similar, and cover the same areas. Catering establishments eligible for certification include restaurants, cafés, takeaway places and public and private caterers that prepare and sell organic foods to the general public.

- Either the whole establishment, or specific dishes or menu items and other foods and beverages that are prepared and sold on the premises as organic or containing organic ingredients, may be certified. In either case, in order to be eligible for organic certification, the dishes, the menus and ingredients, and the premises, must conform to all the relevant standards.
- If a restaurant is not certified, it cannot legally use the term 'organic' when describing its dishes, etc.

- Where a restaurant is serving both organic and non-organic ingredients, those ingredients must be stored and prepared separately. According to the Soil Association, a non-organic ingredient cannot be used in the same premises and at the same time as the same organic ingredient, e.g. if a restaurant is using organic potatoes, it cannot also be using non-organic potatoes; or, in the case of Organic Farmers & Growers' regulations, a restaurant would be allowed to serve the same ingredient but only in a different format – e.g. organic chips could be served as well as non-organic mashed potato.
- Any lapse in the continuity of the organic supply must be clearly notified to customers; full records must be kept of the efforts to source alternative organic supplies, of the non-organic replacements obtained and the duration of the lapse. If the restaurant is certified with Organic Farmers & Growers, no substitution of this kind is allowed. To qualify as an organic meal, they also require, say, organic goulash to be served with organic rice or vegetables.
- Wild-caught fish, shellfish and wild game and other identified products gathered locally from the wild may be used in organic menu items, but must be clearly labelled as such – e.g. wild-caught, not organic. Reared game may not be used in organic menu items.
- The use of microwaves, currently permitted, is under review at the Soil Association.
- Records must be kept identifying the organic and non-organic ingredients and foods purchased and used, both the overall quantities and those used for each specific recipe or menu item.
- Where a premises, menu items, foods or beverages have been independently certified, the certifier's symbol can be used and the word 'organic' can be used in the establishment's names, menu items, etc. and promotional literature.
- The annual certificate of registration must be displayed clearly, along with a description of the nature and scope of the certification, the organic purchasing policy, an up-to-date list of the organic ingredients and products used; and, if applicable, complete and up-to-date list of any non-organic ingredients used.

Many catering establishments purport to offer organic options that have not in fact been certified, and therefore they cannot necessarily prove that the ingredients they are using are organic. Strictly speaking, they are acting illegally; if you want to reassure yourself that the food they are offering *is* organic, check with them personally. If you feel there is a possibility of fraud, seek advice from your trading standards officer.

PROFILES: TWO ORGANIC DIVAS

Two pioneering organic restaurateurs who deserve special recognition are Carol Charlton who runs Hugo's Café-Bar Restaurant in London, and Daphne Lambert who runs Penrhos Hotel in Kington, Herefordshire. Both have led the way in organic catering: their restaurants serve delicious food and represent everything you would wish for when eating out organically.

Hugo's Café-Bar Restaurant, tel: 0207 372 1232 (formerly The Organic Café) in London is a bright, modern restaurant with an up-to-the-minute menu, tucked down a small mewsway at 25 Lonsdale Road, Queens Park, NW6, opened by Carol Charlton and her family in 1995, with the aim of making organic food 'more available, more tasty and part of everyone's lives'. Though no longer certified or exclusively organic, the restaurant is a fusion of the modern organic lifestyle: relaxed, informal and dedicated. The menu changes daily, uses mainly organic ingredients, and has an extensive selection of organic wine and beers. Dishes range from caramelised turnip soup, pistachio nut-crusted chicken breast with roasted peppers, all day breakfasts, sausages, sandwiches, and eggs florentine. Open every day 9.30 am–4 pm; 7 pm–11 pm. They also do outside catering. Their second café-bar, in the Goethe Institute, Exhibition Rd, SW7 tel: 0207 596 4006 is open 9 am–11 pm every day, serves all-day food, brunch, lunch, bar snacks and dinner. The café serves more than sustainably grown food: the stylish tables and seating are made from reclaimed floor boards, the cushions, aprons and napkins from organic cotton, dyed with low-impact dye, the glasses from recycled glass, the menus from hemp, and the bar is made from 'storm' oak, a casualty from the great storm of 1987. Carol Charlton has also written two organic cook books, *The Organic Café Cookbook*, and the *Organic Family Cookbook*, both published by David & Charles.

Penrhos Court Hotel, Kington, Herefordshire.
Acclaimed organic heaven on earth, this idyllic and lovingly restored medieval farmhouse serves fine organic food by chef, nutritionist and cookery author Daphne Lambert, and excellent organic wines. It was the first hotel and restaurant to gain the Soil Association symbol in 1999, won the Millennium Marque Award for environmental excellence in October 2000, and in November 2000 was nominated one of the *Observer/Good Hotel Guide's* best 50 hotels in the UK. A remarkable place by anyone's standards, Penrhos (which has 15 rooms) offers a peaceful and civilised retreat for anyone who enjoys good food and wants to take care of their health – and the environment.

The food is simple, innovative, seasonal – and delicious: from butternut squash soup with toasted coconut, and rogan josh chicken with red rice, to roast beetroot with couscous and horseradish creme fraiche, grilled sea bass with ginger bok choy, and maple syrup and pecan ice-cream. Herbs and salads come straight from the garden. Daphne Lambert cooks special diets to order. Ingredients are sourced locally as far as possible, and all the food is organic.

Daphne Lambert's first book *The Baby and Toddler Organic Cookbook* received the Live Gourmand Best Book for Parents award in September 2000, and her latest cookbook, *Little Red Gooseberries*, is published by Orion. She and co-owner Martin Griffiths also run the Green Cuisine School of Food and Health (residential, giving organic and healthy-nutrition cookery courses), and have a small organic shop selling organic dried foods, organic superfoods, organic seeds and eco-friendly products including organic paints. To find out more, visit their excellent website, **www.greencuisine.org**, which features a daily recipe; you can also subscribe to the regular newsletter and shop online for wines, foods, superfoods and so on. Or contact Martin Griffiths or Daphne Lambert at Penrhos Court, Kington, Herefordshire HR5 3LH, tel: 01544 230720, fax: 01544 230754, email: martin@penhros.co.uk, website: **www.penrhos.co.uk**.

▲▲▲

And . . . more organic London eateries

To give you the flavour of eating out organic style:

Fresh! The UK's first organic café chain, OF&G-certified, with big ideas and simple, stylish eco-decor (wooden cutlery, recycled-coathanger counter-tops and tables made out of yoghurt cartons). They offer fresh, up-to-the-minute sandwiches, wraps, soups and stews of the day, drinks, juices squeezed on the spot and smoothies – all at reasonable prices. Their food is organic except for their salmon, tuna and shrimps, and prepared in their own kitchens and at individual branches. They offer takeaway and platter lunches delivered free to the local area, and for functions – so if you want to throw an organic birthday party here's your chance. To find out more and browse their menus, visit their website: **www.fresh-go-organic.com**. They can also be contacted via email at info@fresh-go-organic.com or feedback@fresh-go-organic.com.

The Quiet Revolution Soups Company now have three of their own organic Soil Association-certified soup cafés to eat in or takeaway, serving home-made soups, hearty broths, fragrant stews, sourdough breads, salads, juices, cakes and other goodies at: The Quiet Revolution, 49 Old Street EC1, tel: 020 7253 5556. Open Mon–Sat 9 am–4 pm, Sun 10 am–4 pm. The Quiet Revolution, 62 Weymouth Street W1 (near Marylebone High Street), tel: 020 7487 5683. Open: Mon–Sat 9 am–6.30 pm. Fully licensed. The Quiet Revolution, 174 High Holborn, Covent Garden WC1, tel: 020 7836 5407. Open Mon–Fri 9 am–7 pm, Sat 9 am–6 pm. For more on their soups, see p. 320.

The Crown, the Duke and the Pelican Three organic traditional Victorian pubs, owned and carefully restored by two young women, Geetie Singh and Esther Boulton, dedicated to providing the highest-quality organic food and drink, at reasonable prices, and in a welcoming and comfortable environment: no jukeboxes, pinball machines, muzak or TV, either – just the buzz of happy people. The pubs are certified by the Soil Association and are totally organic. Their modern blackboard menus change twice daily, with the Crown offering breakfast as well: organic cinnamon toast with maple syrup for breakfast, pumpkin and roast-pepper risotto for lunch, rib-eye steak with chips and Caesar salad for dinner, and apple crumble with custard or lemon polenta cake for afters. High-chairs for babies and smaller meals for kids; organic wines, organic beers and lager on draught, worth a detour any day. For details see directory.

Sauce barorganicdiner, 214 Camden High Street, London NW1 8QR (SA), tel: 020 7482 0777.
All-day modern eatery: breakfast, brunch, lunch and dinner – soups, big sandwiches, home-made beefburgers, organic fries, homebakes, juices, smoothies and other drinks. High-chairs and children's menu too. Open: Mon–Thurs 12 noon–10.30 pm, Fri and Sat 12 noon–11 pm, Sun 12 noon–4.30 pm.

Plus:

Sainsbury's, Otford Road, Sevenoaks, Kent TN14 5EG, tel: 01732 742561.
A first for a supermarket, their in-store restaurant is certified by OF&G to serve organic food. It offers hot organic ready meals all day from 11.30 am: toasted ciabatta with various fillings such as Camembert, wild rocket and dried apricot, with organic salad garnish; toasted bagel with smoked salmon and cream-cheese, and simple snacks, desserts and drinks. Prices are reasonable and the staff – sporting their organic try-me aprons – have been specially trained. All organic pukka, as Jamie would say. Opening hours: Mon–Thurs 8 am–7 pm, Fri 8 am–7.30 pm, Sat 7.30 am–7 pm, Sun 9.30 am–3.30 pm.

See also: UK's first organic catering company, Organic Xpress, p. 432.

6: Organic Vegetables, Fruit and Herbs – and Seeds to Grow your Own

The vast majority of consumers who change to organic food start by buying organic fruit and vegetables – and so popular are they that they account for around 70% of all organic food sales. The insatiable demand is good news and consumers can feel very proud that the many thousands of hectares now growing organic crops where there used to be conventional ones, and the many new and exciting organically minded initiatives that are now taking place all over the world, are entirely due to their support.

The demand for organic produce has another important spin-off. As noted earlier, until recently research and development into organic farming, and particularly vegetable and fruit crops, has been minimal. But with more large-scale growers converting and adapting their expertise to organic methods has come the much-needed impetus to find new sustainable solutions. Though some supermarkets have funded specific organic R&D projects, now for the first time we are beginning to see organic R&D taken seriously by governments. Our government lags behind many, but consumer pressure will send the clearest message possible that they need to take their share of the responsibility for moving agriculture forward.

RANGE, AVAILABILITY AND SEASONALITY

The range of organic products available today is staggering: everything from seasonal delights such as chestnuts, walnuts, coconut and cranberries to persimmons, bilberries, six varieties of mushrooms, five varieties of avocados, organic squash, kohlrabi and celeriac, as well as standard fare such as bananas, pineapples, watercress and fancy salad leaves. Fresh organic herbs are a joy and are regular features in supermarkets. Waitrose have pioneered organic Jersey potatoes, and Sainsbury's organic strawberries from Hereford, a project that included such nice touches as enlisting local hedgehogs to help cope with slugs. Waitrose's forward-thinking policy is to replace conventional produce with the organic alternative as sufficient supplies become available.

At the moment, all their fennel, prepacked (500 g) carrots, seasonal white onions, prepacked shallots, seasonal bunched carrot, and celeriac are organic – another illustration of how far the availability of organic produce has advanced in two short years.

I have bought organic Italian radishes and French beans in January. Organic tomatoes are available all year round, and baby sweetcorn from Egypt and asparagus from Chile have become regular features. But apart from the tomatoes, which I find useful, the development of year-round organic everything I do not welcome – do we really need imported courgettes, even organic ones, in the depths of winter? But this development is both a sign of the times and a reflection of the success and importance that organic produce now enjoys. All the same, Fresh & Wild in London, for example, try hard to resist this, holding back on buying imported produce when they can and encouraging their customers to wait until the English version comes on stream; but it's difficult . And if you too feel this is a retro step, the best thing to do is to use your purse power and choose not to buy out-of-season produce if you can do without it.

Inevitably, popular fruit and vegetables and those easiest to grow or most plentiful will feature on the shelves most regularly. Fresh organic peas, UK organic asparagus and fruit generally, and organic chillis, however, are still rare treats. As always, the range available depends on where you live. South East England, Devon and parts of Somerset have become organic cornucopias. So has Edinburgh. Elsewhere, apart from most major cities, it becomes more patchy, but these days you don't have to go very far to find staples such as organic potatoes, carrots or mushrooms. Except in far-flung corners, especially with the rise of local box schemes, availability has improved substantially. National box schemes, home delivery and Internet shopping plug any gaps.

Imported fresh produce

Though things are improving slowly as more UK growers convert, the amount of home-grown organic produce compared with produce grown conventionally is tiny – about 5%. Around 70–80% of organic produce is imported, with tomatoes nearer 95%. This includes everything from spring onions (Egypt and Mexico) to Brussels sprouts (Holland), and covers over 50 countries, with Dutch imports featuring prominently. All major retailers have expressed concern about the situation, and all now say they have a policy of buying British whenever they can – though often they can't because the produce isn't there. It has to be said that some imported produce is very good: German and Austrian organic potatoes are one shining example. A friend speaks highly of Israeli organic strawberries, and I find their tomatoes and herbs excellent, too. This gives you a clue to one of the reasons why organic Dutch glasshouse crops do not always live up to expectations – Israel has lots of warm sunshine, Holland much less.

British grower initiatives

Though imported organic produce looms large on supermarket shelves, there are large-scale UK grower co-operative initiatives that could provide role models for the future. Through his franchise system, Guy Watson of Riverford Farm in Devon has helped put the county on the organic fresh-produce map: he runs the UK's biggest box scheme providing machinery, temporary labour and expertise to other growers, who then provide the crops for his scheme. In Herefordshire, the Green Growers' Co-operative, who supply box schemes up and down the country, have done exactly the same. Visit Prospect Growers, for example and you will see the kind of expertise, dedication and care that go into producing first-class home-grown organic crops.

QUALITY AND FLAVOUR

Substantial improvements here too. Appearance, consistency and overall professionalism in grading, trimming and packaging have also improved as the market has grown and supply chains become more regular. For sheer vitality, you can't beat locally bought produce.

The flavour of organic food is discussed in detail in chapter 3. Generally organic produce does, I believe, taste better – why, otherwise, would the countless thousands of people who regularly buy organic vegetables and fruit continue to do so? There is, though, more variation in flavour than there used to be. The reason for this, again, is simply expansion: so many more large-scale growers have recently converted, and fresh produce is now coming in from all corners of the globe. Also, the flavour of a crop varies from season to season, and this variation is often more apparent in organically grown crops precisely because they are grown more naturally. In addition, they are grown over a wider range of soils than non-organic crops, some of which are not as suitable as others for a particular crop – and, as any gardener who has grown vegetables and fruit in different parts of the country will tell you, soil type can have a marked effect on flavour too.

Here are some general points to bear in mind.

- Imported and larger-scale commercially grown organic produce is variable; it can be excellent, but is sometimes no better in flavour than conventional produce.
- Flavour variations show up more in some vegetables – tomatoes, carrots, potatoes and certain lettuce types – than others.
- Organic apples and pears, the two most commonly available fruit in supermarkets, are usually imported and are better at certain times of the year than at others. Organic oranges generally have a wonderful flavour, and organic peaches, nectarines and apricots can be superb. Many people rave about organic bananas, too.

How well does fresh organic produce keep?

This varies. Generally, and contrary to popular opinion, organic produce stores better and often keeps its good condition longer than conventional produce. The exception is crops like potatoes which do not last as long because, unlike their conventionally grown equivalent, they are not sprayed with post-harvest chemicals to prevent moulds or sprouting. Organic food keeps better partly because crops are not forced and are generally grown in 'healthier' soils, so often contain more dry matter and less water. The keeping quality also depends on the kind of crop and how it has fared post-harvest: that is, the amount of care that has been taken to ensure freshness from the moment of picking and to keep it in the correct controlled storage conditions until it is sold. Turnover may be slower, which means that most organic produce stays on the shelves longer.

Remember, anyway, that fresh produce is not meant to last and nor should you want it to, and though you can slow down the staling process, the sooner it is eaten, the better. Generally speaking, apart from winter squashes, the fresher it is the higher the vitamin and mineral content – and the better the flavour.

Pre-prepared and frozen organic vegetables

Though they may seem a far cry from the organic ideal of fresh and unprocessed, ready-prepared vegetables such as carrot batons, stir-fry mix and broccoli florets can be found in the chilled section in major supermarkets, organic supermarkets and some organic shops, and the Farm-a-Round box scheme in London also supplies them. Unlike with conventional prepared fresh foods, washing in chlorine is forbidden; instead, a dilute solution of citric acid is used.

Frozen organic vegetables, including chips, are becoming popular. Frozen peas remain my favourite, though they are rarely as tender as the Bird's Eye kind – major supermarkets ad organic supermarkets and shops stock them. Spinach, corn, green beans, cauliflower, petits pois, mixed vegetables, chips and roast potatoes, both branded and supermarket own-label, are also available.

▼▼

HOW TO BUY AND WHERE TO BUY

HOW TO BUY

The best approach to buying organic produce is to be an opportunist. As when buying fish, the golden rule is to buy what looks freshest and healthiest on the day.

- Snap up local when you can.
- Take advantage of seasonal produce and special offers.
- Don't worry about minor cosmetic blemishes, irregular sizing, minor bruises or the occasional insect. Do look for the occasional slug and caterpillar – remove them immediately as they will continue to eat their way through the leaves.
- Store properly.
- Eat fresh.

WHERE TO BUY

The best place to buy spanking-fresh produce is undoubtedly from the local grower direct, either via a box scheme or from the farm gate or farmers' market. And don't forget that box schemes and organic shops provide interestingly different ways to shop. Of the major multiples, Sainsbury's and Waitrose, as already noted, have the largest range of organic fresh produce. Each produces an organic leaflet listing their complete range.

- Major cities and towns are well served, as is any part of the country where there are clusters of organic growers such as Devon, Somerset, and parts of Kent and Wales.
- The kind of outlet you buy fresh organic produce from is important. Here, freshness and the number of links in the distribution chain after the produce has been harvested are the key.
- Shop around if you have the time, and seek out shops or supermarkets with a wide selection and good turnover.
- If you don't have a local organic shop or a supermarket with a reasonable selection, check out box schemes, home delivery and shopping on the Internet.

The displays of produce in London's flagship organic supermarkets have to be seen to be believed. London's organic markets are well worth visiting, too. The selection in wholefood and healthfood shops varies; some are excellent, others rather limited. Many operate a home delivery service. Though there are exceptions, greengrocers still do not generally stock organic fresh produce. If none of these outlets is available to you, or if you want the convenience of not having to go out to shop, mail order and Internet shopping could be your answer. See chapter 15.

▲▲

Peakfresh preserving bags

These roomy green plastic bags, made in Australia and organically certified, are designed to keep produce fresher and crisper, claim to preserve vitamin C, and can be washed and reused for up to two months. They are impregnated with oya stone, a pulverised mineral from Japan that absorbs the age-accelerating ethylene gas given off by ripening fruit and vegetables; they have also been treated with an anti-fogging substance to inhibit bacterial growth and to allow the passage of gases from the inside of the bag to the outside. Some moisture does collect on the inside and it is worth wiping the bag out with kitchen paper. It's also important to make sure the produce is cold before putting it into the bag. Full instructions are included. Available in packs of ten from Planet Organic, other good retailers and the Fresh Food Company, tel: 0208 969 0351.

ORGANIC VEGETABLES: A SELECTION OF THE BEST

Celery If you've never experienced the real thing – freshly dug home-grown organic celery in early autumn – you may be in for a surprise at how green, earthy, crunchy, flavourful and aromatic this amazing vegetable can be. British is best, although the outside stalks may be tougher than you are used to, and it will require more trimming and often more cleaning. Otherwise, it's imported from Spain and Israel. I find it invaluable for crudités, for adding flavour to casseroles, for stir-frying or just to chop and add to any kind of vegetable or meat dish.

TIP: Use the outside leaves and stalks for juicing, or in soups and stocks; scatter the inner tender leaves, finely chopped, over salads and cooked meat dishes.

Chinese leaves Box schemes often contain an assortment of peppery Chinese leafy vegetables such as mizuna, pak choi, mustard, komatsuna and chrysanthemum greens. Pick over and use as soon as possible.

TIP: Small tender leaves are good for salads. Otherwise, shred and stir-fry for a couple of minutes with ginger, garlic and soy sauce, or with a sweet-sour Chinese sauce.

Cucumbers Organic cucumbers have an excellent flavour, though they have thicker skins and sometimes come in weird and interesting shapes. Several varieties are available, such as Danima mini-cucumbers and Flamingo long ones.

TIP: If you get a cucumber glut, cool cucumber soups and easy freezer pickles are the best way to deal with them.

Garlic One of the best things about garlic is that it is so easy to grow – simply plant individual cloves from a garlic bulk in early spring, pressing the cloves about 4 cm under the soil and leaving 6 cm between them. Harvest in July/August when the flags have died down. You then have your own supply of the world's best-kept vegetable secret, freshly harvested garlic. This is much easier on the digestion than the dried version, is wonderful roasted whole or separated into cloves, and will transform your barbecues, pestos and garlic mayonnaise (aïoli). Local growers also offer freshly-harvested organic garlic in summer. Imported organic garlic comes from Spain, France and Turkey in summer, and from Argentina in winter and spring.

TIP: Garlic should not be stored in the kitchen but somewhere cool (use the salad drawer of the fridge if you have nowhere else that is suitable).

Sprouting cloves are well past their best – they are too strong and rancid to eat – but plant them in a pot of compost or in the ground, and the garlic-flavoured shoots can be used as a springtime herb.

Greens Organic cabbages, purple and white sprouting broccoli, Brussels sprouts, spring greens, Swiss chard, spinach beet, black-green cavolo nero (perfect for Tuscan bean soups) and vivid green and purple kales all contain fistfuls of vitamins and antioxidants and are generally superb. All, but especially the brassicas, should either be cooked very quickly – shredded and stir-fried is fast and easy – or long and slowly to break down the sulphur compounds that produce unpleasant flavours and are difficult to digest. Once found only in box schemes, organic Swiss chard is now being grown for supermarkets. Organic Brussels sprouts often come attached to their stalks (a sure sign of freshness). Of all the brassicas, sprouts store least well, but cabbages will store well for a week or so in the fridge; other greens should be picked over, examined carefully for insects, and stored in Peakfresh bags (p. 119) or similar.

Leeks Organic leeks often come with more green flag than you may be used to (great for soups and stockpots) and, if from a local grower, will need careful washing. A simple leek and potato soup, or leek, potato and tomato, takes some beating. Leeks also make an elegant substitute for onions.

Lettuce Though best in its natural season – spring to autumn in the UK – imported organic lettuce from Spain, Italy and France and elsewhere means year-round availability. Because they are grown in soil, and never as a forced monocrop or hydroponically, they have a firmer texture and a flavour more like home-grown. In summer, home-grown lettuce is easy to come by. If buying from a local grower you may need to discard the outer leaves – and do watch out for the odd friendly insect or slug. Best-selling organic varieties are Little Gem and the various red and green filly ones such as Lollo Rosso and Verde, and oakleaf. Different mixes of pre-prepared organic salad are popular, expensive and widely available.
TIP: To crisp up a floppy lettuce – surprisingly – douse in warm water for a few minutes, then dry carefully.

Mushrooms The development of cultivated organic mushrooms has been a great success – so much so that they have become an organic stalwart, readily available all year round and a good first choice for everyone. Varieties include brown-caps, buttons and shitake.

Except for shitake, which are grown on logs, they are grown on composted straw in specialised mushroom sheds; they take 5–6 weeks to grow, and the spent compost is recycled for use as a soil conditioner and fertiliser. None of the many conventionally approved chemicals for mushroom production is used, whether in the compost, sprayed on the crop or as a fog. Instead, pest control is achieved by using air-filters and by biological means. This requires much higher standards of farm hygiene than if chemicals were used. Any sign of disease is removed by hand and up to four times as many people need to be employed to constantly monitor the crop. Only biodegradable disinfectants are used to clean sheds between crops.

Many mushroom producers have converted and many more are considering it. However, a change in the EU organic standards could halt this: the substrate that organic mushrooms are grown on, which is always composted first, will have to be made from organic straw. Though no-one is denying the desirability of this, at the moment organic straw is in extremely short supply and will add an extra cost to the producers of 15p per pound.

UK producers argued for a phased and progressive changeover, but this was rejected, though they have won a derogation allowing them to use in-conversion straw, reviewed annually. On the continent, however, the situation is better and so probably means more imported organic mushrooms. In the UK, retailers are also encouraging their conventional mushroom producers to produce both conventional and organic mushrooms – and, because organic production is only a part of their total production, to effectively absorb the extra costs. For the brave producers who gave us organic mushrooms in the first place, this change will make commercial life extremely difficult. What consumers can do to help here is to buy British organic mushrooms wherever possible, and ask their retailers to continue to support dedicated organic mushroom suppliers.

TIP: Mushrooms need to breathe, and quickly deteriorate if stored in clingfilm or plastic bags. Take them out of their wrapping and store in a brown paper bag in the salad drawer of the fridge, or loose on a plate lined with kitchen paper. They will keep for 4–5 days. They do not need peeling – just wipe with a damp cloth or vegetable brush.

Peas and beans Organic sugar snap peas, mange-tout and French beans from

South Africa, Zimbabwe, Egypt and Kenya are available most of the year and sold through supermarkets, box schemes and Internet suppliers. Don't frown, but this winter for the first time I bought the odd packet of French beans – and found them extremely useful cooked and chopped, dressed with vinaigrette or a spoonful of bottled organic mayonnaise, to use in mixed salads as a simple first course. Peas, broad beans and yellow, purple and green French beans, and occasionally beans for drying such as borlotti, are some of summer's delights when it comes to local box schemes. Because organic peas and broad beans are grown naturally, they do not all ripen at the same time, which means more variation. French beans should always be cooked until just soft and not crunchy: they taste better that way.

TIP: Frozen organic peas are invaluable: always keep some in the freezer. A shake cheers up any winter braise or stir-fry; and they go with everything.

Onions Because organic onions are not treated with post-harvest chemicals, keep them dry and well ventilated to prevent moulding. They also sprout faster than conventional ones – snip the sprouts off and use them like chives for soups and stir-fries.

Potatoes The production of organic UK potatoes is gradually increasing, though no one should underestimate the difficulties this can pose for commercial growers who have converted, especially in very wet seasons or when blight is prevalent. Potatoes are an organic basic, and taste tests consistently show that the maincrop ones especially are superior in flavour, with none of that chemical taint that can sometimes be detected in non-organic ones. If you eat the skins, always choose organic maincrop so as to avoid potential contamination from post-harvest insecticides or sprout-suppressants.

Organic potatoes are rarely cosmetically perfect and are usually more variable in size. Popular commercial varieties include Nicola, Santé and Cara. Local growers and box schemes often sell traditional and heritage varieties. Bagged organic potatoes come washed, though unwashed potatoes always store better and often have the edge on flavour. Maincrop potatoes are imported from Germany, Holland, Austria, Spain and France; new potatoes from Egypt, Israel, Italy and Morocco. Their flavour can vary – a function of the usual factors. Special commendation to Waitrose, who have worked with their Jersey growers to produce organic Jersey Royals – available for one month of the year only, and a taste of how Jerseys used to be.

TIP: Potatoes should be stored in the dark and kept cool at all times. Remove from their plastic bags and keep in a closed cardboard box or thick brown paper bags in the garage, for example, or an unused north-facing room in summer. New potatoes can be kept for a short time in the fridge.

Peppers Peppers have so many uses – they've become almost as essential as tomatoes. The best way to treat them, if they are particularly delicious, is to cut them into strips and enjoy them raw as crudités; otherwise, chargrill or roast in the oven, peel off their skins, and use the cooked flesh in salads, dips and pasta dishes. Keeping the cooked strips covered with olive oil makes them extra good.

Imported organic peppers – Dutch, Italian, Spanish, Israeli or Egyptian – mean a more or less continuous supply, and UK peppers are available now through the summer months. The only two important things you need to know about peppers is that the green ones are unripe (for which read less flavourful, and more indigestible for some) and that, like tomatoes, a pepper needs a long season and plenty of warmth to give of its best. Our own home-grown peppers, for example, in Henley-on-Thames, do not ripen up until late summer and are usually at their best throughout autumn. For this reason, though organic peppers are generally an improvement on conventional ones and the best are fantastic, they are not inevitably so.
TIP: Always store peppers at room temperature: it is surprising how long they last, and continue to ripen.

Spinach Recent research has indicated that organic spinach had almost 100% more iron and manganese than conventional samples. Like other organic green leafy produce, spinach is also lower in nitrates. It should be eaten as soon as possible. Wash the leaves thoroughly before using.
TIP: For extra tenderness, remove the stems from the large leaves first. For the best results when cooking, either stir-fry or blanch briefly in a pan of water, gently squeezing out the excess water. Spinach also freezes very well.

Summer roots Seasonal bunches of organic baby beetroot, turnips and carrots are a joy. None needs peeling, and they often have their leaves attached (a sure sign of freshness). Wash with a brush and cook simply in butter with a few chopped herbs. A pinch of organic sugar will bring out their sweetness. Local box scheme growers often grow yellow and striped varieties of organic beetroot, as well as kohlrabi. Baby beet leaves should never be wasted – they are as tender as spinach. Baby turnip leaves can be stir-fried.

Tomatoes It would be wrong to pretend that all organic tomatoes taste wonderful or that significant progress has not been made in the conventional industry. The British tomato industry, at least, has made huge efforts to improve both the general quality and the flavour of their tomatoes. Today, glasshouse tomatoes are grown hydroponically but use biological controls instead of pesticides, and are pollinated by bees. However, whether grown in glasshouses or not, only organic tomatoes are grown in soil and fed organically approved nutrients.

Organic tomatoes are now available all year round. I buy them sometimes in winter to chop and add to winter salsas, or to add a bit of freshness to organic tomato sauces and dishes using tomatoes. In summer, organic tomatoes are grown locally or imported from Europe, and in winter they are usually brought in from the Canary Islands, Italy, Israel and Morocco. The number of varieties has increased, too. Organic plum tomatoes and vine tomatoes have arrived (in my supermarket, vine tomatoes from Israel arrived in January). People often want to know whether vine tomatoes are any better than the rest. The answer is that they should be, and often are – first because different varieties are used and, second, because they are left on the plant longer.

Whatever the variety or shape, the riper tomatoes are, the better the flavour. The best single piece of advice that can be given, therefore, is that if they are unripe when you buy them, keep them for a few days at room temperature until red-ripe, for their flavour to develop fully. Cold damages the texture of tomatoes and blunts their flavour. For this reason, don't keep tomatoes in the fridge unless they are very ripe and you want to hold them for a few days. Organic tomatoes often have more texture. And the best are *the* best, with a sun-sweet intensity of flavour. Cherry tomatoes are naturally sweeter than other varieties, and have the highest vitamin C content.

Watercress John Hurd's Organic Watercress at Hill Deverill, near Warminster, Wilts, tel: 01985 640260, continues to be my favourite salad vegetable and typifies the organic approach. John Hurd has been growing watercress in the traditional way for 40 years, using the classic late-flowering variety rather than the newer ones that are sown repeatedly and mechanically cropped when very young. Needless to say, no chemicals are used. The watercress is grown naturally, unprotected, so it is entirely weather-dependent – which is why it is not available all year round (it is cut by hand from March to early December). It is delicious, and has the true peppery kick that watercress should. Waitrose, organic retailers and box schemes stock it. It is also available from the packing sheds direct and from the nearby Deverill's Trout Farm.

Watercress is one of nature's superfoods – new research has highlighted its cancer protection properties – and can be used in many ways other than soup. Chopped, it adds an instant fresh green pepperiness to salads, vegetable soups, winter salsas or pestos, and is good scattered over fish and chicken dishes, or as a simple side salad. The stalks have as much flavour as the leaves.

TIP: Watercress is fragile and has a very short shelf life, no more than 2–3 days at most. Keep it in the fridge, in a box or thick plastic bag and wash it in a bowl of water and pick over the leaves before you use it.

NOTE: Occasionally (though this has never happened to me) a bunch may contain the odd freshwater shrimp or insect. To remove, wash the leaves in weak salty water.

Winter roots There is nothing finer or more packed with earthy sweetness and flavour than freshly dug organic carrots, parsnips, beetroot or celeriac from a local box scheme or local grower, so seek these out whenever you can. Carrots are available all year round and so vary the most in flavour. They are imported from various countries including Holland, Austria, Spain, Italy and France. All should be stored dry – unwashed roots last better than washed ones – and in the dark or in the refrigerator (remove them from their plastic bags first). I leave mine, for example, in the salad drawer. Organic carrots and beetroot can often be bought in bulk for juicing.

TIP: Finely grating root vegetables brings out their sweetness. The best way to wash muddy roots is to immerse them in a bucket or large bowl of water for a few minutes to loosen the dirt, then hold them under the tap to wash away the rest before scrubbing or peeling in the usual way.

Winter squashes Organic squashes are one of the best winter vegetables, if not *the* best. They can regularly be found on supermarket shelves and are a popular box scheme vegetable. The orange-fleshed varieties such as Kabocha (the type most supermarkets sell, imported from New Zealand) and Crown Prince are cook's choice.

Squashes are the ultimate convenience vegetable. They store well –

improving in flavour – until spring, and have a rich, satisfying taste and a smooth dense texture. They are highly nutritious, rich in beta carotenes, and are wonderfully decorative too – they can be left on the kitchen table until needed. Once cut, store in the refrigerator. They make superlative soups and ambrosial purées and risottos, and are excellent roasted: cut into wedges, brush with olive oil and roast in the usual way.

TIP: Add cubes of winter squash to spiced meat stews and braises: they add sweetness and act as a natural thickener. You won't need potatoes as well.

ORGANIC FRUIT

Organic fruit is a treat at any time. Though there is still far too little to meet the demand, the range we can now regularly enjoy has increased enormously, as has availability – organic apples, for example, come high on the list of top organic sellers in supermarkets. These are pipped only by organic bananas, which have been a huge success, and should make everyone who has bought them feel extra-good (for why, see p. 134). For the ultimate luxury, hand-picked and hand-packaged organic Medjool dates from Israel and California, each plump fruit nestling in its own paper case, take some beating.

Worldwide, the production of organic tree fruits – apples, pears and citrus, and stone fruits such as plums, apricots, peaches and nectarines – is gathering momentum. Organic orchards and fruit holdings are being planted everywhere, and conventional growers are beginning to convert in large numbers. In the UK, though increasing, production is still tiny so that almost all of our most popular top fruit – apples, pears and plums – as well as soft fruit, is imported, and that if you want to buy organic fruit at all most of the time you will be buying organic apples from, for example, Argentina and organic strawberries from Spain and Israel.

In many ways, the UK is a special case. It is technically more difficult in our unpredictable climate (our growers often suffer late frosts or wet seasons) to produce perfect organic fruit, especially orchard fruit, than in sunny, dry countries. Further, UK government aid for organic conversion is still minimal compared with the rest of Europe – for orchard fruits, for example, one-tenth, one-ninth and just over one-fifth of what is given in Holland, France and Spain, respectively. For organic fruit to blossom, therefore, there is a crying need for government to fund organic R&D, and to bring aid for our fruit growers into line with the rest of Europe – otherwise, we cannot expect the situation to improve significantly.

Growing organic fruit

It's not generally appreciated how difficult growing fruit organically is, or rather, how difficult it is to grow organic fruit commercially, especially to all-year-round standards of cosmetic perfection and uniformity that has sadly become the hallmark of quality. Conventional fruit is literally cocooned by chemicals, every problem solved by a spray of some kind – and, as one grower explained, most consumers and retailers alike are so attached to cosmetically perfect fruit that they are willing to eat organophosphates for the privilege.

Unlike with most vegetables, which grow quickly and are in and out of the soil within a few months, growing most fruits is a long-term project that requires far higher investment and is far more unpredictable. Though strawberries can be (and are) grown as an annual crop, even most soft fruit takes 2–3 years to become productive, and orchards can take 5–8 years. Managing crops organically doesn't just mean not using harmful synthetic pesticides or artificial fertilisers, either. You can't rotate an orchard, or shoo the pests away. Instead, building up biodiversity becomes critical, and pest management requires dedication, continuous monitoring and constant new, creative solutions.

It's the same story with fertility-building and weed management: removing weeds by hand from freezing-cold bogs in order that we can enjoy organic cranberries, or spreading muck manually in steep hilly olive groves, is not something many of us stop to think about. Instead of maximising yields, organic growers concentrate on building up the health of their orchards, by instituting fertility programmes, spraying with seaweed-based foliar sprays and encouraging natural predators. In Austria and Switzerland, organic orchards are a riot of wild flowers. Nor, probably, do we reflect much on the fact that growing organic fruit takes up to four times the manpower and even more guts and dedication – for the organic grower, unlike his conventional counterpart, does not benefit from the faster-growing trees, higher yields and larger fruits that the use of artificial fertilisers brings.

This is why organic fruit is so special and why every organic grower is a brave-hearted pioneer – wherever in the world he or she lives. It is also why, whatever our misgivings about long food miles generally, it makes sense for organic fruit to be grown in areas that suit it best climatically, and it is why we should welcome initiatives to pioneer organic fruit-growing in new areas – for example, organic grapes in Egypt where the usual pests are not found.

The difference here between the conventional and the organic approach is that whereas the former relies on the quick chemical fix and, at worst, can result in pillage of the local environment, the latter is designed to be ecologically and socially sustainable in perpetuity.

Buying organic fruit thus means changing the world one fruit at a time. Now that it is generally available, make sure you include some in your shopping basket every week.

NOTE: To overcome fungal diseases, organic growers, including wine-growers, use two permitted natural fungicides – namely, sulphur and copper sulphate. The use of both is restricted and copper sulphate is being phased out. For more on pesticides used in organic farming, see Appendix.

Quality and flavour

Generally this ranges from average to superb. The main fault I find with top (orchard) fruit is bruising. The skins of most imported apples and stone fruits are also quite thick and tough – but this means the fruit is naturally better protected. UK top fruit tends to be smaller and more variable in size, and can be less blemish-free.

All fruit needs to be ripe to be sweet and flavoursome – and this means sunshine and warmth as well as a healthy, fertile soil. So it shouldn't come as a surprise that, like organic vegetables, organic fruit grown outside its natural season does not taste as good. The easiest way to improve flavour in most fruit, including bananas, is to leave it to ripen at room temperature.

Local organic fruit

Any locally grown fruit is a precious gift and it's a privilege to be able to buy it. Fortunately, the upsurge of farmers' markets, combined with more growers converting and the strong revival of the 'go local' movement, has made it more widely available. Farmers in mid-conversion, too, often sell their fruit at farmers' markets. Though they are not yet certified organic, do give them your support: it's the best way to say thank you for having the vision and the courage to go organic.

You will find a much wider range of varieties to try when you buy locally, and you'll be able to learn from the producer how he grows his crop. For example, new UK organic apple orchards have to be planted with varieties chosen to suit local conditions and that are disease-resistant, such as Worcester and Discovery rather than Cox and Gala. A few organic growers operate pick-your-own systems – an extra bonus, and superb value for money. Finally, one more good spin-off: more organic apple and other fruit growers are making delicious bottled juices from their own fruit.

Its natural shelf life

One of the biggest differences between conventional and organic fruit generally is shelf life. This has come about primarily because the modern experience of buying fruit is buying from retailers rather than locally, and we have got used to most conventional fruits being treated with post-harvest fungicides, or, if they have to travel long distances, they may have been treated with chemicals that inhibit ripeness. Also, many fruits, including citrus, apples, peaches and melons, are waxed. Waxes may contain shellac, paraffin, palm oil, synthetic resins and (in some countries) a range of fungicides such as benomyl and diphenyl.

Since organic fruit, like organic vegetables, is not subjected to any post-harvest treatments of this kind, you cannot automatically judge its keeping qualities. Again, as with organic vegetables, this does not necessarily mean that organic fruit always has a shorter shelf life – rather, it has a more natural one. I have bought organic lemons that develop moulds in one week flat, and others that I have kept for several weeks and that still refuse to go bad but just sit in the kitchen and dry out slowly. Then take strawberries, which like all soft fruits, are very fragile and if bought from a retailer should be kept chilled and eaten as soon as possible. But if you've bought them direct from a local organic grower, picked fresh that morning, and you treat them gently, they will last in the fridge for 2–3 days. They will also last longer if they are not red-ripe (in which case it pays to leave them somewhere cool, but not the fridge, for a day until they are). Further than this, using your common sense is the best guide and will teach you, naturally, how best to store organic fruit.

WHAT CAN YOU BUY

A. Generally available (most or all of the year)

Clementines, grapes, mangoes, melons and plums have become much more readily available. Organic dates are now available all the year, and clementines, grapes and mangoes for most of the year. Most retailers, including supermarkets, stock most of the following for some or much of the time:

apples	dates	lemon
avocados	grapefruit	oranges
bananas	grapes	pears
clementines	kiwi fruit	plums

B. At selected shops, but generally available in season

You can expect to find these in all good organic supermarkets and shops. Sainsbury's, Tesco and Waitrose stock almost all of them. Other major multiples stock some, especially summer fruits such as organic peaches. Imported strawberries are now available for around 10 months of the year, so expect to see more of these in future.

apricots	grapes	pineapple
blueberries	greengages	raspberries (imported)
cherries	mandarins	satsumas
coconuts	mangoes	seville oranges
cranberries	melons	sharon fruit
dates	nectarines	(persimmon)
figs	peaches	strawberries

C. Local and exotic

Organic fruits that you will not find very often.

blackberries	guava	passion fruit
blackcurrants	loganberries	quinces
chinese gooseberry	lychees	raspberries
dragon fruit	papaya	red and white currants
gooseberries		

▲▲▲

ORGANIC FRUIT: A SELECTION OF THE BEST

Apples Organic apples, available just about all year, are imported from North and South America, Europe, and most recently New Zealand. Gala, Golden Delicious, Granny Smith and Bramleys, are all common varieties

A recent five-year study, carried out in Washington and reported in *Nature* magazine, showed not only that the organic apple orchards there were better from the viewpoint of both environment and energy efficiency, but that they achieved yields similar to those of conventional orchards. Furthermore, mechanical analysis backed up by tasting panels found the organic apples to be sweeter.

Organic apples do not have shiny waxed skins, but they keep very well. The most important thing to understand about storing them is that different varieties have different keeping qualities. If you buy apples in bulk from a local grower, check the variety and how long they will keep: early varieties last only a couple of weeks, but late ones can last for months if stored correctly. To do this, keep them in the fridge in a sealed roomy plastic bag punctured with a few pin holes.

For health, organic apples are exactly what the doctor had in mind. The small ones are exactly right for children. There is no need to peel them, whereas a recent report showed that almost half of the conventional apples tested contained pesticide residues, including the organophosphate (OP) chlorpyrifos, and some had multiple residues.

Avocados Avocados are a superfood and have everything you could possibly want – they are delicious, highly nutritious, rich in vitamin E and essential fatty acids, convenient, and perfect for salsas, dips and salads or for the lunch box. Mashed avocado makes one of the best natural face masks, too.

Organic avocados, I find, are generally creamier and have a fuller flavour. They are big business in New Zealand, Israel, Spain and Mexico. Two big differences between the management of organic avocado orchards and that of conventional ones is that the former use no aerial spraying or OPs. Natural leaf mould, home-made composts and organic liquid foliar feeds provide fertility, native wild-flower mixtures encourage natural predators, and natural pesticides include neem oil and the biological control, Bacillus thuringiensis (see Appendix 1). Well worth the extra ten pence or so that organic avocados cost.

The three main organic varieties are Hass, Ettinger and Fuerte. Recently, two more, Ardith and Gween, from Israel, have started to appear. You will regularly find them in supermarkets, often on special offer. The flavour depends in part on the variety. Hass have the edge on creaminess and are my personal favourite, whilst Ardith are less rich and have a lighter texture. They also divide in thick-skinned (Hass, Ardith, Gween) and thin-skinned (Ettinger, Fuerte). For obvious reasons, the thick-skinned varieties are best for the lunch box or if serving avocados in their skins as a starter.

TIP: Avocados are one of the few fruits that are picked unripe. At room temperature, they take around 1–2 weeks to ripen – and they do need to be ripe, that is, slightly soft, in order to become creamy and to mash easily. The main problem is that, once ripe, they do not keep (look for signs of blotching or brown spots, and beware of excessive softness), and should be eaten as soon as possible. There is a handy tip passed on to me by New Zealand's best-known avocado grower, Douglas Brown: once ripe, to keep them in prime condition, put in the fridge and they will hold for 2–3 days without spoiling.

Bananas Most retailers now stock organic bananas as often as they can. Those sold in Europe come from the Dominican Republic, but they are also grown in Brazil, Israel, Mexico, Martinique, Egypt and Honduras.

As one friend, who has recently started buying organic bananas and who does not buy much organic food, said, once you've tasted an organic banana, there's no going back. Moreover, because they are one of the world's most important commodities (they are our most popular fruit) and because we each eat 10 kg per year, choosing to buy organic or fair-trade bananas really does make a difference.

TIP: Bananas are another 'superfood', one of nature's original fast foods, high in potassium and with almost as much vitamin B6 as liver. They are usually sold unripe. The ripe way to eat them is to wait until the skins are dappled with light-brown spots. Cold damages bananas – store them at room temperature and let them ripen naturally.

WHAT'S WRONG WITH CONVENTIONAL BANANAS?

A few large banana companies produce around 80% of the bananas that are sold worldwide. Most of these come from South and Central America. Over the last 30 years, production methods have changed drastically. For example, in Costa Rica, the second-largest exporter after Ecuador, until 1960 bananas were grown in relatively low-impact ways. Forest areas were cleared slowly, agrochemicals were little used, and yields were around 20 tonnes per hectare. Today, bananas are grown highly intensively as a monocrop, causing one of the highest rates of deforestation in the world. In addition, they are often cultivated near watercourses or on steep hillsides where soil erosion is severe, using high-yielding varieties that have low natural resistance to pests and diseases and employing up to twenty times the amount of pesticides – many of which are highly toxic – per hectare that industrialised countries use on their own territory. As a consequence, about 60% of reported pesticide poisonings in Costa Rica are of banana plantation workers. Other daily violations of human and labour rights are widespread in Central and South America.

HOW WE CAN HELP

- World trade in bananas is dominated by Chiquita, Del Monte, Dole, Fyffees and Noboa. If enough of us choose organic or fair-trade labelled bananas, these companies will receive clear messages to improve their production and working practices, and we will be helping to improve both working conditions and the environment.
- If you do buy conventional bananas, buy those from the Windward Islands, which are produced by small family farmers in conditions less harmful to the environment.
- Tell your friends about organic and fair-trade labelled bananas.
- Contact Banana Link for banana action updates: email: blink@gn.apc.org; website: **bananalink.org.uk.**

Growing organic bananas

The banana is a perennial plant that dies back every year after it has fruited, and grows a new trunk every year. The organic plants are grown far less intensively and, managed organically, are excellent soil builders as the crop debris builds up humus. Fertility is provided by a variety of local sources, including green manures, coffee bean husks, guano and seaweed. In some plantations nitrogen-fixing trees such as *Acacia Negra* are planted to help build soil fertility and provide shade. Weeding is done by hand, while mulches suppress weeds and prevent nutrient loss after heavy rains. Biological controls and good management practices replace the barrage of pesticides normally used on banana plantations. Like conventional bananas, they are picked green, but unlike conventional ones they are not sprayed with post-harvest chemicals to retard ripening.

Sainsbury's and Waitrose are developing their own initiatives that will bring more organic bananas on to their shelves. Sainsbury's are working with the government of the Windward Islands on the feasibility of widescale conversion to organic banana production, as well as on diversification into other exotic fruits. Waitrose's Organic Banana project, also in the Caribbean, includes introducing innovations such as flood irrigation and nematode control. Waitrose have also introduced new guidelines for their conventional banana plantations in the Windward Islands: they've stopped aerial spraying and use of pesticide bags over the fruit, and introduced the concept of rotation. These are excellent examples of how consumer demand for crops grown by sustainable methods can reap fruit for everyone.

▲▲

Citrus fruits A full range of organic citrus fruit is now available – grapefruit, oranges, Seville oranges, clementines, satsumas, limes and lemons. Depending on the usual factors, such as variety and where the fruit has been grown, organic citrus fruits are generally sweeter, tangier and juicier – fruitier, in other words – than most conventional ones, which can often appear watery in comparison. Organic juicing oranges are available in bulk – try them, and discover the taste difference for yourself. As a precaution, once ripe, store in the fridge.
TIP: Use organic lemon peel to flavour meat and vegetable dishes, in desserts, in drinks, or to make candied peel and Moroccan preserved lemons. Orange peels are good dried and stored in a jar to flavour Provençal meat braises.

Exotic fruit Organic pineapples, mangoes and papaya are the all-time treat. Because of their tough skins, they can be stored at room temperature to ripen to perfection. Organic pineapples come from Guyana and Papua New Guinea. Like papaya, they are an aid to digestion so make the perfect ingredient for sweet or savoury dishes. Organic mangoes and papaya come mainly from the Gambia: both make wonderful fruit fools blended with organic cream or crème fraîche.

Grapes Organic grapes are plump, juicy, the best are bursting with natural fruit flavour. Most come from South America, but new vineyards are also being planted in Egypt. Because grapes are generally sprayed so extensively throughout their growing season, although they are expensive, choose organic when you can.

TIP: Grapes taste best when chilled slightly (ditto fresh cherries).

Kiwis Organic kiwis are grown in Italy, France, Chile and New Zealand. As well as having a better flavour when organically grown, they are one of the most valuable sources of vitamin C, so make them part of your regular diet. In its natural habitat the kiwi is a trailing plant that lives for thirty years. In organic orchards weed populations are allowed to flourish, helping to keep soil structure intact, reduce the risk of botrytis and provide a natural habitat for predators (herbs may also be planted to help encourage them). The kiwi seed heads provide food for local birds.

TIP: Kiwi fruit should be eaten when slightly soft. As an organic kiwi grower in New Zealand explained to me, they will last well for up to a month, with no loss of vitamin C. No need to put them in the fridge, either; just store them at room temperature until they soften, then put them in the fridge and eat soon. If you want to ripen them faster, put them in a sealed bag with an apple for a couple of days.

Soft fruit Apart from strawberries, the availability of home-grown organic soft fruit is still severely limited. Imported soft fruit, especially raspberries and bilberries, is becoming more widely available. To make them go further, team them with organic cream or crème fraîche.

Stone fruit Organic apricots, peaches, nectarines, greengages and plums are in scarcer supply than some exotic fruits, but they are worth seeking out as their flavour is generally excellent. They bruise easily, so take extra care. And if they need to be riper, leave for a little longer at room temperature. Dried organic apricots have a superb flavour, too. Keep a pack handy in the store cupboard for breakfast, savoury dishes and desserts.

FRESH ORGANIC HERBS

Fresh organic herbs are wonderful, and have become much more widely available. Growing your own, or buying your own plant of, say, sage or rosemary, will bring you much pleasure. Organically grown seeds are readily available (for addresses see below). Jekka's Organic Herb Farm, Alveston,

Bristol, provides excellent mail order herb plants. For local herb centres where you can buy organic plants, see directory.

Buying fresh organic herbs

Three years ago, a bunch (or packet) of fresh organic herbs was a novelty. Today Sainsbury's, Waitrose, Tesco and others, sell a wide variety regularly, so much so they have become part of my weekly shopping basket over winter and early spring, when my own supply is sparse. Because the UK fresh organic herb industry is still in its infancy, almost all on sale in supermarkets are imported, usually from Israel. I find the quality very good. Most organic retailers and supermarkets also stock them. New from Waitrose are attractive organically raised herb plants in pots from Italy: the rosemary can be planted out in your garden, solving the problem of ready fresh rosemary once and for all.

Local outlets

The best way to buy UK grown organic herbs when you get the chance is to buy them locally – they come by the bunch rather than a packet, and are cheap at the price. Farmers' markets and your local organic/wholefood shop or farm shop are good places to start, both for fresh herbs and herb plants. Local box schemes include bunches of seasonal home-grown fresh herbs, as do many local organic shops and farm shops. The range will vary and depend on the time of the year, and what grows well and is easy to grow for each supplier – favourites include sage, thyme, mint, rosemary and parsley, plus perhaps tarragon, chervil, oregano, dill and sometimes the ultimate treat, basil, and even coriander.

Storing

Fresh herbs should be picked over, and any damaged or rotting leaves removed. Store green fleshy herbs in a thick plastic bag or box lined with kitchen paper in the fridge. Use fresh herbs with fragile leaves such as dill, chervil, basil and fennel as soon as possible, within 1–3 days. Other fresh herbs such as parsley, coriander, tarragon, and chives will last up to one week. Tough-leaved herbs such as oregano, thyme, sage, rosemary and bay leaves will dry naturally in the kitchen and do not need to be stored in the fridge. Despite what people say, fresh herbs do not freeze well.

TIP: Fresh dried herbs

This is a good tip to know, especially when you are fortunate enough to have too many fresh herbs to use. It works especially well for oregano, mint and parsley. Chop the herbs finely, spread out on a work surface and leave to dry overnight. Store in the fridge. They keep their fresh dried quality for a month or so.

ENJOYING ORGANIC HERBS

In my own kitchen, I use fresh herbs as other people would salt and pepper. The fact that they are organic is the icing on the cake. A few other favourite ways to use them are:

- Fried sage leaves – wonderful with pasta, veal, pork, chicken or cheese dishes. Fry in a little olive oil, and put in a low oven to crisp.
- Salsa verde – for asparagus, barbecued chicken and fish, and organic salmon.
- Instant tartar sauce: add chopped organic tarragon, capers, a tiny bit of finely chopped onion, or chopped chives, to your favourite bought organic mayonnaise.
- For an instant lift, stir in some extra olive oil and add some extra chopped fresh herbs to bought pasta and other sauces.
- Pestos (think watercress here, too: watercress and walnut pesto, for example, is superb).
- Tomato and herb salsas.
- Fried parsley, either on its own – yummy scattered over salads, or a good handful, finely chopped, thrown into a pan with a couple of fresh anchovies, olive oil and frizzled – use to dress broccoli, French beans and cauliflower.
- Basil purée: whizz basil with melted butter or olive oil in a blender to a thick emerald paste. Use to stir into rice, risottos, for boiled potatoes, fish, or anything else you want to taste fragrantly of basil. A good way, also, to freeze basil for those fortunate enough to have a glut.

For information on buying dried herbs, see chapter 10.

ORGANIC SEEDS

The following specialise in mail order organic seeds – vegetables, salads, herbs and unusual varieties.

Ferme de Sainte Marthe, PO Box 358, Walton, Surrey, KT12 4YX
tel: 019322 2666360; fax: 01932 252707
email: chaseorg@aol.com.
Sainte Marthe is a French organic seed-producing farm which specialises in saving old, rare and forgotten varieties.

Future Foods, PO Box 1564, Wedmore, Somerset, BS28 4DP
email: enquiries@futurefoods.com; website: **www.futurefoods.com**
Specialist eclectic catalogue full of weird and wonderful edible delights for your garden – all the food plants you've heard about but never thought you could grow, plus mushroom spawn and kefir, kombucha, viilli (Finnish yoghurt culture) and vinegar mother ferments. For a catalogue, please send SAE and 4 first-class stamps, or visit their fascinating website. You can also order via email.

The Organic Gardening Catalogue, Riverdene Business Park, Molesey Rd, Hersham, Surrey, KT12 4RG
tel: 01932 253666; fax: 01932 252707
email: chaseorg@aol.com; website: **www.organiccatalogue.com**
The official catalogue of HDRA, includes tried and tested organic varieties from Seeds of Change, USA.

See also: Tamar Organics, Tavistock, Devon, and Jekka's Organic Herb Farm, Alveston, Bristol, in the directory.

7: Organic Dairy Produce

For consumers, organic dairy produce is good news all the way. The last couple of years have seen substantial numbers of farmers convert, and 2002 will see even more, such that dairy is now the second-largest organic sector. The ensuing proliferation of ranges and brands brings with it a much wider choice and greater availability of organic milk, soft cheeses such as fromage frais and cottage cheese, butter, cream and yoghurt. Chilled fresh organic dairy desserts are the latest addition and are becoming more sophisticated by the day: Joubère have just introduced three individual packs which you can turn out on to your best china plate so that no one will know. Meanwhile organic kefir (a traditional Russian fermented milk product), yoghurt with ginseng, and yoghurts made with probiotic cultures are just around the corner.

After fresh produce, organic dairy products are the most popular choice, and if you're not yet converted it's an easy switch to make. They offer all the guarantees of organic farming, ensuring high-quality milk and animal welfare, and minimum food processing. And about every mother I've talked to finds that organic dairy products, particularly milk and yoghurts, taste better than the ones they bought previously.

Changes and developments

The organic dairy sector is a fast-moving business, and many changes are taking place. More European milk and dairy products, especially cheese, are being exported to the UK and imported milk is being used to make some UK organic cheeses. Whereas previously most organic dairies were small concerns, bigger dairies now also process organic milk. More brands have come onstream, notably the Danish brand Harmonie (organic milk, soft cheeses, grated mozzarella, yoghurt and butter), the French brand Vrai (organic crème fraîche, yoghurts); Müller organic fruit yoghurts; and in Scotland, a new organic dairy brand, Rowan Glen (milk, cream, fromage frais, cottage cheese and yoghurts), who use only Scottish organic milk.

Two of the best-known organic dairy pioneers have been taken over by other companies: Rachel's Dairy in Wales is now owned by Horizon, one of America's leading organic dairies, easily recognised by their happy cow motif; and Rocombe Farm ice-cream is now owned by Britain's best-selling yoghurt brand, Yeo Valley. Takeovers are always received with mixed feelings, and suspicions that organic values (and products) may be diluted. My personal view is that until one knows all the facts, it is unwise to jump to conclusions. Nor would any sensible manufacturer dilute a well-known brand by making the products inferior. In these two cases, Horizon has invested heavily in helping Welsh dairy farmers to convert. Yeo Valley's integrity cannot be faulted, and few companies are better at marketing their products and sharing their organic ethos with their customers. The fact that Yeo Valley is now the UK's brand leader for all plain yoghurts is a tribute both to the company and to how far, with consumers' help, the organic dairy sector has advanced.

ORGANIC MILK AND CREAM

The starting-point for all organic dairy products is organic milk. This comes from cows that are raised organically, that graze organic pastures with their rich complex of nutritious plants, and are fed hay or silage supplemented with natural non-GM feeds. On average in the UK, an organic dairy cow produces around 5,000–6,000 litres of milk a year. Organic herd sizes vary from tiny to large. As mentioned earlier, none are pushed to produce milk to the limit of their genetic potential. Day-to-day management – involving feed, medication, welfare considerations and husbandry practices – is designed to ensure the maximum health of the cow, and therefore of the milk.

The daily organic pinta

The daily organic pinta is now a fact of life: all multiples sell it, as do Express Dairies (who also sell Yeo Valley's products), Unigate, Wiseman Dairies in Scotland, and most recently Dairy Crest – which means you can now have organic milk delivered to your door if you want. The sandwich chain, Prêt à Manger also sells organic milk in all its stores. Currently, a pint of full-cream organic milk costs around 10–12p more than the conventional equivalent. Measured by the amount you put in your tea or coffee, this is very little when you consider what you get (see below how organic milk is produced).

Fresh milk is available as whole, semi-skimmed, or skimmed. Most is homogenised. A small amount of green-top (unpasteurised) milk can still be bought, though only direct from producers: these are included in the directory. Semi-skimmed organic milk is the most popular choice. The introduction of long-life and powdered milk has been the subject of intense debate within the organic movement. It is there because people want it and because they prefer an organic version to a non-organic one. A sign of the times – organic milk from selected farms, thus enhancing the link between consumer and producer – is a welcome trend. Currently four brands are generally available, Manor Farm from Dorset, Duchy Original's organic Ayrshire milk from Highgrove, sold in Waitrose, in addition to their own Select Organic whole milk; and Konhess Organic Farm milk from Scotland. All these milks are also non-homogenised, as is Horizon's 'shake and pour' whole milk, which means you get delicious milk with its own delicious cream on top.

Why organic full-fat milk is best

As health and beauty journalist Sarah Stacey wrote recently, if you're trying to be healthy, forget skimmed milk and drink full-fat organically produced milk instead. This is because it contains unsaturated conjugated linoleic acid (CLA), essential for good health. CLA helps natural weight control by enabling the body to burn more fat, helps the liver detoxify, and protects against a range of conditions such as heart disease, cancer and joint stiffness. There is some evidence that it helps in treating inflammatory conditions such as asthma, especially in children. CLA levels increase in milk with the amount of grass, hay or silage in the cows' diet – which is why organic milk has higher levels. Conventional dairy cows kept inside and fed concentrated soya and maize produce in their milk contain significantly less CLA and correspondingly more saturated fat. E-coli 0157.H7 can be another by-product of feeding cows concentrates. Children should always drink full-fat milk because it is more nutritious.

Why organic milk costs more

As we have already seen, organic farming is a system that doesn't – can't – cut corners, and milk is a classic example of the differences that count and of why the organic version costs more to produce. Just not using routine antibiotics necessitates the constant individual personal care and monitoring of animals. Herds are about half the size of conventional herds, their feed costs at least twice as much as conventional feed, and labour costs are around one and a half times greater. Small welfare details such as feeding calves wholemilk for twelve weeks instead of five contribute to the many hidden costs that organic farmers absorb as a matter of course. Add all of these together and you begin to understand how it is that organic milk offers good value for money. With organic milk, too, you can be sure that farmers are receiving a fairer return for their labours.

Imported organic milk

As far as I am aware, imported organic milk is used to make dairy products such as yoghurts and cheese. However, you may like to know that imported organic milk is subject to the same stringent controls as the UK's. Any importing manufacturer must notify their certification authority, who will check that the milk has been produced to equivalent standards. Manufacturers themselves make additional checks on delivery. The milk is imported fresh in chilled containers, and since it travels from dairy to dairy direct it is often no more than a few hours older than if it had travelled within the UK.

PROFILE: THE ORGANIC MILK SUPPLIERS CO-OPERATIVE (OMSCo)

Organic farming is a co-operative movement in the best sense of the term. One very good example of how this works in practice is OMSCo, whose logo appears on Yeo Valley products and Sainsbury's milk. Run by farmers for farmers, OMSCo is the UK's leading organic milk-marketing organisation, and many organic dairy farmers and manufacturers, including Duchy Home Farm, support them. Yeo Valley was instrumental in helping to set up the organisation. Without OMSCo's vision and its commitment to getting a fair long-term price for organic farmers' milk, the organic dairy market would not be as well developed today. In March 1999, OMSCo and Sainsbury's formalised a ground-breaking agreement whereby Sainsbury's have guaranteed a fixed price for organic milk over five years – something that has never happened before – giving farmers confidence and helping them to plan for the long term. This initiative alone, now involving 250 farmers, has significantly helped increase organic milk production from a starting point of a million litres to upwards of 130 million.

OMSCo collect and market the milk, give technical advice to existing organic farmers and to those in conversion, and act as guardians of organic dairy-farming standards. All farmers receive the same guaranteed price for their milk. Their motto, appropriately enough, is 'Putting the heart back into farming'. To find out more about them and the organic farmers producing your organic milk, visit their website at **www.organicmilk.co.uk**. Their new campaign 'I think, therefore I drink organic' says it all.

▲▲▲

Flavour

The defining characteristic of organic milk and cream for me is their sweet, clean flavour – in fact I find ordinary milk flat, sickly and watery by comparison. Flavour also depends on the breed, and on who has produced it.

- Standard organic milk, collected from various sources, pasteurised and cartoned in the same way as conventional milk, loses any flavour nuances it may have had. Semi-skimmed pasteurised organic milk, unless bought direct from a small producer-retailer, tastes the same as good-quality conventional semi-skimmed milk.
- The best organic milk, from small organic dairies, especially green-top producers like Court Farm in Bristol, and Honeybrook Organics at Burwash, East Sussex, both Organic Food Awards (OFA) dairy-category winners, is sublime, and has a sweetness and delicacy never found in standard milk.
- Unlike the standard pint of milk or tub of cream, the colour of organic milk and cream varies with the season and the cows' diet, ranging from whitish in winter to deep yellow in spring and summer, when the cows are feeding on fresh grass; this, too, comes through in the taste.
- The higher the fat content of a dairy product, the greater the difference between what it *can* taste like and what it often *does* taste like. Organic cream from small producers is a revelation to those who haven't tasted it before; here the richness depends on the breed, Jersey or Guernsey being the most delectable.
- Whether the milk has been homogenised or standardised – that is, has had its cream removed and then put back at the standardised amount of 3.5% – also affects flavour.

The crème de la crème

Organic unpasteurised (green-top) milk and cream are the finest in the world and farmers producing it, organic and conventional, should be cherished. Because so little exists, both the milk and the cream are rarer than truffles, almost. If you get the opportunity, buy some. Small pockets of green-top producer-retailers, who have their own milk rounds, still exist (just) in parts of West and North Yorkshire, Lancashire and Cumbria. Keep your eye open, too, for individual green-top producers on your travels, or at farmers' markets. A list of all green-top producers can be obtained from the Association of Unpasteurised Milk Producers and Consumers (AUMPC), Hardwick Estate Office, Whitchurch-on-Thames, Reading RG8 7RB, tel: 0118 984 2955, fax: 0118 984 2968, who also publish a booklet, *The Case for Untreated Milk*, by Dr Barbara Pritchard, £2 inc. P&P (cheques payable to AUMPC).

The enforced demise by health officials of unpasteurised milk is one of the worst dairy crimes of the modern era. Pasteurisation denatures milk, reducing its nutritional value and flavour. In addition, it kills the beneficial bacteria that protect milk from foreign bacteria so that, contrary to popular mythology, fresh unpasteurised milk and cream – as I know from my own experience – are far more likely to keep fresher longer than pasteurised equivalents. Unpasteurised cream can be sold through shops, but unpasteurised milk cannot, except through producer-retailers who have their own milk round or retailer outlet. And, unbelievably, it has to carry a health warning. So I should point out (otherwise this paragraph will not get printed) that although some of the healthiest people I know, including an octogenarian, have drunk unpasteurised milk all their lives, the official advice is that infants, pregnant women and the elderly or infirm should not drink unpasteurised milk and cream.

HOMOGENISED v. NON-HOMOGENISED MILK

Mass homogenisation of milk is a recent phenomenon. It is a process that breaks up the fat globules in the milk (the cream fraction) into smaller droplets and distributes them uniformly throughout, achieved by pumping the milk very fast through tiny holes under extreme pressure. Homogenisation is the kind of issue that the organic food debate throws up that we wouldn't normally think about. As Sophie

Poklewski Koziell has explained in the Soil Association's journal *Living Earth*, it wasn't so long ago that the 'top of the milk' was a treat, and that milk quality was measured by the amount of cream floating at the top of the bottle. But the arrival of plastic containers created a huge change in milk-drinking habits: the cream got stuck, clogged up the neck of the container and was apparently no longer wanted, so supermarkets asked dairies to homogenise the milk instead.

At the same time, semi-skimmed milk became fashionable, so dairies started homogenising this too, so as to make any remaining fat invisible. Because the cream was now dispersed throughout the milk, the milk had a better mouth feel and was thicker. Homogenisation also breaks down carotene, making milk whiter – considered a plus point as it then looked 'pure' – and making tea and coffee seem whiter, too, which apparently is also what consumers wanted. Nor, unlike unhomogenised milk, does it separate out when you freeze it.

As a result, today most milk and cream is homogenised. However, as Ms Poklewski Koziell also explained, it is an unnecessary cosmetic process, requiring expensive equipment and high energy input. It also makes milk likely to sour more quickly, so homogenised milk has to be heat-treated if it is to be stored for long periods. 'Standardised' – milk with its unvarying cream fraction of 3.1%, could be said to cheat the consumer out of the variations in cream content that nature intended. Though there is no conclusive evidence, some doctors believe that homogenisation may be linked to allergies and is not beneficial for people with arthritic conditions. As far back as thirty years ago, Dr Oster, an American cardiologist, postulated that homogenisation may increase the rate of heart disease.

Because conventional milk is homogenised, commercial pressures ensure that so is most UK organic milk. Many people believe that it should not be homogenised. Organic standards, as mentioned earlier, require minimum processing and state that foods should remain as whole and as 'vital' as possible; in Norway and Denmark the organic certification bodies forbid the homogenisation of organic milk, as does one of the large US certifiers. At the moment the brands mentioned on p. 142 are non-homogenised, as is organic milk from local dairies or green-top producer-retailers. More pressure from consumers would bring us more non-homogenised milk, so seek out and support the real thing when you can. In the meantime, the Soil Association is reviewing whether to continue to permit the process; and if so, it will consider labelling homogenised products certified by them as 'homogenised'.

▲▲▲

Organic crème fraîche

Luscious stuff – most supermarkets stock it. Rachel's Dairy is the best-known full-fat brand; Sainsbury's do an own-brand; Vrai is a new organic crème fraîche from Normandy that comes in bottles; and if you want a lighter half-fat alternative, Yeo Valley healthy crème fraîche is excellent. You can use it as you would cream, for a slightly sharper flavour.

Organic clotted cream and other creams

Though not widely available, organic clotted cream and Jersey cream are produced by Conhess; Biona produce organic sour cream; Yeo Valley produce an extra-thick cream which is very popular with their customers (though I do not like it). Apart from supermarket own-brands, Loseley's is becoming a major brand of organic double and single cream (all their milk and cream is UK-sourced).

Organic goat's milk and sheep's milk

Drumboony frozen organic goat's milk is available in selected outlets. Hollypark Organics, Guestling, near Hastings, tel: 01424 812229, is a find. This third-generation Demeter-registered family smallholding produces unpasteurised biodynamic goat's milk, yoghurt and cheese, lamb and poultry and salads. Their goat's milk is available in pints, fresh or frozen, at organic stores in London, at the farm gate and at local farmers' markets.

I have not yet come across a commercially available organic sheep's milk, though organic sheep's milk yoghurt (Vrai and Woodlands) can be bought.

▼▼▼

PROFILE: TWO ORGANIC MILK AND CREAM PRODUCERS

Ivy House Farm, Beckington, nr Bath, Somerset (SA), tel/fax: 01373 830957, website: **www.ivyhousefarm.com**.
Recently converted family dairy farm, with their own Jersey herd. They produce clotted cream, unpasteurised creams, non-homogenised milks, plus brandy clotted cream and clotted cream butter, available locally

and Harrods (milk), Fortnum & Masons (clotted cream) and Neal's Yard Dairy (milk & cream) in London. The Monmouth Coffee shop, owned by Neal's Yard use their Jersey milk, also. Here is what the producers, Geoff and Kim Bowles, say:

> *'Our unpasteurised creams are very much thicker than pasteurised creams because they have not been heat treated and are made within 10 minutes of leaving the cow. Our clotted cream is cooked over boiling water in stainless steel vessels, potted and blast chilled. The cream sets, forming a crust to seal the cream. Our milks are non-homogenised so you always get a rich cream layer, which is the top of the bottle that we used to fight over as children. Jersey milk has a unique taste due to the very large fat globule within it and its colour comes from the high level of natural carotene which comes from its fodder. Our skimmed milk retains its taste due to its freshness at separation and lack of mechanical processing. It also has a higher level of protein and calcium than any other cows milk and is cheaper than calcium enriched water. We deliver into London three times per week and each consignment from milking is less than 24 hours old – we would like to use a better word than fresh but we cannot think of one.'*

Konhess Organic Farm Creamery, Lockerbie, Dumfries (SA), tel: 01461 600227, website: **www.borderorganic.co.uk**.
Another farm creamery, with their own herd of Jersey cows, and the only dedicated organic creamery for liquid milk in Scotland. Their non-homogenised, award-winning Jersey milk (full cream, semi-skimmed and skimmed), cream and butter, is available throughout Scotland and nationwide. Their milk and cream is also used in Baby Organix and Simply Organic Baby Foods (and currently in Loch Arthur cheeses).

Buying and storing

Given the choice, I would buy full-fat organic milk every time. Organic pasteurised milk has the same storage life as conventional milk; how fresh it is when you buy it is the critical factor. For this reason, buy your organic milk from a retailer with a swift turnover, and check the sell-by date. A few other tips:

- For maximum enjoyment, always buy the freshest milk you can and consume it soon.
- Store in the coldest part of the refrigerator – fresh milk will keep for four or five days.
- Cream from full-fat milk can be spooned off to enrich soups, sauces, dips and dressings.

ORGANIC BUTTER

Until recently there was very little organic butter generally available and even less choice of style or brand. This has changed dramatically, and consumers can now buy salted, unsalted, French sweet cream and Vrai Normandy butter; Bridel 'Beurre de Barrate' unsalted butter from Waitrose and Danish organic butter as well as organic Anchor and own-label organic butter from some supermarkets such as Sainsbury's. Other major brands include Dairyland, Harmonie and Naturemaelk from Denmark; and UK brands Yeo Valley, Lye Cross, Hergest Court Farm based in Hereford, Highgrove Dairy in the West Country, and Castle Dairy and Rachel's new Welsh organic butters. Organic butter is made by large and small dairies and has all the advantages of organic milk. Though prices have come down because of greater supplies, they still vary depending on the outlet; the best advice here is to shop around. Prices at supermarkets are usually lower than elsewhere. Make it a part of your weekly shopping basket.

Handmade farmhouse butter

This is a luxury food and therefore expensive. It can cost three or four times more than cheap butters but is about the same price as up-market French butters – and is worth every penny. Produced and churned in the traditional way, it is not pasteurised and varies slightly with the seasons. The main organic producer is the Elms Dairy, near Shepton Mallet in Somerset. Other organic butters are made locally and sold at the farm gate, at farmers' markets and through farm shops or local stores.

Buying and storing

Commercial organic butter is made from pasteurised milk and has the same shelf life as conventional butter. Hand-made farmhouse butter is a different product entirely: gloriously sweet and creamy when freshly made, it does not keep well and should be bought as fresh as possible and eaten within two weeks. For this reason, only buy when very fresh. Two tips:

1 Always store butter in the fridge well wrapped in greaseproof paper; this protects it from absorbing other flavours.
2 The best way to store hand-made organic butter is to cut it into conveniently sized small blocks, wrap well in greaseproof paper and keep in a box in the freezer. If you use only small quantities anyway, do the same with other organic butters.

ORGANIC CHEESES

Compared with two years ago, the number and variety of organic cheeses now available – even in major supermarkets – are remarkable, and putting together an organic cheeseboard has never been easier. If you wanted to, you could easily assemble blue, soft, hard, traditional, classic, British or European cheeseboards that would each feature organic cow's, goat's and sheep's milk cheeses. Quality is excellent, and organic cheeses now regularly win prizes at major cheese competitions. Major UK brands, in addition to the pioneering Lye Cross of Staffordshire, that now offer organic cheeses, include Belton in Somerset, Fountain Dairies in Wensleydale, North Yorkshire, Pilgrim's Choice from North Downs Dairy at Sittingbourne in Kent, and Coombe Farm in Somerset. Evernat have also added four cheeses to their range.

This year Duchy Originals introduced their first cheese, organic Stilton made by the country's smallest independent Stilton dairy, Webster's in Leicestershire, using milk from native shorthorns, a rare breed kept at the local agricultural college. It's sold at Sainsbury's and at independents, and is delicious, creamy, full-bodied and nicely blue. Cropwell Bishop organic Stilton, from Nottingham, won the organic Food Awards 2001 cheese category, together with – a sign of the times – Futura organic mascarpone (available in some Sainsbury's). The best-known European brands that you will see on supermarket shelves are the Danish Harmonie and Dairyland, who both produce a very good range of soft and blue cheeses. Harmonie's soft cream-cheese is excellent. Their organic grated cow's-milk mozzarella in resealable packs gets my stamp of approval, too, as do the two Stamp Collection cheeses in chic designer packs – Troy (hard sheep's cheese) and Priscilla (soft goat's cheese, complete with a tiny pressed flower in the centre). The new cheeses to look out for? Artisan Spanish organic cheeses.

How they are made

Organic cheese uses milk from animals raised and managed as described on pp. 10–11. Cheese-makers who have switched from conventional to organic milk remark on the difference it has made to the flavour of their cheeses. In addition, these cheeses conform to all the usual organic standards, and in the UK only vegetarian rennet is used, so all UK organic cheeses are suitable for vegetarians. If no organic equivalent is available, up to 3% of non-organic ingredients such as garlic, herbs and spices is permitted – though this is increasingly rare now that the organic version of most ingredients can be obtained.

Though larger dairies are increasingly adding organic cheeses to their range, many are still made by individual cheese-makers who use milk from their own animals, or buy accredited organic milk from known producers. The remainder are made in small and medium-sized dairies, including the rising number of imported organic cheeses coming on to the shelves (imported cheeses, made to similar exacting standards, are generally of very high quality). Cow's milk accounts for about one half of the cheeses available, goat's and ewe's milk the other. About half are unpasteurised.

The range

There are getting on for a hundred organic cheeses to choose from. They include all the traditional hard cheeses from Cheddar to Wensleydale and Double Gloucester, Gouda and Edam, Brie and Camembert, blue-veined cheeses including Roquefort and Gorgonzola, smoked goat's cheese, havarti and mozzarella, and cheeses flavoured with herbs, garlic and spices such as caraway seeds. There are three sorts of organic feta (made from cow's, goat's or sheep's milk), French mountain cheeses, and Gruyère and Emmental. Some imported cheeses use animal rennets, so if you're a vegetarian you may want to check first. Many more imported hand-made cheeses from small dairies are now available, some at Sainsbury's, Tesco and Waitrose. Organic parmigiano, cut to order (Waitrose and Sainsbury's sell it), is superb. And organic French reblochon has many fans, too. Prepacked organic cheese is readily available.

Lye Cross have increased their range and now make four types of organic farmhouse Cheddar (mild to vintage), farmhouse Red Leicester and Double Gloucester, Wensleydale, Lancashire, Caerphilly and Stilton – all delicious. Pilgrim's Choice produce farmhouse Cheddars and Red Leicester. Fountains

Dairy also produce a range of organic regional cheeses: Wensleydale original (made from 100% Wensleydale milk), three varieties of Cheddar, Red Leicester, Double Gloucester and White Cheshire. Popular Irish cheeses include Desmond and Gabriel Cheddar, St Tola goat's milk log cheese from County Clare, and Orla sheep's milk pecorino-style cheese from County Cork.

Organic soft cheeses – fromage frais, cottage cheese and cream-cheese – are impressively good and widely available. You can also buy organic mascarpone, ricotta and quark. Loseley produce both organic cottage cheese and full-fat soft cheese. The award-winning Pant-ysgawn soft goat's cheese, available in packs (but also cut to order in the cheese section of Waitrose, and it is Sainsbury's own-brand soft goat's cheese), remains my favourite soft cheese – what I would have done without my daily fix while writing this book I do not know.

Buying and storing

The same rules apply to organic cheeses as to any other high-quality cheeses. When buying loose cheese, look for one that is in good condition; avoid dried-up, sweaty or obviously unloved cheese; ask to have it cut on the spot rather than taking a pre-packed piece; always taste first, and seek advice if you need it.

Any high-quality cheese must be stored at the correct temperature; this varies with the individual cheese, but is usually around maturing temperature, 10–14°C/50–60°F. Whenever possible, check with your cheesemonger. A cool larder or, failing that, a plastic box in the salad drawer of the fridge is acceptable. It must also be wrapped well; waxed paper is by far the best – plastic film is not a good idea and in time will make the cheese sweat. Neal's Yard Dairy recommend storing cheese wrapped in greaseproof paper in a cardboard box, to create the right humidity. Allow it to come to room temperature before eating. A few tips:

- The softer the cheese, the fresher it must be and the shorter the shelf life.
- If buying a whole cheese, ask how long it has been matured for, when it will reach its peak and the best way to store it.
- Soft curd cheeses are best bought prepacked.
- Once cut, use hard cheese within 7 days; soft cheese such as Brie or soft goat's cheese within 3–5 days; curd cheeses and crème fraîche as soon as possible.

Price and availability

Organic cheeses are all high-quality, predominantly farmhouse cheeses. Those already made in relatively large quantities and stocked by supermarkets, such as Lye Cross and organic Brie, represent excellent value and cost very little more than conventional equivalents – 5–10% at most – and in some cases less (Lye Cross Cheddar is approximately the same price). Organic farmhouse cheeses come in the same price range as other high-quality cheeses. Look out for promotional offers in shops and specialist cheese stores.

Popular stalwarts like organic Cheddar, and often Brie, are sold by most major multiples, and some have their own brands. Sainsbury's sell 37 different organic cheeses and Waitrose around 20. Cheese is often an expensive purchase and you need to be sure you're getting it in good condition. Specialist cheese shops, which usually sell some organic cheeses, are the best place to try – failing that, go for shops that are cheese enthusiasts. Planet Organic and Fresh & Wild in London have an excellent selection. Organic and wholefood stores and some healthfood shops stock organic cheeses.

Many box schemes now include organic cheeses (some do a dairy box), and they can be bought by mail order on or the Internet. Finally, don't forget that the cheapest and one of the nicest ways to buy cheese is direct from the producer at the farm gate.

PROFILE: LOCH ARTHUR CREAMERY, Beeswing, Dumfries and Galloway (Demeter)

At Loch Arthur Camphill Community, where they farm biodynamically, producing good food is a way of life. Their creamery and creamery shop are well known, and all their products receive high acclaim. Like many craft cheese-makers, they use unpasteurised milk for their delicious hard and soft cheeses, collected from their own native Ayrshire cows. Sadly their herd was culled during the foot and mouth crisis, so they are temporarily buying in local organic milk. The range includes an award-winning traditional Cheddar (about as good as it gets), available plain or with herbs or caraway seeds, a twelve-month-aged Cheddar, a small soft cheese called Crannog, available plain, herbed or with green peppercorns, a semi-soft rind-washed cheese called Criffel and a smooth, creamy, pasteurised fresh curd cheese. They also produce hand-churned organic butter, yoghurt and home-made muesli, run a monthly meat box scheme, and they have their own organic bakery that offers freshly baked wholemeal, sunflower and honey bread at their creamery shop. Widely distributed throughout Scotland, including Iain Mellis's cheese shop, and Neal's Yard in London, which stocks Loch Arthur Cheddar. Their cheeses, including mixed-cheese platters and baskets, can be bought through mail order, tel: 01387 760296.

SPECIALIST CHEESE SHOPS

The shops listed below specialise in British farmhouse cheeses, including farmhouse organic ones, matured in their own cellars.

The Cheese Shop, Chester, tel: 01244 346240.
Stocks over 150 British cheeses, is particularly strong on Welsh ones, and includes a dozen organic farm-made cheeses such as Staffordshire, Penbryn, Llangloffan, Bourne's unpasteurised Cheshire, St Tola and Pant-ysgawn. They also sell organic butter, biscuits, chutney, oils and wine. Mail order service available: the cheese is cut and dispatched to order, then sent in chilled packaging to reach customers within 24 hours.

Their new restaurant, Elliot's, situated around the corner, tel: 01244 329932, serves organic dishes using many basic organic ingredients, and also offers B&B with organic breakfast.

Iain Mellis, Edinburgh and Glasgow tel: 0131 226 6215.
Scotland's premier cheese merchant, with shops in Edinburgh and Glasgow. They stock 70–80 farm-made cheeses, including organic Loch Arthur, Staffordshire and Orla Irish sheep's-milk cheese. They also sell organic olive oil from Spain, oatcakes, Loch Arthur organic yoghurt and Rachel's Dairy products. Excellent catalogue, and a cheese mail order service.

Neal's Yard Dairy, Covent Garden, London WC2, tel: 020 7240 5704.
A mecca for anyone who loves real cheese. Their organic cheeses include Loch Arthur cow's-milk cheese, Plaw Hatch award-winning unpasteurised Cheddar, St Tola goat's-milk cheese (seasonal) and Penbryn cow's-milk cheese. Plus Neal's Yard own organic creamery Ragstone and Perroche goat's cheeses, Wealden Round and Finn (made from double cream) cheeses, and their equally delicious organic fromage frais, Greek yoghurt and crème fraîche. They publish a comprehensive catalogue and advisory

leaflet, *Taking Care of your Cheese*, and run an excellent mail order service: the cheese is freshly cut to order, wrapped well and packed in a cardboard box (for keeping it in at home), and arrives next day. The shop also sells organic red wine vinegar, French Dijon mustard and preserves, and L'Estornell Spanish organic olive oil. For cheese mail order tel: 020 7645 3555, email: mailorder@nealsyarddairy.co.uk.

Their sister shop, tel: 020 7645 3554, is opposite Borough Market and sells the same range.

Ravens Oak Dairy, Nantwich, Cheshire (SA) tel: 01270 524624.
Another find. Dairy farmers and cheese-makers who have their own excellent country farm shop. They make award-winning Ravensoak soft cheese and Burland Green mould-ripened organic cow's-milk cheese from their own milk, plus Spurstow and Brindley buffalo-milk cheeses using local Welsh buffalo milk, and 3 goat's milk cheeses using goat's milk that comes from two miles down the road. In addition, their extensive cheese counter has around 20-plus British cheeses, predominantly organic, including the Staffordshire ones and Cropwell Bishop's extra-creamy organic Stilton.

▲▲

ORGANIC YOGHURT

'Right from the start, as a family, we were never tempted by chemical shortcuts and were raised to believe that health depended on a cycle of natural replenishment, and nurture began with the soil. My grandmother and mother also believed passionately, as I do, that food should be pure, natural and healthy. When we started making yoghurt I was determined not to compromise this. I believed that's what consumers want and have always used it as my guiding principle.'
Rachel Rowlands, founder, Rachel's Dairy

Yoghurt is the most popular organic food you can buy, available everywhere. These days there is all the choice you could wish for: Rachel's bio-live fat-free fruit yoghurts, baby yoghurts, frozen yoghurts, drinking-yoghurts, and yoghurts in dinky recyclable glass pots by the French brand Vrai (and perfect for home-made organic jams and jellies), as well as extra-large, good-value 1 kg pots of Harmonie natural yoghurt – these are the innovations. Cream o'Galloway's frozen yoghurts are sold in 100 ml impulse tubs and 500 ml takeaway home packs, and come in scintillating flavours such as elderflower cordial (made with spring water), lemon meringue, and honey and stem ginger. Loseley's, meanwhile, have combined organic yoghurt and crème fraîche to produce two new layered dairy desserts, one with strawberries and one with chocolate sauce.

For anyone new to organic food, yoghurt is the perfect thing to try first. Healthy, convenient, delicious and *not* expensive, unlike conventional yoghurts it contains only real ingredients, no refined white sugar (organic yoghurts tend to add less sugar, anyway) and is free from artificial flavourings and additives. Almost all widely available organic yoghurt is produced from cow's milk. Vrai and Woodlands have recently introduced an organic sheep-milk yoghurt, which is excellent news. Elm Farm organic goat's milk yoghurt is the most widely available. All of these are to be found at organic retailers, not supermarkets.

What is and isn't in organic yoghurts

By law all organic yoghurt must contain 95–100% certified ingredients, though most contain 100%, or all but. Only organic milk, milk powder, cream and fruit can be used. Non-organic ingredients may include added pectin or starch in fruit yoghurts. Many – Yeo Valley, Rachel's, Harmonie and Vrai, for example – do not use milk powder at all, but make all their yoghurts from liquid milk.

Types available

There are two broad types. Commercial organic dairies produce cow's milk yoghurts of the same smooth, thick style as conventional yoghurts. They are available plain and flavoured, whole-fat, low-fat and frozen. Yeo Valley and Rachel's are leading brands – they are both dedicated organic companies, as is Vrai, whose organic yoghurts receive warm praise. Vrai (meaning 'true', and 'real' in French) started producing the first organic dairy products in Brittany twenty-five years ago, and now have dairies in Normandy and Haute-Savoie in the French Alps as well. Loseley now have an organic range, which is also popular, and other brands include Biona Demeter whole-milk yoghurt and kefir in glass pots, Biyo, who produce drinking-yoghurts, the Irish brand Gleniska, and a new Scottish brand Rowan Glen. The up-and-coming Harmonie yoghurts, sold in most major multiples including Tesco, are made in Denmark from milk from their own organic farmers, thereby ensuring that quality and high standards are maintained. Their excellent low-fat yoghurt is made from whole milk. Harmonie and Vrai also produce baby yoghurts, both without added sugar.

Commercially produced organic yoghurt is excellent value, and is generally approximately the same price as equivalent – that is, premium – conventional brands, with fruit yoghurts only around 5–10p extra. Look out for promotional offers in supermarkets.

The second type of yoghurt is individual producer-made, such as those made by the Elm Dairy, near Shepton in Somerset; Loch Arthur in Dumfries; Sussex High Weald Dairy in Uckfield, East Sussex; Radford Mill Farm at Timsbury, Somerset; and Court Farm in Winford, Somerset. They are usually made from the producers' own organic cow's, goat's or sheep's milk, and mostly plain, but a few producers make a small amount of fruit yoghurt. They tend to be more like home-made yoghurt, with a creamy crust if made from whole milk and a slightly thinner, grainier texture that traditional yoghurt aficionados appreciate and that is best for eating rather than cooking with. Like hand-made cheese, this kind of yoghurt may also show seasonal variations. It's the crème de la crème of yoghurts, made in small batches, thus costs a little more (large tubs are more economical). It is sold through local outlets and organic supermarkets.

Quality

Like ice-cream, yoghurt has become a debased product commercially, a world away from the original simple food made from cultured whole milk – and because the word sounds so natural, few of us bother to read the labels. Organic manufacturers (though they, too, produce low-fat yoghurts, sweetened yoghurts and so on) try harder than many to retain the nutritional integrity of their products, and the quality of organic yoghurts is generally excellent. A word, however, about children's yoghurts, and especially yoghurts for babies. The general consensus is that babies up to twelve months old should not have sugar, organic or not, and that children's yoghurts should contain as little as possible. Dentists recommend no sugar until the age of about two and a half. So to be sure to check the label that you are happy with the nutritional profile.

Storing

Organic yoghurt has exactly the same shelf life as good-quality conventional yoghurts. Unopened, plain yoghurt stores very well in the fridge for two to three weeks, but changes in flavour, becoming more acidic with time and gradually thickening. Fruit yoghurts should be eaten as soon as possible.

PROFILE: RACHEL'S ORGANIC DAIRY AND YEO VALLEY

Britain's two leading brands of organic yoghurt are dedicated organic companies. Both have done an enormous amount not just to develop the market for organic yoghurt but, like OMSCo (see p. 143), they epitomise the organic working ethos and through their investment, hard work and long-term trading support have encouraged many more dairy farmers to convert – a process that continues.

Rachel's Organic Dairy (SA) Rachel's Dairy's organic roots stretch back over three generations. In 1984 Rachel made her first batch of organic yoghurt on the kitchen Aga from milk from their organic Guernsey herd, which had been started by her remarkable grandmother who introduced the first Guernsey herd into Wales and bred them for over thirty years. Today, though Rachel Rowlands remains a director, this award-winning Welsh dairy is owned by an American organic dairy, Horizon, who are expanding into Europe.

For their yoghurts, especially, they have become a household name, synonymous with the best quality; the yoghurts contain no added thickeners, pectin, stabilisers or artificial anythings, and are sweetened with organic raw cane sugar. The fruit ones contain whole pieces, cooked first to a jam. New varieties include Greek-style yoghurt, sweetened with honey, wholemilk with maple syrup, and low-fat with real vanilla. They also produce excellent crème fraîche, double cream and Sainsbury's own-brand organic yoghurt. Recipe leaflets are available. Tel: 01870 625805, email: enqs@rachelsdairy.co.uk, or visit their excellent and informative website at **www.rachelsdairy.co.uk**.

Yeo Valley (SA) Yeo Valley, the country's most successful organic dairy business, whose products can be found in major supermarkets including ASDA, Budgens, Safeway, Sainsbury's, Tesco and Waitrose, started buying organic milk from local dairy farmers in Somerset to make organic yoghurt in 1993. They have built their business on long-term contracts which guarantee fair prices for their milk suppliers, who also receive an additional annual payment based on the company's profitability. Their mission – to deliver to consumers competitively priced, high-quality organic food – has made them the brand leader for all natural yoghurt, and they now outsell all other brands, including long-established non-organic ones.

Their name and their eye-catching, innovative packaging make their yoghurts easy to recognise on the shelves. Their range also includes extra-thick cream, butter, healthy crème fraîche and their very popular fruit compotes. Recent additions are frozen yoghurts, children's fruity fromage frais (equally appealing to grown ups – I eat lots) and ice-cream – sold under both Yeo Valley and Rocombe Farm brand-names. Their yoghurts use organic fruit and sugar, sometimes a little pectin or organic lemon juice, and some contain organic corn starch or apple juice for thickening or sweetening. They also have one of my favourite (award-winning) websites, which combines visual and audible entertainment with clear information, and an excellent children's section. Visit them at **www.yeo-organic.co.uk**.

▲▲▲

PROFILES: THREE SMALL-SCALE YOGHURT AND DAIRY PRODUCERS

The Elms Organic Dairy Ltd (OF&G), Friar's Oven Farm, West Compton, Shepton Mallet, Somerset, tel/fax: 01749 890371 produce excellent organic goat's- and sheep's-milk yoghurt and goat's-milk cream from their own herds, organic cow's-milk and soya-milk yoghurt, and organic milk, cream and delicate-flavoured, unsalted hand-churned butter; plus a small amount of sugar-free organic fruit yoghurt – the fruit is home-grown. All produce is pasteurised and made on the farm. Available in the South West, the South East and London, including Planet Organic and Fresh & Wild.

Sussex High Weald Dairy (SA) A small family-run dairy at Putlands Farm, Duddleswell, Uckfield in East Sussex, tel: 01825 712647, producing a range of sheep's-milk and organic cow's-milk dairy produce. The organic range, sold under the Putlands Farm label, includes creamy, thick-set, low-fat bio-yoghurt made with Guernsey milk from which the butterfat has been removed; low-fat fromage-frais-based soft cheese (plan, and garlic and herb), pasteurised organic Guernsey cream; small quantities of Guernsey unsalted butter, and the superb and delectably rich Ashdown Foresters hard cow's-milk cheese. All their products are excellent; the low-fat ones do not taste low-fat. Their foods can be bought from the farm direct, are widely distributed throughout the South, and their hard cheeses are available by mail order.

Old Plaw Hatch Farm (Demeter) Voted by *Harpers & Queen* magazine the best farm shop in the country, Old Plaw Hatch Farm at Sharpthorne, East Grinstead, tel: 01342 810652, is a biodynamic farm under the ownership of a charitable trust and specialising in dairy produce – unpasteurised milk and cream, ice-cream, yoghurt, quark, award-winning Cheddar-type cheese – and vegetables. They sell single, whipping and double cream (so thick it should be called quadruple), plain full- and low-fat yoghurt, and pure 100% organic fruit yoghurts made with UK-produced fruit, mainly their own, and organic sugar. Their dairy produce is sold through the farm shop, throughout the South-East in small outlets, and in London. They are now in partnership with another nearby biodynamic enterprise, Tablehurst Farm, selling beef, lamb and pork.

Others include Court Farm, Winford, Somerset; Loch Arthur Creamery, Beeswing, Dumfries; and Radford Mill Farm, Timsbury, Somerset. For details, see directory.

ORGANIC ICE-CREAM

The nation's favourite dessert has now gone seriously organic. This means more brands and more flavours, supermarket own-brands – and more variations in price and hence in perceived quality. I say 'perceived' because all organic ice-cream starts at a much higher base level than any mass-produced so-called ice-cream; and at this level it's mainly a question of personal taste and whether you are looking for a high-quality or a gold-star ice-cream. Recommended popular brands include Green & Black's and Rocombe Farm's luxury ice-creams. Yeo Valley have introduced three good-value one-litre tubs, vanilla, chocolate and caramel. Two others are Finest Organics' new range which includes vanilla and raspberry-twist ice-cream, and Bio Line. Sainsbury's, Tesco and Waitrose sell own-brand organic ice-cream; all are good – to prove the point, Sainsbury's organic chocolate ice-cream won the dairy category in the 2000 Organic Food Awards.

Local brands made by enterprising dairy farmers are also beginning to make their mark. Three – September Organic Dairy in Hereford, Cream o'Galloway in Scotland, and Meadow Cottage Dairy Ice-Cream (who also supply British Airways) in Hampshire, all of whom have recently converted – are featured below. Other small organic producers such as Old Plaw Hatch Farm, East Grinstead, also make their own organic ice-cream.

The differences that count

Organic ice-cream is made from organic cream, milk, sugar and fruit, and contains minimal added ingredients and no artificial flavourings or additives. Different proportions of the basic ingredients produce different styles, with the best superbly rich, clean and delectable. As with anything else, the label will reveal what you need to know. Comparing organic with non-organic ice-creams, there are two other important things to note:

- The vast majority of conventional ice-creams are made with a range of artificial emulsifiers and stabilisers. Their function is to enable a maximum amount of air to be incorporated and to develop a creamy feel in products that do not necessarily contain any cream. The only stabilisers allowed in organic ice-cream are guar, xanthan and locust bean gums, the only emulsifier, lecithin; all are natural products.
- Ice-cream is sold by volume, not by weight. Cheap ice-cream can contain up to 120% more added air. To judge the quality of any ice-cream, feel the weight of the tub. The lighter it feels, the more removed from the real thing and the poorer the quality.

NOTE: Organic ice-cream is made with a minimum of 95% organic ingredients. Non-organic ingredients may include pasteurised free-range eggs (this is because pasteurised organic eggs are still in very short supply).

Organic ice-cream sells at around the same price as premium conventional ice-creams such as Häagen-Dazs, though own-brand varieties are cheaper. All are excellent value for what you get.

Storing

Whether organic or not, it's important that ice-cream should be well wrapped and got home as quickly as you can. Commercial organic ice-cream has a storage life of 9–18 months, depending on the brand; unless the box says differently, farm-made ice-cream is best eaten as soon as possible. Ice-cream should not be eaten straight from the freezer but allowed to soften and 'ripen' for a few minutes, to bring out the flavour. Three tips:

- Ice-cream must be stored in the freezer at a minimum temperature of −18°C. It will keep unopened, but once opened should be eaten as soon as possible, as constant softening and rehardening leads to deterioration of taste and texture.
- To prevent ice crystals forming on top of the ice-cream, keep the tub covered at all times.
- Never refreeze ice-cream that has thawed; this can be a health hazard.

Ice-cream desserts and confectionery

Not content with just organic ice-cream? Look out for Finest Organic's vanilla and chocolate or vanilla and strawberry ice-cream cakes and Loverendale's (Demeter) ice-cream lollies and choc ices. Who said organics hadn't arrived?

PROFILE: THREE LOCAL GEMS

Family-run dairies are precious. Three not to be missed (featured in the food maps at the end of the book) and whose products are becoming widely available:

Cream o'Galloway, Castle Douglas, Dumfries (SA) tel: 01557 814040 website: **www.creamogalloway.co.uk**.

The award-winning Cream o'Galloway Dairy has been farmed by the Finlays for three generations – since the 1920s – and they have been making ice-cream since 1994. Conservation has always been a passion and the farm is a local tourist attraction featuring nature trails and playground areas as well as their shop and dairy, where you can see their ice-creams and frozen yoghurts being made. The farm has recently become organic. All their ice-creams are made with milk and cream from their Ayrshire cows. Their organic range is currently vanilla, strawberry pavlova, chocolate and cappuccino (for their organic frozen yoghurts, see p. 155), sold at some Sainsbury's and Safeway stores in Scotland, and widely available in London.

Meadow Cottage Dairy Ice-cream, Bordon, Hampshire (SA) tel: 01428 712155 website: **http://members.netscapeonline.co.uk/weydown**.

One of the few remaining dairies where you can buy fresh untreated Jersey milk and cream straight from the dairy. They've been making ice-creams and sorbets since 1984, which are well known locally and in the South of England. The farm has recently completed organic conversion, and uses its organic Jersey milk and cream in all its ice-creams; they currently have one full organic ice-cream, vanilla, and are developing others. Strong supporters of Hampshire local fare, they sell their products at all the local farmers' markets. Their farm shop is open 8 am–6 pm every day except Christmas Day, and also sells local cakes and eggs. For directions and a list of local farmers' markets, ring direct or visit their website.

September Organic Dairy, Almeley, Hereford (SA) tel: 01544 327561 website: **www.september-organic.co.uk**.

This small family dairy, situated on the Welsh Borders, sells their exquisite ice-creams from the farm direct. All the milk, eggs and cream used are produced on the farm, and all ingredients are 100% organic and they use local organic fruit where possible. Flavours include Brown Bread, Cinnamon Spice and Elderflower Cream.

▲▲

ORGANIC EGGS

The development of organic eggs mirrors that of organic chicken. In the last couple of years organic eggs have become commonplace in supermarkets and, like organic chickens, have come under increasing scrutiny. The same reason for this scrutiny applies to both – there are two types of organic eggs: those produced by small producers and organic farmers who keep a few chickens to sell locally as part of their mixed-farming system, and those of medium-sized specialist egg producers who mainly supply supermarkets, and are available at a price that more of us feel we can afford. The same issues are common to organic chickens and organic eggs, including the question of standards – the Soil Association's poultry standards are higher than the other certification bodies. For all of this see chapter 8.

The fundamental problem is that conventional eggs, like conventional chickens, have become so cheap that few consumers are prepared to pay the necessary extra for eggs produced in the best ways possible; and any system that tries to produce a better egg not only seems expensive – it *is* expensive. High quality food always costs more. Put bluntly, we pay too little for our eggs, and have done so for a considerable time. Although it merely reflects the latest food fashion, one of the more welcome developments of the last two years is the gradual appearance on the supermarket shelves of various brands of up-market eggs, of specific breeds and produced by exacting standards, whether organic or not. Waitrose, for example, stock Columbian Blacktail and Old Cotswold Legbar eggs. These delicious, though not organic, eggs are raised in similar free-ranging conditions to small organic laying flocks, and actually cost more than the standard organic eggs on sale in my local branch.

Why do organic eggs cost more?

The extra costs are mainly due to lower stocking densities and more expensive feed (a good-quality conventional non-GM feed costs £130 per tonne, compared to £250 for organic feed). In addition, Soil Association regulations state that the birds must receive a minimum of 8 hours of darkness in 24. The Stonegate story is told below. Because this company produces conventional free-range as well as organic Columbian Blacktail eggs, for once we can make an exact comparison. It currently costs Stonegate 42p extra to produce a dozen organic Blacktail Columbian eggs. Apart from the difference in feed costs, this is because their conventional birds are contained in fixed housing at a stocking density of 10 hens per square metre, and lay 302 eggs per bird, whereas their organic layers, stocked at 6 hens per square metre, lay 280.

Organic standards v. the rest

The debate mainly applies to commercial organic eggs, rather than to those from small producers. As with chickens, in practice it is how each organic producer actually runs his operation rather than which logo the eggs carry that is the most important factor. All producers of organic eggs subscribe to organic farming principles. But some compromises are inevitable. It is not often appreciated, for example, that at the moment (though this will change) unless a producer raises his own pullets (young birds) because there are no commercially raised organic pullets to buy, conventionally raised pullets (up to sixteen weeks old) have to be bought in; after six weeks, their eggs receive organic status.

The hens have constant access to organic pastures and are fed a natural diet comprising a minimum of 80% organic feed. Note also that all organic eggs are produced in free- range systems. The birds have up to twice as much room as their conventional counterparts – in other words, stocking densities, both inside and out, are up to half that of conventional free-range systems (some small organic producers have stocking densities of one-third less).

- Prophylactic and routine medication of flocks is forbidden; if medication is used to treat individual hens, withdrawal time before the sale of their eggs is two or three times longer than with conventional systems.
- In-feed medication, growth-promoting agents, yolk-colorants and animal wastes, including feathers, are forbidden.
- Artificial light to extend day length is allowed, but not for as long (16 hours maximum) as in conventional systems, which extend light hours from 18 hours (Freedom Foods) to 23 hours (standard conventional layers). Soil Association standards require that the day must end with a natural dusk.

- Organic poultry and non-organic poultry are not allowed on the same holding.
- Once the laying cycle is completed, pasture must be rested for a minimum of nine months.

For a detailed comparison of organic and conventional standards, see Appendix, p. 378.

A good egg

A good, fresh organic egg from a small producer, who keeps a small flock, is a revelation: an extra-thick yolk that becomes an intense yellow in early summer, and a creamy white whose delicacy defies description. Such eggs are easily the best in the world. Make mayonnaise with one of them and you will immediately see what a good egg is all about. Whatever the price (and it is not usually all that much for such an outstanding product), it is worth it. And yes, one of these eggs is better than any commercial organic egg from a supermarket.

Buying and storing

Stored properly, a fresh egg will keep perfectly for a month. Keep cool at a constant temperature, or in the least cold part of the fridge. Allow to come to room temperature before using. Note that:

- The thicker the shell, the better the eggs will store and keep their eating quality. Many organic eggs have thicker shells than conventional ones on account of the quality of the calcium feed in the hens' diet.
- Avoid buying eggs in recycled egg boxes, which may be contaminated with bacteria, including salmonella, or with broken egg remains from previous eggs.
- Keep the egg shelves in your fridge door clean so as to avoid contamination from, e.g. spilled yoghurt or dripping meat, which can cause bacterial build-up in eggs.
- Cracked eggs should be used only for cakes and for other cooking where the eggs are cooked thoroughly, and should be used as soon as possible.

Organic egg producers

There are many ways of producing an organic egg. Commercial producers produce them to either Organic Farmers & Growers' or Soil Association standards. The eggs are boxed and sold to wholesalers, who sell them on to retail outlets including supermarkets. All eggs carry the appropriate symbol on the box. If it's the SA symbol it means that, except where they fulfil extra conditions, the eggs come from small flocks and have been kept almost always in mobile houses; if they carry the OF&G symbol they are likely to (but don't always) come from larger flocks and live in fixed houses with pop-holes. The Soil Association recommends 500 birds per house as a maximum (but allows up to 2,000). UKROFS regulations, which OF&G follow, allow a maximum of 3,000 birds per house.

The three examples that follow illustrate what's been done to move the egg production debate forward, and how – particularly in the Stonegate example – consumer demand for organic eggs has resulted in new role models for better egg production systems all round.

Cherry Tree Eggs (OF&G) A good example of eggs from a small producer. Featured on the BBC's *Food and Drink* programme, the eggs are produced by Growing Concern, Loughborough, Leicestershire (see p. 421), who have been producing top-quality organic eggs for many years. The hens are kept in movable houses, 100 in each, graze on organic pastureland and are fed home-grown organic wheat. The eggs are available at Planet Organic and Bumblebee healthfood shops in London, in local shops and from the farm direct.

Columbian Blacktail Organic eggs The first organic eggs sold by a supermarket (exclusive to Waitrose) to gain Soil Association accreditation, these are produced by Stonegate egg producers, who are the first to have developed their own breed specifically to suit commercial organic egg production. They are also the first to have their own breeding flock and to raise their own stock, which results in a closed organic cycle (they don't have to buy in conventional pullets), as well as the first to produce their own electricity for the houses from solar panels and windmills.

Any chicken-fancier who has kept rare-breed chickens (I have and now miss them sorely) will immediately recognise the Welsummer pedigree with a dash of others such as Light Sussex and Rhode Island Red. The Stonegate birds are kept in large mobile arks, 1,500 to each, and have constant access to ample permanent pasture. They are mainly produced on mixed farms in the locality, where it may be 18 months – sometimes years, even – before the chickens return to the same piece of pasture. Once the laying cycle is completed, the arks are moved on to fresh pastures, for the next flock. They have now introduced brown eggs from another special breed 'Speckledy' hens, developed from the Maran breed. In developing this system, Stonegate have made significant advances in trying to resolve some of the most important issues: namely, the question of breed; mobile housing, which means better management of land; and the move away from specialist units and back on to mixed farms. The solar-powered electricity is the icing on the cake.

Straw-bale organic free-range eggs A couple of OF&G farmers, including their chairman Charles Peers, who have sizeable flocks, are experimenting with housing their organic layers in biodegradable straw-bale housing. After the laying period (12 months), the houses are dismantled, the straw burnt, and the droppings collected and composted to provide fertiliser for the farm. Each house is one-storey, with a sloping roof covered by tarpaulin and pop-holes for outside access. Inside, a third of the space is set aside as a scratching area, which provides a permanent dust-bath, and the remainder has perches. To prevent waterlogging, a deep trench is built around the outside to form a moat, and the chickens go out to the field over duck-boardings erected across it. Once the house is dismantled, the ground is left to rest and another straw-bale house built elsewhere. Stocking densities inside and outside and all other aspects adhere to UKROFS regulations.

8: Organic Meat, Game, Poultry and Fish

ORGANIC MEAT

Over the last couple of years the organic meat industry, though still small, has come of age, and consumers are now enjoying more and more organic meat. This is partly because more farmers have converted – which means more local organic meat – but also because the 'big three', Sainsbury's, Tesco and Waitrose, have worked hard behind the scenes to build up regular supplies. Sainsbury's were the first to supply fresh organic meat from the butchery counter at their Cromwell Road store in London. Safeway also sell a wide range of organic meat; ASDA and Marks & Spencer sell a little. The result is that, though only sold in selected stores, it is now much more widely available. More butchers are also now selling it, which is excellent news. One enterprising company, Organic Kosher Ltd (see p. 188), is supplying organic kosher and halal meat suitable for the Jewish and Muslim communities respectively – and everybody else as well.

Predictably, organic chicken (and turkey at Christmas) is the most popular, followed by sausages, beefburgers and lamb kebabs. With increased availability comes more choice. There are more prepared organic meats and meat-based convenience meals. Pure Organics were the first company to introduce a children's range, their popular For Georgia's Sake brand. Swaddles Green have followed and Eastbrook Farm have introduced children's organic burgers and sausages.

Why organic meat?

Though various meat-production schemes now offer improvements in the areas of animal welfare and environmental sustainability, as well as other 'farm assurances', no other farm-to-table production system in the UK offers such a comprehensive and legally binding set of guarantees. In addition to all the welfare advantages of organic farming that have already been mentioned, all mutilations, such as tail-docking, keeping the animals on slatted concrete floors and permanent tethering are banned.

In addition, organic meat-producers tend to have smaller herds than many conventional farmers, often favour the more flavoursome, traditionally slower-growing domestic breeds, and use small local abattoirs where possible. At slaughter, everything is done to ensure that their animals experience minimal stress, which is critical to the eating quality of the meat. Most kill a few beasts, or just one at a time; local organic farmers have their own butchers and sell their own meat, which is often hung for longer than conventional meat; generally the whole carcass is hung in the traditional way, to help ensure optimal eating quality.

Buying and selling organic livestock

The recent foot-and-mouth epidemic has brought into sharp focus the traffic of livestock up and down the country and the hundreds of miles that animals travel just to be bought and sold at markets. The organic system works differently: animals are generally bought from one farmer by another, then sold in the same way, without recourse to markets. This considerably reduces the risk of disease and is far less stressful for the animals. The year 2000 saw the first UK organic livestock markets, in Wales and Carlisle. They were strictly regulated, but have caused considerable disquiet amongst many organic farmers, who feel that to go down this particular conventional route is a retrograde step. At the time of writing, no such further markets were planned.

Slaughter

How an animal is slaughtered is of prime concern to the organic producer. All abattoirs used must be approved by a registered organic certification body. Where animals cannot be slaughtered locally, the maximum travel time allowed for any one journey is eight hours. Organically reared animals are kept apart from conventional ones, are generally the first in the day to be slaughtered – and in small numbers rather than in hundreds. Mobile organic slaughterhouses that would slaughter animals individually could be an option for the future. After slaughter, the organic ones are separated from non-organic animals and stamped with a seal certifying their organic status.

Under the Soil Association's regulations, organically raised animals are not allowed to be exported live for slaughter. In the light of the 2001 foot-and-mouth epidemic, this particular ruling has special significance. From the animal welfare point of view, clearly the less an animal has to travel in crowded conditions out of the farmer's control, the better. And surely, in terms of disease prevention too, the time has now come for the transport of livestock within a country to be severely curtailed. Compared with the cost of foot-and-mouth or of whatever disaster may hit next, the loss of income is tiny. Such a move would also help to put back on the agenda, in all EU countries, the issue of local meat and how to make that market flourish.

The plight of small abattoirs

Producing organic meat on a commercial scale poses many challenges, not least the time it takes to convert. One major issue for organic farmers has been the plight of small abattoirs and the fact that so many have closed down on account of changes in EU legislation and the indifference shown by government when it comes to supporting this vital rural resource. There are now only around 250 left in the UK; ironically, if all animals were slaughtered locally, we would have been able to contain the foot-and-mouth tragedy. After a two-year battle, led by Bob Kennard of Graig Farm Organics and Richard Young of the Soil Association, small abattoirs have been reprieved, and changes made in the way they work should enable them to continue in business. To ensure that they thrive, it is even more important that we support local and organic meat producers, who use local abattoirs, when we can.

Organic meat and health

The whole subject of organic food in relation to health is one of the main threads of this book's argument, and even scientists agree that grass-fed animals are better for you (see p. 63). Common sense says that meat produced from animals that have received a natural diet and have grazed organic pastures, that were not stressed or constantly dosed with antibiotics, has to be better for you; and that healthy meat makes for healthier people. Deficiencies in minerals, for instance, affect animal as much as human health. The application of minerals such as zinc and copper to fields in which sheep are raised has been shown to result in increased lambing, to halve early mortality and to double the lambs' growth rate. Organophosphates, widely used in conventional farming as we have seen, bind selenium to the soil, leading to selenium-deficient meat (a lack of selenium has also been implicated in falling sperm counts in Western males); kiln dust containing carcinogenic waste has been used as a fertiliser and as a cattle-feed binder; excess free nitrogen may trigger some forms of cancer; and it has now been shown by a group of EU scientists that hormonal growth-promoters in beef can be carcinogenic. Unfortunately, too little work has been done in this field, and meat production methods and their effects are currently not a factor in scientific investigations into health. We are now being told that eating too much red meat causes stomach and colon cancer. Is it beyond the bounds of scientific probability that intensive practices may be a contributory factor?

TWO ISSUES THAT COUNT

1. GM Animal feeds

GM animal feedstuffs are banned in organic farming. The position elsewhere is as follows . . . Most GM soya finds its way into animal feed, and most animals are fed GM feed. The banning of feeding meat and bone meal to animals as a result of BSE also means that substantially more GM animal feeds are being used than previously.

Because consumers have made their distrust of any genetically modified ingredient used in the production of their food clear – when ASDA conducted their own shopper's poll, two thirds said no to GM diets for animals as well – just about every major supermarket, including ASDA, Marks & Spencer, Sainsbury, Tesco, and Waitrose, has declared a ban on GM feedstuffs for their own brand meat. But apart from these and organic meat, unless the label expresses says otherwise, or the producer gives you his guarantee, just about all conventional meat and meat products you buy is highly likely to have been produced using GM animal feeds. This includes all other brands of meat and meat products sold by supermarkets, the NFU's new 'food you can trust' Red Tractor and Freedom Foods labels, and also applies to any meat you eat in restaurants, pubs or cafés.

It will be some considerable time before we know whether feeding animals GM feed is safe or not. Friends of the Earth (**www.foe.co.uk**) and Greenpeace (**www.greenpeace.org.uk**) both campaign on this issue. For the latest developments, visit their websites.

2. The routine use of antibiotics

One of the fundamental differences between organic and conventional farming is the approach to, and the use of, antibiotics in livestock. Antibiotics have been used as growth promoters in farming for nearly fifty years, since they were first made legal in 1953. Today, just over 60% of all antibiotics are used on animals, and 80% of these are given routinely in feed or water on a daily basis, to promote growth, as a preventative measure against possible disease, or to treat illness. This includes poultry, pigs, beef, dairy herds and fish. Organic farmers, by contrast, only use antibiotics to treat illness, and on an individual basis.

The issue surrounding routine use of antibiotics is not about residues in the meat you eat – these are very rarely recorded – but is potentially much more serious. Bacterial resistance to antibiotics is a fact of life: salmonella resistance to drugs, for example, has increased from 5–95% in the last twenty years. The problem is that antibiotics used in human medicine are often similar to, or even the same as, those used in farming. Resistant bacteria in farm animals can easily affect humans via other bacteria who develop the resistance, either through food which is not properly cooked, or from the environment, for example people working with animals or processing raw meat. Resistant bacteria (commonly known as superbugs) in hospitals are already a major headache. The concern is that if antibiotics continue to be used to treat farm animals at the current level, resistance could spread to life-saving antibiotics used to treat humans, and we could have a health epidemic on our hands.

After many years lobbying, the issue is now being taken seriously. The EU has now banned 7 out of the 11 permitted antibiotic growth promoters. The Soil Association, spearheaded by their campaign adviser, Richard Young, has led the campaign against the routine use of antibiotics and presented two detailed reports to the House of Lords. But though the House of Lords Select Committee agreed that there is a continuing threat to health from the imprudent use of antibiotics in animals, the fundamental problem remains. Routine antibiotics are a major prop of intensive systems, and these systems could not operate without them. Routine use of antibiotics thus continues, and antibiotics known to be cross resistant with important medical drugs continue to be added to livestock feeds under veterinary prescription. The only long-term solution to this gathering crisis is to stop routine farm use of antibiotics – Sweden did so for their poultry in the late 1980s. Supporting organic farming, and farmers who do not use antibiotics routinely, by buying their meat wherever possible will provide an impetus for this change.

▲▲▲

EU livestock regulations, and what they mean for the consumer

In August 2000, EU regulation 1804/99 came into force, covering livestock and livestock products, including the inspection of permitted feedstuffs. Livestock standards are mind-bogglingly complex; to add to this complexity, for the first time member states have been allowed to set higher standards where it seems to them desirable, with the result that almost all have done so, but not in the same areas. The net result is that some standards have been raised and others lowered. For details, see Appendix 1.

For UK consumers, at least in the short term, the introduction of the EU regulations means potentially more confusion. My advice, as before, is to buy local where you can, which permits you to find out exactly how the meat you are enjoying has been raised; and if you buy your organic meat from a supermarket, check with them. Use the information in the Appendix, and in the section on organic principles (pp. 10–11) to guide you. At the moment, the Soil Association has overall the most stringent livestock standards in the UK; but remember that individual farmers registered with other certification bodies may be raising animals to standards as high or even higher. With respect to imported organic meat, the Soil Association is proposing that the country of origin for all primary ingredients be labelled – which, if approved, means you will be able to tell at a glance if a meat is imported.

What the EU regulations mean in practice is that, as noted previously, some standards have been raised and others lowered. This does not mean disaster – the UK bodies have all agreed not to water down UK standards – but it does make it easier for more average organic meat to be produced in other countries, and for producers to operate to the minimum standards rather than aspiring to the highest. The two areas to be most aware of are organic pork standards, and the question of whether an animal has been 'born organic' or 'converted'. The prohibiting of synthetic amino acids has an unwelcome side-effect: until other acceptable supplements can be found, the use of fishmeal as a substitute is affecting the flavour of some organic chickens, and may cause the same with pork.

Imported v. British

I would not buy imported organic meat – not because it is inferior (most of what is currently imported is not) but because I believe in supporting British organic farmers. In doing so, it helps raise meat production standards generally and helps ensure that we shall have a better environment and countryside for our children.

Buying British also means indirectly helping to nurture pioneering initiatives such as the investment that Sheepdrove Organic Farm in Wiltshire has made in organic chicken production, and the decision by Eastbrook Farm Organic Meats to join forces with one of the UK's leading free-range pork producers and processors, BPQ, to fast-forward the development of organic pork. In addition, in order to encourage more producers to convert and develop a stable and committed UK organic meat market, four major meat processors have formed a link with the Organic Livestock Meat Co-operative (OLMC), who act as brokers and marketeers for many organic farmers. It's through co-operative measures like this, and the Graig Farm Organics Producers' Group in Wales and Organic Farmers Scotland, that the future of British organic meat is assured. To further the 'buy British' initiative, discussions are underway to develop a British organic logo that will appear on every pack of meat that has been reared on organic farms to UK organic farming standards.

But, in the short term, to meet the consumer demand for organic meat, a fair proportion (some estimates say up to 50%) is being imported, particularly pork from Denmark and Germany and beef from Argentina. Whether this will become a fixture or not is too early to tell – all the supermarkets I talk to say they want a 'buy British' policy and are working towards it. But let's squash one myth. Just because it's foreign doesn't mean it is not high-quality, or is produced to lower organic standards. The imported meat sold in the major supermarkets has to meet all their standards, and is often certified by an IFOAM-affiliated UK standards authority also. If you are concerned, ask the supplier or supermarket to explain exactly what their standard-controls are.

Although imported meat is on sale in supermarkets, most is sold through catering and processing outlets. With catering establishments you can ask them. Unfortunately at the moment standards do not insist that the country of origin appear on the labels of processed organic foods, though this is expected to change.

European meat: a bird's-eye view

Tim Finney, managing director of Eastbrook Farm Organic Meats, has travelled extensively in Northern Europe, looking at organic livestock operations. This is his report:

> *'Livestock standards in Northern Europe are very mixed. On the whole, beef standards across the EU are compatible with and equivalent to those in the UK, except there are more animals housed than is the norm in the UK, but the cattle buildings are very good. One area where the Europeans tend to be a little more rigorous than us is in their dietary requirements for animal feed – they generally seek at least 85% organic in the diet, by dry matter weight, whereas in the UK we're still at 80% for most of the time, with targets to get to 90% and above in the next couple of years. The problem for the UK has primarily been cost. Sources of organic protein here have been limited and hence more expensive, but this is changing, and I think we shall soon see more feed suppliers supplying organic rations, and more sensible pricing, allowing the non-organic ingredient percentage to fall more quickly. The UK is the major producer of sheep within Europe, and standards don't seem to vary very much.*
>
> *With pigs, it's different. There is a deliberate loophole in the new EU regulations which allows young pigs to be taken off conventional farms at weaning stage, say 4–5 weeks, and put into an organic unit. This was expressly allowed because it was thought to be a good method of increasing supply quickly while demand was strong, without considering fully whether the integrity of the product, of the "organic" brand, would be harmed. On the whole – though there are some shining exceptions – pigs across Europe, except in the UK, tend to be housed in not particularly nice buildings, with access to outside runs, usually concrete. This means better feed-conversion ratios, lower labour costs – and cheaper organic pork. Because, unlike the UK, the conventional systems of pig-rearing*

in many countries are so disgusting, organic pig-rearing is seen to be relatively close to heaven (even though it's not very close to the UK pig's idea of heaven).'

Eating quality

Organic meat often looks and eats differently from standard meat. Butchers who have experience of both wax lyrical about the difference in muscle tone and the sheen of the carcass. This is because the animals have been reared more slowly and have had more exercise. How *much* difference depends on the age and breed of the animal and, most importantly, on the butchery skills employed, including maturation. Size and age, too, vary more than with conventional meat. This makes buying organic meat a bit more complicated, so it's important to choose it carefully.

For the thousands of people who buy organic meat, its flavour is one of the main attractions. Comments from satisfied customers testify to this. Compared with cheap mass-produced meat, all organic meat has incomparably better flavour and eating quality, particularly pork and poultry. Compared with the highest-quality conventional meat, though, this may not always be the case. Generally speaking:

- organic meat is denser and less watery than most other meat. When cooked, shrinkage is about 10% compared with 30%
- organic meat often has a richer, more fulfilling meaty flavour and is often closer-grained, giving it a more toothsome texture. It is more satisfying to eat, and goes further
- the fat is creamy and the meat has good marbling
- it can be darker-coloured, and dulls more quickly from bright to dark red on the slab.

  NOTE: Because organic meat sold by supermarkets is stored using modern methods, in vacuum packaging and for a shorter time, its eating quality is more consistent with conventional supermarket meat.

All this is very good news for anyone who enjoys traditional meat. If, however, you prefer less robust, very lean, or conventionally tender meat you may find that some organic meat is too chewy, or even has too much flavour. If so, the organic meat sold in supermarkets, or organic meat raised from modern rather than traditional breeds, may suit you better.

Price

As mentioned earlier, organic meat is the most expensive food purchase you will make, and can cost anything from 50 to 100% more than standard mass-produced meat – though if you compare organic meat prices with those of other high-quality, non-intensively produced meat the differences, if any, are minimal. The reasons for this we have already discussed – namely, that better animal welfare (fewer animals per hectare, feeding them a high-quality, predominantly organic diet, and so on) costs significantly more. This means that organic meat will never, can never, be cheap. As the small conventional meat producers who produce meat to their own exacting standards have known for a long time, it can be an uphill battle to persuade consumers that real meat is, in real terms, good value for money. The reward is not just meat you can trust but meat you can enjoy at every level. As first BSE and now the foot-and-mouth tragedy have taught us, the price we pay for cheap meat – now well over £4 billion for BSE alone – is far too high. Going organic in the meat department is our best guarantee that crises like these will never happen again.

Buying and storing

Inevitably, the best source of organic meat is the expert, be it a butcher who specialises in it, or a producer who understands the butchery side of meat production as well as the rearing. Never be afraid to ask questions – about the breed, how long the meat has been hung, or how to cook it. Buying organic meat by mail order is usually very reliable, though it's always worth checking out the supplier first. Unless it is packed well, try to avoid buying frozen organic meat as it can be difficult to see the quality clearly (for one exception, see Lower Hurst Farm, Buxton, p. 186). Wherever possible, if you are buying fresh meat and intend freezing it, ask to have it vacuum-packed.

My own view, borne out by experience, is that as long as you store it correctly, organic meat keeps better than most other meat. All meat should be stored in the fridge. Joints and whole chickens should be stored on a clean plate, uncovered, with plenty of air around them. Small pieces of meat, including sliced meat such as steaks, should be oiled and wrapped in non-PVC cling-film and used within 2–3 days. Minced meat, sausages and burgers should be eaten as soon as possible, or frozen. Mail order meat is usually vacuum-packed. Freeze any you do not want to eat immediately (vacuum-packaging is ideal for freezing).

Remember the following points as well:

- Unless it is vacuum-packaged and you want to freeze it, always remove meat from its wrapper, and put it in the fridge well away from any cooked meat or other food.
- Organic meat bought by mail order will come with full instructions on how to store and, usually, how to cook the meat.
- Organic chicken should be eaten within 2–3 days; remove any giblets immediately and wipe out the cavity with kitchen paper. Pork will keep for 3–4 days, lamb and beef for 5–7, depending on the cut.

Vacuum-packaged meat

Joints or slices of meat will keep perfectly in the fridge for 7–14 days, depending on the meat; you will find that meat 'ages' in the pack and in time develops a stronger smell and a slightly richer flavour. This applies only to meat where the seal is airtight; if the seal has been broken, take the meat out, wipe it dry, put it on a clean plate and store it in the fridge in the usual way. Vacuum-packed sausages and minced-meat products should be used as soon as possible, or frozen.

GETTING THE BEST VALUE OUT OF YOUR ORGANIC MEAT

Prices are beginning to stabilise. However, there is still a large amount of variability – which is why it pays to shop around. A small local producer selling his own meat at his farm shop or at a farmer's market will invariably be able to sell it more cheaply than a specialist supplier operating a professional mail order or Internet service. The same goes for retailers. A retailer sourcing his organic meat direct from the producer is able to sell it more cheaply than a retailer who sources it through intermediaries.

Bear these points in mind:

- Braising joints are proportionally cheaper than the most popular cuts such as steak, chicken breasts, pork fillet and prime roasting joints.
- Mail order and home delivery services have regular special offers including family packs.
- Small producers are usually happy to sell half or a whole lamb, half a pig and sometimes half a cow, which is far more economical for the customer than buying separate joints. You can usually arrange to have

the animal cut as you want. This is a good option for people joining together to share the cost.

- If you *can* buy large quantities, and have a freezer to match, small producers such as the award-winning Higher Hacknell Farm in Devon offer outstanding value – high-quality fresh meat boxes at prices every serious meat-eater can afford.
- Supply is not as consistent as with conventionally-reared meat. Prices may come down when there are gluts and go up when supply is poor; when buying meat direct from a farm, check the best time to buy.
- If you are buying meat by mail order, get as many leaflets as you can before making your decision. Prices vary!
- Online food companies often have promotional offers.

▲▲

Is selling organic meat in supermarkets a good idea?

The fact that it's on sale in supermarkets is a confidence boost for organic meat, and means that the market for it will develop much faster. Supermarkets have all the necessary resources, the infrastructure and the expertise, and employ witheringly strict codes of practice – all of which bode well. However, the more organic meat is sold through supermarkets, the harder it is for anyone else to sell, and the more control over the sector supermarkets exert, the more pressure there will be – because price is the determining factor – to produce organic meat more economically. The answer, as usual, is in consumer hands: spread your buying, and support independents as well.

Organic butchers

Butchers selling organic meat, and especially dedicated organic butchers, are our knights in shining armour. A supermarket may offer convenience, but a butcher has *knowledge*, and having access to an expert who recognises what good meat is, who will hang it properly, give you advice on how to cook it and, like mine, Bailey's in Henley-on-Thames (tel: 01491 573214), displays the name of the producer on the wall for customers to see – *and* smile at you when you come in – is worth his or her weight in gold. Though the occasional butcher will buy direct, most use an intermediary like Pure Organic Foods (p. 192) or Black Mountain Foods (p. 193), who market the meat of several farmers.

PROFILES: THREE PIONEERS

The retail organic meat sector is dominated by a few well-known pioneers, who have not only developed the mail order market and thereby helped provide a living for many more local producers, but through their own integrity and commitment have also helped to ensure that organic meat standards in this country are second to none. All have won many awards for their products. They offer a friendly, efficient service and advice, special requests are catered for and credit cards are accepted. They supply excellent literature – or visit their websites – and you will learn all you need to know about organic meat, how it is reared and how to cook it.

Graig Farm Organics, Dolau, Powys (SA), tel: 01597 851655, website: **www.graigfarm.co.uk**.

It is difficult to praise Graig Farm Organics too much – for the service they provide; for the quality, especially, of their award-winning meat and meat products; for encouraging the development of a thriving network of local Welsh organic meat producers; for their tireless campaigning, together with the Soil Association, to save our small rural abattoirs; and for the excellence of their literature and their website. Established in 1988, they are one of the most successful and long-standing organic delivery companies: butcher, baker, pie shop, organic fishmonger, grocer, greengrocer, dairy, wine merchant; and purveyor of local cosmetics made with organic ingredients, organic woollens, Soil Association-approved native tree seedlings, local sustainably produced charcoal, and wormeries for making your own worm compost.

Specialities include Welsh Mountain mutton and lamb, certified wild fish from St Helena (see p. 208), traditionally hung chicken and the South African delicacy biltong, and they also offer a wide range of ready meals and other prepared dishes. They operate an extensive home delivery service and have around 100 retail outlets, plus a well-stocked farm shop, open Mon–Sat 9 am–5.30 pm.

Eastbrook Farm Organic Meats, Bishopstone, Wilts (SA), tel: 01793 790460, helpline: 01793 790340,
website: **www.helenbrowningorganics.co.uk**.
Eastbrook Farm is one of the most inspirational and innovative organic farms in the UK, regularly visited by government ministers and the like. Helen Browning, who farms it, is one of the country's best-known organic figures and is currently chairman of the Soil Association.

No one has done more for the development of UK organic pork than Eastbrook. They have also pioneered a unique organic veal system (each calf has a nurse-cow to suckle from). They hold regular open days, and visitors to their website can find the dates there, and learn more about the philosophy of the farm. They also run a very successful home delivery service, selling their own pork, beef and lamb. Their information pack includes special offers and a newsletter designed to brighten up your day and make you smile.

Helen Browning's Totally Organic range of pork products includes dry-cured ham and bacon, and sausages; and her very good kids' burgers and bangers are on sale in major supermarkets.

Swaddles Green Farm, Buckland St Mary, Somerset (SA), tel: 01460 234387, website: **www.swaddles.co.uk**.
Described once by the *Sunday Telegraph* as 'gastronomes who produce the kind of food people go to France for', Swaddles Green is an organic gourmet's delight. So you will not be surprised to learn that the owners, Bill and Charlotte Reynolds, are keen food lovers. For my money, they also have one of the best websites, which includes shopping à la carte and a cook's section, full of the kind of information that every cook needs, as well as very good recipes. None of their products contain any nitrites – they refuse to use them.

In addition to a complete range of meats, poultry, cured meats and bacon, and some of the best organic sausages you can buy, they produce an impressive range of home-made organic everyday and special-occasion ready meals (meat and vegetarian) – which came out top in a recent *Time Out* tasting of organic ready meals – excellent organic pâtés, thirteen different pies, pizza, soups and desserts, all made on the premises. The meat is raised on neighbouring organic farms, to their own specifications so as to ensure highest eating quality; for example, all beef is from traditional beef breeds, has the proper conformation of fat and is hung for three weeks; all meat is cut to order. They also sell organic chicken bones for stock (a bargain), stocks, dairy produce, eggs, chutneys and relishes, and organic beer, wine and cider.

They deliver in and around London in their refrigerated vans on Wednesday, Thursday and Fridays, and by overnight courier for the rest of the UK.

Plus:

Meat Matters (SA), Wantage, Oxon, tel: 01235 762461, freephone: 08080 067426, website: **www.meatmatters.uk.com**.
A very good home delivery service, established for ten years, with the emphasis on customer choice: meats are butchered to order, and there is no minimum order. Their list includes a full range of organic meat (mainly from Welsh Hook Meat Centre), poultry, French organic pâté, fresh fish from Looe (delivered to your door within 36 hours of being landed), plus organic trout and Irish smoked salmon, mixed fruit and vegetable boxes, local eggs, dairy and other groceries. Nationwide delivery, free delivery in their refrigerated vans within the M25, and in Berks, South Bucks, South Herts and Oxon.

▲▲

Beef

Since the BSE crisis, sales of organic beef have continued to soar. Organic beef comes with a BSE-free guarantee. The eating quality varies, but can be glorious – this is particularly true of traditional breeds. Until very recently, most organic beef came from specialist beef suckler herds, in which the mother rears her own calf for up to eleven months before it is weaned. Specialist beef breeds have large backs and rumps, where the prime joints are. Though such breeds are still the main source of organic beef, it comes increasingly from dairy calves; interestingly, in blind tastings these have performed very well. Organic animals are not killed until 20–24 months old, or 30 months in the case of a traditional breed (most conventional beef is killed at 12–15 months old).

▼▼▼

PROFILES: SEVEN OF THE BEST

There are many fine organic meat-producers in the country. These give you the flavour of what you can expect from the best featured in the directory.

Kites Nest Farm, Broadway, Worcestershire (SA), tel: 01386 853320. One of the UK's foremost organic beef farms, run by Mary Young and her son and daughter Richard and Rosamund. The farm has been featured often on TV, and is renowned for the rare wild flowers and wildlife that thrive there. Cattle are raised in family groups, usually three or four generations together, and each animal is known by name. They are free to wander, and spend a good deal of their time in the farm woods as well as on the grazing pastures. The herd has been 'closed' since 1987, and is given only home-grown organic feed. In fact, no feed concentrates or bought-in feed have ever been given. Their farming system is unique, even by organic standards. Ironically, their meat is no longer technically certified. This is because most of their local abattoirs have closed, and they refuse to send their animals on longer journeys to the nearest organically certified one.

Their richly flavoured beef is sold through the farm shop only, and is excellent value. It is butchered and hung on the premises, can be cut to particular requirements, is available fresh when butchered, and frozen at other times. The shop also sells suet, and wool from their own sheep. Visitors are made welcome.

Churchtown Farm, Lanteglos, Cornwall (SA), tel: 01726 870375. A 350-acre clifftop model organic farm, owned by the National Trust and run by husband and wife team Mark and Charlotte Russell, who have been organic farmers for 14 years. All their animals are fed home-grown organic feed, and they raise traditional beef breeds – South and North Devon, and Aberdeen Angus, which are killed and butchered locally and hung for 2–3 weeks. Their award-winning meat is available at the farm, at local stores and National Trust restaurants, and from Riverford Farm Shop in Totnes.

Northumbrian Quality Meats, Hexham, Northumberland (SA), tel: 01434 270184, website: **www.northumbrian-organic-meat.co.uk**. An example of how local is not only best but can be innovative too. Steve Ramshaw is a hill farmer in the unspoilt and isolated uplands of Northumbria, producing the highest-quality meat possible from traditional breeds, using low stocking densities and selling to consumers direct. The animals live a totally natural life, roaming freely and grazing a natural diet of grasses, mosses and herbs (numbering over a hundred species). The unique traceability system used on this farm traces each animal's pedigree back for several generations. Uniquely, too, they offer heather-fed or clover-fed lamb and mutton. The meat is butchered on site, well hung in the traditional manner, then vacuum-packed and sold in meat boxes (in 10–14 kg packs). A selection of cuts is available Sept–March, but there is a limited supply. Home delivery throughout Northumberland, or by national carrier throughout the UK. 10% of their profits are pledged to conservation projects on the farm.

Heritage Prime Earnestly British Meats of Rare Quality, Bridport, Dorset (Demeter), tel: 01297 489304.
A small biodynamic farm, acknowledged by MAFF to practise a unique system of animal husbandry, committed to raising meat to the highest welfare standards possible, and they use homoeopathic remedies only. They rear rare and traditional breeds – Portland Down and Dorset lambs, Shorthorn and pure Aberdeen Angus cattle, Tamworth pigs, kept in family groups – and occasional seasonal poultry. Their meat is highly sought after (food writer Nigella Lawson is a customer), well hung and available direct from the farm by mail order.

Providence Farm, Holsworthy, Devon (SA), tel: 01409 254421, website: **www.providencefarm.co.uk**.
An idyllic 20-acre, organic farm that produces sublime award-winning pork, chickens, ducks and guinea-fowl plus beef and lamb. As farmers Pammy and Ritchie Riggs explain, their animals receive lots of love, which they believe makes a world of difference to the quality of the meat. Their poultry is raised in small mobile houses in batches of 120–

150 at a time, and range freely in large fields from about three weeks old. When the time comes they're dispatched to one of the few remaining local poulterers and killed individually, then hung to develop their flavour further.

All their animals are reared in small numbers – around 20–24 lambs and 120 or so pigs per year. They also produce a gaggle of geese for Michaelmas, which they sell at the local Tavistock pannier's market for their annual traditional 'goosey fair', and they have a laying flock of 60 Blackrock hens. Their meat and eggs are available from the farm direct, at Tavistock market on Fridays, and at the local farmers' market in Okehampton. They also supply various sorts of good-value meat boxes by mail order.

Sheepdrove Organic Farm, Lambourn, Berkshire (SA), tel: 01488 71659, website: **www.sheepdrove.com**.
Organic farming is partly about finding new solutions, and wherever it is practised you will find ground-breaking initiatives being undertaken that are moving it on to ever greener pastures. Sheepdrove Organic Farm, surrounded by the Wiltshire prairies, is, like nearby Eastbrook Farm, in the vanguard. Unlike most organic farms, this one is large – 2,500 acres. They produce beef, lamb, mutton, pork, chickens and turkeys, and use traditional breed crosses such as Tamworth-Oxford Sandyblack pigs. What makes them special is that, though producing livestock on this large scale, they are working to Soil Association standards, as well as processing them on site in their state-of-the-art plant. They are also engaged in one of the largest compost-making ventures in the country, incorporating local waste, and are setting up their own biodiversity centre.

The way they rear their chickens demonstrates their devotion to the organic ideal. They produce up to 2,000 birds per week, and from the minute the day-old chicks arrive, they live an idyllic life, housed in modern mobile French chicken houses and ranging as far as the eye can see on fresh pasture containing a rich mix of clover, sheep's parsley, yarrow, chicory, salad burnet and bird's foot trefoil, from which they derive minerals and nutrients. They grow slowly and naturally, and are killed and processed with minimum stress on the farm at twelve weeks old. The eating quality is excellent. All their meat is available from the farm direct or through mail order, and visitors are welcome. Their chickens are sold at Sainsbury.

Lower Hurst Farm, Hartington, nr Buxton, Derbyshire (SA), tel: 01298 84900, website: **www.lowerhurstfarm.co.uk**.
New interesting meat venture. Grass-fed pedigree Hereford cattle, that range freely in idyllic surroundings, reared in small numbers (50 per year), and culled at 24 months at the local abattoir. To optimise flavour and tenderness further, the meat is hung for a minimum of 3 weeks. Then, following recommendations from the Food & Nutrition department from Oxford Brookes University, to ensure their meat reaches customers in perfect condition, the meat is blast frozen, packed like a 'mini deep freeze', and delivered overnight. Most cuts are individually boxed and all their meat comes with a full ID, date of birth and slaughter on each label. Sold primarily through mail order and their excellent website, but can also be collected from the farm by prior arrangement. They also produce a top quality handmade organic steak and cider pie, with butter pastry, using their own beef and Dunkerton's organic cider, which also comes in its own box.

▲▲

Other inspirational organic farms selling their own meat include Domini Quality Foods, Diss, Norfolk; Growing Concern, Loughborough, Leicestershire; Manor Farm, Leicestershire; Elmhurst Farm, near Coventry; Howbarrow Farm at Howbarrow, Cumbria; Higher Hacknell Farm in Higher Hacknell, Devon; Abbey Home Farm at Cirencester, Glos.; Luddesdown Farm in Kent; and the remarkable Longwood Farm at Bury St Edmunds, Suffolk. For further details, see directory.

Veal

Organic veal is produced the way veal *should* be produced. Unlike with 'welfare-friendly' veal, organic calves are suckled entirely by their mother or replacement mother, and enjoy freedom throughout their lives. At Eastbrook Farm they are kept inside in small groups in roomy pens when the weather is too bad for them to go out, but otherwise range freely. Their diet comprises whole organic milk and organic pasture. They are usually killed at between three and six months old and hung for around 10–14 days. The result is a deep-pink meat, best thought of as beef-veal, which offers a very different eating experience from intensively raised veal. Because the animal has spent its life running around it has a much firmer texture, and can have a far more 'beefy' flavour.

Not surprisingly, it is also the most expensive organic meat you can buy, and you can expect to pay up to 50% more than for crate veal. Eastbrook Farm Organic Meats is the major producer. Temple Farm, Marlborough (Wilts) and Little Warren Farm, Newick (Sussex) both produce veal 'sous la mère'. See the directory for details. Individual producers, such as Domini Quality Foods in Norfolk, may have the occasional veal calf for sale from time to time. The loin and escalopes are extremely expensive. Pot-roast cuts are more manageable; minced veal, usually good value, makes excellent hamburgers, and ragù for pasta and risotto.

Lamb

Because sheep are still largely raised extensively, there is far less difference between the way conventional and organic lambs are produced than with other meats. Nor can it be said that the flavour differences are that marked; here it depends more on breed and whether the sheep are upland (more flavour) or lowland (milder flavour).

Mutton

Produced in small quantities, mainly by Graig Farm Organics and Sheepdrove Farm, it comes from lambs raised organically that are over two years old, and is good value. Mutton at this age is not tough, has a gorgeously rich flavour, and is less fatty and therefore a drier meat. You can cook it in exactly the same way as lamb, and you will find that it roasts just as well – roast at a moderate temperature until slightly pink. It responds to gentle cooking and is excellent for braised and spiced dishes.

Pork

If you have never bought organic meat, and have forgotten what pork should taste like, then try UK organic pork. Don't forget that because there are no fillers or added water in organic hams or bacon, and the meat is usually hung for longer, weight for weight you are getting more for your money.

UK organically reared pigs meet all the livestock regulations already discussed.

- Many producers use traditional breeds such as Gloucester Old Spot, Berkshire, Tamworth and British Saddlebacks, favoured for their flavour and ability to thrive when reared in natural ways.
- Organic pigs are typically killed at four and a half to six months instead of the conventional 16 weeks.
- They are fed a diet that includes 60% fresh green food or unmilled forage – a mix of wheat, barley, triticale, oats, peas and beans. They also forage in their pastures for food such as insects.
- The use of concrete slatted floors is forbidden.
- Tail-docking, routine teeth-clipping and nose-ringing are banned (as is castration, which is allowed in organic standards abroad).
- For social as well as welfare reasons, organic pigs are kept in smaller groups, a maximum of 30–40 for fattening, plus ten breeding animals per group.
- Farrowing crates are forbidden. Piglets are weaned when their digestive systems are sufficiently well developed, at 6–9 weeks instead of 2–3. The sows have only 2 litters a year instead of the average 2.5.

The result of all this is pork with real flavour and texture, that is neither pappy nor wet, that has a creamy rather than a pasty white fat, and that smells wonderful while it is cooking.

Offal

The liver and kidneys (the excretory organs) have to deal with toxins – most of the testing for antibiotic residues is done on conventionally reared offal. So eating organic rather than conventionally-reared offal helps to minimise your intake of these. If you are an offal fan, you'll find the organic version deliciously clean-flavoured, with no taint. Organic chicken, lamb and pork livers, and lamb, pork and ox kidneys, are readily available from mail order meat specialists and are usually excellent value. Organic calves' liver has a darker colour and a stronger flavour than conventionally reared Dutch, and commands the same premium.

Organic kosher meat

High-quality organic kosher (OK) poultry, lamb and beef are supplied by Organic Kosher Ltd: in boxes or as individual cuts, fresh or frozen, in chilled packs, and delivered by nationwide couriers. Business is booming!

They pay regular visits to the farms and their meat comes with a double approval – organic plus official kosher certification (Manchester Beth Din, Machkzikei Hadath and London Beth Din) and is available from various kosher butchers in London and elsewhere. They also supply organic smoked salmon and gravadlax, and are planning to supply other organic kosher foods also. To find out more, ring freephone 0800 458 K-O-S-H-E-R (that's 0800 458 5-6-7-4-3-7), or tel: 020 8441 1983, fax: 020 8441 5484, email sales@organickosher.co.uk, or visit their website and order online: **www.organickosher.co.uk**.

Sausages

Organic bangers are probably the most popular organic choice of all: as a result, most supermarkets now sell them; they come in many variations, and are made not just from pork but from lamb and beef as well. Quality has improved significantly, though as with conventional sausages there is still too much variability, and not all organic sausages thrill. Sausage-making is an art, and often it isn't so much a question of this one being better than that one, but of style and price.

Most producers make their own from organic minced meat, organic rusk or ground rice, organic flavourings and natural casings. They contain none of the conventional chemical additives, nor do they contain soya proteins, carcass scraps or mechanically recovered meat (MRM). To cater for different tastes, the meat content varies – the label will tell you – as does the texture. The higher the meat content the more like a continental sausage it will be, whereas the traditional British banger is softer and has a higher rusk content. Some are too fatty for my taste, but the best, such as Swaddles Green Farm's handsome, hunky sausages that carnivores dream about, or Planet Organic's, are superb. Organic sausages sold in supermarkets are generally very credible, honest bangers – which is not surprising as they are mainly made by the same specialist sausage producer, who makes slightly different recipes for each retailer.

Organic sausages have a short shelf life and should be eaten as soon as possible (within 2–3 days) or frozen. The meaty ones go further, and two per person is usually enough. They are superb on the barbecue, especially with aïoli (garlic mayonnaise). Pork sausage meat – remove the skins from sausages if you have none – is excellent for pâtés and rissoles, and for stuffing vegetables.

How a sausage is packed makes a difference. Vacuum-packed sausages are fine, but get very squashed; the sturdy shrink-wrapped trays in which supermarket organic sausages are sold offer a better and more caring way to pack and send them, and have the advantage that you can see for yourself exactly what they look like.

Close scrutiny of various ingredients lists reveals that the three binders most often used are organic rusk (breadcrumbs), rice flour or oats, and occasionally potato starch. These don't seem to affect the flavour as much as the texture of the sausage. Many commercially made ones also contain water (though this is not necessarily declared on the label), and some contain ascorbic acid (vitamin C) as a natural permitted preservative; very occasionally you may also find ones that have maltodextrin as a sweetener.

The VFM factor

With sausages, value for money is not necessarily obvious. If you divide the cost by the number of sausages you've bought, for example, and then look at the meat content, often the most expensive, such as Swaddles Green Farm's, turn out to be the best value. Comparing mail order organic sausages with those on sale in supermarkets also reveals that there's very little difference (1–5p).

Bacon, gammon, ham and other cooked meats

Produced from organic pork and cured in traditional ways using salt or brine, or, in the case of a special cure, using salt, organic sugar and herbs or spices, the hand-carved roast ham (and pork) on sale in major supermarkets – tender, sweet, and with a good dry flavour – has become a favourite of mine, and I find it useful to cut into small shreds to scatter over salads for a starter. Organic bacon can be superb – try Duchy Originals, wrapped in greaseproof paper, or Swaddles Green Farm's, for example. None contain polyphosphates or added water.

Sliced organic cooked meats – chicken, pork, turkey, ham – and deli meats, such as organic salami and excellent Parma ham, can be found in the chiller cabinet or at the deli counter of major supermarkets. Many of these cooked meats are made from imported organic meat – check the label to see if you're happy with this. Waitrose sell organic chicken pâté. Organic meat producers often offer their own cooked meats.I once came across organic

Gloucester Old Spot roasted on the spit at a farmers' market, which made the best takeaway bun ever.

Sodium nitrite

One change that has not met with universal approval is that, in order to kill the *C. botulinum* bacillus and impart the characteristic familiar red-pink colour, standards now allow small amounts of sodium nitrite and nitrate and potassium nitrate (derived from mined saltpetre) for the curing of organic hams and bacon. There has been a long-running debate about the safety of these substances, which are used throughout the conventional food industry, as they are known to be carcinogenic in animals. Infants and children are particularly susceptible to nitrates, and the possibility that they may be indirectly linked to stomach cancers has received considerable attention. Not every producer uses these substances – Swaddles Green Farm is one that doesn't – so that hams and bacon from such suppliers will be greyer when cooked. If you feel strongly about this, contact the Soil Association, who will furnish you with information on why they decided to permit it; and Swaddles Green Farm, who will explain why they do not use it.

ORGANIC GAME

Standards do not exist for wild game, so apart from game reared on organic estates, there is no organic game to speak of – only wild or farmed game. Farmed pheasants, which account for about half the pheasants we eat, are not necessarily reared extensively. Though the majority are reared and released birds managed by gamekeepers, the Farm Animal Welfare Network (FAWN) reports instances of game being kept in large numbers, where debeaking, routine medication, growth-promoters in feed, and other practices associated with intensively reared chickens, have been found.

Because wild game is 'natural', we also presume it to be 'pure'. Alas, this is not so. As the Game Conservancy Trust is aware, game are in the front line when it comes to environmental pollutants. The increase use of pesticides, for example, has been partly responsible for the severe decline in wild partridge numbers, and antibiotic residues in pheasant and partridge are monitored. DDT, for instance, has been found in pigeons, which are migratory birds and can pick up pollutants on their regular route between here and Scandinavia. The best course is to buy game from organic estates and farms when you can.

A note on farmed venison

Farmed venison is raised extensively in this country, given no routine medication, and fed a natural diet. It is one of the healthiest meats you can buy, being naturally higher in polyunsaturated fatty acids and low in cholesterol. Organic standards are currently being finalised for it. Many venison farmers are interested in gaining organic status; when the time comes, the major stumbling-block will be finding supplies of organic feed – hay, potatoes, carrots, apples – especially for producers in marginal areas of Scotland, for example, who are unable to grow it themselves.

Specialist suppliers

These companies specialise in buying and preparing organic meat to sell to independent butchers and organic outlets:

John Bryan Organic Meats, Biggar, Scotland (Demeter), tel: 01899 221747, fax: 01899 221518, email: johnbryan@scottishorganicmeats.com, website: **www.scottishorganicmeats.com**.
They supply Scottish organic meat and specialise in biodynamically raised meats such as those from Loch Arthur Camphill Community. They buy from farmers direct, and the animals are slaughtered in a Demeter-registered abattoir. Beef is hung for 21 days, and lamb and pork for 10 days, and all is supplied vacuum-packaged. The company also makes organic bacon, sausages and burgers. They mainly supply independents in Scotland, plus a few outlets in London. They also supply direct through mail order.

Pure Organic Foods Ltd, near Leiston, Suffolk (SA), tel: 01728 830575, email: enquiries@pureorganicfoods.co.uk, website: **www.pureorganicfoods.co.uk**.
A label you may see in leading London stores including Harrods, Partridges and Fresh & Wild, in selected Tesco and Budgens stores in the South East and on the websites of home delivery Internet companies such as Simply Organic. The company sources its meat and poultry from small farms, and has its own dedicated organic processing and packing plant. Their charcuterie range includes organic salamis, and oak-smoked chicken, and popular lines include their chicken kiev, lamb and mint sausages, and beef kebabs with peppers – all 100% organic. They also supply meat and good-value meat boxes, dispatched overnight in refrigerated vans. Online ordering. Phone or email for your nearest stockist.

Black Mountain Foods, Talyllychau, Dyfed (SA), tel: 01558 685018, email: mynyddu@aol.com, website: **www.blackmountainfoods.co.uk**.
Purchase meat from selected small Welsh producers, which is then aged and prepared by themselves and sold to around twenty independent high-quality butchers, primarily in London and along the M4, and to home delivery companies. They also make sausages and burgers. Their leaflet is available at the butchers that they supply. Phone or email for your nearest stockist.

Welsh Hook Meat Centre, Haverfordwest, Pembrokeshire, tel: 01437 768876, website: **www.welsh-organic-meat.co.uk**.
Third-generation family farm. They produce their own lamb and beef, use local pork and poultry, and make their own hams and cooked meats. They have a farm shop (p. 528), supply Meat Matters and other organic farm shops, and run an online mail order service.

Organic butchers

Dedicated organic butchers are still few in number, though an increasing number of independent ones, especially those that belong to Q Guild, an association of high-quality butchers, sell some organic meat, including that from Prince Charles's organic farm, Duchy Home Farm. Telephone the butcher to check opening times and the choice of organic meat available. Pure Organic Foods and Black Mountain Foods above are happy to tell you the name of your nearest supplier. Planet Organic in Westbourne Grove, London, has an exceptional meat counter. Butchers selling organic meat are listed under speciality providers in the directory.

ORGANIC POULTRY

Chicken

The nation's most popular meat is still the most expensive to produce organically. Nevertheless, because demand has been so great, organic chickens have become much more widely available in the last two years; Tesco, Waitrose, Safeway, Marks & Spencer and Sainsbury's stock them routinely. The last two years have also seen a gathering cloud of confusion over organic chickens in terms of exactly what the standards are, and how much better they are – or aren't – than those of conventional systems. So I have covered them in detail in this book. All the general standards apply to other poultry, such as geese and ducks, as well.

The background

Before the advent of modern production systems, chicken was an expensive luxury, and all poultry production was small-scale. Today, chicken is a cheap mass-market commodity – we eat over 600 million a year. It is cheap because modern hybrids have been bred to be super-efficient feed converters – in other words, to grow as fast as possible; and flock sizes are enormous, reaching up to 50,000 or more. The birds have an in-built leg weakness that is now a major animal welfare issue, but have big breasts. They reach table weight in 35–42 days, and spend their short lives permanently housed in state-of-the-art bio-secure conditions that, however hygienic, few of us would want to see.

Because chicken production has evolved this way, the reality is that all chicken production, even organic, means compromises – and usually hefty ones. Put simply, the larger the flocks and the more you can control their environment, the more economic they become. Conversely, the minute you start giving chickens more houseroom, reduce the flock size, improve their diet, let them go outside and give them more land to roam, the more slowly they grow and the more costs escalate. So that the nearer the ideal, the more expensive they become. Rearing birds in mobile housing as opposed to fixed housing has various knock-on effects, which escalate costs further. The dilemma for all chicken producers is balancing this against what the consumer will pay. Every small high-quality chicken producer, organic or not, finds himself at the sharp end: the base line is so cheap that anything else looks expensive. This is why we now have a bewildering number of 'natural' options, each offering a different version of improved animal welfare at a slightly different cost.

Against this background, how does an organic chicken differ from other chicken production systems?

First, it is not true that all organic chickens are raised in small flocks or live idyllic lives. Most are produced by commercial chicken producers, adhering to the same basic organic standards as small producers, but trying to produce organic chickens at a price more of us feel we can afford. Nor are organic chicken standards always superior to those of other high-quality free-range chickens – the major difference lies not necessarily in chicken 'quality', but in the fact that organic producers subscribe to a farming system that is environmentally sustainable in the wider context. Third, it's important to realise that standards always represent *minimum* guidelines; in practice, many organic producers, irrespective of which certification body they are licensed with, operate above these, and, as with all food and wine, it's the individual producer who makes the difference here. Finally, size matters: a small producer is obviously differently placed than the specialist poultry farm producing 1,000–2,000 organic birds a week.

The differences that count

There are, of course, essential differences that set organic chickens apart from the rest, and many of those are common to all organic livestock.

- Since permanent housing is forbidden, there is no such thing as an organic broiler and all organic chickens are free-range, having access to outside grazing for some or most of their lives.
- Pasture management is a key feature: except where flock sizes are small and the chickens are not kept in runs but roam freely, pasture must be rested between batches.
- Diet is mainly organic (minimum 80%) and must be GMO-free (this will change to 100% organic by 2005).
- No in-feed additives of any kind, including synthetic yolk colorants.
- Mandatory lower stocking densities than all other systems except small private producers.
- A minimum of eight hours' darkness, per 24 hours.
- The minimum age of slaughter is 81 days (as opposed to 35–42 for broilers and 56 days for standard free-range).
- All mutilations are forbidden.
- The injection of water into the carcasses is forbidden.

For details on poultry standards, including flock sizes, differences between organic and 'standard', 'traditional and 'total freedom' free-range; and the Soil Association's own particular standards, see Appendix.

Can there ever be a 100% organically fed chicken?

Chickens need about 5% grit in their diet, which serves rather like teeth in their crops; this means effectively that, unless gravel pits become certified (which seems like overkill), around 95% certified organic is about as near as you will get.

Which certification bodies for chicken?

The Soil Association and Organic Farmers & Growers between them certify most organic chickens, both table birds and layers; though not a hard-and-fast rule most smaller-scale producers are registered with the Soil Association and most commercial producers, who supply supermarkets, are registered with OF&G.

Do organic chickens always have extra flavour?

Because it grows much more slowly, lives twice as long, receives an excellent diet, suffers less stress and doesn't have 5% water injected into it, the average organic chicken is a marked improvement on the standard broiler. *How much* better it is depends on all the usual factors, including breed. An organic chicken from a small producer, especially if it has been hung for a few days, will usually be glorious. It will also be expensive, so treasure it accordingly.

Which should I choose and how much will it cost?

Because of the way they are reared, organic chickens will cost 50–100% more than a standard broiler, though compare them with chickens produced the way you want them to be and the extra costs are minimal.

Once you decide that organic chicken is for you, you have various options: a supermarket; an organic supermarket or shop; or mail order, either direct from the producer or via a home-delivery service. I buy from all of these. For convenience, I buy from a supermarket; I make a point of buying a whole chicken from my butcher or from an organic shop, so I'm supporting them; and I seek out organic chickens from small producers whenever I can, or buy mail order if there's a chicken that I specifically fancy trying.

How much you pay will depend on the outlet and on whether the bird is a superb hand-crafted one or a mass-produced one, which will give you a reasonable flavour *and* the satisfaction of being grown in a decent system. Basically, as with conventional chickens, you get what you pay for. The most expensive bird is Kelly's, who have a reputation second to none and have recently gained organic certification; it is a wonderful chicken. As far as the 'everyday' organic chicken is concerned maybe the only way the huge demand for it can be satisfied is to have more specialist commercial producers. Because these are the large-scale producers they are the only ones able to produce organic chickens at a more realistic price. As stated earlier, a balance has to be struck between maintaining organic standards and producing chickens that more of us can afford. Though not the perfect solution, the result is that more and more conventional chicken producers are converting to an organic system.

When buying organic an chicken, remember:

- more butchers now sell organic chickens
- some producers hang their chickens for a few days, to develop the flavour further; I find these easily the tastiest of all, though if you are unused to them you may not like the smell when raw, and you may find they have a slightly gamier taste
- slow-growing and traditional breeds have leaner breasts and larger thighs.

If you want to know how the chicken you are buying has been produced and whether the producer's standards come up to scratch (or exceed yours), ask him (or her) – base your questions on the information given earlier in this chapter, or see the Appendix.

Turkeys

The organic Christmas turkey has arrived: Sainsbury's, Safeway, ASDA, Waitrose and Tesco stock them. They are available from all meat mail order and home delivery specialists, and from an increasing number of local producers. Turkeys, being semi-wild, are naturally more aggressive than other poultry, especially when kept in confined conditions. Most conventional ones are raised as intensively as chickens. Modern varieties are bred to have super-huge breasts, because this is what consumers prefer; unless the birds get regular exercise, they are so large that they can have difficulty in walking. Traditional 'farm-fresh' turkeys are reared according to much higher welfare standards than these. Organic turkeys, bronze- and white-feathered types, are raised to the same standards as organic chickens, and cost more than other high-quality turkeys, primarily because of the extra feed and labour costs involved. They enjoy natural daylight and ventilation and are kept in much smaller flocks – one-tenth the size of intensively raised flocks. They may be killed at around 4–6 months, and are generally hung for 7–10 days, to acquire maximum flavour.

NOTE: Scientific studies at Bristol University have shown that hanging turkeys in this way is the safest way to produce a Christmas turkey, because the gut becomes acidic and inhibits the growth of bacteria.

Geese

Organic geese are generally available at Christmas from mail order meat suppliers and a few independent organic farmers, who raise a few to sell locally. They are raised just like other organic poultry.

Ducks

Organic ducks are delicious, but in limited supply. Available from Swaddles Green Farm, Providence Farm Organic Meats, whose ducks (and guinea fowl) won 2001 Organic Food Awards (poultry category), and Welsh Haven Poultry, whole or jointed. For suppliers of geese and ducks, see directory.

Guinea fowl

Guinea fowl are precocious birds and notoriously difficult to raise organically on a commercial scale. Providence Farm have succeeded and offer a few superb birds.

Quail

I have not yet found a producer of organic quail, though a couple of producers are thinking about it.

Organic poultry producers

The number of specialist producers, small, medium and larger-scale, is increasing all the time. These profiles give you a flavour of the variety to be found in organic chicken-rearing today.

Kelly Turkey Farms, Danbury, Essex CM3 4EP (SA). Farmgate sales and mail order, tel: 01245 223581, website: **www.kelly-turkeys.com**. Paul Kelly is a maverick who cares passionately about how chickens are produced and who makes no compromises, in terms either of animal welfare or of other quality factors that count, such as how the birds are killed, plucked and how long they are matured for. A poultry producer for some 30 years, his turkeys have won universal acclaim and his chickens are every bit as good. As I noted earlier, they also the most expensive. Flock sizes are small (500 birds per house, mainly in mobile housing), have ample range and are fed 100% organic feed. Paul Kelly has developed his own breed, KellyBronze™, Christmas turkey, and his KellyChicken™ is a French breed. His chickens are killed at around 13 weeks – which makes them very large by most standards. They are killed on site, dry-plucked by hand, then matured for 7 days. In 2000 he gained organic accreditation. He sells only whole birds: his organic 'special roast' chickens are produced seasonally, from October to April. Available from butchers and direct through mail order, they arrive in their own box, wrapped in greaseproof paper, and offer you everything you could ever want in a chicken (including delicious livers, wrapped separately). They absolutely deserve their luxury status. In addition to his regular KellyBronze™ turkeys, which are franchised and produced by other local poultry producers to his standards, Paul's organic KellyBronze turkeys are available via mail order direct from the farm. They are killed at around 23 weeks and matured for 7 days. He also produces Duchy Original Christmas Turkeys. Website includes stockists and online ordering.

Springfield Organic Poultry near Leominster, Herefordshire (SA).
Another specialist poultry producer whose label you will see on organic chickens. Flock sizes are no more than 500, the chickens receive 100% organic feed, and are hung for 1–7 days depending on customer requirements. Sold via wholesalers and independent butchers, and available widely in the South but also elsewhere.

Welsh Haven Poultry, Little Haven Pembrokeshire (OF&G), tel: 01437 781552, email: Welshhaven@aol.com.
Situated in an enviable position in the Pembrokeshire National Park, these specialise in organic Christmas chickens, turkeys and geese. They are also one of the leading producers of ostrich, which also range on organic pastures. The chickens live in movable houses, are raised in flocks of 200 and range on grass. They are killed and prepared on the farm at 10 weeks old and hung for 3–7 days. Their geese are fed organic corn, dry-plucked and wax-finished, and hung for 7 days (as are their turkeys). Their poultry and ostrich products are available at their farm shop or direct by mail order. They also operate gastronomic weekends featuring local foods, B&B and self-catering cottages. To find out more, or to order online, visit their website: **www.welshhaven.freeserve.co.uk**.

See also: Sheepdrove Organic farm (p. 185).

The future

The poultry issues that everyone needs to address, including consumers, are those concerning breeds, stocking densities and the desirability of a move away from specialist production units to incorporation of poultry in mixed farming systems. Modern hybrids, designed merely to produce cheap meat as fast as possible, are clearly not suited to organic systems, and great efforts are being made at the moment to find sturdier breeds.

ORGANIC FISH

Having evolved from very tentative beginnings, organic farmed salmon and trout, fresh and smoked, are now on the UK menu, and have been selling fast in supermarkets since they were introduced in 2000. Early in 2001 the world's first organically certified prawns, from Ecuador, went on sale at Sainsbury's. Next on the menu could be organic carp from Germany and Austria, and organic mussels from Ireland, certified by Naturland.

It has not been an easy journey, and the few brave fish farms that have converted to organic aquaculture, both in the UK and elsewhere, deserve praise. In the future, other organically farmed fish could include sea bream and sea bass, oysters from New Zealand, as well as shrimps, mussels and carp, a freshwater fish that has been farmed since the Middle Ages. Though there is an ongoing international debate about whether farmed fish can ever strictly be 'organic' – and about whether organic standards should include carnivorous fish such as salmon (see p. 201) – for consumers, going organic means a significant leap forward for farmed fish production generally, resulting in a better deal for the fish as well as a better-quality product. The industry, though set to grow fast, is still in its infancy. All I can say is, try some: most people, myself included, find that organically farmed fish have a more delicate flavour, better texture, and are less flabby than most of the conventional equivalent.

The perennial issues regarding fish, to do with industrialised fishing methods and overfishing, the continuing pollution of our seas and the build-up of toxins in the fish we eat, remain as urgent as ever. The state of fishing stocks, in particular, is now an international crisis. Over a hundred species appear on the International Union for the Conservation of Nature (IUCN) red list, which catalogues the world's most threatened animal species; and about 30% of the world's fish stocks, representing nearly half of the landings, are classified as overexploited or depleted. Meanwhile, on the horizon can be glimpsed genetically engineered fish – already a reality, though not yet on our plates.

As a consequence, as with meat we need to start to be more choosy and to ask more questions about where and how the fish we are buying was caught. (For more on this generally, I recommend Joanna Blythman's excellent chapter on fish and shellfish in *The Food We Eat*, published by Penguin.) Buying locally caught fish whenever you can, and supporting fishmongers who buy their fish from day trawlers, is one way to support sustainable fishing. The Marine Stewardship Council have also designated certain fisheries and fish species as sustainable: currently there are three – wild Alaskan salmon, Western Australia rock lobster and Thames herring. Look for the MSC logo, and ask your fishmonger for details. Their initiatives are also supported by major supermarkets such as Tesco. To find out more, visit their excellent website, **www.msc.org**. You may also want to consider using your purse power to avoid buying Indian or South East Asian tropical prawns, the intensive farming of which has caused tremendous environmental and social upheaval; and buy Icelandic cod when you can, which is all caught sustainably. Many organic retail outlets such as the Fresh Food Company (p. 361) and Planet Organic in London sell only sustainably caught or organic fish. Planet Organic, for example, sell line-caught wild fish and have full traceability back to the boat or farm for all their fish.

As consumers we see the end product, but behind the scenes many other related initiatives are in train. One benefit, for example, of a more positive environmental approach to fish farming is the development of organic biochemical and naturopathic non-polluting products to replace the usual chemical armoury. Green Aqua Ltd are one company developing eco-friendly products for tomorrow's fish farms. To find out more – and to glimpse the future – take a quick peek at their website: **www.greenaqua.com**.

THE ISSUE: ORGANIC OR NOT?

Though organically farmed fish aims to offer a better alternative, it does not resolve all the objections that fuel the current controversy. Friends of the Earth Scotland, for example, are just as much opposed to organic farmed salmon and trout as they are to the conventional sort. They argue that containing migratory carnivorous fish dependent on fast-diminishing marine resources, in relatively high densities, whether conventional or organic, is hardly Nature's way; and point to the environmental damage that all farmed fish cause. The controversy mainly surrounds salmon but applies to most farmed fish. If you agree with Friends of the Earth, you would be best advised not to eat farmed fish at all. I believe that organic standards do address all the major issues responsibly and represent a first and important significant step forward. For an alternative view and to find out more about the Scottish Friends of the Earth position, visit their website: **www.foe-scotland.org.uk**.

Organic fish standards

Although there are no EU-wide standards yet, a common set of organic standards for farmed salmon and trout in particular has been developed collectively by the Soil Association, the Organic Food Federation and Food Certification Scotland. For consumers this means that all UK organic farmed salmon and trout certified by these three bodies is reared to the same set of standards.

More generally, national aquaculture standards are being developed in the USA, and the Danish government has also shown interest. IFOAM has drafted a basic framework for organic aquaculture standards, on which UK common aquaculture standards (see below) are based. One of Germany's best-known certification authorities, Naturland, which is also accredited to IFOAM, has been a pioneer of organic aquaculture standards and is currently the major private fish certification body in Europe; it is also running projects in various tropical countries for shrimp species and tilapia fish.

Organic standards, which exist for farmed fish only, initially came about as a response to consumers who wanted to be able to buy organic fish. In developing the standards, the aim was to go back to first principles and produce the best possible living conditions for the fish that would minimise adverse effects on the environment and provide the highest-quality product. The core principles underpinning organic aquaculture are:

- the development of a sustainable aquatic system
- the healthy use and proper care of water, water resources and all aquatic life
- maintenance or enhancement of water quality.

To devise the current standards, which cover every aspect of fish breeding, rearing and management, as well as water quality, environmental impact and the use of local resources, environmentalists, vets, fishermen, fish scientists and Compassion in World Farming were consulted. Consequently, the basic aims and characteristics of all organic fish-farming systems set down in the UK aquaculture standards are:

- the production of prime-quality fish, free from artificial additives and with minimal contamination from the environment
- production methods that use natural substances and minimise the use of external resources
- management procedures that ensure minimal effect on the local environment
- the promotion of the health and welfare of the fish by minimising stress, reducing the incidence of disease, and nurturing vitality by meeting the physiological and behavioural needs of the fish
- high standards of management so as to minimise the need for veterinary intervention
- the prohibition of pesticides
- the application of appropriate standards to the goods and services used by organic fish farms
- the encouragement of the use of local resources and services

Translated into practice, what you get when you buy organically farmed fish is:

- fish raised only in exceptionally pure water, monitored by the Environmental Agency for purity and sustaining natural populations
- exceptionally low stocking densities, with fish occupying no more than 1.5% of the available water
- fish fed high-quality natural and GM-free feed; fishmeal must be made from by-products of fish caught for human consumption, preferably from northern waters
- no pesticides to control lice, no routine use of antibiotics to control disease, no kind of artificial colouring
- fish culled humanely, either individually or in small numbers
- for salmon, there must be very strong natural currents for them to swim in

NOTE: These standards represent a 'best start', and will be refined further. Since they still need to reflet organic principles more fully, the Soil Association consider them as interim. The debate about issues such as recycling and feed contamination, for example, needs to be resolved.

Organic farmed salmon

Produced mainly in the Orkneys, with a little in the Shetland Isles and on the west coast of Ireland. Maximum stocking densities – 10 kg per cubic metre of water (2–3 fully grown fish per large bathful) – are half that permitted for conventionally farmed Scottish salmon. The fish are usually culled at around 3–5 kg – they are individually stunned and bled by hand – which is swift, and less stressful for the fish.

Organic farmed salmon costs around £1 more per 500 g from a supermarket and less from a producer direct, expensive organic feed and lower stocking densities accounting, as with other livestock, for most of the extra costs. It is now available as whole fish, steaks and fillets, and is sold by Sainsbury's, Waitrose, Marks & Spencer and Tesco.

Colour and flavour

Colour – a small point, but a highly visible one. Wild salmon derive their deep pink from their diet, which includes crustaceans. With organic farmed salmon, artificial colorants are not allowed, and pigmentation can be achieved in two ways: by the use either of natural crushed prawn shells (Soil Association-approved), which give the salmon a pale pink hue – much paler than conventional farmed or wild salmon – or of a derivative of phaffia yeast (Natura- and IOFGA-approved), which gives the more familiar bright orange-red. What colour your organic farmed salmon is, therefore, depends largely on whose organic symbol it carries.

As far as flavour differences are concerned, I haven't quite got to the bottom of this. What I can say is that, though both are produced to the same high standards in similar strong tidal waters, the organic farmed salmon from the Orkney Isles that I have eaten tastes as well as looks different from the Irish equivalent. I'm told it is mainly to do with the feed. The Scottish organic salmon is more like a delicate sea trout than like ordinary farmed salmon. I like it steamed, and served with a simple creamy herb sauce or tomato salsa, for example. Irish organic farmed salmon, and the smoked salmon made from it, are deeper in colour and have a richer – you might say more typical –

salmon flavour. I like these done in all the usual ways, including barbecued. Because they manufacture their own feed, with a lower oil content, Glenarm organic salmon are most like wild salmon in eating quality. These flavour differences also come through in smoked salmon.

Two Irish producers

Clare Island Irish organic salmon. Certified by Naturland and IOFGA, reared off the west coast of Ireland in the pristine grade-A waters of the Atlantic Ocean. The area is recognised as the most exposed in Western Europe, with very strong currents that ensure that water continually flushes through the cages, preventing the accumulation of parasites and pollutants. The fish are fed an organic GM-free diet, by hand, by local fishermen. Sold primarily to Europe but available in the UK from Rockport Fish Ltd, Tunbridge Wells, tel: 01892 533855, and online from the Fresh Food Company, tel: 00353 9533 501. Clare Island salmon is also used by Kinvara Smokery and Summer Isles Smokery.

Glenarm organic salmon. Glenarm have been at the forefront of salmon farming for years and have only ever produced salmon to very high animal welfare and environmental standards. They are unique in that they control the whole operation, raising their own fry and, through their sister company, producing their own organic feed. They are now certified by IOFGA. They have two sites in County Antrim – at Glenarm and Red Bay. As with Clare Island, the fish are reared in the grade-A waters of the Atlantic, under similar strong tidal conditions. Their feed includes less fish oil (24% compared with the usual 30%), which means that the fish grow more slowly than most, contributing to their fine flavour and eating quality, which is more like that of wild salmon. Glenarm salmon is generally available in London, at retailers including Planet Organic, Selfridges and Harvey Nichols, as well as at a few good fishmongers; and in Northern Ireland at Tesco and Sainsbury's. Smoked and fresh, it is available by mail order from Severn and Wye Smokery, Glos., tel: 01452 760190. A detailed leaflet on the production process is available on request from Glenarm, tel: 028 28 841 691, fax: 028 28 841 637, email: northern.salmon@btclick.com.

Organic farmed trout

Whereas four years ago organic trout was a rarity, supplies are increasing daily and trout farmers are working together to keep supermarkets regular supplied, with the result that Booth's, Safeway, Sainsbury's, Tesco and Waitrose all stock it.

Most people agree that organic standards point the way forward for trout farming generally. Because trout, like chicken (and salmon, for that matter), has become a cheap, mass-produced commodity, conventional trout farmers, for their own survival, have been forced to adopt 'pile-'em-high, sell-'em-cheap 'economics; going organic will mean a fairer return for them and a much better deal for the trout.

TROUT; THE DIFFERENCES THAT COUNT

The key to organic farmed fish is freedom of space, alleviating the need to suppress disease, and means the fishes' own immune system function as normal. For Nigel Woodhouse, Hawkshead Organic Trout Farm, Cumbria (see p. 454) the first trout farmer to go organic, this meant cutting stocking densities to one fifth of what they had been – with dramatic effects. Previously, the trout were dull in colour and apathetic by nature. Because they were crammed so close, their fins could get nibbled by other fish, rendering the fish susceptible to infections. Lowering stocking densities resulted in alert, healthy fish. Nor are they any longer fed with rapid weight gain in mind (an overfull fish needs all the energy it has to digest the food, which leaves none to fight off disease). A more natural feeding regime that allows adequate growth means the fish are better able to protect themselves and keep themselves healthy. Their natural pink hue is due to the wild shrimps found in the streams that flow through the trout ponds, and they have a much better flavour. Whereas it was customary to kill 5,000 trout at a time, which were left to asphyxiate in an ice slurry, now they are humanely electrocuted a few at a time as needed. The organic trout farmer has also had to revert to using natural, mixed sex fish. Unlike conventional trout farmers they cannot manipulate their gender, rendering them all female. Hawkshead Organic Trout are sold at the farm, mail order (direct and through companies such as Graig Farm Organics and Swaddles Green Farm), and are widely available through box schemes, organic shops and supermarkets. Tel: 01539 436541, website: **www.organicfish.com**.

▲▲

Organic smoked salmon and trout

Both are smoked naturally in the traditional way – and are delicious! Organic smoked salmon is in high demand. Both are available from Sainsbury's and Waitrose. Those I have tried have a natural creaminess and are neither heavily smoked nor heavily salted. Orkney organic smoked salmon is particularly mild. Food writers, including Nigel Slater, rave about Kinvara and its delectable creaminess. Glenarm smoked salmon is equally rich and delicious, and slightly more oaky. Organic kosher smoked salmon is also available.

Organic prawns

A first from Sainsbury's, who started selling ready-to-eat cooked organic prawns in 2001, from the world's first organic shrimp farm in Ecuador, certified by Naturland. The prawns cost just 50p extra per 125 g. They have a slightly sweet natural flavour with no chemical undertones, a firm texture, and are succulent and not in the least bit flabby or watery. Add organic avocado and mayonnaise, and you have the world's first organic prawn cocktail (or try prawn risotto).

The shrimps are raised on a wildlife farm that has become an eco-tourist attraction, alongside aloe vera, almonds and mangroves, which act as a biofilter and food source. The shrimp waste is recycled for fertiliser to feed the other crops.

Compare this with the industrialised farming of tropical prawns in Asia, for example, and it is easy to see why organic prawn farms offer hope for the future. Once a sustainable cottage industry, the large-scale farming of tropical prawns, dubbed the 'blue revolution', began in the 1980s. In order to create the prawn ponds, half of Thailand's mangrove forests – a vital part of the tropical ecosystem – have been chopped down, coral reefs have been plundered to provide lime, and leaked salt water from the ponds has ruined the surrounding agricultural land, which the local populations depend on for their food. The intensive use of chemicals (including pesticides, antibiotics and chlorine) is required to control disease – which has become so rife on these farms that many have now been abandoned. Industrialised shrimp farming is increasing alarmingly, too, in North East Brazil and Ecuador. To find out more, visit the Industrial Shrimp Action Network's website: **www.shrimpaction.org**.

By contrast, organic prawn production puts a high priority on maintaining the ecosystem. Here is a summary of some of the differences that count, supplied by Dr Stefan Bergleiter of Naturland.

- No more cutting down of mangroves; farms operating conventionally must be reforested with mangrove to at least 50% coverage.
- Herbal and mineral alternatives are used in the ponds instead of chemotherapeutics.
- No wild larvae are caught for stocking the ponds.
- Natural pond food resources – plankton and algae – are used.
- Only approved non-GM organic feed and fertilisers, containing very little fishmeal, can be used. No fishmeal from industrial harvesting operations – fishmeal must come from local artisanal sources, or from the trimmings of fish caught and processed for human consumption.

South Atlantic St Helena fish

The remote British island of St Helena is a unique source of pure, sustainably caught fish, which also provides a valuable, non-exploitative income for the islanders. The fish are caught in the clear, unpolluted island waters, using rods and lines or small boats, are landed within 4 hours, processed or frozen immediately, then shipped to the UK via the island's main link with the outside world, the Royal Mail ship. Because the fish are caught and processed on the island, the economic benefits go direct to the local community. The range comprises several varieties of tuna, wahoo (related to the mackerel), grouper, bull's-eye and smoked mackerel. Imported exclusively by Graig Farm Organics (see p. 180), who have published a detailed leaflet, and available in many organic supermarkets and shops.

Canned Alaska salmon

Produced from wild salmon. Brands include John West, Prince's and own-labels such as ASDA, Co-op, Safeway, Sainsbury's and Tesco.

Buying and storing

The same rules apply whether fish is organic or not. It is only worth buying when it is very fresh, it should be kept chilled at all times, and eaten as soon as possible. If you buy from the farm direct, when it will have been killed there and then (or at most a few hours earlier), it will be fine to keep for 24 hours or so. Whenever possible, ask for whatever fish you buy to be vacuum-packed – this will keep it in the best condition. It will also freeze much better – so much better that I would not now freeze fish *unless* it was vacuum-packed.

If you do freeze it, remember that a freezer does not so much keep food fresh as slow down the staling process. Unlike meat, fish is delicate, so use it as soon as you can. The oils in fish such as salmon develop taint quickly, so don't keep it frozen much beyond a month or two if you can help it.

Sealed vac-pacs of smoked salmon and trout keep quite happily in the fridge – for a week or so beyond their sell-by date if necessary. Once opened, use as soon as possible.

Suppliers

If you have no local fishmonger or have to rely on supermarkets – and presuming you have a freezer and don't mind freezing fish – mail order solves the question of sourcing local fish in quantity. Otherwise, you can buy direct from most fish farms and smokeries.

Cornish Fish Direct, The Pilchard Works, Tolcarne, Newlyn, Cornwall TR18 5QH, tel: 01736 332112, fax: 01736 332442, email: dee@cornishfish.com, website: **www.cornishfish.com**.
The last family to salt pilchards in the traditional way, they also supply fabulous freshly caught fish landed at Newlyn by local boats. The fish is prepared to customer requirements and packed in chilled polystyrene boxes, then sent by overnight courier on Thursdays, together with an information and recipe leaflet. The minimum order is £40. Orders are taken up to 4 pm on Tuesdays. Or you can buy direct and visit their award-winning working pilchard museum and factory on the same premises.

The market fish shop, Victoria Road, Dartmouth, Devon TQ6 9SE, tel/fax: 01803 832782.
Run by Jenny Mackesy, who supplies local restaurants. Specialises in local

caught fish, including dived scallops, crabs, lobster and John Dory in season, plus home-made fishcakes and pies. Offers customised mail order service at shop prices. Fish is prepared as you want – gutted, filleted etc. – then vacuum-packed in chilled polystyrene boxes, to arrive next day. Both fish and service are splendid. There is no minimum order, but carriage costs are around £10.

For organic smoked salmon:

Kinvara Smoked Salmon Ltd, Kinvara, Co. Galway, Ireland (IOFGA), tel: 00353 91 637489, fax: 00353 91 638193, email: smokedsalmon@eircom.net. Delicious organic smoked salmon and gravadlax, using traditional methods (long, slow cure), and locally produced County Clare organic salmon. Order direct via mail order or via their UK supplier, Pure Organic Foods (see p. 192). To find out more, visit their website: **www.kinvara.co.uk**.

Severn and Wye Smokery, Chaxhill, Westbury-on-Severn, Glos. GL14 1QW (OF&G), tel: 01452 760 190, fax: 01452 760 193.
A traditional family-run smokehouse, selling a full range of smoked products, who have been involved in fishing for 40 years. They have their own line-caught sea-bass boat and supply local fresh and smoked wild salmon as well as fresh and smoked organic Glenarm salmon, and organic trout. Their salmon is available any way you want – whole, steaks, filleted; ditto their smoked salmon (whole sides, sliced or not, or smaller packs). Best value for fresh salmon is to buy a whole fish and let them prepare and vac-pack it for you.

See also: Summer Isles Foods, Achiltibuie, Highlands (p. 516).

9: Organic Bread and Flour

'Industrial farming treats the soil as a resource to be mined for immediate profit, not conserved for future yield. Industrial baking has turned the staff of life into a tasteless, cheapened apology for real food. In the headlong rush for profit and instant gratification, we fail to take proper care of our own bodies and souls, not to mention the precious environment on which we all depend. By contrast, a field of organic wheat and a loaf of bread made with patience and integrity bring long-lasting joy and satisfaction.'

Andrew Whitley, founder, Village Bakery

ORGANIC BREAD

For most people in the West, bread is the most important staple. Increasingly, too – as supermarket shelves and the number of well-known conventional bakeries that now produce an organic range show – the daily loaf is becoming organic and the range expanded far beyond the familiar wholewheat, brown and white. There is now almost every conceivable kind of organic bread and other baked goods that you could possibly want to try (including gluten-free), from everyday kinds to handcrafted, including three brands of organic naan and some wonderful new par-baked artisan grain breads from Le Fournil de l'Eau Vive bakery in the French Alps, made with natural leaven, alpine water and sel de Guerande (sea salt). A new European organic artisan 'bake-off' bread – bread that is part-baked and then finished off in store – to look out for is the Dutch Odenwald brand. 'Bake-off' is a favourite supermarket way of selling organic bread that has shown rapid growth (Sainsbury's ready-to-bake ciabatta won in the bread category in a recent SA Organic Food Awards). Happily, the appearance of mass-produced organic bread has been matched by small artisan bread-makers who are also flourishing: Hobbs House Bakery in Chipping Sodbury, another OFA winner, is one example. The Celtic Baker, the Authentic Bread Company Flour Power City and the newest, Artisan Bread in Whitstable (p. 469) are six more of the best.

Recent changes

The emergence of mass-produced organic bread has meant other changes. It wasn't so long ago that all organic bread could claim to be 'traditional', and it was certainly distinctive. This is no longer the case. Though large commercial bakeries like Warburton's and Harvestime should be commended for bringing organic bread to the general population, mass-produced bread (as in the classic sliced white), organic or not, has essentially the same hallmarks of mediocrity, as well as being cheaper than a handcrafted organic loaf. Since the standard organic supermarket loaf is made to be more like, and to taste like, a conventional loaf, it is also more likely to contain organic soya flour, fat or sugar, and sometimes vinegar or added vitamin C. These help to give it volume, speed up fermentation times, increase shelf life, and so on. That any organic bread should aspire to be just like conventional bread many find a worrying trend, and it is confusing for consumers who are new to organic bread and expect something distinctively better. Nevertheless, from two important stances – lack of 'nasties' and environmental benefits – organic, mass-produced is a significant improvement on its conventional equivalent. Besides, everybody's taste and idea of the perfect loaf varies. The choice is yours. Having tried umpteen organic breads, the best advice I can give is to read the labels. Generally, the fewer added ingredients that sound as if they don't belong in bread, the higher the quality and the more like traditional bread it will taste. (An example of what I mean is given below.) To find the ones you like best, try as many different organic breads as you can. If an ordinary organic loaf disappoints or doesn't meet your organic ideal, there are plenty that will. Which leads me to . . .

A plea for real bread

As Andrew Whitley at the opening of this chapter poetically explains, real bread is a wonderful food, and like good wine, has a sweetness, balance, complexity and length of flavour that surpasses all others and nourishes soul and body alike. It is also easily digestible – unlike many mass-produced breads. Real organic bread gives you the best of both worlds: the best bread, from ingredients produced in the best possible way. Support local organic bakers when you can and your enjoyment of bread will be much enhanced.

The campaign for better bread raises other issues. Freshness, for one. As Andrew Whitley also points out, good bread ages with dignity and should be appreciated more as it gets older. Modern breads do not have this quality, and our notions of freshness have become distorted. Loaves may last (commercial bakers are being expected to provide breads with a 7–10-day shelf life) and stay 'fresh', but they offer no pleasure or interest. The use of enzymes – not declared on the label, and also permitted in organic breads – to improve shelf life confer that claggy softness which is becoming the hallmark of modern breads but which is the antithesis of what good bread should be. This is one of the issues that organic breadmakers need to address. Andrew Whitley – good bread is his life's passion – asks whether, in order to prove bread quickly, we are using too much baker's yeast. What about wheat varieties? Have we hybridised wheat beyond the capacity of the human gut to easily digest it? As with wine, maybe the organic loaf of the future will return to its roots, and organic bakers will be the first to produce loaves from named varieties of wheat and other grains.

Why buy organic bread?

Organic bread is the natural alternative for people who care about their health and who care about the environment. Suffice to say that, worldwide, cereal crops are among the most intensively produced and intensively sprayed, and more than other crop have irrevocably changed the face of the landscape for the worse – from the vast American dust bowls to our own East Anglian prairies. The result has been massive soil erosion and the loss of precious biodiversity, as well as all the feel-good factors that a mixed landscape brings.

Organic bread offers many other advantages. It does not contain the plethora of chemical-improvers, dough-conditioners, additives and artificial flavourings that are standard in much bought bread. Mass-produced organic breads can be made fast and using just as modern technology, but only a few permitted processing aids are used. The Enjoy Organic Company's breads, on sale in most supermarkets, are made with a 'mother' sponge, are given a long, slow mix and a short rise, and are proved in the usual way for up to an hour before being baked. Enjoy Organic receive many letters of support from their customers – try everyone's favourite, their tasty multiseeded brown-batch. In addition, the numerous small independent organic bakers are dedicated to producing the best loaf they can, which usually includes long fermentation to ripen the dough and develop the flavour. Except for soda bread, where baking powder is the raising agent, many organic breads (including the Village Bakery's) contain none of even the permitted processing additives. The Village Bakery has just produced the first organic loaf made with Bioreal organic yeast, too, on sale in Sainsbury's. Sink your teeth into one of these loaves and you will re-discover bread that is twice as satisfying to eat, with real flavour and texture.

NOTE: Many shops and small bakers, and some supermarkets, sell bread made with organic flour. This may be excellent bread, but it is illegal to sell it as 'organic bread', since it has not been certified, and it may contain other, non-organic ingredients and non-permitted chemical agents.

How organic bread is made

Many bakers producing organic bread make non-organic breads and other baked goods as well. All of their organic ingredients must be kept separate at all times, by using separate storage facilities and by shutting down and cleaning the bread-making units before baking the organic breads. In addition to the premises having to be registered, every organic bread and baked good must be too – this is to avoid any confusion with other loaves and to provide the consumer with an extra guarantee. The actual process of bread-making is the same as for conventional bread, whether the bread is being made by a small baker or a medium-sized bakery or a large bread-processing unit.

The extra ingredients

Ascorbic acid, fat, soya flour, sugar and vinegar are the main extra ingredients you will find in organic breads that class as processing aids. Their functions are as follows:

Ascorbic acid (Vitamin C) Acts as a catalyst and helps the gluten to develop faster, thereby considerably shortening the time dough needs to be left before being knocked back for the final proof. It also strengthens the gluten of weaker flours, producing a bolder, airier loaf.

Fat Non-hydrogenated vegetable fats are added to give the loaf better mouth feel and flavour, but they also improve dough structure and gas retention and give a smoother, silkier loaf.

Non-GM soya flour Contains natural enzymes and emulsifiers, which act as natural dough-improvers, helping the bread to achieve more volume and to produce a softer loaf.

Sugar Makes a loaf sweeter, which many people prefer, and produces a darker, more golden crust.

Vinegar Acts as a natural preservative. It has been used in breadmaking for over a hundred years and is a natural mould-retardant.

In addition:

Enzymes Derived from cereal or fungal sources, enzymes such as alpha amylase and hemicellulase make the gluten in bread dough more elastic and 'tolerant' during the proving process. They can also be engineered to delay the rate at which starch stales after baking. Often sold to bakers as 'crumb-softeners', they are widely used even by craft bakers and lead to that ubiquitous clagginess characteristic of modern breads. Pressure from large commercial bakers has resulted in enzymes (though not genetically modified ones) being allowed under organic standards, and they do not have to be declared on labels because they are considered a 'processing aid' rather than an ingredient.

Organic bread facts

Organic breads carry a double guarantee. Both the bakery, and the ingredients of each individual bread (or other baked goods) must be approved by a registered certification body (which includes, as for all other organic goods, a full audit trail of all ingredients). All organic loaves, buns, biscuits and cakes contain 95–100% certified organic ingredients and:

- are made from flour milled exclusively from organically grown grains
- may include only a few baking aids, such as vitamin C, calcium carbonate and permitted raising agents (see p. 388), which must be clearly listed with their chemical names on the packaging
- contain no artificial additives, hydrogenated fats or white sugar; and no GM ingredients or derivatives.

Some craft organic bakers such as Paul's and the Celtic Bakers use filtered water for their breads.

The range

The image of the classic wholesome but dense organic loaf, fit only for those as hefty and robust as itself, has gone. These days organic breads are lighter, and many are much more interesting. High-quality bakers are producing their own: Maison Blanc, for example, bakes a Boule Bio and Miche Bio made with stoneground organic flour, freshly made wheat leaven and sel de Guérande. Most supermarkets and bakers stock an organic loaf of some kind; many now stock a range, including the excellent Village Bakery and Duchy Originals, as well as their own-brand breads. These are made either by dedicated organic or by commercial bakeries, and each own-brand loaf will be made to that supermarket's specification.

The range available includes everything from everyday white and wholewheat loaves and packets of mixed organic rolls, to country bread made with natural leavens, Irish soda bread, sourdough ryes, mixed-seed breads, Italian breads, enriched breads and fruit breads, long-life breads, breads made from sprouted seeds, imported continental breads, and many excellent crispbreads and crackers. Waitrose's new range of traditional German pumpernickels is excellent. You can buy organic pizza bases (though not all are good), excellent organic crostini from Tuscany, hand-made Italian spelt pizza bases, organic pittas (Evernat's are nutty and have a nice large pocket for stuffing), and organic breadcrumbs and croûtons. Organic breads for special diets are well catered for. In America you can get 'women's breads', nutritionally formulated to contain, for example, more phyto-oestrogens. The latest arrival here? Hempseed and seaweed breads.

The range of buns and other baked goods has similarly expanded. These days, Easter would not be complete without organic hot-cross buns. Tesco sell their own organic crumpets.

TWO FAMOUS BRANDS

Duchy Originals

Duchy Originals is a company created by Prince Charles in 1990 as a high-quality food and drink brand with special emphasis on creating the natural food link and encouraging organic food and farming. All its profits are donated to the Prince of Wales's Charitable Foundation. Its organic breads, made by the well-known La Fornaia craft bakery in London, have become very popular, are available nationwide and are sold at Safeway, Sainsbury's, Tesco and Waitrose. The only flour-improver they use is one specially developed for them, based on wheat flour (to replace soya flour). Their organic artisan-type breads comprise malted oat bread and rolls, sunflower-seed and honey bread and my favourite, their latest delicious mild sourdough wheat and rye bread, the first ready-to-bake bread of its type, designed to do for sourbreads what ciabatta did for white. Other organic products in their range are chocolates, biscuits (including their new chocolate orange biscuits), sausages, bacon, and their new gammons and hams. Lemon Refresher and two new dairy products, non-homogenised milk and Stilton, deserve similar praise for the thought and integrity that have gone into each of them. Their new Christmas fare includes hampers, turkeys, Christmas puddings and cakes. For more information about Duchy Originals, visit their website: **www.duchyoriginals.com**.

The Stamp Collection

Given that 25% of the UK population have an intolerance to wheat, wheat-free breads fulfil a need. The Stamp Collection was created in 1994 by Terence Stamp and Elizabeth Buxton to provide eye-catching, chic, high-quality, special-diet foods that taste good for those who, like Terence Stamp, cannot eat wheat or dairy products, and come highly recommended. Available at Sainsbury's, the range includes organic wheat-free bread with rolled-oat topping (also available with poppy-seed and sunflower-seed topping), and a new easy-to-make wheat-free soda-bread mix (two varieties).

Other Stamp Collection goodies are wheat-free flour, easy-mix pasta flour and pastas, dairy-free chocolates and sheep's milk cheeses. They publish a newsletter, *Stamp News*, and for information about all their products, including stockists and recipes, visit their website: **www.stamp-collection.co.uk**.

Price

Organic breads are very good value. Glance along the supermarket shelves and compare prices, and you will find virtually no difference between the organic wholewheat loaf and the conventional premium equivalent. And organic breads can be considerably cheaper than the top-of-the-range 'gourmet' hand-baked kind. Organic white is more expensive than organic wholemeal, because only 70% of the grain is converted into flour as against 100% for wholemeal. Supermarket own-label is often the cheapest organic bread you can buy.

NOTE: Do not compare the price of organic bread with the standard sliced mass-produced loaf. This is often sold as a loss-leader at below-production cost in order to attract customers into the store.

Buying and storing

Except where it is baked on the retail premises, organic bread is usually wrapped and clearly labelled. Most keeps fresh for 3–4 days; rye loaves keep well for up to a week, as do naturally leavened breads.

- Artisan organic breads are good to eat both fresh and a few days old, and do not go stale so much as grow old gracefully.
- The best way to store bread is to freeze it; divide large loaves into smaller portions, and you can be sure of very fresh bread, every time.
- Don't keep bread in the fridge; this will dry it out sooner.
- To refresh bread, place it in a hot oven for 7–10 minutes.

TIP: passed on by a friend from the Flour Power City Bakery. To defrost bread straight from the freezer, throw a small glass of water over it and put it in a moderate oven for around ten minutes.

Getting the most out of your organic bread

Good organic breads should never be wasted. A few tips:

- Old bread is perfect for baked croûtes.
- Turn leftover bread into breadcrumbs – use a food processor, or simply grate it. Use to strew over gratins or baked vegetables, or in stuffings. Fried breadcrumbs are extra-good with pasta or scattered over salads. Caramelised breadcrumbs – breadcrumbs and a little organic sugar toasted under the grill – make a delicious topping for poached fruit and fruit fools.
- Use organic bread for bread-and-butter pudding and summer puddings, in stuffings and meatballs, and on bruschettas.

Organic bakers

Dedicated bakers that produce only organic breads and other baked goods, or that are primarily organic bakers using organic flour and other organic ingredients wherever possible, baking their bread in the traditional way, are a national treasure. Most of their output is sold through independent organic outlets and through box schemes or other home delivery services, and via Internet retailers. Many make a mouth-watering range, such as:

The Authentic Bread Company, Strawberry Hill Farm, Strawberry Hill, Newent, Glos. (SA), tel: 01531 828181, fax: 01531 828151, email: info@authenticbread.co.uk, website: **www.authenticbread.co.uk**.
An award-winning small traditional baker, producing superb breads made with Shipton Mill organic flours, including speciality breads, pasties and cakes. Available locally, via home delivery companies including Graig Farm Organics, box schemes, and mail order. The range includes fougasse (a Provençal bread containing olive oil and flavoured with aniseed), all-butter croissants, pain au chocolat, French sticks, a malted-grain loaf, black-olive and pumpkin-seed and rye and wholemeal. Phone for stockists. And do visit their lovely website, too.

The Brilliant Bread Company, Hope Enterprise, Wigan, Lancs (SA), tel: 01942 768803, fax: 01942 208801.
A small organic baker producing excellent breads with Shipton Mill flours, using traditional methods. The range comprises white and wholemeal, with or without sesame or sunflower-seed toppings, baps, granary and rye loaves, and fresh white and wholemeal pizza bases. They supply local wholefood and organic shops and delicatessens in Liverpool, Manchester and Warrington.

The Celtic Baker, West Hendon, London NW9 (Demeter and SA), tel: 020 8202 2586.
An acclaimed, small, dedicated organic baker, one of my favourites, producing delicious, richly flavoured, traditionally handmade breads using minimal yeast and long fermentation. Their English muffins win rave reviews. Over twenty-five different organic breads and rolls, including barley bread, natural sourdough ryes, olive and pumpkin and cheese and onion bread, wholemeal croissants and a dairy-free Irish soda-bread without salt. They also produce organic cakes. Available widely in London, including their stall

at Spitalfields Market, and the South-East generally, plus a few outlets elsewhere.

The Engine Shed, Garvald Community Enterprises Ltd, Edinburgh (OFF), tel: 0131 662 0040, fax: 0131 667 5319.
A community workshop based on Rudolf Steiner principles, which includes an organic bakery producing innovative and traditional breads and baked goods, available at their vegetarian organic café, through their wholefood shop at 124 Bruntsfield Place in Edinburgh, and throughout Scotland. There is a tofu-processing plant here too. They produce around a dozen different organic breads, using strictly traditional methods, including Demeter loaves, oat and herb breads, a five-grain bread spiced with star anise, fennel and coriander, and sourdoughs. No improvers or additives of any kind are used. They also make organic flapjacks, oatcakes and other baked goods using organic ingredients.

Flour Power City, 228 Hoxton Street, London N1 (OFF), tel: 020 7729 7414. Also at Flour Power City, Tunbridge Wells, tel: 01892 547456.
Difficult to beat by anyone's standards. This superlative artisan baker specialises in pain au levain and sourdough breads. Their exceptional range of breads and other baked goods includes brioche, pizzas, bread-and-butter pudding and difficult-to-resist chocolate tart and pecan pie. Breads include sourdough rye and sourdough wheat, best ever pain de campagne (so big you can buy it by the quarter), baguette, ciabatta, and spelt bread with pumpkin seeds. Visit their amazing stall at Borough Market in London, or see them at Henley-on-Thames farmers' market (third Thursday in the month). They also supply Fresh & Wild and Neal's Yard Dairy in London.

Paul's, Snow Hill, Melton Mowbray, Leics. (SA) tel: 01664 560572.
Renowned small baker and tofu producer. Makes an impressive range of traditionally baked breads and other baked products, using organic flour from local miller Nigel Moon, ionised water and sea salt. All their products are either 100% organic or 100% organic except for cooking oils. Available from the bakehouse and Melton Mowbray farmers' market. All breads are available salt-free, and sliced to order if required. The range includes excellent white and other yeasted breads, rolls, baguettes and tea-cakes; fancy breads, focaccia, olive and basil breads, and sourdough or yeast-free, including barley bread and pain de campagne. They also bake three yeast-and-gluten-free

breads, including a chickpea, rice and corn bread; and very good tortillas. Their breads are widely available at independent organic/wholefood/healthfood shops throughout Greater London, Essex, Cambridgeshire, Lincolnshire, Leicestershire, Nottinghamshire and the West Midlands; also from Ryton Organic Gardens in Warwickshire and through local home delivery and box schemes.

Sunshine Organic Bakery, The British School, Stroud, Glos, tel: 01453 763923 (SA).
Another first-class small traditional family-run bakery, producing excellent breads and other baked goods for their Sunshine Health Shop in Church Street. They bake thirty certified organic lines daily, including wheat, rye, oat, spelt, multigrain, sprouted-wheat and soda-breads, rolls and baguettes. The mainly organic lines – 75–90% organic ingredients – include focaccia, Bara Brith and cheese bread, vegetarian savouries, cakes and biscuits. Selected breads available also at the Cheltenham Nutrition Centre in Bath Road and at Malmsbury Wholefoods in Winchcombe Street, Stroud.

See also: Artisan Bread, Whitstable, Kent, p. 469.

PROFILE: THE VILLAGE BAKERY

'The only climate we want to change is that of public opinion – in favour of sustainable ways of making our daily bread.'

The Village Bakery at Melmerby, Penrith, Cumbria, has become a legend. Established twenty-five years ago, this inspirational initiative has become a role model for how to produce artisan breads with true organic integrity on a commercial scale, while providing local employment and collecting numerous awards along the way. It has an award-winning restaurant, an extensive mail order catalogue, runs the highly successful *Bread Matters* bread-making courses and is opening its own Organic Centre of Excellence education centre for the public. Recently it has formed a partnership with another local baker – Bells of Lazonby – who are now 20% organic. In January 2001 Prince Charles, whose Duchy Home Farm at Highgrove supplies much of the rye for the Village Bakery's famous Russian-style breads, visited Melmerby to open the company's new shop and restaurant and to mark the commissioning of Bells of Lazonby's new computer-controlled wood-fired oven, the first made in Britain, designed to minimise emissions and to use sustainable fuel.

At the Village Bakery, taste and integrity go hand in hand. The heart of the bakery, apart from their wood-fired oven, is their belief in bread as the staff of life and their conviction that the best bread requires nothing more than excellent organic flour, natural leavens ('mothers') or yeast, salt and time. Village Bakery breads are made with traditional long fermentations, giving them a finer, moister texture and subtler flavour. Where a loaf of industrially baked bread can take under 2 hours from start to finish, theirs takes anything from 4 to 24 – as you can tell by the flavour and the deeply satisfying texture.

Their equally well-known range of cakes and biscuits (over 50 in total), including their award-winning Christmas and best-ever chocolate cake – made with Green & Black's chocolate, almonds, eggs and sugar, topped with chocolate ganache – and Christmas puddings, are widely available in supermarkets, leading independent shops, coffee-houses and tea-rooms, and via box schemes. Their mail order brochure contains a full list of stockists. Their contact number is 01768 881515, email info@village-bakery.com, website: **www.village-bakery.com**.

▲▲

Plus:

Cranks, London.
A popular vegetarian restaurant chain selling four organic breads – wholemeal, honey and sunflower, wheat and rye, and malt and brown granary-style – certified by the Soil Association and made for them by a traditional bakery in London and another small baker in Devon. The bread is used in their restaurants and widely distributed in major supermarkets and organic/wholefood/healthfood shops and delicatessens in London and the South East, and locally around Brixham, Devon.

St Fagans Museum of Welsh Life, St Fagans, Cardiff.
Though not certified organic, the museum's reconstructed bakery, producing fresh bread in the old-fashioned way, uses organic flour in a wood-fired oven. You can see the bread being made and buy it in the tiny bakery shop next door.

Finally, as my researcher Jane Faulkes commented, bakery is one of the more happening organic sectors, simply because most organic bakers keep a firm grasp of the fact that it is good quality, as well as organic status, that matters. Because of the relatively unperishable nature of the product, mail order proliferates, especially through second parties such as home delivery companies, or on-line. For more bakers that sell organic bread direct from their bakeries, or through local outlets and farmers' markets, see the directory.

ORGANIC FLOUR

Organic flour has become a staple ingredient and is part of the core range of basic organic foods that most supermarkets sell. Over the last two years, the range of organic flours – particularly speciality kinds such as special-diet and organic pasta flours for home-made pasta buffs (available at Waitrose) – has increased, and the packaging has got snazzier. Two organic brands, Doves Farm and Shipton Mill, dominate the market, both excellent. For extra interest, and the sheer pleasure of visiting a local mill and buying the real thing, take the opportunity to do so whenever you can.

For consumers, what's important is having the choice: read about how conventional wheat is grown, and you'll need no further incentive to switch. Buying organic also offers a catalyst for change in the larger sense: a move towards growing cereals within mixed farms and towards developing traditionally based varieties of wheat and other grains that may suit sustainable farming methods (instead, as is now the case, of breeding varieties to suit chemical agriculture and the Chorley Wood bread-making process) and, in addition, a move towards a resurgence of local cereal farms such as Rushell Farm in Wiltshire and Pimhill Farm near Shrewsbury, which bake their own products while developing the local market. All of which adds a spark of much-needed individuality to the food chain, and bodes well for better and more interesting bread and baked products.

Something not generally appreciated is that all white flour, including organic, has chemical nutrients added to fortify it, namely: ground chalk (calcium carbonate), iron, thiamin (vitamin B1) and nicotinic acid. The government is thinking of adding to this list folic acid (about which there is much controversy and that many organic millers feel unhappy about). Because these are statutory additions they do not have to be declared on the label. Organic millers such as Shipton Mill believe that the sooner legislation is changed to remove all statutory ingredients, the better. To raise awareness of these hidden additives, Doves Farm have become the first millers to list them on their packaging. Hopefully, their action will encourage more millers to follow suit, and the debate about whether they are truly necessary can then begin.

Quality and flavour

Organically grown wheat, flour and other cereals generally have a depth of flavour and character absent from the mass-produced versions. This can be summed up in one word – they are *nuttier*, and with a natural, earthy sweetness. This is partly due to the fact that organic millers mainly use traditional techniques to grind the wheat slowly so as to preserve maximum flavour and nutrition, and bleaching agents are prohibited in organic white flour. However, it isn't quite that simple. The quality of flour is also measured by its protein content; wheats imported from countries with sunnier, drier climates contain more protein, and so it is these that are used in most flours, organic or not.

Who mills organic flours?

Organic flour is mainly produced by registered organic commercial mills whose flours are available nationwide; then there are the small independent traditional millers, often open to the public, who mill flour on a small scale and sell it at the mill or locally. You will find these in the directory. Some operate a mail order service, which is economical and gives you the opportunity of buying freshly milled flour – a real treat if you bake bread – without having to lug it home. Here, bread buffs and fledgling enthusiasts need look no further than Shipton Mills' remarkable selection of flours (see p. 228). In addition, large conventional operations such as Allied Mills, using modern milling techniques, are increasingly producing organic flours; here, as always, organic and non-organic grains must be kept separate at all times, and to avoid contamination there must be a thorough clean-down of all machinery before milling the organic grains.

ORGANIC WHEATFLOUR

For general use, organic wheatflours perform exactly the same as non-organic ones. From the bread-making point of view, they fall into two broad groups: native organic flours and blended ones.

Native flours

Milled exclusively from English wheats which, as just mentioned, have a lower protein content than 'hard' organic wheats. Our native organic flours vary with the season and with the wheat variety, as well as with the part of the country in which it has been grown. These flours are full of character, have a beautiful sweet flavour, but make less buoyant loaves than blended flours do. The protein content is typically 9–11%. This is the flour commonly found in small independent mills. We are lucky in having a few organic farms such as Pimhill and Rushall Mill that both grow and mill their own wheat. Pertwood is another UK brand producing home-grown stoneground organic flours, this time milled locally. Such flours are rare treasures, so seek them out when you can.

Blended flours

Milled usually from a blend of English wheats and imported Canadian, North American, East European or Australian organic wheats. These grains, with their higher protein content, are physically harder than the native kind – hence the term 'hard' wheats. They make the well risen, lighter bread that everyone has become accustomed to, and are blended so as to be consistent and thus satisfy consumer demand and commercial baker alike. The protein content is typically 11–13%. All commercial organic millers produce these flours, and they are the ones you will mainly see for sale in shops and supermarkets.

NOTE: Do not confuse 'conservation-grade' flour with organic flour. Conservation-grade wheat is grown using fewer chemicals, but is not organic.

Imported organic wheats

Unless you buy your organic flour from the local millers, using UK wheat described above, you will be buying the blended kind using imported wheats. There are two reasons for this. Harder, imported wheats are more suitable to modern-day commercial and domestic baking needs, but also the supply of UK organic wheat doesn't begin to meet the demand (don't forget, there is an equal demand for organic cereals to feed livestock, so consumers and animals are chasing the same resource).

OTHER FLOURS

Organic barley, rye, buckwheat, millet, maize, potato, spelt, kamut, brown-rice, corn and soya flours and oatmeal, grown to the same organic standards as wheat, are all available. Many are gluten-free. Many, too, have a delicious nutty depth to their flavour; organic oatmeal, for example, is a revelation compared with the ordinary packet stuff. You cannot buy these flours in conventional supermarkets – the best places are wholefood and specialist organic shops. Doves Farm gourmet flours include buckwheat, rice and gram flour – which makes delicious socca and chickpea fritters. Shipton Mill sells semolina, and chestnut flour from the Ardèche region of France.

Spelt is an ancient variety of wheat that has an intense wheaty flavour, contains more protein, fat and fibre and can be tolerated by some with gluten allergies. Spelt flour, available from Doves Farm, can be used for bread and cakes. Food writer Annie Bell is a fan, and recommends it for cheese scones and pizza bases. Kamut is another ancient Egyptian variety known as 'sweet wheat', a hard, crisp durum wheat that bakes very differently from ordinary wheats and makes a toothsome pasta. Shipton Mill sell it when they can.

Gluten-free flours

These are becoming more popular; they are made by blending various non-wheat flours such as barley, rice, millet, potato, buckwheat and maize. Major brands are Doves Farm and the Stamp Collection organic and wheat-free soda-bread mix. The mix comes with impeccable instructions, takes a minute to mix and around 40 minutes to bake, and produces a lovely nutty soda-bread. Shipton Mill and Joannusmolen also make a gluten-free baking mix.

Price

For all the reasons outlined here, organic flours represent excellent value. Given that most people use comparatively little, buying organic flour instead of conventional is an easy switch. If you make bread, it is especially good value. Flour is sold in 500 g, 1 kg and 1.5 kg bags – bear this in mind when comparing prices. Standard organic wholewheat flour bought in supermarkets will cost you the same as, or a few pence more than, equivalent non-organic flours. Otherwise, expect to pay 10–20% extra; as with conventional flours, speciality blends and flours cost more. Loose flour is cheaper than ready-bagged. Flour bought by mail order direct from the miller is the best value; bulk orders can be 30% cheaper. Note that prices also vary depending on the retail outlet, and on whether the flour has been bagged by the wholesaler or by the miller. Remember, too, not to compare the price of organic flour, especially white, with cheap mass-produced flour, because this is another product that is often sold as a loss-leader and whose shelf price may bear no relation to its actual cost.

Buying and storing

Organic flour has the same shelf life as non-organic. Organic wheat and rye flours are often available in small bags, bulk bags, or loose; if you bake bread, bulk-buying is much more economical. If buying loose, buy from a shop with a good turnover and check the date stamp on the bag. This is most important; ideally, aim for a stamp that has six months to go for white and three for wholemeal or wheatmeal. Speciality flours keep for 3–6 months, depending on the kind of flour and whether it was milled from whole grain. If you use a lot of flour, buy from the miller direct. Always store flour in a cool, preferably dark place and in paper bags or sacks. The same applies to all cereals.

TIP: Remember that any flour that contains the germ of the grain – and so this applies to grains too – is perishable, and that though starch is stable, the oils in the grains deteriorate fairly quickly.

Will it bake the same?

The quality of organic flour, especially that from well-known commercial organic millers, is excellent, and generally you can expect the same results with your normal brand. The major difference that you will find has already been mentioned: bread baked from flours milled from native English wheats do not rise as well and so produce a different kind of loaf. Such flours, however, make wonderful biscuits. If in doubt as to which flour is best for your purpose, seek advice from your supplier.

▼▼

PROFILE: BRITAIN'S BEST-KNOWN ORGANIC MILLERS

These two pioneering millers have done more than anyone to develop the market for organic flour and cereal products in the UK. As with everyone mentioned in this book, taste, integrity and commitment to the highest organic standards are foremost.

Doves Farm Foods Ltd, Salisbury Road, Hungerford, Berkshire. tel: 01488 684880, e-mail: mail@doves-farm.co.uk.
A family firm run by Clare and Michael Marriage, Doves Farm is the UK's leading organic flour and baked-goods company, whose brightly coloured packs of flours, biscuits, cakes and breakfast cereals can be found nationwide, including at most major supermarkets.

They produce 10 organic flours, amongst them home-grown organic grain; and 4 non-organic gluten flours. All are specially blended to give optimal baking qualities. Their new gourmet range includes organic pasta and spelt flour. All are available from Simply Organic and the Organic Shop online supermarkets. For more information, including a comprehensive list of stockists and recipe leaflets, contact them direct or visit their website: **www.dovesfarm.co.uk**, which includes an interactive recipe section (there are recipes on the packs also).

Shipton Mill, Tetbury, Gloucestershire, GL8 8RP, tel: 01666 505050, fax: 01666 504666.
Established in 1981, Shipton Mill is everything a bread buff could ever wish for. Its descriptions of rare and speciality flours, personally sourced by the owner John Lister and second to none, are so appealing that you will want to rush to the kitchen and start baking bread instantly. They produce both organic and conventional flours, all stoneground in the traditional manner in their restored eleventh-century mill. Their bread flours are specially blended from home-grown and imported wheats to give optimal baking quality, and are used by many master bakers. Their mail order service, Flour Direct (minimum order 5 kg), is unique. It features over 20 mouth-watering speciality flours, packed in small quantities and including (a real treat, this) fresh organic wheatgerm, milled to order, as well as the fabled Maris Widgeon (the traditional wheat variety) organic cake and biscuit flours, plus a range of children's baking mixes to encourage children to bake. Full descriptive leaflets are included, and personal advice on bread-baking given. Contact Rachel Walker for Flour Direct, or their resident baker Clive Mellum for bread-baking queries. Their organic wheatflours are widely available nationwide from independent outlets.

Shipton Mill is a delight to visit. They like visitors, the staff love talking about flour and bread – and there is even a nice gate to lean on and a stream to dream by. You can buy direct from the mill, or email John Lister at jlister@shipton-mill.com.

▲▲▲

Local millers

A full list of all millers who belong to the Traditional Cornmillers' Guild can be obtained from The Windmill, Swaffham Prior, near Newmarket, Cambridgeshire. There are five producing flour (available nationwide) from native-grown organic wheats.

Maud Foster Mill, Boston, Lincs. (SA), tel: 01205 352188.
Run by James Waterfield and his parents, this is one of only four commercial windmills in the country. All their flours are organic, milled from local grain. Their range includes wholemeal, white and rye; plus maize-meal, pancake and chapati flours, and organic muesli, available locally and in their own delightful vegetarian tea-room. Mill and tea-room are open all year round, Wed 10 am–5 pm, Sat 11 am–5 pm, Sun 1 pm–5 pm.

Little Salkeld Watermill, Penrith, Cumbria (SA), tel: 01768 881523.
One of a few working traditional water-powered mills that specialise in mail order; in addition, they produce a newsletter and run baking courses. They mill only British organically grown grain, of either Soil Association or Demeter standard, and produce a wide range of specialist stoneground organic flours including white and wholemeals. Four-grain blend, Granarius malted flour, barley flour, semolina, oatmeal, porridge oats, wheat and rye grain for sprouting, and muesli. The flour is freshly milled to order. The mail order catalogue also includes organic dried fruits, pasta, pulses, nuts and seeds, chocolate, sugar, herbs, spices, tea and coffee – all available from their mill shop and tea-room.

Perry Court Farm, Chartham, Canterbury (Demeter), tel: 01227 738449.
A Rudolf Steiner bio-dynamic farm, that produces its own stoneground wheatflour. The farm also produces its own beef, for sale in the shop at Wincheap Butchers in Canterbury, and runs a subscription vegetable box scheme.

Pimhill Mill, Lea Hall, Harmer Hill, Shrewsbury, Shropshire (SA), tel: 01939 290342.
A pioneering organic family who have been milling their own home-grown grain exclusively for fifty years. The stoneground 'soft' flour, which produces a bread renowned for its flavour, is freshly milled to order. Their full range is

available locally and nationwide through Suma Wholefoods. It comprises organic wholewheat and fine brown (85% extraction) flour; organic bran; organic wheat grain; organic groats, oatmeal, porridge oats and jumbo oats. They also produce Pimhill muesli, which is not certified organic but is made with organic grains and no added sugar. All Pimhill products can be added to basic bread recipes to create different loaves, and can also be used in biscuits, tea-breads and cakes.

Rushall Mill, Rushall, Pewsey, Wilts (SA), tel: 01980 630335.
Produce stoneground wholewheat flour from their own home-grown organic wheat, available from the farm shop and by mail order. They also bake from their organic flour a wide range of breads, tea-breads, scones, pizza bases and garlic croûtons, for sale at the farm shop, which also stocks their own meat and local produce.

And finally . . .

Mills are wonderful places to visit and from which to learn more about how flour is milled and what makes a good flour. The mills listed in the directory produce and sell organic flours – please ring first for opening hours. Many supply their products to local outlets, and some operate mail order.

10: Organic Tea and Coffee, Sweeteners, Dried Herbs and Spices

TEA AND COFFEE

Most people reading this will probably by now have drunk organic tea and coffee. Certainly, you will have seen a selection of both in your supermarkets (own-brand, too). You may also have noticed that major conventional brands such as Ridgway's, Twining's and Taylors teas and – the ultimate sign of acceptance – Kenco and Nescafé instant coffee have gone organic. In addition, organic tea and coffee are now available in many cafés and restaurants. The UK's largest coffee chain, Costa, with 200 stores nationwide, has established a partnership with the leading Fairtrade coffee company, Café Direct, to create the first organic fairtrade blend, Organic Espresso, regular and decaffeinated – which is what you call progress.

Why buy organic tea and coffee?

Like bananas, sugar and cocoa, tea and coffee are part of the basic global organic shopping basket that has come under intense scrutiny in recent times – and with good reason. The intensive production of most tea and coffee causes devastation of the natural environment. Working conditions often leave a lot to be desired, and the constant use of toxic pesticides is a major health hazard for the plantation workers. So, as with all tropical food commodities, though pesticide residues may or may not harm those drinking the tea and coffee (residues are often present in tea, but not normally in coffee), they are a major problem for those growing them.

Organic tea and coffee offer a much fairer choice all round – yet they cost almost nothing extra per cup. The fact that they are the world's most popular beverages – in Britain alone, every day 185 million cups of tea and 28 million cups of coffee are drunk – means that choosing organic and fairly traded tea and coffee is a powerful catalyst for change for the better. Moreover, so many stories that you read are an inspiration as to what can, and is, being achieved, be it the farmers in northern Peru who once grew coca (the plant from which cocaine is produced) and who now cultivate organic coffee beans, some of which find their way into Clipper's instant coffee; or Equal Exchange's 'girl power' initiatives in Darjeeling, enabling women for the first time to train as managers; or the wildlife that is returning to the landscapes, and the many educational, social and medical improvements with which the security of fair trade empowers communities.

Standards

Growing tea and coffee organically means far more than not using artificial fertilisers and pesticides. As with the other tropical products discussed, it embraces everything from the prevention of soil erosion, the use of legumes to improve soil fertility and shade plants to protect the crops, and the selection of the plant varieties suited to local conditions, to the living standards of the workers. As yet there are no common worldwide standards, though current efforts by IFOAM to harmonise and simplify them should bear fruit.

Where and how organic tea and coffee is grown

Organic tea and coffee are grown mainly in remote and isolated places, often at high altitudes amid breathtaking scenery, and sometimes surrounded by virgin forests. Organic tea is grown mainly in India, but also in China, Nepal, the Seychelles, Sri Lanka and Japan (a small amount). Organic coffee is grown in Latin America, especially Mexico, in east Africa and other exotic locations such as the highlands of Papua New Guinea, St Helena and Sumatra. Though there are some large organic tea estates, plantations tend to be smaller and they aim to be self-sustaining. Tea and coffee are grown as a cash crop for clothing, medicines and education alongside other crops such as bananas, maize, pineapple and, in Peru, potatoes as well as animals that provide food and milk, and dung for fuel and soil fertility.

Growing tea and coffee organically means adopting many practices designed to keep the plants and soil healthy and to avoid erosion. Farmers use natural composting, natural animal manures and mechanical weed control, and make maximum use of forest shade and mulches. They grow legumes between the bushes to provide fertility, use other natural fertilisers, and to get rid of pests they use various plants and herbs to attract natural predators. Biodynamic tea estates such as the Makaibari (which supplies Hampstead Tea & Coffee) in Darjeeling, and the Iddalgashinne tea estate in Sri Lanka, go further, employing a lunar calendar to help them determine the best time for sowing, planting and harvesting, as well as bio-dynamic preparations made on the estates to treat the tea bushes and the soil, applying them in homoeopathic quantities to enhance their vitality.

Sri Lanka, which produces organic teas of remarkable quality, deserves a special mention. The island as a whole does not use pesticides except as a spot treatment, and has been leading the way in natural predator control by encouraging beneficial insect populations. For example, since the 1960s they have been growing sunflowers to provide shade for the wasps that attack the leaf-rolling tortrix moth. If other tea-growing countries had applied their vision, just think of where we could be now.

What makes organic coffee so special?

Growing coffee organically is not easy. The coffee tree takes eight years to mature and is subject to a multitude of pests and diseases. For any chance of success, the plantations need to be isolated and generally at high altitude, which makes transport more difficult and costly. Organic growers do not use pesticides, defoliants, fungicides or synthetic fertilisers, a combination which produces a 50–100% increase in yields and that is offered to growers under various low-cost, buy-now-pay-later schemes. With organic coffee growing there are no economies of scale, the conversion period is a minimum of three years, and land, compost and beans have to pass the purity test before official organic status by either the Organic Crop Improvement Association (OCIA) or Demeter is granted. A full audit trail from plantation to processor to importer has to be set in place, and at no stage in its production may the coffee, as beans or in any other form, come in contact with any non-organic coffee or any other non-organic products.

The best of both worlds: organic and fair trade

Choose organic and fair-traded when you can. Organic tea and coffee producers are not immune to the vagaries of world trade – for example, prices for both organic and conventional coffee recently dropped to a record low. Having both fair-traded and organic status provides producers with the best shield against price fluctuations, ensuring a stable and fair price for their goods. The development of fair-traded and organic alongside each other is necessary for the long-term sustainability of these two most important commodity crops. Having both delivers the best of both worlds to all concerned; and choosing both will make this fusion happen faster. Look for the Fairtrade label on tea and coffee from Café Direct, Clipper, Equal Exchange, Percol, Hampstead Tea & Coffee and Ridgway's. Brands such as Fertilia, Simon Levelt, Seyte and Rapunzel operate their own fair-trade policies, as do Taylors snazzy Feel Good Teas. For more on fair trade, see p. 81.

Quality and price

Because of where and how they are grown the quality of organic teas and coffees is generally good. And supplies have increased, so quality has improved further.

Organic teas usually have clean, pure flavours and coffee a fine, rich flavour. Most organic coffee, including instant, is made from arabica beans, which are the best quality you can buy and better for your health. Decaffeinated organic coffees are made using the Swiss water process which does not involve the use of chlorine. As with conventional tea, different grades and leaf sizes represent different qualities – and are reflected in the price. You will never get the same aroma or quality from a tea-bag as you will from loose tea. With coffee, aroma and lack of bitterness are the two most sought-after qualities. The aroma and nuances that give each type of coffee its distinctive flavour and subtlety are locked into its essential oils, and fade with time. This is why, to appreciate coffee at its best, it should be freshly ground.

Now that many more brands are available, at varying prices, you will find that some are better or more to your taste than others. As a general rule, if, like me, you are used to drinking high-quality first-flush leaf tea, weak and without milk, organic tea-bags are never likely to thrill you much: so I recommend you go straight to Hampstead Tea & Coffee biodynamic teas. Again, if you yearn for something absolutely authentic, unusual and traditional, you couldn't possibly do better than Clearspring's Japanese teas; whereas if your tipple is strong teas, organic tea-bags will provide you with happy hours of drinking. It's the same with organic coffees, which range from the headily exotic to the familiar and popular blends.

With pack sizes and prices varying quite a bit, the best advice is to shop around. Prices have also become much more competitive – supermarkets often have the keenest, and promotional offers are regularly to be found in them and in independent shops.

Variety

The decision these days is not whether or not to buy organic, but which of the bewildering selection of teas and coffees to choose.

Latest upmarket arrivals on the organic tea scene include 'mood' teas, green teas, low-caffeine teas, spiced chai blends, superior tea-bag teas and ready-made organic iced teas. Clearspring's iced-tea Thirst-Quenchers for example, come in glass jars and two flavours – peach (made with organic Ceylon tea), and mint and jasmine (made with organic green tea). Organic Kombucha, the coming health craze – fermented sweetened black tea – is now available: Golden Temple offer three varieties of green tea and Kombucha tea-bags. Long Life Herbal Teas, appropriately, offer green tea-bags combined with ginseng and ginkgo, while Higher Living offer Ayurvedic tea-bags, and so on.

Organic coffee – available as beans, ready-ground, decaffeinated and instant freeze-dried powder or granules – has developed along similar lines. Packaging has come of age and, increasingly, nice-to-knows such as the country of origin or details of how the coffee or tea is grown are included too. If instant coffee is your tipple, you may like to know that, apart from the famous ones mentioned above, there are four other organic brands: Café Direct, Clipper (regular and decaffeinated), Mount Hagen (Demeter-registered) and Natura. Rombouts have gone one further and introduced the first individual organic filter coffee – all you do is pour boiling water through the filter into your cup. Treat-yourself individual sachets of ground coffee are also becoming popular.

More kinds and brands of tea

'Chais': These Indian teas blended with warming spice mixtures and drunk with milk and sugar are becoming the latest drink craze to sweep the USA, and are catching on in Europe and Japan too. Starbucks have started to sell them. Organic chais include those from Equal Exchange, Hampstead Tea & Coffee, Dragonfly and Clipper.

Clipper Teas: One of the best-known organic brands, who employ fair-trade policies and whose teas and coffees have notched up a dozen awards in the Organic Food Awards, including the best hot-beverage category for their roast ground arabica Papua New Guinea coffee in 2000. They sell over thirty varieties of teas and coffees – including seven teas with the Fairtrade logo –

from single-estate and herb and fruit teas to their award-winning instant coffee. Their new upmarket range of superior tea-bags – premium organic, 'summer', exotic and decaffeinated – is good. Available at all major supermarkets, including Budgens and the Co-Op, and at independents. Or you can order them online, or join their Tea Club. To learn more about them and see their growers, visit their colourful and informative website at **www.clipper-teas.com**.

Equal Exchange: Founded in 1979 and based in Edinburgh, Equal Exchange, along with Café Direct, is one of the heroes of the fair-trade movement. Equal Exchange specialises in high-quality teas and coffees, is the leading organic Fairtrade brand and offers a wide range of both, including jasmine, mint and lemon green teas and masala chai, and two new gourmet coffees – their gold-star (wrapped in gold foil) first-ever Fairtrade organic coffee from the rainforests of Sumatra, and one from Colombia. Their coffees are packed in stylish silver-coloured one-way-valve packs which ensures one year's shelf life. As part of their 'girl power' policy of providing better training and employment prospects for women, their loose green tea is now packed on site by a new Fairtrade business run entirely by women at the Samabeong Tea Gardens in Darjeeling, thereby guaranteeing both freshness for the consumer and better opportunities for their female workforce. They do not supply supermarkets but are widely available at independent stores. To find your nearest stockist, tel: 0131 220 3483, or visit their website at **www.equalexchange.co.uk**, where you can also learn more about their growers and products.

Flavoured teas: These are black teas – that is, the fermented kind with which we are most familiar – with natural flavourings. The main brand is Seyte, who offer vanilla-, orange-, mint-, cinnamon- and lemon-flavoured.

Green teas: Green tea – tea leaves in their natural unfermented state that have simply been dried, then rolled or cut – is being promoted as another health drink, as having powerful antioxidant and antibacterial properties as well as the ability to lower blood cholesterol. It is also said to have anti-cancer properties and to help reduce tooth decay, contains very little caffeine, and is a rich source of vitamins and trace elements. It is a costly tea, most of it Japanese, though more Chinese, Darjeeling and fair-traded green teas are also available. Green tea is drunk on its own. As with black tea, the larger the leaf, the better the quality. It is not as mild or as delicate as its name suggests, but has an astringent quality – slightly bitter, even. Apart from the well-known organic brands already mentioned, others are Bradley's, Long Life, and Qi Herbal Health. Green teas also come in other health blends combined with herbs, or flavoured – for example, Long Life Green Tea with ginkgo, ginseng, jasmine and lemon grass.

Golden Temple Natural Products: You can't but find these pleasant, specially blended Ayurvedic organic green teas and herb tea-bags intriguing. Three formulations are available: Green Balance, Green Power and Green Guardian. Ayurvedic Yogi teas, blends of organic green tea and Ayurvedic spices – a personal favourite – offer something different from the normal flavoured teas; they include Classic (cinnamon), Licorice (Egyptian spice blend), Jamaica (mocha spice blend) and Choco (Aztec spice blend).

Hampstead Tea & Coffee Co.: This remarkable company, passionate equally about biodynamic farming and fair trade, sells finest-quality, top-grade (first two leaves and buds only) award-winning Darjeeling, and Oolong and Earl Grey teas from a single estate – Makaibari – the first Demeter-certified biodynamic Fairtrade tea estate in the world, personally managed by the owner, Mr Rajah Banerjee. Many loyal customers (including myself) find their teas superb. Their range includes spiced Biochai, English Breakfast, and the first biodynamic mint green tea. Available at independents, at Selfridges in London, by mail order and online, tel: 020 8731 9833, email info@hampsteadtea.com. Waitrose now stock their green and Darjeeling tea.

Japanese teas: There is a small range of these very special teas. In Japan, Sencha green tea is a prized commodity served in high-class restaurants and to honoured guests. It has long been used by Zen monks to promote mental clarity and calmness. Clearspring is the major brand; their Nagata Sencha green tea, available loose in foil packs and as tea-bags, is grown by the Nagata family on a remote mountain-top plantation, using home-made compost and natural mulches. Only the first tender leaves are used – hand-picked, then briefly steamed and rolled into thin curls and dried slowly in the oven. It has an exquisitely delicate flavour and a lovely calming influence. Also available are Kukicha loose (Western Isle) and Kukicha tea-bags (Lima); Hojicha tea-bags (Clearspring).

Kombucha: Billed as more than just a drink, Kombucha is a special kind of fermented tea used for over two thousand years in the East, surrounded in mystery and with many vitalising health-giving properties. It acts as a cleanser, an aid to digestion, and a mild antibiotic, and contains B vitamins, beneficial yeasts and bacteria. In ten years' time it will probably become a cult tea and be on sale at Prêt à Manger. In the meantime, organic Kombucha, from Kombucha Health Ltd, made from filtered water and Japanese Sencha tea, can be bought from organic outlets. If you want to make your own, you can buy Kombucha ferment from Future Foods website: **www.futurefoods.com**, who supply full instructions.

Robert Wilson's 'Ceylon' Teas: An old-fashioned, ex-tea-planting-family tea merchant, specialising in high-quality teas from Sri Lanka, grown on model tea estates where workers receive social, educational and medical benefits. Their teas, packed on site, have been praised by food writers. The range includes the biodynamic green tea, loose and as tea-bags, from the exceptional mountainside Iddalgashinne estate surrounded by virgin forests, and two other organic black teas. Informative leaflets are available. For mail order details and for London and nationwide stockists, tel: 01460 77508, or visit their website: **www.wilstea.com** – one of the most interesting and comprehensive sites I have found about tea, and highly recommended for anyone interested in quality teas.

Finally, two special types of tea that do not neatly fit into any category:

Maté: The national drink of South America, especially Argentina, this tea consists of the dried leaves of an evergreen shrub belonging to the holly family that grows wild in this part of the world. Plantations were first developed by the Jesuits in the seventeenth century. It has detoxifying properties, a pleasant green-tea 'grassy' flavour, which some may find slightly bitter, and is a natural stimulant. It should be made with hot but not boiling water, can be drunk with milk, hot or chilled, or sweetened. It is traditionally drunk in a special gourd, and drinking it is a communal activity signalling hospitality and friendship. ChéMaté is the up-and-coming organic brand. To find out more about this fascinating beverage and its customs, and for your nearest stockist, email info@chemate.com, or visit their website at **www.chemate.com**.

Rooibos* and *Honeybush teas: These teas from South Africa are mild, clear, bright and soothing, low-caffeine and rich in antioxidants, and fast becoming popular under the Dragonfly brand. Rooibos (red bush) tea, drunk by the Dutch during the early years of colonisation in the eighteenth century, is made from the fermented leaves of a legume indigenous to the Cape of Good Hope, and drunk with or without milk, or iced. Organic supplies come from certified plantations. Honeybush is similar but rarer and more delicate, and grows high in the South East Cape coastal mountains. The first plantations have just been established. Honeybush teas come from sustainably harvested bushes that are organically certified as pure: an important point, because some honeybush tea is being overcropped, damaging the mature indigenous honeybush populations and seriously affecting the local ecology. Dragonfly's teas are available at independent outlets – to find your nearest stockist visit their website at **www.dragonflyteas.com**. Alternatively, Waitrose stock their honeybush and their Capa Malai rooibos chai. Organic rooibos is also sold by other brands such as Clipper and Biona.

Organic herbal teas

Judging by the explosion in organic herbal teas to have hit the shelves recently, they are the new lifestyle drink. At the last count, I noted over a dozen brands, including well-known ones such as Dr Stuart, the London Fruit and Herb Company, Heath & Heather, Twining's and Jackson's, who've each added one or two organic varieties to their range.

Organic herbal teas are made with only certified organic or wildcrafted herbs and natural flavourings. They are guaranteed to be free of irradiation, and sold in non-chlorinated tea-bags. One of the reasons for their popularity is that they all provide a natural caffeine and tannin-free alternative to tea and coffee; the other is to do with their health benefits, which have been recorded since times ancient. Peppermint and camomile remain the most popular (some supermarkets sell own-brand), but there are many others to try, including newly revived traditional herbal brews such as nettle, Essential's new biodynamic Egyptian 'Kakade' (hibiscus) tea, and their best-ever spearmint and peppermint teas, as well as other exotic and medicinal blends created for your every mood and need. Lemon verbena is one of my favourites, and packs a fragrant lemon punch. Sometimes I find herbal tea-bags not strong enough; obvious, I know, but if you find the same try using two instead of one.

Along with Hambleden Herbs, brands you will find in organic retail outlets include Essential, Evernat, Golden Temple, Yogi, Piramide and Kitchen Garden (see p. 252). Piramide is a specialist Dutch herb company who work with small-scale organic growers world wide and import organic herbs direct. Their herbs carry the SKAL, ECO or Demeter symbol. In addition, they operate their own independent quality controls – every batch is checked for purity.

Ayurvedic organic herbal teas are becoming increasingly popular – and, I suspect, will become more so. One nice-to-know brand is Golden Temple – see p. 237. Higher Living have a range of three Ayurvedic tea-bags, 'higher calming', 'higher vitality' and 'higher stomach cleanse'. Though not yet organically certified, a specialist Ayurvedic company, Asmita, in Hove, Sussex, who also run their own Ayurvedic health clinic and sell a range of aromatherapy oils, offer Vata, Pitta and Kapha Balance tea powders, as well as ginger and mint tea powder, by mail order. For more details, tel: 01273 298286. Finally, if you are a mum-to-be, you might like to know that a new company, Welcome World, currently undergoing organic certification, specialises in herbal tea formulas for pregnancy and birth. Phone for mail order brochure 0117 977 6220. They also operate an advice/helpline Mon 10.30 am–3 pm, on the same number.

TIP: Herbal and spiced teas give a new twist to fresh fruit salad mixtures and compotes. Make them strong, sweeten to taste, allow to cool and add chopped organic fruit. And use camomile as a rinse for fair hair.

Organic coffee substitutes

Various 'no-caff' organic coffee-look-alike drinks made from blends of grains, chicory roots and sometimes figs and chickpeas are available; most have roasted flavours. They include Nambu, Malt Fit, Yannoh, and Prewett's organic malted chicory drink, on sale at Sainsbury's, Whole Earth's Nocaf, on sale at Waitrose, and their Wakecup taste similar to the real thing, but you need to make them strong. Kitchen Garden have recently introduced organic fair-traded Sycaf, made from slowly roasted soya beans, as beans or ready-ground.

Independent tea and coffee shops have not yet generally embraced organic teas and coffees, primarily because to sell them loose they would need to be certified, even if they only had a couple of varieties each. One exception is:

The Tea and Coffee Plant, 170 Portobello Road, Notting Hill, London W11 2EB (OF&G), open Tues–Sat, 9.30 am–5.30 pm.
They stock ten organic coffees and over twenty teas and herbal teas, many fair-traded. They also supply Fresh & Wild own-label coffee as well as restaurants and offices, and have a stall at Spitalfields organic food market on Sundays, 10 am–4 pm. They offer mail order and an online ordering service, tel: 0207 221 8137, email: coffee@pro-net.co.uk. For more details, including price lists, visit their website: **www.coffee.uk.com**.

SWEETENERS

Sugar

Organic sugar has come of age. Pioneered by the unrefined heroes of the sugar world, Billington's, who produce a range of organic sugars that are available at most major retailers, it is now sold by other well-known brands such as Whitworth's, Tate & Lyle and, most recently, Silver Spoon. Demand for organic sugar is currently rising by around 50% a year. Until recently most was produced from cane sugar, but now the spotlight has turned to organic sugar beet. After extensive trials by the British Beet Research Organisation, in 2001 the first organic sugar beet was being grown in the UK for British Sugar by over twenty farmers, to be processed and used in manufacturing. The amount being grown is expected to double by the end of 2002, and to account for several thousand hectares within the next decade. This is welcome news, because it means less imported organic sugar and more organically grown crops on our farms, but, as explained below, things are not as organically sweet and simple as they may sound.

Cane or beet?

Broadly speaking, there are two kinds of sugar in this world: refined cheap white sugar, produced either from sugar beet or from predominantly large sugar cane plantations, such as those in the Dominican Republic; and unrefined cane sugar of various hues, from pale-golden granulated to dark, sticky molasses. All standard sugars, refined and unrefined, are generally grown intensively, with all the knock-on effects that brings. In addition, on some sugar cane plantations workers are not given adequate pay or working conditions. In the EU, conventionally grown sugar beet is one of the most profitable crops for farmers and processors; and it swallows up significant quantities of pesticides, and twice the average amount of herbicides used on other crops.

The upshot of all this is that the consumer is likely soon to have the choice of buying unrefined organic cane sugar, unrefined conventionally grown cane sugar from agribusinesses who run large sugar plantations, or cheaper organic sugar made in Europe from sugar beet processed with fossil fuels. Clearly, choosing which organic sugar to buy will be more complicated than it's been in the past, calling perhaps for an appraisal of the particular brand's organic pedigree and a consideration of whether their marketing of organic sugar is born of sound principle or of commercial opportunism.

The imminent arrival of organic sugar produced from sugar beet, which is being actively encouraged in the EU, raises a dilemma. Though far better for the environment from the agricultural point of view, the production of sugar from sugar beets, even organic, is not as wholesome as one might imagine. To be edible, beet sugar needs to be fully refined, which strips out all the nutrients and sucrose, using large amounts of fossil fuel in the process. By contrast, in producing unrefined sugar no part of the cane is usually wasted: the fibre is used to fuel the boilers and power the mill, the solid residues are returned to the fields as fertiliser, and the surplus molasses is fed to livestock or may be distilled to make rum. But to prevent organic unrefined cane sugar from competing 'unfairly' with European organic beet sugar, the EU imposes a levy of nearly £300 per tonne, which places an extra financial burden on the developing countries where organic sugar cane is grown.

Why buy organic sugar?

Organic cane sugar is currently produced in Argentina, Paraguay and Brazil. It is grown on plantations separate from conventional sugar, and unless planted on virgin land where no synthetic fertilisers or pesticides have been used, the plantations usually undergo a five-year conversion period during which they are managed organically and then certified by IFOAM-accredited organisations or by the Soil Association. The estates are small, and often sustainably managed. Billington's, whom they mainly supply, operate their own code of social and environmental practice, which embraces fair-trading, pay, health and safety, and the protection of children.

Organic cane sugar is extracted from the cane in exactly the same way as is conventional unrefined cane sugar: the canes are collected from the fields, taken to the local mill, the juice pressed out, clarified, and the sugar crystallised from the clarified syrup. If the same machinery is also used for conventional sugar, the machinery is always cleaned first to avoid contamination. The only processing aid allowed is lime, in the form of calcium hydroxide. By contrast, refined white sugars undergo another dozen refining processes.

Because it is far more costly to produce and grow in small quantities, organic sugar is about a third more expensive than equivalent unrefined sugars and can be at least twice as expensive as white sugar – mainly because, like sliced white bread, sugar is a 'loss leader', sold by major retailers deliberately cheap. Consumers in the know choose unrefined sugars for preference because they contain minerals which refined white sugar does not, are minimally processed, and have a better flavour – unless it says 'unrefined' on the pack, incidentally, brown sugar is invariably refined white sugar that has been coated brown with something like cane syrup. Unless your household uses vast amounts, the extra cost of organic sugar is hardly going to break the bank, and will not, unlike most conventional sugar, cost the earth either.

What does organic sugar taste like?

Organic sugars come in various sorts. They taste the same and can be used in the same way as other unrefined and ordinary sugars, including preserving. Of course, they do not give a colourless syrup and so produce slightly darker results – though, in fact, because every batch is slightly different, some being almost pale-tea or coffee-coloured, the colour difference may be barely noticeable. The only advantage of preserving-sugar, incidentally, is that it's jumbo-sized crystals are less likely to 'catch' when heated in the preserving pan, but if you melt it carefully, granulated sugar is just as good. Organic icing sugar (milled from organic demerara sugar) will not give you a pure white topping for your fairy-cakes, but can be coloured and flavoured if you want.

Billington's A family firm who produce minimally-processed high-quality natural cane sugars, and the first major sugar brand to market a whole organic range (they do not sell any refined sugars). Their range includes organic granulated (500 g and 1 kg packets), caster and demerara, plus their dinky stick sachets and wrapped cubes; their demerara is darker and fuller-flavoured. For information about their organic sugars (including production details) and about stockists, as well as recipes by well-known chefs, or to join their unrefined sugar club, visit their website: **www.billingtons.co.uk**.

Rapadura unrefined organic cane sugar, produced by Rapunzel and available in organic shops and supermarkets, is a muddy-brown colour, has an attractive slightly fudgy flavour, and is powdery with tiny pebble-like lumps that give it a gritty texture. I like it very much, but some may find it strange. It is made by pressing sugar cane to release its juice, heating the juice gently in large pans until it dries into cakes, then finely grating to produce Rapadura.

Other brands : Suconat and Biona produce unrefined cane sugars.

Honey

Organic honey is pure and natural. It comes to you just as nature intended, and is one of the best foods you can eat, both nutritionally and as far as the bees who produce it are concerned. EU honey standards, which are very stringent, came into force in August 2000; they ensure that organic honey is of the highest quality, and that the bees receive the best care throughout their life-cycle. Bees, the EU standards point out, are one of our most valuable agricultural assets and should be treasured. Unlike most commercially produced kinds, organic honey comes from hives situated in remote and unpolluted areas, well away from any industrial sites or intensive agricultural or horticultural farming. No insecticides, antibiotics or chemical repellents are used, the wood for the hives comes from untreated timbers, and organic beeswax is normally used to make the combs.

There are other key differences. In conventional honey extraction, generally the maximum amount of honey is taken from the hives, and the bees are given refined sugar as a replacement to feed on over winter. In organic production this is forbidden, and sufficient honey and pollen must be left in the hives to nourish the bees; in emergencies such as extreme climatic conditions, they may be fed organic honey, and in some cases organic sugar syrup or molasses.

Though all honey is natural, not all of it is pure. Most commercial honey is a devitalised product that has been flash-heated to 70° to keep it runny, a process that destroys the individual flavour as well as the nutrients. It is then passed through very fine filters to make it clear, which removes its valuable pollen grains. Standard honey is often a blend of honeys from various countries. Most organic honeys, by contrast, tend to be individual and are produced with a minimum of heat treatment and filtering. Organic honey also comes in recyclable glass jars rather than plastic ones.

Honey, one of nature's finest foods, should never be debased. It ranks in importance with organic bananas in its good-for-us-all-ness. Organic honey also enables many traditional beekeepers in tropical countries to earn a living, continue their customary lifestyle, and stay in their local communities. In this way, too, traditional methods of beekeeping are kept alive and we can enjoy a far greater range of honeys. Organic honeys are no more expensive than many other unblended kinds and are widely available, including at major supermarkets (Waitrose, for example, sells excellent Turkish pine honey and organic forest honey from Zambia). Buying them preserves many good things, and will bring you far more pleasure than your average jar.

The HMF factor

This mysterious term is one of the most important indicators of honey quality. HMF is a refined glucose molecule present in honey that increases as the honey is heated. It is used as a measure of how much degradation honey has undergone due to heat treatment; so, broadly speaking, the lower the HMF factor the better quality the honey. New Zealand organic honey has one of the lowest HMF ratings, at 8 mg/kg; most EU countries allow 40 mg/kg in organic honey, while UK regulations allow 80 mg/kg to be present. Major organic producers like Allos and De Rit test for its presence in their honeys, and include the HMF rating on the label.

Wild honey

Wild honey – that is, honey collected from out-of-the-way places – is deemed to be organic by virtue of its isolation, and may be certified as such as long as it meets the other organic requirements.

The threat from GMOs and other contaminants

The threat of contamination from GM plants such as rape is very real, especially for UK beekeepers, and some have already suffered the contamination of their honeys. Organic regulations stipulate that organic hives and apiaries must be situated sufficiently far away from any GM crops to avoid such contamination.

Because Britain is such a crowded island that there is nowhere safe from aerial contamination of one kind or another, there are no certified British organic honeys. Some organic farmers sell honey from their own hives, but it does not qualify as organic.

Flavours galore . . .

Because it is a totally natural product, one of the remarkable things about honey is that its flavour, like that of wine, depends on the country it comes from and the season, as well as the kinds of flowers the bees collected the nectar from. This is why unblended honeys are much more interesting. For organic honeys, which come from the four corners of the earth, this ranges from delicate or buttery New Zealand honeys and named aromatic monofloral ones such as acacia and lime blossom, exotic honeys like manuka (tea tree), valued for its extraordinary antibacterial properties, to medium-weight Mexican and resinous pine honeys, through to full-bodied tropical honeys. African honeys, for instance, are very different from European ones and may seem strangely strong. Forest honeys are also very strong, as they contain a high proportion of honeydew, a sticky substance excreted by aphids that bees also collect. As with wines, which honeys you find appealing is very much a question of personal taste, so seek advice and try different ones when you can.

Brands

Four organic brands of particular note, to appeal to honey buffs in particular, are De Rit, who also produce the widest range of other honey products, and Allos; and two New Zealand brands, the New Zealand Natural Food Company and Wild Honey New Zealand Ltd. All are specialist honey producers, passionate about quality and producing first-class, cold-extracted unblended honeys of exceptional purity and with low HMF factors. They are worth looking out for – you will find them in independent outlets. Many other brands – such as Rowse, Epicure and Evernat – also sell organic honeys.

Allos A specialist honey company supplying high-quality honeys, cold-extracted, unblended and with a maximum HMF factor of 15. All their honeys undergo testing for residues and radioactivity, the results of which can be obtained from Allos by quoting the number on the jar. They offer an extensive range comprising ten honeys, including Eucalyptus, Canadian, Maya and Argentinian Wildflower, and Bio Blossom.

De Rit Another specialist honey company, this one claims to supply the best honey money can buy because of the unique process the honey undergoes, which guarantees that it is pure, unblended and cold-extracted, and that its natural enzymes and nutrients are all retained. Though fully organic, it is not certified because De Rit prefer to maintain their own independent standards. The HMF content is a maximum of 10 mg/kg. The range comprises 21 honeys, from acacia and wild-flower from Hungary to lavender, sunflower and fruit blossom from France and forest honey from Greece, all supplied to them by known producers.

New Zealand Natural Food Company The major specialist supplier of organic New Zealand honeys. All of their honeys are untreated and of the highest quality; each jar can be traced back to the beekeeper. Available only through independent healthfood stores, their range comprises Organic Manuka, Honeydew, Native Flower and Tawari honeys and delicious raw organic honeycomb in small boxes. They also offer a mail-order service, tel: 01730 81342. For more, visit their website, **www.nznf.co.uk**.

Wild Honey New Zealand Ltd. A collective of 4 family beekeepers who produce a range of delicious honeys imported by Essential Trading. They produce informative literature. Email: wildhoney@wildhoney.co.nz.

Honey products

Honey, nature's original sweetener, is used as a healthier alternative to sugar by many organic manufacturers in cakes and biscuits – look out for delicious honey-cakes and waffles especially – in confectionery, including honey marzipan made with organic ground almonds and honey, in organic honey halva, and in some jams and spreads. Organic mead, brewed by Broughton Pastures from tropical forest honey, raisins and cane sugar, is available exclusively through Vinceremos wine merchants (p. 264), and Fullers have introduced Organic Honeydew Golden Ale, brewed from organic English malt, hops and honey.

Other honey know-how

- Throughout history many cultures have attested to honey's magical healing and cosmetic powers. It is a natural antiseptic and mild antibiotic.
- Honey is an important ingredient in many cuisines and can be used for all your cooking, from salad dressings and fragrant Middle Eastern casseroles to desserts, cakes, biscuits, smoothies and drinks. Different honeys match different dishes. Plain yoghurt and honey are a marriage made in heaven.
- Honey in its natural state may be runny, grainy, viscous or solid, and varies in colour from white through amber to dark caramel. Crystallisation is natural, and a sign that it has not been over-processed. To make it runny again, immerse the jar in hot water for a few minutes.
- Honey is its own natural preservative, and does not go stale. Store at room temperature, not in the fridge.

ORGANIC HONEYS WORLDWIDE

These examples show what a precious product organic honey is:

New Zealand

New Zealand has vast areas of unpolluted natural bushland and breathtakingly isolated landscapes, and is the world's leading high-quality organic honey producer, where 'man, mountains and nature' work together with the rhythms of the seasons. Organic honey production is carried out by small family concerns on both the North and South Islands. Hives are situated in uncultivated remote regions, and every organic beekeeper must produce 'land user statements', guaranteeing that no toxic chemical sprays have been used in the area within a minimum 5 km radius – a bee's natural foraging distance. All sites are approved by the organic certifying body, Bio-Grow New Zealand, and no organic hives are allowed to be used for the pollination of conventional orchards, which are a prime source of additional income for other beekeepers. To confirm purity, every batch of honey is rigorously tested for residues and GM contamination, and HMF tests are undertaken. The bees are allowed to live out their natural life-cycles. In each hive, 15–20 kg of honey is left to feed the bees over winter, and extraction is carried out as naturally as possible to preserve the honey's maximum nutritional and curative properties. It is never heated beyond natural hive temperature (38°C) or finely filtered, so as to retain the precious pollen grains. Every jar can be traced back to the beekeeper and the site.

Conservation of the natural landscape is taken seriously, too, as native forests are a major source of honey. For example, the Project Crimson Trust (**www.projectcrimson.org**.nz), supported by the beekeepers of the Wild Honey Company, is one ongoing initiative to save the spectacularly crimson-flowering native pohutukawa or Christmas tree, and the rata tree, from extinction (these are found on the coastal areas, particularly in the northern part of the North Island).

New Zealand honeys from the Wild Honey Company include:

- Manuka – known as the 'healing' honey, with a rich barley-sugar flavour
- Alpine-clover – gathered from pure alpine regions of the South Island, with a sweet, traditional flavour
- Wildflower – a mix of NZ native bush and manuka varieties, with a rich, mellow flavour
- Tawari – a deliciously sweet rosehip flavour
- Pohutukawa – a light, buttery flavour, often said to have a hint of the sea in it.

South East Asia, Africa, India . . .

Organic 'wild' honeys from tropical countries such as Borneo, Zambia, the Solomon Islands, India and Vietnam, produced by traditional small-scale and village beekeepers, are becoming more popular – Waitrose, for example, sells one from a Welsh company, Tropical Forest, which specialises in importing these kinds of honeys. The honeys, collected from hives situated deep in the forests, have strong, complex flavours. The hives are hand-made using forest materials. In Africa, for example, bark is formed into a cylinder and closed with a grass door; the hives are then hung up trees to protect the bees from honey-badgers and other predators. To harvest the honey, the beekeeper ties a bundle of leaves to a fibre rope, lights them and leaves them to smoulder, then climbs the tree and scoops out the honey with one arm, into a bucket.

Also, many tropical honeys, like Oxfam's or Equal Exchange's (Fairtrade) organic honey, are fair-traded, which helps to further support the local economy and infrastructure. The trucks that collect Oxfam's fair-traded organic honey from Zambia, for example, also deliver essentials such as salt and bicycle tyres to the villages – and it's small details like this that, as the beekeepers themselves point out, make a world of difference. As they also point out, the market that we provide by buying their honeys is essential to their survival.

Other sweeteners

Organic molasses, golden syrup and maple syrup (now in squeezy bottles), of which there are several brands, are the other well-known organic sweeteners. Clearspring (p. 301) also sell various toffee-sweet syrups made from grains: corn and barley, brown rice, barley, malt, Japanese millet and rice malt, which are popular macrobiotic sweeteners and can be used in the same way as the others. Only organic sugar, honey and the other sweeteners described above are used in organic manufactured foods such as cereals, cakes and confectionery. Note that organic sugar does not affect the flavour of foods in any way.

DRIED HERBS AND SPICES

Information on fresh herbs can be found in chapter 6, but there are also many reasons for choosing organically grown herbs and spices for your store cupboard, including their intense flavour. Herbs and spices are nature's healers, and their efficacy, as well as the concentration of their natural oils and hence their flavour, depends on the way they are grown. Organic herbs and spices are able to draw up naturally a pot-pourri of trace elements from the soil. Many believe that for this reason they are more potent; certainly, this is borne out by the organic spices I have tried. As you would expect, unlike their conventional equivalents, they are not irradiated or treated with chemicals such as etherol (a ripening agent sprayed on at harvest time), ethloxyquin (an antioxidant) or chlorine (a cleaning agent).

Both are widely available, are on sale in some supermarkets, and cost no more than those you can buy in fancy jars. The latest arrival, organic saffron from Hambleden Herbs, is superb. Being light, they make admirable gifts and are ideal to buy via mail order.

'Wildcrafted'

With the ever-increasing demand for organic, the issue of 'wildcrafted' herbs – that is, wild herbs gathered from their native habitat – has become particularly important. The term denotes herbs that have been correctly identified and conscientiously harvested from isolated places unpolluted by roads, industry or conventional farming, under strict regulations that ensure natural purity and preservation of the natural habitat. Gathering takes place at the peak of each herb's growing cycle, and must not deplete the natural plant populations. To protect from exploitation and guarantee purity, the wildcrafting of herbs is now embodied in organic standards, which means that all wildcrafting operations must be certified and adhere to the regulations outlined above.

Quality

Dried organic herbs and spices are a high-value, labour-intensive crop and are sourced from over thirty countries. Import and quality-control regulations are strict, and they are regularly tested for purity. All must either be grown to organic standards or are wild-crafted. The demand for organic herbs and spices is currently growing at a rate of 50% a year. Inevitably, as more become available there will be greater variation in the raw materials, and whereas only five years ago the few organic herb and spice producers around the globe were committed pioneers, the mass-market ethos means increasingly that organic herbs and spices are treated as commodities like anything else. This means greater choice and cheaper prices – but expect more variations in quality.

WHERE ORGANIC DRIED HERBS AND SPICES COME FROM

- **Austria** – coriander seed
- **Egypt** – camomile, basil, marjoram, spearmint, fennel, coriander leaf, coriander seed
- **Hungary** – paprika, parsley
- **Indonesia** – cardamom, ginger

- **Madagascar** – cinnamon, cloves, vanilla
- **Malawi** – lemon grass, bird's eye chillis, hibiscus, annato
- **Pakistan** – turmeric, powdered chilli
- **South Africa** – thyme
- **Spain** – bay leaves, rosemary, tarragon, sage, thyme
- **Sri Lanka** – black pepper, nutmeg, ginger
- **Uganda** – ginger
- **USA** – peppermint, onion, garlic

▲▲

Brands

Hambleden Herbs (see p. 253) is the leader. Others are Barts, who now have an organic range, De Rit biodynamic herbs, spices and spice pastes, and Lebensbaum, who produce a full range of organic herbs and spices, including Herbes de Provence and organic curry powder. Kitchen Garden fair-traded organic herbs and spices are produced in Zimbabwe, by small-scale farmers on company-owned farms. The plants are processed on site and the range includes herbal condiments such as minced garlic and fresh minced basil, and a variety of herbal teas. To learn more, visit their website: **www.kitchen-garden.co.uk**.

Ready-made spice blends – and three more brands

The latest development is ready-to-use authentic spice blends to add that essential exotic flavour to your organic food, produced by people who are passionate about spicing – for example:

Archiamma, Sittingbourne, Kent (SA), tel/fax: 01795 520504, email: info@archiamma.co.uk.
A first. Must-have, fragrant handmade organic spice kits for creating authentic Sri Lankan food, produced by a small family business. Beautifully packaged, and excellent product – the spices are freshly ground, made in small quantities every week, and have a deliberate, short shelf life (6 months). Each packet comes with its own recipe sheet (the best I have come across), plus organic coconut butter. Supporters of fair-trade, also. On sale in Fresh & Wild, selected outlets, mail order and on line. For more, visit their lovely website: **www.archiamma.co.uk**.

Chiman's, Cleave Farm, Barnstaple, Devon (SA), tel: 01271 883864, fax: 01271 882843.
A small specialist spice-blend company, who have now introduced their organic Indian recipe blends. The spices are blended by hand and come in lovely serene packaging, depicting traditional Indian scenes. Each one, commendably, has the recipe on the back – they are all family recipes that work, and are easy to follow. Their organic blends include Bombay Potatoes (winner, Organic Food Awards 2001), Spicy Chickpeas, Bean Curry and Chicken Madras. Available at organic retailers and independents; and by mail order – ring direct.

Seasoned Pioneers Ltd, Northwich, Cheshire, (OF&G), freephone: 0800 0682348, fax: 0151 709 9330, email: info@seasonedpioneers.co.uk.
This new company, passionate about authenticity and who dry-roast their spices in cast-iron pans, have come up with snazzy, dinky resealable foil pouches of various mixes that have received praise from food writers such as Nigella Lawson. Their organic blends include Indian masalas, African Berber and Moroccan La Kame – all handy and fragrant. They also stock Chinese mandarin peel and two sorts of organic chilli. You'll find them at independent retailers, and Fresh & Wild stores and Bluebird in London. To find out more, to shop on line, to find your nearest stockist, for recipes and spice know-how and much more, visit their great website: **www.seasonedpioneers.co.uk**.

▼▼

HAMBLEDEN HERBS

Established in 1982 and winners of over twenty-five awards, Hambleden Herbs, Milverton, Somerset, TA4 1NF, are Britain's leading organic herb and spice company. Like all the organic pioneers in this book, they have single-handedly created the UK market for their chosen product, and have worked tirelessly in developing organic standards and ethical trading, in maintaining organic integrity and improving quality. They source worldwide, predominantly direct from growers, dealing with long-established and committed producers.

The Hambleden Herbs range of 135 organic herbal products includes teas, infusions, culinary herbs and spices, herbal tinctures, mulling spices and Christmas incense, frankincense and myrrh, all of which are available from independent retail outlets nationwide.

As the Organic Herb Trading Company they supply the country's largest range of organic dried herbs, spices, tinctures and plant-derived products to organic food, herbal medicine and cosmetics manufactures. On the farm they grow 100 varieties of medicinal herbs, from which they produce their fresh herbal tinctures, made with the addition of organic alcohol. They have their own drying barn.

To receive a list of stockists, tel: 01823 401205, fax: 01823 401001, or email: info@organicherbtrading.com. To learn more, visit their website: **www.organicherbtrading.com**.

THE WIDER PICTURE

An important but often overlooked feature of organic farming is the positive changes it is making in underdeveloped countries. These often go unnoticed on the supermarket shelf, if mentioned on the packaging, but such changes, though small, are hugely significant. New organic herbs-and-spices projects taking place in Africa, for example, are not only providing valuable jobs and income, but developing new sustainable agricultural practices that reverse soil erosion and are helping to revitalise rural economies in areas such as Malawi, Zimbabwe, Zambia and Namibia.

The Devil's Claw project is one such ground-breaking initiative, in which over 300,000 hectares of semi-desert in Namibia have recently been certified organic for the sustainable harvesting of devil's claw, a valuable herbal remedy for arthritis. Funded by local and international agencies, the project has resulted not only in better-quality devil's claw, but in increased prices for the harvesters, who are able to maintain their traditional nomadic lifestyle and receive proper training in managing their resource. Previously there was no control, natural stocks of the plant were dwindling because of over-picking, and the harvesters were not receiving a fair price – hence their need to pick more devil's claw than was sustainable. The project is now providing a fair-traded stable income for some of the country's poorest rural communities, who now trade direct with the exporters – who contribute to a community-controlled fund that is helping to develop other community benefits.

Storing

Keep your herbs and spices in a cupboard, not on show; stored properly – somewhere cool and dark – whole dried organic herbs and spices have a long shelf life (around 18 months for herbs and two years or longer for spices). Ready-ground spices and powdered herbs have a shorter shelf life, 12–18 months maximum. Once opened, they gradually lose their potency and should be used within 3–6 months if possible.

11: Organic Alcoholic and Soft Drinks

Once organic food becomes part of your diet, organic drinks become the next natural switch. They offer the same benefits as eating organic: the confidence that what you are consuming you can trust. All conform to organic processing standards – for instance, the use of GM yeasts in brewing is prohibited. Many are produced by small, dedicated producers and manufacturers, which has particular benefits where wine is concerned. Though it would be wrong to pretend that every organic drink tastes wonderful, converts favour the cleaner flavours that many organic drinks express; and just about everyone susceptible to hangovers votes for organic wines every time.

Though slower to develop than organic food, organic drinks – by which I mean wines, beers, cider, spirits and soft drinks of all kinds (tea and coffee were discussed in Chapter 10) – have paralleled organic foods in their range and scope. There is now an organic option for every kind of drink imaginable, and the choice expands daily. Because of increasing demand, conventional drink manufacturers (and supermarkets) are also developing organic lines; Tesco have their own organic vodka, Waitrose their own champagne, and so on. The UK has two organic vineyards, Avalon in Somerset and Sedlescombe in East Sussex, and its first dedicated micro-organic brewery, Pitfield Brewery in Pitfield Street, Shoreditch, London. The most famous organic soft drink has to be Whole Earth's cola: and before you raise your eyebrows, it's not only a great product – it shows what you can achieve if you apply the organic ethos and add a splash of creativity.

A note for vegetarians and vegans. Most wines, beers and lagers are clarified using fining and filtering agents. These include isinglass (made from fish bladders), egg whites (not commonly used in the UK) and gelatine, all approved under organic regulations. Alcoholic drinks excluding animal ingredients will state so on the label: otherwise, it's safe to assume that one of these will have been used. For more information, contact the Vegetarian Society, tel: 0161 928 0793, website: **www.vegsoc.org**.

ORGANIC WINES

There are now thousands of organic wines produced in the world, stretching from Germany to the tiny island of Waheki in New Zealand, where the fabled Stonyridge wines have been produced organically for the last twenty years. Because in the UK we know and like French wines best, most organic wines on sale in the UK come from France (look for the words *vin biologique* on the label), but Italy, and recently Spain, are becoming major players, and providing potential organic wine buffs with many happy hours of discovery. Rioja, for example, has just produced its first 4,000 litres of organic wine, from the Grajera winery and using Tempranillo grapes from thirty-year-old vines. Organic wines are also being imported from South Africa, Chile, Germany, Tunisia, Australia, New Zealand and, of course, California. The full range includes reds, rosés, whites, sparkling wines (from France, Spain and Italy) and champagne – around half a dozen at the last count. For once, the first own-label organic wine (from La Mancha, in Spain) came not from a major retailer (though Tesco and Sainsbury's do now both have them), but from one of the country's best-known organic wine merchants, Vintage Roots. A cause for celebration, we think.

What is an organic wine, and why buy it?

Organic wine is made in exactly the same way as conventional wine: the grapes are harvested, pressed, fermented, filtered (occasionally you may find a wine that has not been filtered, but this is a curiosity these days), and bottled. An organic wine is simply a wine made from certified organic grapes; and the logo on the bottle refers to this, not to how the wine was made. The reason for this is that wine-making is a very individual process – every grower makes his wine slightly differently – which changes from season to season. And the wines range from those made in high-tech stainless steel wineries to traditional ones made in tiny cellars using minimal, or sometimes no, technology. Because of the great variation in climate and growing conditions, too, standards vary in detail from country to country, and sometimes from region to region.

All the same, general principles still apply. For example, read the standards of a certifying body such as OGWA (Organic Grapes into Wine Alliance) in California, and you will find them every bit as detailed as other organic standards. In this case, every stage of the operation is specified from the origin of the grapes to the harvesting and crushing, and recommended corking materials and cleaning agents. Generally, then, when you buy an organic wine this is what you're getting:

- minimal use of sulphur dioxide: typically, one-third less than that conventionally employed
- minimal use of permitted additives, e.g. fining agents: those most often used are betonite, kieselguhr clays, egg whites and isinglass
- apart from sulphur dioxide, no artificial additives or chemical preservatives.

Organic wines have other advantages. Though there are a few large wineries committed to organic wine, such as the splendid Fetzer in California and Penfolds in Australia, the majority of organic wines are made by small producers. This means that they are more individualistic. As conventional fine wine-makers, who often mirror organic principles in their own vineyards, know only too well, the best way to improve quality is to reduce yield, and the simplest way to do this is to use no artificial fertilisers and to adopt the kind of pruning methods that organic producers use as a matter of course. This means, a priori, that organic grapes tend to be of better quality than most conventionally produced grapes. As all wine writers are keen to point out, remember too that whereas great grapes can be turned into indifferent wine, indifferent grapes can never make great wine and the skill of the wine-grower is paramount.

All these are positive reasons for buying organic wine. Another reason, of course, is that conventional wine production is highly intensive. It is estimated that vineyards account for only 10% of arable land but over three-quarters of herbicides and nearly half of all pesticides used. A recent three-year study of French farmers has concluded that there is a significant link between bladder cancer and pesticide exposure in vineyards. Residues are frequently detected; the last time wine was tested, in 1993, half of imported red and white samples and three out of five English samples contained fungicide residues. In addition, a cocktail of chemicals, often including high levels of sulphur, is used in the production of cheap wine – if you get a headache from drinking wine, this is the likely reason.

If you are a wine enthusiast, remember, too, that GM vines are being trialled: if they become a reality, then much of the reason for buying wines – their age-old individuality – flies out of the window, and wine will become as standardised as ball-bearings. Buying organic wine now means safeguarding choice for the future.

Biodynamic wines

These deserve a special mention. Several of the top wine-makers in the world use biodynamic methods in their vineyards, some having converted from conventional ones. The reason is very simple. If you want to make the finest wines, there is a growing opinion that biodynamic methods produce the best results. As Renée Eliott, wine writer and founder of Planet Organic, points out, wine-makers have long known that the phases of the moon, which affect atmospheric pressure, have a bearing on racking and bottling times, as well as on when a wine 'opens' and 'closes' in the bottle. Grapes, even more than food crops, express their sense of place, and have a depth of complexity that defies description. Vines are long-lived plants and, like people, they mature and grow more complex with time. Part of the skill of a wine-maker is to capture this, and to produce a wine that will express the ultimate in harmony and balance. As explained previously, biodynamic crops regularly show more harmony and vitality than others. The enhanced microbiological life (see p. 16) that you achieve when applying biodynamic methods to the soil – which will affect the grapes' health, vigour and vitality – may be one of the secrets, and is certainly another reason why wine-makers believe that biodynamic is best.

Sulphur dioxide

Sulphur dioxide has been used to preserve wine since ancient times – it was used by the early Egyptians, the Greeks and the Romans. Headaches aside, because it is recognised as a health hazard, organic wine-makers use the minimum. In America, for example, it is not allowed in organic vinification at all, and many other organic wine-makers also choose not to use it. In the UK, labelling laws exempt alcoholic drinks from listing ingredients, which means that you have no idea how much sulphur dioxide is present in your bottle of wine. As a precautionary measure, it is a good idea to choose organic or to seek advice from your wine supplier as to which wines have low levels of sulphur and which do not.

Though wine can be made perfectly well without sulphur dioxide, it does not keep or travel as well. While this is of no consequence for wines made and consumed locally or for fresh wines meant to be drunk young, it does make it difficult for wine merchants and means that you need to check how soon you should drink your organic wine rather than assuming that you can leave it in the rack for that gloriously sunny day or special celebration.

Organic vineyards

Walk into any organic vineyard and the differences that count are immediately visible. Absent is the scorched-earth policy whereby the vines are surrounded by bare soil and nothing lives between the rows, and where if you drive through you frequently encounter warning signs saying 'spraying in progress'. Organic vineyards are full of life – weeds flourish, as do cover-crops to fix nitrogen and herbs and flowers to attract predators; in high summer the air is filled with the noise of insects, and spiders and all manner of life crawl around in the undergrowth. A couple of years ago I visited Richmond Plains vineyards near Nelson in the South Island of New Zealand, run by the Holmes brothers from Yorkshire, who make beautifully pure-tasting wines. There the local Maoris come every year to pick one of their favourite food plants, for which these vineyards provide one of the few remaining local refuges. The brothers showed us a clump of their soil: rich, crumbly and full of humus. To see more of how their wines are made, visit their website: **www.organicwines.co.nz**.

The other immediately noticeable difference is the way the vines are pruned and held on their supports. For an organic wine-maker, keeping lots of air moving through his or her vines is paramount if the various fungal diseases that blight wine production are to be controlled. This means that the vines are less crowded, which produces fewer grapes, but of better quality. The health and overall vigour of the leaves, and the way they support themselves on the vine stems, are generally noticeable, too.

Organic vineyards are not perfect. Weeds are managed by various mechanical means, including mowing, which compacts the soil. Fungal diseases are currently controlled using Bordeaux mixture (copper sulphate and lime, developed in 1885), though this will be removed from the permitted lists shortly.

English vineyards

We have two:

Avalon Vineyard, East Pennard, Shepton Mallet, Glastonbury, Somerset (SA), tel: 01749 860393.
An organic vineyard and fruit farm, producing organic white wines, traditional cider and mead, and organic fruit wines – apple, gooseberry, tayberry and raspberry, made from their own and local fruit – plus ginger wine and a new one made from vine leaves, called Folly Wine; and once the orchards have completed conversion they will add plum wine, made from local cherry plums, to their organic list. Available by mail order, by the case and direct from the farm shop – visitors welcome, but please ring first.

Sedlescombe Organic Vineyard, Cripps Corner, Robertsbridge, East Sussex (SA), tel: 01580 830715, freephone: 0800 980 2884.
Described as a magical experience, Sedlescombe Vineyard near Bodiam Castle is one of the most idyllic locations in southern England. They started with 2,000 plants on one and a half acres in 1979; today the vineyard extends to fifteen acres and is still growing. It is a major tourist attraction, with vineyard tours and regular tastings. They produce red, white and sparkling wines, fruit juices and cider. Their vineyard shop stocks an extensive range of organic wines and other items. Mail order catalogue available. To find out more or order online, visit their equally magical website (enjoy the groovy music, too) at **www.EnglishOrganicWine.co.uk**; there's also a good links page.

Quality, flavour and price

All the organic wine merchants I speak to agree that the quality of their wines is improving all the time, as organic wine-makers get better and better at their art. The best are now taken seriously by many wine writers, and regularly win awards. Wine experts comment on their purity, finding that they typically have a fresher taste, express the grape variety and *terroir* better, and do not give you a headache. The reason is simple: the more you remove the cushion of chemicals, the more care and extra attention to detail the *vigneron* has to apply to produce decent grapes and make decent wine. Experts also point out that organic wines are honest with your taste buds – there's often more difference between the vintages in organic wines – which is the way it should be. Remember, not everyone agrees.

Given the way the grapes are grown – costs in an organic vineyard can be 35–40% higher – and the way the wine is produced, organic wines also represent very good value for money. On average, you can expect to pay only 5–10% more, and less for wines over £5. But don't expect wonders from an organic wine at £2.99, even if you manage to find one. According to Lance Pigott of Vintage Roots, who tips organic Spanish wines as the ones to watch (his top tip is Penedes Lignum from Albert I Noya), some of the best-value fine organic wines are in the £5–7 bracket.

Where to buy

Major supermarkets stock a handful of organic wines (Waitrose with around 25, currently stock the most, followed by Sainsbury's and Tesco, who have 15 plus), and are a very useful first port of call, though an organic supermarket (and some organic shops) will have a much broader selection. For example, Planet Organic in London stock around 150 wines at their Westbourne Grove store, As Nature Intended over 200, and Fresh & Wild ten different champagnes. High-street wine merchants also stock some organic wines. Waitrose and Tesco sell organic champagne, and all Waitrose's wines are also available from Waitrose Wine Direct.

Thereafter, to discover the joy of organic wines, the best advice is to seek out specialist mail order organic wine merchants. Buying wine through mail order is accepted practice, and works very well. They try to stock as many different wines from each other as they can, so it's a good idea to get all of their catalogues. Often, too, they stock other products such as organic oils, vinegars, pasta products and juices, and organic spirits, liqueurs and fortified drinks. Online organic retailers offer wines by the case, as do the major home delivery companies.

NOTE: Wine merchants are increasingly stocking eco-friendly wines, which are not certified organic but are made from grapes that may be grown using organic methods, for example, or using minimum inputs. The merchant will usually be able to tell you exactly how the wine qualifies for its eco-status.

Serving wine

Wine is a living product, and should be treated gently and with respect. Reds need to be served at room temperature, whites slightly chilled but not, except for the very sweet ones, too cold for enjoyment. Don't overfill the glasses –

it's easy to drink too much, and having less in the glass tends to make you savour it more.

Sometimes an organic wine, like many fine wines, throws a sediment – tiny crystals that settle in the bottom of the glass. These are nothing to be concerned about and are completely natural. If decanting, check for sediment first, then pour the wine carefully into the decanter, holding the bottle at an angle so that the sediment collects in one corner, and leave it in the bottle.

A good wine book

The best way to learn about organic wines is to invest in an organic wine book. Monty Walden's excellent *Organic Wine Guide*, published for Friends of the Earth by Thorson's, covers the whole world thoroughly, has profiles of over 400 organic wine producers and 2,000 organic wines, and includes a very good section on biodynamic wines. The other good book that I recommend, which is shorter and more basic but covers the essentials, is Hilary Wright's *The Great Organic Wine Guide*, published by Piatkus; it includes 150 best-buys. Both are very readable and tell you what organic wine is and isn't and how it's grown, and give comprehensive details about organic producers and wine merchants.

PROFILE: FETZER WINES, CALIFORNIA

Fetzer, of Hopland, California, who are acknowledged to have been at the cutting edge of organic wine-making for several years, are probably the world's best-known and largest organic *vignerons*. Officially acknowledged, also, as one of the top ten recycling companies in California, their commitment to recycling is equally strong. Every year they compost over 10,000 tonnes of grape skins and pips, recycle their wine bottles, cartons and waste paper, and use wax seals instead of lead capsules on their bottles.

The original vineyard was started in 1957 by a lumber merchant, Barney Fetzer, who with his large family began making wines. Today all their vineyards (360 acres) are managed organically; in the late 1980s they created a five-acre organic kitchen garden and a state-of-the-art wine-and-food visitor educational centre, overseen by one of America's top chefs, John Ash, which is open every day and is now world-famous.

Their delicious and stylish red and white Bonterra ('good earth') wines are stocked by many wine merchants and major supermarkets, packaged in recycled glass bottles with labels made out of keanf (hemp) and printed with soya-based ink. To find out more – and see the vineyard and garden for yourself – visit Bonterra's or Fetzer's excellent websites: **www.bonterra.com** and **www.fetzer.com**.

▲▲

ORGANIC WINE MERCHANTS

The three main organic wine merchants (see below) all sell through mail order and online, and their catalogues have helpful symbols for everything including which wines are suitable for vegetarians and vegans. They offer mixed cases, and stock Sedlescombe's English white wine.

The Organic Wine Co., PO Box 81, High Wycombe, Bucks. HP13 5QN, tel/fax: 01494 446557, email: afm@lineone.net.
A small organic wine merchant, supplying around 300 wines in total, including five wines in ten-litre box, plus beers, Sedlescombe cider, apple and pear juice, spirits including grappa, port, liqueurs and bottled French fruit and vegetable juices. They produce a small, closely worded catalogue, plus an occasional newsletter. They also, handily, stock glasses and some prized organic olive oils (and drizzlers): Tuscan Il Casale (plus their excellent oak-aged organic wine vinegar), Mas de Gourgonnier's fabulous Provençal olive oil, Agriverde from Abruzzo, and Terres de Solence from Côtes du Ventoux. They also sell wines 'in bond'. For more, or to order online, visit their website at **www.organicwinecompany.com**.

Vinceremos Wines and Spirits Ltd, 19 New Street, Leeds LS18 4BH, tel: 0113 205 4545, fax: 0113 205 4546, email: info@vinceremos.co.uk.
A well-known organic and speciality wine and spirit merchant (spirits not organic, but this means you can try Russian vodkas, too), established in the mid-1980s, their catalogue is jam-packed with a range of over 200 organic wines, plus organic beers, ciders, and their non-organic juices and spirits. Should you need any more persuasion, their catalogue includes comments on various wines from experts who have tried them. Vinceremos also run the HDRA Organic Wine Club: the email address is hdrawine@bottlegreen.com. To find out more about their wines or to order online, visit their easy-to-use

online shop at their website **www.vinceremos.co.uk**, chosen by the *Independent* as one of their top ten food-and-drink sites.

Vintage Roots Ltd, Farley Farms – Bridge Farm, Reading Road, Arborfield, Berks, RG2 9HT, tel: 0118 976 1999, fax: 0118 976 1998, freephone: 0800 980 4992, email: info@vintageroots.co.uk.
The original organic wine specialists, who have been selling organic wines exclusively since 1986, when they set up business with an enterprise allowance. They produce a stylish catalogue, bright and cheerful, featuring over 250 wines, plus beers, ciders, spirits, liqueurs, juices, oils and vinegars. They are the exclusive supplier of Broughton Pastures fruit wines and mead, and now have their own-label organic bianco from Italy, plus own-label beer and lager – all proving very popular. To find out more about their wines or to order online, visit their easy-to-use online shop at **www.vintageroots.co.uk**.

Also:

The Pure Wine Company, Unit 18, Woods Browning Industrial Estate, Respryn Road, Bodmin, Cornwall PL3 1DQ, tel: 01208 77219, freephone: 0808 100 3123, fax: 01208 79393, email: service@purewine.co.uk, website: **www.purewine.co.uk**.
Specialist organic, vegetarian and vegan wine merchant, with over 200 selected organic wines from around the world (strong Italian selection).

Rose Blanc Rouge, 2 Bedale Street, London SE1 9AL, tel/fax: 020 7403 0358, email: contact@rose-blanc-rouge.com,
website: **www.rose-blanc-rouge.com**.
A small French company specialising in fine organic wines from France and elsewhere. Also sell organic beers, Sedlescombe organic cider and James White organic juices. Attractive, informative website.

Divine Wines Ltd, Divine House, 6 Hornbeam, Leighton Buzzard, Bedfordshire LU7 8UX, tel: 01525 218100, fax: 01525 218100, email: enquiries@divinewines.co.uk, website: **www.divinewines.co.uk**.
An online organic wine merchant, run by Julie Pearson, specialising in affordable wines. Also stock small range of organic country wines, port, spirits, juices, Rock's cordials, and beers. Groovy, relaxing website.

ORGANIC BEERS

There are around forty or so bottled organic beers, lagers and ciders now available, both UK and imported. Bottled beers include Caledonian Golden Promise, Sam Smith's Organic Best Ale, Brakspear's organic beers, Fuller's Honey Dew Ale, Wychwood Brewery's Circle Master Ale, which uses malted barley grown on the Prince of Wales's Duchy Farm Estate in Gloucestershire, and their new Kiwi Organic Ale; and St Peter's Organic best Bitter and Organic Ale.

Pitfield and Brakspear's produce draft cask-conditioned organic real ales; Fuller's have recently introduced theirs on draft, too. Brakspear's, Sam Smith, Freedom Brewery and Vintage Roots offer organic lager. There are excellent imported organic beers and lagers, mainly German but also Belgian and Australian, and you can even buy organic hemp beer – Cannabia is the main brand; and Motherhemp sell one, too (don't worry, it's approved by the Home Office).

Organic beers and lagers are now sold in supermarkets: Tesco sell their own organic beer, they and the Co-op sell organic lager, made for them by Caledonian. Sainsbury's and Waitrose stock St Peter's and Wychwood's Circle organic ales (St Peter's Organic Ale contains no finings and is suitable for vegans). Organic supermarkets such as Planet Organic and As Nature Intended sell a good selection, around twenty or so. The amazing Cook's Delight organic shop in Berkhamsted also stocks around twenty, all suitable for vegetarians; their customers' favourite tipples are Sam Smith's Best Ale and the delicious Riedenburger unfiltered lager from Germany. Serious beer buffs, meanwhile, should head for the Beer Shop attached to Pitfield Brewery (p. 268), who sell all the organic beers it is possible to buy.

How organic beers are made

The brewing methods and ingredients for making organic beer are exactly the same as those for any real ale: fermented malted barley, hops and yeast, plus permitted fining agents to clarify beers and lagers if that is their style. The main problem is securing supplies of organic hops, and hops of the right variety (as with wine, the variety is all-important). Hops take three years to come into production, and are prone to a variety of pests and fungal diseases – which makes growing them extremely difficult and precarious, and yields unpredictable. This is especially so in the UK, where our climate is more unpredictable than most, and the only brave heart currently producing them is the award-winning fruit grower Peter Hall, in Kent, who also grows organic apples. His hops (variety Target) are used in Brakspear's organic beers. The native shortage means that organic hops are imported from several countries, including Germany and New Zealand. Head brewers I have spoken to are generally impressed by their quality, especially the aroma differences they can detect and the liveliness that the imported hops can impart to the beers. Certainly, those I have tried have very clean, fruity flavours.

Though the brewing process is the same, because there is more variability from batch to batch of ingredients organic brewing is more of a challenge. As my local head brewer put it, 'You can't leave it on autopilot, it just won't work'. Because supplies of hops are limited, the organic brewing sector at the moment is still very small, and the production of organic beers is suited only to small-scale and regional breweries – which means more choice of local brews for the consumer.

Just so that you're clear, the fining agent used in brewing is isinglass: this binds with the yeast cells that are deposited during brewing and causes them to settle to the bottom of the cask more quickly; brewers who don't use it (thus making their beers suitable for vegetarians and vegans) just use gravity, substituting time for the fining agent.

Another difference worth pointing out is to do with whether a bottled organic beer is the equivalent of real ale – that is, bottle-conditioned and hence 'live' – or pasteurised. Neither Pitfield nor Brakspear's pasteurise their beers, but just about everybody else does – so if you're a real-ale enthusiast, these are the ones for you.

The cost

Organic beers cost a lot more to make – organic hops and malted barley can cost up to three times more than conventional equivalents. However, because beer is taxed more than foods, this cost is diluted, so that as far as consumers are concerned organic beers are very good value and generally should cost around 10% more; if the mark-up is substantially more, then, allowing for distribution costs, it's the retailer you need to query. The two breweries producing the widest range of organic beers are:

W. H. Brakspear & Sons, The Brewery, New Street, Henley-on-Thames, Oxon RG9 2BU tel: 01491 570200, website: **www.brakspear.co.uk**.
This fiercely independent regional real-ale brewery currently produces five

organic beers: their award-winning Ted and Ben's, available as cask and as bottle-conditioned; their award-winning Live Organic, also bottle-conditioned (on sale at Safeway); their Natural lager, brewed exclusively from organic English ingredients, including Peter Hall's Kentish hops – this one is described (like Live Organic) by their head brewer Peter Scholey as made in the 'modern "up-front" style, with a big lively hop flavour'. The fifth is Vintage Roots own-label organic beer.

All their beers are suitable for vegetarians and vegans and none are pasteurised (indeed, they don't own a pasteuriser). All are widely available through Brakspear's outlets and at their brewery shop, situated next to the brewery in the brewery yard.

The Pitfield Brewery, 14 Pitfield Street, London N1 6EY, tel: 020 7739 3701, fax: 020 7729 9636.
A three-man, award-winning, eighteen-year-old microbrewery run by the owner, Martin Kemp, brewer Andy Skene, and Steve Christopher, manager of their gaily painted (bright red) Beer Shop. The first brewery to convert completely to organic brewing, they use New Zealand hops, malted by traditional UK maltsters, and brew a range of beers, pale ale, stout and lagers. They don't use finings and all their beers are suitable for vegetarians and vegans. Their bottled beers are bottle-conditioned.

Their beers include Eco Warrior, their first organic beer made with pale malt and Hallertau hops; East Kent goldings pale ale; Shoreditch stout; and a local speciality, 1850 Porter stout; plus seasonal beers and one-off brews including a Christmas beer and Millennium Ale, and bespoke beers for pubs and private clients.

Their specialist beer shop stocks a full range of organic beers and lagers, organic wines and ciders, plus home wine and beer equipment. All their beers are available through the shop, and can be ordered online through their website: **www.pitfieldbeershop.co.uk**. Cases can be mixed and orders can be phoned or faxed to the shop. In all, they stock over 500 bottled beers. Opening hours, 11 am–7 pm Mon–Fri, 10 am–4 pm Sat.

ORGANIC CIDERS

Making cider is a very simple process. Basically, you take apples, press out the juice, then ferment it – but much cider on sale today has been adulterated with various chemicals, contains preservatives, and is usually made with concentrates. Organic ciders are primarily made by small traditional cider-makers, who in continuing to make their cider have prevented many cider and other apple orchards from being grubbed out. No organic ciders contain preservatives; a very small amount of sulphur dioxide is permitted during the fermentation process, but does not survive into the bottle; and malic acid (the natural acid found in apples) can be added if the acidity is too low. Note that large companies like Bulmer's and Weston's use imported organic apple concentrate from Turkey and elsewhere.

How traditional cider is made

This is how Robert Crone's cider is made, and the process is essentially the same for all traditional cider-makers.

Their traditional Norfolk Cider is produced from a blend of fresh dessert, cooking and cider apples (a local biodynamic apple-grower provides some too). The apples are first washed and milled (minced to a pulp), then wrapped in cloths which are stacked on top of each other, before being subjected to moderate pressure – they are pressed in the traditional way, using a small modern mill. No chemicals, animal finings or concentrates are used.

The resulting juice is the equivalent, as far as quality is concerned, of extra-virgin olive oil. It is then fermented with natural yeasts. The unfiltered cider is matured for 8–14 months and allowed to clear naturally. Just before bottling, a small amount of organic unrefined demerara sugar is added. Most conventional cider is flash-pasteurised at 75–85°C, then bottled and often carbonated to make it sparkling. Crone's cider and apple juices are bottled first, then gently pasteurised at lower temperatures (71–72°C) for 20 minutes, to preserve their fresh flavour.

Local cider-makers

Dunkerton's, Aspall's, Luscombe's, Heron Valley and Crone's are small traditional cider-makers; Avalon and Sedlescombe are wine-makers who also make their own traditional ciders. All use local organic apples (a good reason to choose their ciders) – either their own or bought in. Steve Christopher, who used to make traditional cider but is now manager of the Beer Shop at Pitfield Brewery, pointed out to me that cider-makers in the West of England use predominantly cider-apple varieties, which, because they have more acidity, give a more complex end product. Cider-makers in Kent and elsewhere use a mixture of eating and cooking apples, and sometimes cider apples; these produce more rounded, winey ciders.

Aspall's, Stowmarket, Suffolk (SA), tel: 01728 860510.
Makers of the famous organic cyder vinegar, they also produce Aspall's organic Suffolk cyder, from a blend of local dessert, cooking and cider apples, including two cider varieties from their own orchards, Medaille d'Or and Tom Putt, planted by their great grandfather. Available in local stores, organic retailers and selected Sainsbury's. To find out more, visit their website: **www.aspall.co.uk**.

Avalon, Shepton Mallet, Somerset (SA), tel: 01749 860393.
Produce a dry (unsweetened) organic cider from their own local cider apples, sold mainly as draft farmhouse scrumpy cider from the farm. For their wines, see p. 261.

Crone's, Kenninghall, Norfolk (SA), tel: 01379 687687.
Robert Crone and his family first began producing their traditional Norfolk organic cider in 1984 and delicious apple juices ten years later. Both have won major awards, and today they produce a range of both. This year, in addition, they began making unpasteurised cider vinegar. Their unpasteurised barrel cider is sold to local pubs. Their apple orchards – growing Bramley, Spartan, Grenadier, Warner King and Laxton apples – are forty years old, and have been managed organically for fifteen years. Their cider varieties include Yarlington Mill, Kingston Black, Dabinett and Brown Snout. For more information, their website is: **www.crones.co.uk**. For their location, see the directory on p. 414. Their products are sold locally in the South and in Eastern England, and through organic retailers. Callers are welcome – but phone first.

Dunkerton's, Leominster, Herefordshire (SA), tel: 01544 388653, who describe their ciders as essentially 'sophisticated farmhouse ciders', produce around ten different kinds made exclusively from their own organic and local Soil Association-certified cider orchards. Each variety is pressed individually, then blended later. Three of their ciders are single-variety: Breakswell Seedling, Court Royal and the now rare Kingston Black. They also produce the even rarer Perry, made from evocative-sounding varieties of organic perry pears such as Redhorse, Merrylegs, Barland and Painted Lady. For details of their must-visit shop and restaurant, consult the directory. Their ciders are available nationwide, and they also offer a mail order service.

Heron Valley Juices and Ciders, Loddiswell, Devon (SA), tel: 01548 550256. A family firm producing still and bottle-conditioned sparkling cider using traditional cider apple varieties from local organic orchards, plus a small range of award-winning apple juices, including apple and pear and apple and grapefruit. Sold locally in Devon and also in London, or from the farm direct. For location, consult the directory.

Luscombe Organic Drinks, Buckfastleigh, Devon (SA), tel: 01364 643036, produce a dry as well as a slightly sparkling medium-dry cider, from hundreds of different varieties of organic cider apples with wonderful names such as Devon Crimson, Sops-in-Wine, Pig's Snout and Tale Sweet, from their own and other local farms. They do not sell direct, but their ciders are widely available in local shops throughout Devon and the South, and also in some London food shops such as Villandry. They also produce juices and other drinks (see p. 342).

Sedlescombe Organic Vineyards, Robertsbridge, East Sussex (SA), tel: 01580 830715 (for full entry, see p. 261).
Produce dry and reserve farmhouse (still) ciders from local apples, mainly Cox and Bramley, available nationwide through independents, by mail order and online from **www.englishorganicwine.co.uk**. Their dry cider is also on sale at Waitrose.

Plus:

Thatcher's, Sandford, Somerset, tel: 01934 822862.
A traditional family company, now the fifth-largest cider-maker in the UK; they use only English apples in all their ciders and have recently introduced their organic cider (on sale at Waitrose and some Somerfield stores). They also have a cider shop. To find out more, visit their website: **www.thatcherscider.co.uk**.

Weston's, Much Marcle, Ledbury, Herefordshire, tel: 01531 660233.

The largest of the small producers, Weston's have been producing high-quality cider for 120 years in the time-honoured way, milling and pressing the fruit, then fermenting the cider in old oak vats. Their ciders are high in fruit (around 60%), and their award-winning organic cider has been a runaway success. An unpasteurised, filtered cider, it's made from locally grown bitter-sweet organic cider apples, including those from their own orchards; because demand is so high, if necessary they add up to 10% high-quality apple concentrate imported from Germany. Their cider mill is open all year round. For more, visit their website: **www.westons-cider.co.uk**.

Buying

Browse through the drinks section of organic-loving supermarkets and you will find not one but a selection of organic ciders. Most – Dunkerton's, Aspall's, Thatcher's, Weston's, Bulmer's – are well-known brands. Organic wine merchants have a good selection too, as do organic retailers of all kinds, who also sometimes stock French Normandy cider made by small producers.

Cooking with cider

Just to remind you that cider is as good as wine for cooking. It's perfect for pork, gammon, chicken and white fish and for making an onion fondue; and it can be used in apple cakes and for poaching really good sausages. Browse through your recipe books and you will find many other ideas. For general purposes a medium cider is best.

ORGANIC SPIRITS AND OTHER DRINKS

It wasn't so long ago that organic fortified drinks and spirits simply didn't exist. Today, you can stock your drinks cupboard with organic vodka, gin, rum, cognac, calvados, grappa and a Millennium organic whisky, Da Mhile, now so rare it's a collector's item and costs £100 plus per bottle. Sainsbury's sell Juniper Green Organic Gin, UK5 Organic Vodka, Tesco their own-brand gin, and Waitrose own brand gin and vodka.

Organic aperitifs include sherry, Pineau des Charentes and Muscat de Riversaltes; and two others even more unusual from France – Vinoix, made from organic walnuts and red wine, and Cerise, made from organic cherries and red wine, both available from Vintage Roots. For dessert there's organic port, and a growing range of sweet liqueurs such as Crème de Cassis (blackcurrants), organic kir and Crème de Pêche, all from France, and Schoko (chocolate) and Café Crême liqueurs, both produced by a traditional family firm in Steinfort, Germany.

If you require something fruity but less alcoholic, then try organic fruit wines – blackcurrant, elderflower, elderberry – or Broughton Pastures' warming ginger wine or award-winning organic mead, made from fermented honey from the virgin forests of Tanzania and Zambia, or Weston's Spritzer (1% alcohol), a refreshing blend of sparkling water and organic cider available in major supermarkets. All are widely available through organic outlets and organic wine merchants, too. A new find, when you are travelling in East Sussex, is Hidden Spring's apple and pear wines (see p. 467).

A very special whisky

Da Mhile . This single-malt organic whisky (the name is Gaelic for 'two thousand'), the first of its kind, was commissioned by organic farmer and Teifi cheese-maker John Savage-Onstwedder, who supplied his own organic barley, and distilled it at the famous Scottish malt-whisky distillery, Springbank, which became certified by the Soil Association in order to be able to do so. Aged in oak casks for seven years, it was released in 2000 in two strengths (58.6% and 46% alcohol). A second vintage will be bottled in 2003; more is being made this time, and retail prices are expected to be around a more forgiving £30, but it would be wise to place your order now. For more on John Savage-Onstwedder's cheeses and farm shop, see the directory.

Two more exceptional products

This is the life! These two have been an enormous success, and with an impeccable pedigree stretching back to the eighteenth century – great fun, and great websites to boot.

Juniper Green Organic Gin (SA) The family have been making gin in London since 1700, and this is the world's first organic gin. It is distilled and bottled at Thames Distillery in Central London to their centuries-old recipe from pure organic rye, demineralised water and organic botanicals (juniper, coriander, angelica root and savory). It's sold nationwide at ASDA, Booth's, Budgens, the Co-op and Sainsbury's, and its popularity has spread as far as Japan, Zambia and Bermuda. Visit their website at **www.junipergreen.org**, where you will find a rather depressing cocktail of information on pesticides, cheered up with some dream-ticket cocktails (organic fruit and vegetable juices laced with Juniper Green gin to liven things up) and other good recipes – click on 'Naughty but Nice' and choose your menu from the top line – such as scallops in gin and cream sauce, chilled avocado and bean soup, and red pepper, tomato and gin sauce for pasta.

UK5 Organic Vodka (SA) is a premium vodka, produced by the same company and distilled at Thames Distillery to similarly high standards; it is available nationwide at the same outlets as Juniper Green. Visit their website, **www.uk5.org**, and this time not only do you get some more great organic cocktail recipes, but if you run out of what you need and get withdrawal symptoms, you can find your nearest stockist. Link into a kite-surfing site (**www.Kitesurfing.org**); or if you're feeling peckish, order from London's newest food-to-go soups, salads and juice bars website: **www.crussh.com**.

THE PERFECT GIN AND TONIC AND A TRADITIONAL BLOODY MARY
Juniper Green Organic Gin's advice:
Chill the tonic
Put ice in the glass
Pour Juniper Green about one-third up the glass
Wipe lemon (organic) around the lip of the glass
Place lemon slice in the glass
Top up with the chilled tonic

Note: Organic tonic, when chilled, loses its effervescence – so I'm afraid you'll have to use conventional tonic if you want your drink to be super-cool.

UK5 Organic Vodka's traditional Bloody Mary
Their version of the old classic, using the 100% organic vegetable juice available at most supermarkets. Its base is predominantly tomatoes:
One-third UK5 Organic Vodka on ice
Two-thirds vegetable juice
Add salt, pepper, Tabasco and Worcestershire Sauce (to taste)

SOFT DRINKS

Organic soft drinks include everything from fruit cordials and traditional lemonade and ginger beer, to Santa Cruz's fun and fruity canned tropical mixes, the latest-taste Australian wild berry, fruit, lemon and lime fizzies, and four brands of organic cola (Whole Earth, Kicking Cola, Santa Cruz and Natur Frisk). Natur Frisk's cola is one of a range of eleven organic sparkling soft drinks, including several with no added sugar such as Noble Fizz, Iced Tea Lemon and Ginger Ale. Biona's sodas, cranberry, cranberry and blackcurrant and elderflower crushes are sweetened with agave syrup, too. The German firm Voelkel BioZisch have produced the first Demeter-certified orange and bitter-lemon organic sodas. The excellent Duchy Originals Organic Lemon Refresher, made from spring water, organic sugar, organic Sicilian lemon juice and natural lemon oil flavouring, comes complete with a royal pedigree, this time the late Lord Mountbatten. Moulin de Valdonne, a new range of cordials and squashes from Provence, includes Grenadine and cassis cordials.

All are produced with certified organic ingredients and conform to organic processing standards. Ascorbic acid (vitamin C) and tartaric acid (sodium tartrate, found naturally in grapes) are the only natural preservatives allowed. Many organic manufacturers also prefer using honey, apple or argave juice for sweetening. Some of these drinks are healthier alternatives to the conventional versions – though note not all are lower in sugar. Most soft drinks are merely sugared water and flavourings. Generally, organic soft drinks try to do better, though not always. Organic gin may be superb, but organic soda is not.

Coming next? Organic soft drinks with attitude. Three have just been launched. Bionatura's Aloe Vera and Passion Fruit Nutaceutical drink is for those who want something more than just fruit in their drink to help keep them healthy. Free Natural's canned Organic Citrus and Tropical Energy drinks are designed with grab-and-go appeal plus ginseng and guaraná for extra lift; and Weston's canned Organize is a blend of spring water, apple juice, rosewater, camomile, St John's wort, nettle and echinacea. The trendiest soft drinks? Taste Australia on sale in Harrods. The spring water is certified and the fizz comes from a natural source of carbon dioxide from Boggy Creek in Victoria.

Rock's organic cordials, Twyford, Berkshire (SA), tel: 0118 934 2344.
Excellent award-winning cordials, made the old-fashioned way in small batches, with real organic fruit and sugar and a dash of citric acid. Hugh Rock buys his organic fruit from the growers direct – lemons and limes from Corsica and Spain, mangoes and pineapples from the Dominican Republic – as well as using elderflowers from his own farm. Sold at major retailers, the cordials can be used in summer desserts and sorbets, and are easily recognised by their simply gorgeous labels.

Belvoir Organic Cordials and Pressés, Grantham, Lincs (SA), tel: 01476 870286.
The family firm of Belvoir Cordials produces traditional preservative-free, high-quality cordials, using fruit that is pressed on the farm plus other natural ingredients and their own spring water. Their highly praised organic range includes elderflower cordial and their new pressé made from their 80 acres of organically certified elderflowers, old-fashioned lemon cordial and lemonade, ginger cordial and ginger beer and blackcurrant cordial. Available at Sainsbury's and Waitrose. A very good recipe leaflet is also available. For more information, visit their website: **www.belvoircordials.co.uk**.

Organic soft drinks checklist

- Organic sodas, plain and fruity
- Ginger ale
- Lemonade
- Lemon Refresher
- Tropical mixes – mango, pineapple, guava – and more
- Lemon, lime, ginger, elderflower, redcurrant, strawberry, grenadine cordials
- Barley water
- Cola
- Bottled juices – every kind
- Apple juices – 66 varieties
- Freshly squeezed – orange, grapefruit
- Iced teas
- Health teas
- Kombucha – the becoming health craze (fermented sweetened black tea)

- Demeter functional drinks – multi-vitamin, Sport-Isotonic, Vital A-C-E
- Demeter Kanne bread drink.

TIP: Organic lemon cordial is easy to make at home : steep organic lemon rind in a thick syrup made with organic sugar, add the juice, a teaspoon of citric acid, then bottle. Keep in the fridge and dilute to taste.

PROFILE: WHOLE EARTH'S COLA

Founded in 1967, Whole Earth are one of the pioneering organic companies, with an impeccable pedigree and a range of products that always strive to be as healthy as possible. They buy from over 8,000 organic farmers worldwide, practise fair-trading policies and support ethical and environmental charities. Their products include their excellent breakfast cereals, spreads, peanut butter, tomato ketchup, baked beans – and now soft drinks. When they brought out their cola, eyebrows shot to the ceiling – yet this is one of the best examples I know of an organic manufacturer striving to do something better than their conventional counterparts. Whole Earth's canned organic cola contains lemon juice instead of phosphoric acid (which not only attacks teeth but also causes brittle bones) and real cola-nut extract instead of caffeine to give you a natural lift, and to provide a more prolonged energy boost it is sweetened with natural fruit juices instead of refined white sugar. It also has one-tenth the glucose of the average cola, and instead of containing preservatives, it's pasteurised in the can. Great taste, great packaging, great product, comes in four-packs, too. The latest drinks from the Whole Earth stable are sparkling organic gusto energy health drinks.

12: Organic Superfoods

Forget pills. If you want superhealth, superfoods are all set to become part of your daily diet. Superfoods and natural foods and natural food supplements, stuffed full of vitamins, minerals, enzymes and who knows what else, that are easily absorbed, give super-nourishment and promise optimum vitality and health (as opposed to just keeping body and soul nicely ticking over). Whereas vitamin supplements are created in laboratories, superfoods are directly derived from the plant, and because their supernutrients are found naturally together, their bio-availability is high. They are food, not medicine, and are about creating health rather than curing disease. As such, they are a matter of faith, but as the father of medicine Hippocrates maintained, the physician is only nature's assistant – it is the body that heals itself. Proponents of superfoods would certainly maintain that they help to give you the ability to heal yourself, as well as nourish and cleanse you – and are the perfect survival foods to combat the stress and toxins of modern life.

Though called organic, many superfoods are not certified organic: it is up to you to read the labels and make your own decision, and seek advice from the supplier if you want to. If certified, the certification logo, name or number will appear on the label, and 95% or more of the ingredients will have been certified as organic.

In the USA, superfoods are all the rage: visit the search engine **www.google.com**, key in the words 'organic superfoods' and you will find seventy-five pages of books, products and websites devoted to the subject. Here I offer a brief taste of the organic foods that we shall all be hearing more about in future, as well as some easy tips for supercharging your daily diet.

Generally, the processing of superfoods is benign, mainly limited to juicing or pulverising, then drying. How much of their supernutrients survive processing is unclear, though manufacturers take care to retain as much as possible: here the best advice, again, is to check with the supplier. Freeze-dried products are best. Apart from sea vegetables, because they are concentrated foods, you need very little: it's best to start with less than the recommended dose, and build up slowly. Too much of a super-good thing can be quite a shock to the system.

I include here supergreen foods – grasses, sprouted foods, algae and sea vegetables; miso; designer oils rich in essential fatty acids, and hemp; and raw juices. As for those waiting in the wings, watch this space for a revival in interest in Kombucha tea (the organic version is available, see p. 238); kefir, and sauerkraut and other pickled vegetables. All are traditional fermented foods – which completes the circle nicely.

GREEN POWERFOODS

There are three main types of these superfoods: algae, special blends, and sprouted grasses. They are available usually in powdered form or as tablets, and can be bought from the 'well-being' or vitamin-supplement sections of organic supermarkets and healthfood shops. All the powdered forms can be added to smoothies, or fruit or vegetable juices; they can be sprinkled over foods – you can add them to yoghurt, for example – but the simplest and nicest way is to mix them with your favourite fruit juice for an instant power-packed health cocktail. Their taste is essentially pleasantly green and grass-like; not everyone agrees.

The common wonder ingredient of all of these 'green power' foods is chlorophyll. It's what makes plants green and, biochemically, is responsible for plant photosynthesis – the making of simple sugars from sunlight. Pure chlorophyll is a very potent antioxidant and detoxifier. It purifies the blood, cleanses the tissues and cells and rids the body of harmful toxins, has antibiotic properties, inhibits the metabolic activity of carcinogens, and is good for anaemia – and sunburn. To find out more, visit the Xynergy website: **www.xynergy.co.uk**.

Algae

Algae, such as Klamath blue-green, spirulina and chlorella, are one of the earth's original life-forms; they evolved over three billion years ago, and comprise simple but nutritionally potent organisms, microscopic aquatic plants that literally transform the sun's energy into a powerhouse of essential nutrients, including vitamins, minerals, trace elements, essential fatty acids, amino acids (the building-bricks of protein) and glycogen. Algae are also rich in protective plant pigments such as chlorophyll. As such, they are a complete superfood; and are perfectly safe. Sea vegetables are also algae. If you want the simple difference between them, chlorella is better for detox, spirulina will boost your energy, and Klamath blue-green algae is good for brain activity and calming.

Chlorella A single-celled green alga with a hard outer shell, which is removed first to make it more absorbable (though recently it's been discovered that the shell has an effective cleansing property). A powerful detoxer, it is very high in chlorophyll and nucleic acids. Chlorella is now farmed. I have not yet found an organically certified brand, but Eco-Zone (see below) supply one in tablet form, grown in pure crystalline water, on an agrobiological island in Japan in a protected environment, and regularly tested for purity.

Spirulina This is a blue-green alga, also farmed. Amongst many other benefits, spirulina is said to increase the beneficial intestinal bacteria. Its nutritional profile includes 60% protein, essential fatty acids including GLA (gamma linoleic acid), iron, vitamin B12, and glycogen for energy boost: Aztec runners used it. Spirulina is conventionally farmed with the addition of nutrients, including synthetic fertilisers, to the water, and it is becoming an increasingly industrialised operation; organically grown spirulina is fed with nutrients derived from naturally occurring earth deposits or composts, and grown on a smaller scale in specially selected sites. Organic spirulina is available in two main brands; both are grown in Hawaii, which is said to produce the best and nicest-tasting (their high-intensity sunshine produces more beta carotene).

Pure Plant premium spirulina Available from Xynergy, this is said to be the most advanced spirulina product in the world; it is produced in small batches and hand-packaged in deep-violet Miron glass, which gives extra protection against light degradation and maintains biopotency.

Hawaiian Pacifica spirulina Grown organically (certified in the USA, though not in the UK) in ponds of spring water supplemented with pure deep-Pacific sea water to give over 90 extra minerals and trace elements. It's dried by a patented process called 'ocean chilled dried' to protect it from heat and oxidation, and packed in special glass that also contain oxygen absorbers. *Also:*

Eco-Zone spirulina Grown on a site 2,500 metres up in the Andes, in pure air and pure glacial waters, and with 12 hours' sunshine a day, then dried at low temperatures. Eco-Zone also produce Spiruseng tablets, a combination of spirulina and wild Chinese ginseng. For more, including pictures of where their superfoods are grown, visit their website at **www.sea-vegetables.co.uk**. For more on Eco-Zone, see p. 298.

Klamath blue-green algae Described as the most nutrient-dense food on the planet (and selling like hot cakes in the USA), these soft-celled algae grow in the glacial Lake Klamath in Oregon, which is extraordinarily rich in mineral deposits (several feet thick), and is fed by pure streams from the surrounding mountains. It is said that there are enough Klamath algae in the lake to feed the world, and that they are so prolific that they regenerate themselves overnight. The lake is divided into two: the upper lake is pure, the lower lake has some residential development. Organic Klamath blue-green algae, sold by the Really Healthy Company, tel: 020 8780 5200, website: **www.healthy.co.uk**, certified by the Soil Association in the UK, are harvested from the upper lake only and freeze-dried. Every batch is tested for purity. The taste is very mild and you take it by the quarter-teaspoon. Apart from the usual superhealth benefits, Klamath blue-green is said to be particularly beneficial for people under stress or undergoing mental exertion – and yes, it does seem to help.

Special blends

These are concentrated natural food supplements in powder form. Typically they contain amino acids, vitamins, minerals, trace elements, antioxidants, enzymes, sometimes specially selected herbs such as ginseng, ginkgo and echinacea, or probiotics. Their base is usually green foods such as spirulina and chorella, wheat, alfalfa or barley grasses, and/or seaweeds, plus extra ingredients such as royal jelly or pollen grains and essential fatty acids. What they offer is concentrated health and natural nourishment in a bottle: and they are expensive. Purported benefits include increased energy and stamina, a strengthened immune system, sharpened mental powers, detoxification and the elimination of free radicals, improved digestion, increased vitality, improved skin, hair and nails, cancer prevention, help in controlling diabetes – though not, of course, all at once.

The rationale for these blended versions – which are becoming more popular by the minute – is that they offer a convenient way to ensure that you are getting every possible nutrient you could conceivably need, which even if you already have a splendid diet you may not be receiving regularly. At times of stress, or when you're not eating properly (as when writing a book, for example), they save you from worrying. On a slightly more sobering note, as Dolores Riccio, author of *Superfoods for Life*, wrote, it's been calculated that one-third to one-half of the health problems experienced by people over fifty are related directly or indirectly to nutritional deficiencies, and some scientists have begun to think of the ageing process itself as a deficiency disease. Which means that green power foods hold out the promise of eternal life, too.

Like the other 'green power' powdered foods discussed above, the blended versions are usually best taken first thing in the morning on an empty stomach, and usually in liquid form, mixed with water – or, better, organic fruit juice of some kind, such as apple or another non-acidic variety, as many of these foods taste distinctly 'greeny'. Allow twenty minutes or so, so that the body can absorb them, before you eat anything else. You will find several on American websites. My favourite UK organic one is Synergy (sold by Xynergy), a remarkable product with a remarkable story (too long, unfortunately, to recount here). Greens+, Udo's Wholesome Fast Food Blend and Beyond Greens, and Viridian's green food blend are other excellent organically certified products.

Viridian Nutrition, 31 Alvis Way, Daventry, Northamptonshire NN11 5PG, tel: 01327 878050, fax: 01327 878335, email: info@viridian-nutrition.com, website: **www.viridian-nutrition.com**.
A new, young, ethical nutritional-supplement company (vitamins, minerals herbs, oils), committed to recycling, who supply independent shops and ethical businesses and donate 50% of their net profits to charity. Stylish packaging and excellent advice and information. Their list includes three certified organic lines: green food blend (spirulina, alfalfa and bilberry fruit powder), and cold-pressed organic hemp and golden flax seed oils. Phone for nearest stockist.

Xynergy Health Products, Elsted, Midhurst, West Sussex GU29 0JT, tel: 01730 813642, fax: 01730 815109, email: orders@xynergy.co.uk.
Xynergy has been pioneering natural superfood supplements, food-sourced

vitamin and mineral supplements and skincare products for more than twenty years. Their superfoods include freeze-dried organic wheatgrass and premium spirulina, organically grown aloe vera juice, and Pure Synergy, probably the world's ultimate superfood (praised by health guru Leslie Kenton), which, being sweeter than many, I find good to eat too. They sell via mail order, online, and in selected healthfood stores. Many complementary therapists and clinics recommend their nutritional products. A friendly, efficient service, excellent information leaflets and catalogue. To find out more about their products, to have all your questions answered, or to order online, visit their website at **www.xynergy.co.uk**.
Also:

Green People Company Ltd, Brighton Road, Handcross, Haywards Heath, West Sussex, RH17 6BZ, Tel: 01444 401444, fax: 01444 401011, email organic@greenpeople.co.uk.
Apart from their excellent organic skincare, bodycare and other care products, they provide two dietary supplements: Herbal Elixir, made from the cold-pressed juices of a dozen organically grown herbs (suitable for children, too); and organic seaweed (kelp) capsules. For more, and to order online, visit their excellent website: **www.greenpeople.co.uk**.

Greenery, Flat 3, 406 Seven Sisters Road, Manor House, London N4 2LX, tel: 020 8880 1970.
Distributors for the American superfood supplement, Greens+, they offer a synergist blend of over twenty superfood ingredients including chlorella, wheatgrass powder, spirulina, pollen, botanical extracts and herbs, all produced organically or wildcrafted, available in powder of tablet form. For more information, visit their website: **www.greensplus.com**.

Sprouted grasses – green grass power

When seeds first sprout, their nutritional value is at its highest. Sprouted grasses – wheatgrass, barleygrass and others – are no exception, and are becoming one of the new wonder foods, packed with protein, enzymes, natural fibre, minerals, vitamins and chlorophyll. They can be bought as a powder or as tablets. Wheatgrass is the best-known, and most fashionable: visit a juice bar and you are likely to see wheatgrass growing on the counter.

Wheatgrass

If you have ever wondered how cows get to be so big living off grass, it's because grasses are living vitality, a powerhouse of nutrients. Wheatgrass, for example, contains every vitamin and all known mineral elements. It is exceptionally high in calcium, magnesium, phosphorus and potassium, as well as the trace minerals zinc and selenium, and contains sixteen easily-assimilated amino acids (protein), along with the enzymes to help assimilate them. Plus it contains around 70% chlorophyll. Its chemical molecular composition is very similar to that of haemoglobin.

Like all sprouted foods, grasses are quick-energy foods. Unlike ruminants, our systems are not designed to cope with their fibrous nature, so they need to be juiced before they can be digested. The nutrients in wheatgrass juice are completely assimilated by the body in twenty minutes. After being juiced, the wheatgrass is dried and bottled. It's a very light, finely ground green powder that can be sprinkled on food, but is more usually added to liquid such as apple juice, and is specially convenient when travelling. In addition to its other benefits, it is said to protect the lungs and blood from air and water pollution, cigarette smoke, heavy metals and other toxins. It contains the natural rejuvenator hormone DHEA.

A shot of freshly juiced wheatgrass (best sipped very slowly) is strong and quite bitter. For most people's palates, wheatgrass and carrot juice, or carrot and apple juice, make a good blend. To show how concentrated it is, a one-ounce shot is equivalent nutritionally to over a kilo of vegetables: ideally, they say, you need one to two ounces of wheatgrass juice per day. You can also grow your own (see p. 285).

Commercial production and preparation

Wheatgrass for commercial production is mainly grown in Connecticut and Oregon. It is not, apparently, as easy to grow as you would think because it is prone to moulds, so fungicides (as well as fertiliser feeds) may be used on conventionally grown wheatgrass. Organically certified wheatgrass is grown in specially prepared organic composts from organically certified seeds, fed organically approved foliar feeds and receives no fungicides. How young (and therefore sweet) it is, how long the grass is left to grow before being dried, and whether it is grown outside (sown in autumn and overwintered) or as a protected crop inside, all make a difference too. If simply cut and dried, a lot of bulk is created, which means you need to eat more. Wheatgrasses that have been juiced first, and then freeze-dried, like Xynergy's organic Sweet Wheat, are the best. The water from the juice is evaporated under a vacuum at low temperatures; 100% juice yields about 4% dry matter, which means a teaspoon of powder gives you a lot of concentrated goodness. Rehydrated with pure water, it becomes wheatgrass juice again.

Trays of freshly grown wheatgrass can now be bought from:

The Green Seed Company (SA), the Apple barn, Rock Lane, Washington, West Sussex RH20 3BL, tel: 020 8789 7897, fax: 020 8788 4896, email: christopher@green-seed.freeserve.co.uk.
A find: a tiny company, passionate about the health benefits of green shoots, who have been growing wheat, barley and sunflower shoots for eighteen years. They produce organic wheatgrass, using ancient varieties of wheat – spelt is one – including some supplied as seed by organic UK farmers growing it on organically approved compost and feeding it organic nutrients including seaweed meal. Available direct from mail order in trays (sufficient for one week's supply, currently around £15), or from local juice bars and other organic shops for around £12. Ring or email for a list of outlets; they also send you an excellent feature on wheatgrass that will make you want to track down your nearest source immediately – if not sooner. Plus a selection of juicers.

How to grow your own

Friends who have tried have explained patiently that it's not always as straightforward as it seems. Perhaps you need supergreen fingers, too. But these are the Green Seed Company's – who grow eight tonnes and rising a year – foolproof instructions.

1. Use whole organic winter wheat seeds, or a non-hybridised grain variety such as kamut or spelt.
2. Soak 2 cups of the seeds for 6–12 hours in plenty of water in a large jar, then drain them with the jar upturned. (Use an elastic band and a muslin net.)
3. Allow at least 12 hours to sprout, depending on the temperature.
4. When visibly ready and sprouted, sprinkle the seeds evenly to cover a cafeteria-style tray filled with about 2 cm of prepared organic soil, a top-soil and compost mix.

5 Water thoroughly but don't saturate, then cover the planted tray with another upturned tray or plastic sheeting, in order to create a dark, moist environment for the germinated seeds to root. (Trays can be stacked.)
6 Two or three days are sufficient, and when uncovered the grass shoots will be upright and eagerly waiting for sunlight, to start producing chlorophyll.
7 Water daily and watch as your grass greens and matures in about 7 days (climate depending).
8 At about 7 inches tall, harvest at soil level with a bread knife or sharp scissors.

'It is quite possible to grow it with minimum effort in your home, on a shelf or sill near daylight. Seaweed meal is a good feed, as it contains a spectrum of minerals. When you have harvested this crop, recycle all your soil and compost using worm-bins.'

More organic sprouts

Either grow your own, or look for ready-sprouted organic beansprouts, alfalfa, radish, chickpea and mixed bean sprouts in the chilled cabinet of your nearest organic retailers. The main organic brands are Sky Sprouts and Aconbury, and they cost very little more than the conventional equivalent. Worth knowing is that alfalfa sprouts, weight for weight, are much better value than conventional mustard and cress. They have a delicate flavour, are more nutritious, and are a rare plant source of vitamin B12, so particularly important for vegetarians and vegans. Organic mung beans are sweet and crunchy. New flavours include vitamin-packed sunflower-seed sprouts, wheat sprouts and alfalfa and broccoli. Check to see that they're fresh (avoid brown or sad-looking packets). Use in salads and sandwiches. If you want to start from seed, organic alfalfa, cress, radish, mustard and sprouting mix are sold under the *Davert Muhle* brand.

RAW HEALTH: JUICES

A man from Mars visiting London for the first time might be forgiven for thinking that freshly squeezed juices had just been invented. In fact, the use of raw juices both as food and as medicine, and raw-juice therapy to treat a number of conditions including cancers, has been established since the 1920s. The difference now is, first that juices have become trendy, part of the new must-have-health-and-vitality lifestyle; and second, juice extractors have improved beyond recognition. Anyone who tried juicing in the 1980s, as I did, faced with a bulky Heath-Robinson machine that was incredibly noisy and messy and took forever to clean, soon lost the appetite for freshly juiced carrot, however delicious.

Raw juices, vegetable, fruit and blends, are undoubtedly wonderfully good for you: everyone I've ever met who has made them a regular part of their diet has had a wonderful skin, has been youthful and has seemed to enjoy extra good health plus that elusive and highly desirable 'well-being'. A friend who has recently got the juice bug says he feels sixteen. This summer, it's my turn.

Raw juices are super-natural nourishment in highly concentrated form. They contain all of a plant's vitamins, minerals, all-important enzymes and macro- and micro-nutrients, but none of the fibre, which means they are easily absorbed. They should be treated with respect, and sipped slowly (think of them as soup, not drink). Because they are raw and naked, it hardly needs to be said that organic is best.

Often described as the 'fountain of youth', fresh juices are a perfect food supplement. Devotees point out that their nutrients are far more potent that the isolated nutrients found in vitamin pills, stressing the synergistic effect whereby nutrients combined naturally in foods work together more effectively than when they are isolated in a single supplement. They also point out that raw juices provide not only the well-documented benefits of nutrients, but also some that are not yet recognised or understood. As to what makes raw juices extra-special – it's their 'alive' quality: the enzymes are the living component. As one book put it, think of them as the spark-plug for a superfunctioning and healthy metabolism.

Interested? Help is at hand in the form of RAW Health, an organisation of raw-fooders who sell the Oscar Living Juicer (see p. 289) and other essentials, including a leaflet on how to grow your own wheatgrass, plus books about health and raw nutrition. They give regular demonstrations, hold workshops and raw-food parties so that you can try the raw-taste experience for yourself. You can also visit them at Spitalfields Market in London each Sunday. For their catalogue and more information, tel: 0870 800 7020.

Essential know-how

Raw-juice therapists divide juices into cleansing fruit juices, and regenerating and body-building vegetable juices. They are all alkaline (for which read extra-good for combating the rest of your acid-forming diet). Read serious juice books and you will find specific formulas to help with everything from arthritis to gallstones. Many detox diets include juice fast days. Juices help build up your immune system, speed up metabolism, and are often recommended in weight-reducing diets. They are also delicious. The only drawback is that they do take time – washing, cutting, preparing – and you will need an extra-large shopping basket to accommodate all the vegetables and fruit you are about to consume: putting a pound of carrots through a juicer is a bit like giving an elephant a strawberry.

The other thing you need is a good juice book, one that will not just give you a few evocative recipes but will explain the ins and outs and tell you which juices to use for what and in which combinations. Some, for example, like beetroot and watercress, are so powerful that they should only be used in small quantities. It's nice to know, too, which are good for cleansing (celery) and so on. Savant (below) offer a good selection of publications, as do Amazon.co.uk. Other recommended books include Maurice Hansen's *The Complete Raw Juice Therapy*, published by Thorson's, Julie Stafford's *Juicing for Health*, published by Penguin, which includes recipes; and any Leslie Kenton book. Nigel Slater's new book, *Thirst*, published by Fourth Estate is a must-have.

You also want to know which juices taste the nicest. Apples and carrots are the two best bases: they are both sweet and can be combined with just about everything to produce a delicious juice. A friend describes carrot juice as the most feel-good, do-good, of them all. It does discolour quickly, though. Top tip from food writer Nigel Slater, if you want to retain the colour, is to squeeze an orange, or better, a pink grapefruit into the glass first, then let the carrot juice fall into it. As he says, it also stops the carrot juice being too sweet.

For extra zing you can add ginger (good for your digestion). If you like garlic – a superfood in its own right – add a fresh clove; if you don't like raw garlic, absolutely leave it out. For extra potency, a teaspoon of a green-powder food will help you live for ever. Fresh herbs such as parsley are rich in chlorophyll, so experiment with these too. Because raw juices can deliver a shock to a well-fed but undernourished system, at first you may experience side-effects such as headaches: these are quite normal, but it is wise to start slowly and build up your intake steadily.

All raw juices should ideally be consumed straightaway. Once the cell walls of the fruit or vegetable have been crushed, the nutrients are exposed to the air and begin to oxidise, and the juices start to lose their vital properties. Which is why in juice bars they should be, and are, made to order. If you want to reap the benefits, then you need to consume them regularly and take at least 500 ml daily. Apparently, you can't take too much, though you won't have a lot of room or appetite for much else if you do.

That just leaves the mound of debris that's left behind: I'm sure you must be able to use it in delicious cakes or whatever – you can apparently make sorbets with fruit pulp, for example, and stock with the vegetable debris – but the best tip I've been given is to buy a wormery and compost it.

Juicers

You cannot juice without a juicer. These are a serious investment in both money and space, and cost anything from £30 to £400. Seek advice and look at a few before you take the leap – start by visiting the website given below. There are three basic types: the cheapest extract the juice using centrifugal force, shredding then spinning the food very fast; mastication juicers, such as the Champion Juicer, have teeth that shred the food which is then forced through a cone to extract the juice; and the latest generation, trituration juicers, work more slowly, crushing the food (including the cell walls). These are quieter and also the most expensive, but are the best because their gentle action keeps the enzymes intact while producing minimum heat, thereby preserving the maximum amount of nutrients and the living quality of the juices. Juices extracted by this kind of machine can be stored for up to 24 hours if necessary. Two such juicers are the Green Life Juicer, said to be the best you can buy, which includes the latest magnetic 'bioceramic' technology that extends the life of a juice for up to 48 hours; and the Oscar Living Juicer, which is smaller, neater and easier to clean, and comes with attachments included in the price. There are other juicers such as the Waring, available at Divertimenti in London and from Cucina Direct, tel: 0870 727 4300, that use filter-papers, which save on the messy business of cleaning.

Some juicers do more than juice – they can make nut butter or sorbets, homogenise baby foods, for example – and come with various attachments.

For the best website about juicing and juicers, fascinating and exhaustively thorough, visit the American website: **www.discountjuicers.com**.

More points to consider when buying a juicer:

- Some juicers heat up more than others; this is not good for the juice, as heat above 80°C will start to destroy the living enzymes.
- Not all juicers juice everything equally well; and some – the centrifugal and mastication type – will not handle fibrous stuff like wheatgrass or leafy vegetables well. Check that the machine suits your juicing needs (you can always take the wheatgrass in powdered form).
- From a nutritional point of view you want maximum juice: some cheaper juicers produce quite a wet pap of debris, which means that they do not extract as much as they might.
- Check how easy it is to assemble and clean – especially the latter. The juicer needs to be cleaned every time you use it. This is a pain.
- Check how noisy it is.
- Check how much produce it will juice in one go.
- What about the quality of the juice when extracted – that is, how much does it extract from the fruit?
- It's going to be permanently on display. Do its looks please you?
- How long is it likely to last, and how long is the warranty?

Top tips

- You can juice just about anything except the green parts of carrot or potatoes, and rhubarb.
- Avocados and bananas produce no juice; mangos produce very little. Use bananas and mangos for smoothies instead.
- Wash all fresh produce first.
- Remove large pips and stones from fruit.
- Don't include the peel of citrus, but do include some pith; this is a rich source of bioflavonoids, good for lowering cholesterol.
- To make sure they juice properly, mix very soft fruits like strawberries and melons with harder fruit.
- If not drinking straightaway, cover, and keep in the fridge.

Savant Distribution Ltd, 15 Iveson Approach, Leeds LS16 6LJ, tel: 0113 230 1993, fax: 0113 230 1915, email: info@savant-health.com.

A small, super-friendly, high-quality mail order company dealing with nutrition and therapies and supplying life-enhancing products, nutrition books and equipment, including Dr Udo Erasmus's range of products. They also stock the Champion and Green Life juicers, plus several juicing books (a free copy of Michael van Straten's *Superjuice* is included with their juicers), and will give you expert advice on which to choose. Excellent informative brochure and literature, including Udo Erasmus's *Fats That Heal, Fats That Kill*. For their catalogue and literature, or to order online, visit their excellent website: **www.savant-health.com**.

Raw v. bottled juices

To my mind there can be no comparison between freshly squeezed and bottled juices. However, the latter do retain more nutrients than you might think, are healthy enough drinks in their own right, are more convenient and much better than no juices at all. For more on these, and on organic juices in general, see p. 339.

SOME SIMPLE WAYS TO IMPROVE YOUR DIET

Instant detox Start the day with a large glass of hot water with a slice of organic lemon in it.

Start-rite juice Juice together 3 organic carrots, 2 sticks of celery and some parsley.

Dr Sandra Cabot's Instant superfood mix Grind 3 parts organic linseeds, 2 parts sunflower seeds and 1 part almonds. Sprinkle up to a tablespoonful on your breakfast cereals or yoghurt.

Green-power smoothie Blend organic apple juice, a banana and ½–1 teaspoonful of whichever green superfood powder (algae, wheatgrass, sea vegetable) you're using; add a few ice cubes (made from pure mineral water) if you want.

Smoothie of the moment Blend together goat's-milk yoghurt, banana and passion fruit. Add some green superfood, too.

Sunshine plus Blend organic orange of pineapple juice with a few fresh strawberries, mint leaves, and ½–1 teaspoonful of green superfood.

Jungle juice The cheat's organic smoothie, for mind, body and soul, and the first convenience organic superfood drink, from Soma: a heavenly superfood cocktail of apple juice, banana, mango, apricots and strawberries, plus spirulina, kelp, Klamath blue-green algae, and wheat and barley grasses. One of the best products in the book. For more, see their website: **www.somajuice.com**.

▲▲

NATURE'S SUPER VEGETABLES AND FRUIT: THE BEST OF THE BUNCH

Apples: It's true that an apple a day keeps most ills away, and they're a great detoxifier: the occasional 24-hour apple monofast (as many as you like) is recommended by many alternative practitioners.

Apricots: Delicious, loaded with betacarotene (and iron), the best dried fruit for sweet and savoury dishes alike, or on their own as a snack. Try soaked and cooked dried apricots, hot or cold, for breakfast. I eat them hot with Udo's oil (which is better than it sounds).

Avocados: Five-star nutrition that comes in its own serving dish, and not fattening. For your skin's sake, eat as many as possible. An excellent source of protein, vitamin B_2, monosaturated fatty acids and antioxidant vitamins; and easily digested.

Beetroot: An excellent detoxifier, it purifies and enriches the blood and cleanses the kidneys. Apple, pineapple and beetroot make a winning combination.

Celery: Favoured juice combination with carrot and apple. Alkaline and a good detoxifier, and stimulates digestion.

Carrots: Rich in betacarotene and antioxidants.

Bananas: Nature's own answer to food-to-go, for sustained energy. Packed with potassium, and almost as much vitamin B_2 as liver.

Broccoli: A green that is a pleasure to eat. Rich in iron, and in protective superfood anti-cancer agents.

Grapes: A grape fast is as good as an apple fast. Excellent cleanser for the skin, liver, kidneys and intestines.

Kiwi: Contain more vitamin C than just about anything, and as much vitamin E as avocado.

Lemon: An alkaliser, and rich in vitamin C.

Strawberries: An indulgent way of taking your vitamin C.

Watercress: So good for you and good to eat: chop it over salads, in soups and sandwiches. Botanically a member of the cabbage family (crucifer), with the same protective anti-cancer properties, plus iron and vitamins C and A; and a natural antibiotic. Aids digestion, too.

Winter squash: Nature's best-kept secret. Stored sunshine in a shell, and betacarotene by the slice.

The Green People's detox

For an excellent account of what detox is and why the occasional detox is a good idea, plus a simple detox regime to follow, visit the Green People Company's great website, **www.greenpeople.co.uk**. Here, with their permission, are some recommended Green People detox juice cocktails:

- 3 carrots, 1 apple
- 2 apples, 225 g red grapes
- 4 carrots, 5 chopped celery sticks
- 4 carrots, 1 raw beetroot, 3 chopped celery sticks
- 2 apples, 6 lettuce leaves, a small handful of watercress

In all cases, feed the fruit and vegetables into the juicer. Stir. Dilute with mineral water and sip slowly.

DESIGNER OILS

Olive oil may be the oil of choice for cooking, but highly nutritious, state-of-the-art, cold-pressed 'designer oils', brimming with essential fatty acids (EFAs), are what you need for maximum health. Essential fatty acids, namely omega-3s (alphalinolenic) and omega-6s (linoleic), are quite literally the stuff of life, playing a vital role in the renewal of cells and in brain and nerve functions; they are the building-blocks of cell membranes, and help to control the cholesterol level in the body and just about every other life process as well. They cannot be made by the body, so must be supplied in the diet (hence the term 'essential'). Oily fish is a good source of omega-3s, while omega-6s are found in seeds such as sunflower, though for general purposes oils are much more convenient. Omega-6s are also found in nuts and grains; and omega-3s in the leafy parts of dark green vegetables. For health, you need a balance of both omega-3 and omega-6 fatty acids. And this is where designer oils come in, because they are designed to give you both. Imported from the USA and Canada, each brand comprises a slightly different blend of oils and therefore tastes. To keep their nutritional qualities intact, the oils are extracted under specially controlled conditions at low temperatures which safeguards them from the effects of air, light and heat, and they are then hermetically sealed in dark bottles. You use them as a salad dressing (I take mine with avocado, pouring the oil into the stone cavity), poured over tepid vegetables or baked potatoes, or as a dietary supplement. They are expensive, and must be refrigerated once opened.

These oils have pleasantly mild tastes, and which to choose is really a question of personal preference – they do taste different depending on the combination, so try them all before you settle on which one is for you. You can buy them in organic supermarkets, through healthfood shops and some mail order suppliers. Two well-known brands are:

Essential Balance: a blend of flax (i.e. linseed, and one of the few plant sources rich in omega-3 fatty acids), sunflower, pumpkin and borage oils, produced by Omega Nutrition in distinctive dark plastic bottles. Omega Nutrition also produce Essential Balance Junior with butterscotch flavouring for kids, as well as flax and hempseed oils. All are available from Higher Nature, tel: 01435 883484.

Udo's Choice: formulated by Udo Erasmus, the guru of essential fatty acids. A blend of flax, sesame and sunflower oils with added vitamin E and other essential nutrients. Readily available, or can be ordered direct from Savant (see p. 290).

State-of-the-art cold-pressed flax, hemp (rich in both omega-3 and omega-6 fatty acids), borage and starflower oils are also becoming popular and more easily available. All such oils are unstable – which is why they are not for cooking – and need to be kept in the dark.

Also:

Kinetic Enterprises Ltd: 158 Belsize Road, Kilburn, London NW6 4BT, tel: 020 7435 5911, fax: 020 7431 5935, email kinetic@globalnet.co.uk. They supply Health from the Sun's organic FiProFlax food-mix, a powdered way to add the benefits of flax seeds to your diet, plus Total EFA™ Oil, a unique blend of primrose and certified high-lignin flax oils. They also supply the Really Healthy Company's certified Klamath blue-green algae.

Finally, two paperbacks to read: *Fats That Heal and Fats That Kill* by Dr Udo Erasmus (Alive Books); and *The Driving Force* by Professor Michael Crawford (director of the Institute of Brain Chemistry and Human Nutrition, London University) and David Marsh (Mandarin).

HEMP: A SPECIAL CASE

Hemp (Cannabis sativa) could save the world. No other plant has so many important uses, as both food and fibre, or is used to make so diverse a group of products (ranging from ice-cream to bank notes). It grows like a weed (fast and dense), which means that it is eminently suitable for organic cultivation as it quickly forms a canopy shading out other plants, requires few inputs, no upkeep, and suffers from hardly any pests. Its falling leaves return nutrients to the soil, which makes it a good rotation crop. Until the 1930s it was grown extensively, but because of its association with another variety of hemp, marijuana (Cannabis indica), it has since been banned in many countries. In the UK the ban was lifted in 1993, and small pockets of hemp are now being grown. Cannabis sativa has only a fraction (0.3% as against 10–15%) of the psychoactive substance found in marijuana.

As a food, hempseeds have been propelled into the superfood bracket. These small, sweetly nutty-tasting, crunchy seeds with a tough case are an extremely important source of both omega-3 and omega-6 essential fatty acids; they are also a good source of gamma-linolenic acid (GLA), which is used to alleviate pre-menstrual syndrome and skin problems, and is an anti-inflammatory agent, so alleviates joint conditions too. Hemp has the same amount of protein as soya; and as well as being a good source of fibre it contains zinc, iron, calcium and vitamin A. Like soya, it can be turned into lactose and cholesterol free 'milk', from which a range of non-dairy products are made, including excellent ice-cream (in three flavours, vanilla, strawberry and mint choc). Hemp pasta is one of the best non-gluten pastas.

Other organic hemp foods currently available include breads, cereal bars, flapjacks, impressive vegan pestos, and soft hulled hemp seeds that you shake over salads. All are made by the remarkable:

Mother Hemp Ltd, Tilton Barns, Firle, Lewes, East Sussex BN8 6LL, tel: 01323 822909, fax: 020 7691 7475, email: contact@motherhemp.com. Mother Hemp is determined to put hemp in all its forms, and hemp foods, on the map. Their products are available in organic shops. Don't miss their website, **www.motherhemp.com** and their online shop, where you can buy all their hemp foods and oils, clothes, shoes, shower gel, beer and much else for the twenty-first century eco-lifestyle, including hemp guru, consultant and chef Paul Benhaim's book *H.E.M.P.* (*Healthy Eating Made Possible*), published by Vision Paperbacks. They have also recently opened their first shop, Mother Hemp, at 22 Gardner Street, North Lanes, Brighton, tel: 01273 818047, which sells hemp foods, bathroom products, clothes and accessories. To find out more about hemp, visit the Hemp Food Industries Association's highly enjoyable hemp nutrition website (complete with music, rainbows and charts on omega-3 and omega-6) at **www.hemp.co.uk**.

Arriving shortly in the UK, another major hemp brand to look out for is HempNut™, an American operation that has been producing hemp foods since 1994. Their major product is fluffy, shelled, sweet and nutty, organically grown hempseeds, sold in cartons. Other products include HempNut™ burger, hempseed oil, excellent peanut butter, hemp mayonnaise, Chocolatey Whole Food Bar, Chocolate Chip Cookies, the first hemp tortilla chips (Organic Blue Corn), and organic margarine made with hemp oil, sunflower oil and palm oil. To find out more, including more pages of hemp info, visit their website: **www.TheHempNut.com**.

Hempseeds

Use hempseeds in the same way as you would use sunflower or pumpkin seeds – in salads and cooked vegetable dishes, for example. Like those seeds, too, I find they are nice as a snack on their own. To soften the tough seed cases (which make the seeds crunchy), you can soak them first, overnight if possible, then use on top of salads or roast them. Soaking them also releases enzymes which aid their digestion. Alternatively, buy ready-hulled seeds from Mother Hemp. Three more suggestions from Paul Benhaim:

- As an alternative easy snack, roast the seeds in a dry pan with a sprinkling of sesame oil, and add a splash of soy sauce.
- The soaked seeds can be sprouted: put in a jar, and leave for another day or so, rinsing regularly with fresh water until the sprouts have developed.
- Grind the seeds in a coffee-grinder and add to your favourite bread recipe.

SEA VEGETABLES

Although part of the Japanese diet and an important element of macrobiotic diets, sea vegetables – various types of seaweed – have always been a minority food elsewhere. In Britain, we have the Welsh delicacy, laverbread (which you can buy fresh or canned at Swansea Market), and samphire, but these are not widely eaten.

Things are slowly changing, though, and sea vegetables as superfoods are becoming more widely recognised, with sales growing at a steady 10% a year. Their nutritional benefits are immense: they are rich in essential minerals, vitamins, protein, trace elements, antioxidants, iron and iodine and are one of the few plant sources of vitamin B12, all in easily absorbable form. Their minerals are particularly nourishing for skin and hair – sea vegetables are largely credited with giving the Japanese their lustrous locks and smooth complexions. No food has such a comprehensively naturally balanced range of nutrients. They are low in sodium and highly alkaline – the perfect counterbalance to modern-day acidic diets. They are also an excellent source of fibre, cleansing the intestines as they pass through the body.

In the 1930s it was found that Japanese people who ate regular amounts of sea vegetables lived longer; since then, scientists have discovered that they reduce blood pressure and cholesterol, have antibiotic properties and contain a substance called alginic acid, which helps the body eliminate toxins by binding with any heavy metals present in the intestines; other studies have shown that they help protect against certain cancers. Eating them daily in some form or other virtually guarantees that you get all the micronutrients you need.

Cooking and eating

As anyone who has eaten in a Japanese or macrobiotic restaurant knows, sea vegetables can be delicious; but using them does not always come easily to those of us, including myself, more used to land vegetables.

The most popular types are arame, wakame, nori and Hijiki. They all taste – not surprisingly – of the sea, though some are milder, sweeter and more delicate in texture than others. You usually buy them dried in packets and rehydrate them in one way or another. One tip worth noting is to soak them for no longer than the specified time: they are best, I find, not watery-soft. The wafer-thin sheets of nori, used to wrap around rice for sushi, and which can also be bought as a ready-made snack or toasted and sprinkled over salads, are one of the best to try first. The liquorice-like strands of Hijiki have a meaty savouriness, and are good as nibbles straight out of the pack, while the thin, dark shreds of arame are one of the mildest. Wakame is a delicate ribbon type; both it and nori are also cultivated, or 'farmed'. Dulse and kombu are used mainly to make broths and stocks.

Though you can cook sea vegetables Mediterranean-style, and you can also cook them with dried beans, to make them more digestible, I find their traditional partners – toasted sesame seeds, soy sauces, ginger, miso and so on – are the easiest to start with, though visit Eco-Zone's website and try their recipes, and you may not agree. Vegetarian magazines often include recipes that use them, or visit the Clearspring website (see p. 302). A good book to start with is *Simply Seaweeds* by Lesley Ellis, published by Grub Street. Alternatively, most superfood blends contain a fair proportion of super-health-giving seaweeds; or even easier, you can buy them in capsule form – Seagreens, Viridian and Green People do them – as a natural food supplement.

The differences that count

Sea vegetables are wild; they are increasingly harvested (or even farmed) on an industrial scale, and can pick up toxins from their polluted surroundings. Organic sea vegetables, by contrast, are always sustainably harvested from waters officially certified as pure and regularly monitored for purity. They are harvested by hand, cutting them so that the plants can regenerate.

Though various independent organic certification bodies, including the Soil Association, have certified sea vegetables, a recent EU ruling has declared that because they are wild, they do not qualify for organic status. This decision is expected to be challenged (if you can certify fish, you should be able to certify sea vegetables), but for the time being, as far as the EU is concerned, organic sea vegetables are no longer. How this shakes down as far as the products on the shelves are concerned is too early to tell, but the Soil Association have decided that sea vegetables under their licence will be classified in the same way, for example, as garden composts, and will carry the Soil Association Certified-Product wording. Clearspring regularly test all their sea vegetables for purity and sell two certified by the Soil Association, hijiki and arame, both sun-dried for maximum flavour. Manna is another brand of certified Japanese sea vegetables (whose range also includes bio-miso and the first organic Umeboshi plums). Though not certified organic, the other major brand of Japanese foods, Sanchi, also harvest their sea vegetables sustainably from carefully selected sites, and their growers do not use chemicals or added nutrients for the production of nori or wakame.

Eco-Zone Ltd, 12 Snaresgate Street, London W10 6QP, tel: 020 8962 6399, email: ecozone@sea-vegetables.co.uk.

Not certified organic, but a small specialist company with a mission to encourage the use of sea-vegetables in Western dishes. They supply a range of high-quality fresh, ready-prepared punnets of sea vegetables for salads; dried sea vegetables, and products such as certified organic seaweed tartare relish, condiments, par-baked organic bread with seaweed, and seaweed pasta. They also supply superfood supplements such as spirulina (see p. 281). Their vegetables are sourced from north Brittany and Northern Ireland, sustainably harvested and tested onsite during growth and at harvest for purity. Their fresh ones are salted and just need rinsing, and will keep for up to 3 months in the fridge. Their excellent website, **www.sea-vegetables.co.uk** features much sea-vegetable information, and has monthly recipes. Available at organic retailers and independent outlets, or try them for yourself at their stall at Borough Market in London on Saturdays. To order by post, ring or email.

Seagreens. This is the lazy but eminently sensible way to get your daily fix of sea-veg superfoods, produced by a company passionate about the benefits of seaweed as a foundation for good health, and about harvesting them sustainably. They market four products, certified by the Soil Association, widely available nationwide, and easily recognised by their eye-catching deep-blue packaging: Seagreens Table Condiment (a tangy substitute for salt with only 3.5% sodium, compared with 40% in normal salt and 15% in low-sodium salts) and Culinary Ingredient, to use in baking and cooking (both available at Sainsbury's on their Special Selection shelf); and Wild Seaweed and Everyday Food Capsules – all available at organic and natural stores like Fresh & Wild, Planet Organic and the larger branches of Waitrose.

These foods are produced from three varieties of sea-wrack, harvested by hand in remote conservation islands in Norwegian Arctic waters, cleaned, air-dried and processed the same day, then blended so as to taste good as well as being supergood for you. To find out more, including the benefits of sea vegetables, check out **www.seagreens.com**, or email: seagreens@probono.org.uk. For your nearest stockist tel: 01444 400403. They have also recently published a leaflet.

The final word on seaweeds must go to marine biologist and seaweed author S. Surey-Gent: 'Unfortunately,' she writes, 'it is a modern demand that all results must be instant. Better health from eating seaweed as a supplement to a good diet will only come relatively slowly. But the results will be marvellous and long-lasting, and your patience will be well rewarded.'

MISO MAGIC

Miso as superfood and seasoning

Another stalwart of Japanese and macrobiotic cooking, miso is both a superfood and a very versatile seasoning for soups and stews, as well as making excellent dressings for salads, tofu, Japanese noodles, and grains. It is a nourishing, high-energy food that helps maintain health and vitality, and is rich in vitamins and minerals, including iron.

Miso is made by fermenting soya beans, either on their own or with other grains – rice, barley, oats – which results in various types from 'white' (yellow in colour) through to dark reddish-brown. Organic misos are made in the same way as conventional, but using non-GM organic soya beans and other grains. It is important that you buy traditionally made miso, not cheaper versions made on a mass scale; check the label or ask your supplier.

The exact process is best explained by miso experts, John and Jan Belleme:

> ***'Traditionally, miso is made by combining*** koji ***(cultured grain or soybeans, with Aspergillus oryae) with cooked soybeans, salt and water, and allowing the mixture to ferment in wooden casks at natural temperatures. Gradually, enzymes supplied by the koji, along with microorganisms from the environment, break down the complex structure of beans and grains into readily digestible amino acids, fatty acids and simple sugars. By varying the type of koji used (usually rice, barley, or soybean) and the proportions of ingredients in the recipe, traditional makers are able to create a wide range of misos, from light and sweet to dark and robust.'***

Light-coloured 'sweet' misos take 2–8 weeks to ferment, are high in koji and low in soya beans and salt, and are ideal for summer soups, dips, spreads, sauces, pickles and salad dressings. White miso broth can be substituted for fish or chicken stock, and dark miso broth for beef stock; it also makes nourishing, instantly reviving soup. Dark 'red miso', 'brown-rice miso' and 'barley miso' contain more salt, less koji and proportionately more soya beans, are fermented longer – up to 2–3 years in very cold climates – and are excellent for winter soups, stews and sauces.

Misos can be used as a salt substitute, giving a mellower salter tang; miso is also a natural tenderiser. Though the other nutrients are not, the beneficial micro-organisms are destroyed by cooking, so using some in uncooked foods as a dressing ingredient is a good idea. Generally, it is added towards the end of cooking. Like soy sauce, a dash is good added to gravies.

Convinced? For recipe ideas, see Clearspring's or Source's Food website below.

Miso as medicine

Japanese culture has also long valued miso as a potent medicinal food. Recent scientific research in Japan has found that regularly drinking miso soup, for example, helps protect against heart disease, some cancers and radiation, lowers cholesterol and has an alkalinising effect on the system – as the Bellemes put it, it is a natural Alka-seltzer. Unpasteurised miso is full of beneficial micro-organisms and enzymes that aid digestion and food assimilation. During fermentation, the complex proteins, oils and carbohydrates in the grains and soya beans are broken down into more readily digestible amino acids, fatty acids and simple sugars. This is why miso is considered an excellent food for people with a weak digestion and is still used by traditional Japanese women for weaning. Its unique lactobacillus fermentation also kills dangerous pathogens, both in the foods before they are eaten and in the intestines.

For smokers, miso is thought to rapidly clear nicotine from the body, and miso broth is still used in Japan to clean tar from smokers' pipes.

In the UK we are well off for genuine misos, including organic versions. Apart from Clearspring, the other major Japanese brand is Sanchi, who produce organic mugi (barley) miso and excellent instant organic miso soup powder in individual sachets. My current favourite is not Japanese, but French – Danival's whole-barley miso, also imported by Clearspring, which knocks the spots off Marmite any time and has an unctuous not too salty, chocolatey quality. Remember to refrigerate, once opened.

Clearspring: A remarkable company and a major name in Japanese foods, including misos, shoyu, noodles, teas, sea vegetables and other high-quality vegetarian foods. It is owned and run by a long-standing organic pioneer, Chris Dawson, whose wife is Japanese. All their products are personally sourced and meet their own strict nutritional standards; as someone remarked to me, they go the extra mile to make the highest-quality foods available to consumers. Some – such as their artisan Japanese teas, pastas and misos – are unique. All are GMO-free, and many are organic. They have an excellent mail order catalogue, full of useful information about all their foods, and publish similarly informative leaflets. Their website: **www.clearspring.co.uk** is well worth a visit, includes a macrobiotic website link, recipes and online shop. Tel: 020 8749 1781.

Source Foods

A small company based in Wales, certified by OF&G, who specialise in handmade organic misos (eight varieties of fresh miso), including some made with low-sodium sea salt; plus ginger and Mexican chilli misos, instant miso soup and other products such as hemp miso and organic miso mustard. To find out more about all their products and to shop online, visit their new-age website: **www.miso.co.uk**.

13: Organic Baby Foods

Every mother wants the best for her baby, so it is not surprising that organic baby food has become first choice for over 50% of mothers in the UK, and is still rising steadily (at the last count it represented 75% of baby food sales at Waitrose, for example). As Tesco confirms, organic baby foods, along with fresh produce, are the first things that people choose when going organic. In the UK, annual growth is ten times that for the conventional equivalent, and already represents 25% of all baby food sales. In Germany, predictions are that all baby food will become organic in the near future.

As a result, major baby food manufacturers – Heinz, Boots and Cow&Gate (Olvarit) – now offer an organic range, in addition to the leading brands, Baby Organix and HIPP. Incidentally, HIPP, which is also Germany's leading brand, operate sophisticated screening procedures for over 800 potential contaminants, in which every ingredient is tested for purity before being cooked. Major supermarkets all sell a range of organic baby foods – Sainsbury's sell Baby Organix, HIPP, Heinz and Olvarit, and are the first supermarket to sell their own organic range. Other brands include Babynat, the Demeter brand Johannus, and a new brand of biodynamic baby food, Bio Bambini. Not surprisingly, the choice available continues to grow and the range now includes meat and vegetarian meals, both dry and wet; drinks; desserts; cereals, bread sticks, pastas and pasta meals; baby yoghurts and formula milks; and – new from Baby Organix – mini boxes of dried fruit for toddlers.

A major new development, opening up a whole new vista, is chilled fresh baby food pioneered by the award-winning Simply Organic Company under their Original Fresh Babyfood Company range. It is sold at Tesco, Sainsbury's, Safeway, Booth's, Cullen's and organic supermarkets, and by some home delivery companies and specialist food shops. The range comprises ready vegetable meals such as sweetcorn and potato and Caribbean beans and coconut, and puddings such as Simply Fruit pear and apple purée and apricot rice pudding. And we have frozen organic fruit and vegetable purées in handy chunks for babies produced by the Organic

Baby Food company, which are proving popular with mums I have talked to.

Since the last edition of *The Shopper's Guide*, these excellent books on organic baby food have been published, dealing with all the important issues. If you are a parent-to-be, I recommend them highly. They are *The Organic Baby Book* by Tanyia Frost (Green Books), which includes a comprehensive directory of everything you need for the organic baby; and Planet Organic's *Organic Baby & Toddler Cookbook* by Lizzie Vann, founder of Baby Organix (Dorling Kindersley); and, most recent of all, *Organic Baby Foods* by Amanda Grant (Mitchell Beazley). Tanyia Maxted Frost has also published her own informative *Organic Baby & Toddler Cookbook*, with Daphne Lambert, chief proprietor of Penrhos School of Food and Health in Herefordshire (see p. 111).

For consumers, organic baby food offers mothers the peace of mind that comes from knowing that they are giving their babies the best nutritional start in life – free, also, from the nineteen or so processing aids and emulsifiers, such as hydrogenated vegetable fat, demineralised whey, thickeners and approved flavourings that are included in most conventional brands of baby food, especially the cheaper ones. It should be stressed – as all baby books and nutritionists do – that the best and most economic way to feed your baby organic food is to make your own, using branded foods as a supplement. Baby books and the Baby Organix brand provide many simple recipes.

NOTE: Contrary to accepted opinion, babies are very sensitive to taste. Their senses of both smell and taste are developing throughout the first twelve months of life. Research shows that weaning-foods affect food preferences later in life, so that bland, starchy, sugary or adulterated food, for instance, may affect food choices later. Maltodextrins, for example, present in many commercial brands of baby food and in formula milks, are partially broken-down carbohydrates used extensively in food processing. They provide bulk and enhance the flavour of other, often cheap, ingredients, but they have no nutritional function and their presence helps to familiarise infant taste buds with poor-quality synthetic foods.

WHY ORGANIC BABY FOOD?

'Children aged one to five eat about three times more food per unit of body than the national average, and they consume large volumes of water

and reconstituted juices so that the amount of pesticides they encounter is also larger. Many foods that children eat contain multiple pesticide residues. Most research, however, is done on single pesticides, and combinations are not usually studied because interactive effects are not easy to discern. But we have often found six or seven pesticide residues in our patients, some of them in very large quantities.

'The EPA (US Environmental Protection Agency) sets safe tolerance levels for individual pesticides, on the assumption that they occur only one at a time in a serving. But in fact there are often more, and often they are neurotoxic substances. We have found that some people, including children, are more vulnerable to pesticides than others, because they have an impaired metabolic detoxification system. Almost 25% of children now have asthma. How many are being exposed to pollutants in their food which they cannot degrade and which are therefore going to poison them because the backlog will inevitably be neurotoxic effect?'

Dr Jean Munro, medical director, Allergy and Environmental Medicine Ltd (Breakspear Hospital), Hemel Hempstead.

As this quotation makes clear, babies and toddlers are especially vulnerable to chemical toxins, and it is vitally important that they, above all, should be given an organic diet. In particular, they eat fewer foods but far more of them – fruit and vegetables, for instance – where most residues are detected, at a time when they are least able to deal with them.

It seems that the 'cocktail effect' of multiple pesticide residues, referred to elsewhere in this book, could have especially profound implications for babies. Since 1992, at least fifty synthetic industrial chemicals have been shown to interfere with hormones – which are particularly important during the growth and development of the egg, the embryo, the foetus and the baby. Hormone-mimicking chemicals, which include many pesticides, have been shown to have serious effects on normal growth and development and on the reproductive health of many species, including man. The results of this interference include small penises, diminished sperm count, various cancers, nervous-system disorders, birth defects and damage to the immune system.

Most threatening of all, perhaps, is that it's thought that the toxic effect of some groups of bio-accumulative substances can be subtle, and that they may have their maximum effect on the next generation while they are in the womb.

[Material supplied by Dr C. V. Howard, Foetal and Infant Toxico-Pathology, Liverpool University; Green Network papers on hormone-mimicking chemicals; Our Children's Toxic Legacy.]

Mums-to-be should eat organic, too

As Dr Vivyan Howard, head of foetal and infant toxico-pathology at Liverpool University stated recently, one of the most positive things we can do is to eat organic food because it 'considerably reduces the "body burden" of toxic chemicals in both parent and child'. Because babies in the womb derive all their nourishment from their mothers, it is as important that a woman eat organic food *before* pregnancy to help detoxify her body as it is during pregnancy. And it goes without saying that she should stop smoking. Dr Howard also recommends avoiding dieting when pregnant, as this mobilises fat stores, depositing fat-soluble toxins in the blood stream and possibly in the developing baby. For more information see the books mentioned above, and *What Are Babies Eating?*, available from Baby Organix.

What does organic baby food contain?

Organic baby food contains 95–100% certified organic ingredients, and is minimally processed. The number of non-organic permitted ingredients is as strictly controlled as in all the other organic-food sectors. Many people feel that baby food, especially, should not be compromised at all, and though it costs more to produce (permitted non-organic ingredients are cheaper than similar organic ones), it should only ever contain 100% organic ingredients – and though I am not a mum, that is the view I share. Though many or most lines of all the major brands are 100% organic, currently only Baby Organix and the Original Fresh Babyfood Company produce *only* 100% organic baby food – both are committed to making their products completely natural and as pure as possible. Other brands sometimes add a little sugar, natural flavourings or corn starch – so, as usual, you should always read the label to check that you're completely happy with what is inside.

A nit-picking legal point perhaps, but so that you know, to conform to EU regulations, baby cereals have to contain added vitamins (B6 and B1), and certain fruits have to contain added vitamin C. This means that, technically speaking, such products, though made with 100% organic food ingredients, cannot claim to be 100% organic.

Formula milks

Formula milks, even organic ones, are a contentious subject and are not recommended by nutritionists or health practitioners – except for mothers who are unable to breast-feed – as they lack vital elements that breast milk contains, such as antibodies, digestive enzymes and the long-chain fatty acids necessary for brain development. For more information, consult *The ABC of Healthy Eating for Babies and Toddlers* by Janette Marshall (Hodder & Stoughton) and always seek advice from your health expert.

Baby yoghurts

Whether you choose organic or not, since babies need maximum nutrition they should always be fed whole-milk, not low-fat, yoghurts. Needless to say, they should contain no unnecessary flavouring, additives or other ingredients, such as added sugar.

Price and availability

Organic baby food costs approximately 20–30% more than standard commercial brands, but generally no more than 5–7.5% more than premium brands. In practice this works at around 4–10p extra per jar. When used to supplement home-made baby food made with fresh organic ingredients, the extra cost is very little. There are also regular promotional offers in mother-and-baby magazines and other women's publications, special promotions at supermarkets and other retailers, offers of the 'two-for-one' kind, and coupon offers.

Two tips when buying organic baby food:

- Most stockists sell a selected range of brands – ask for a list of their full range. Or if there's a brand that you particularly want to try but haven't located, contact the manufacturer for the nearest stockist.
- Packet and jar sizes vary from brand to brand; bear this in mind when making price comparisons.

Organic baby food can be bought everywhere. Major supermarkets offer free organic baby food in their cafés – isn't that nice? Baby Organix baby foods are given free to babies at all Welcome Break service station restaurants, at Little Chef, TGI Fridays, Beefeater, Brewer's Fayre, Pizza Organic, Fabulous Bakin' Boys, IKEA, Legoland, Debenham's and John Lewis's restaurants, and at some in-store cafés.

BABY ORGANIX

Founded by Lizzie Vann and Jane Dick who, concerned about the quality of commercial brands, started producing organic baby food in their own kitchens and thus, single-handedly – and with extraordinary vision – created the market for organic baby food in the UK today. Committed to organic farming, they work alongside organic farmers and have all their produce grown for them. They have already won countless awards. What makes them so special is their total commitment to providing children with optimum nutrition. This involves making no compromises whatsoever, and to this end they have produced a Charter for Children's Food, published in their annual report, *What are Babies Eating?*

They now have 54 varieties – main meals, cereals, desserts, tiny pasta shapes and pasta sauces, bread sticks, and their mini boxes of dried fruit. All are produced to the highest quality and nutritional standards, are made only with real (primary) ingredients and are regularly tested for absence of residues. They share all their recipes, produce regular reports, and operate a totally transparent policy. Together with Olvarit and the Original Baby Food Company, they are the only baby food manufacturers to adopt the QUID (Quantitative Ingredients Declaration), which commits them to listing on the label the percentages of all ingredients used, so that parents know exactly what they are buying. They have recently introduced children's fruit bars – one of the best I have tasted, and that I now eat regularly. Their excellent free information service on 0800 393511 provides advice from health experts, offers detailed literature on feeding and weaning, and recipe cards. They operate a mail order service for dry products and publish a regular newsletter containing money-off vouchers. To find out more, for online ordering or for your nearest stockist, visit their website: **www.babyorganix.co.uk**

STOP PRESS: Carrots or Chemistry

Lizzie Vann has recently launched a new campaign to improve the quality of children's food in the UK. To find out more, or to sign their petition, visit the Baby Organix website (above) or freephone: 0800 393511

14: The Organic Store Cupboard

At a guess, the number of items you can buy for your organic store cupboard now runs into a thousand or more: certainly, they fill many pages of the organic wholesale catalogues. Large, well-known conventional brands are being matched by a steady stream of gems, mainly from small European producers such as Probios (see p. 313), but there are also some British ones, such as Halen Mon's amazingly good organic sea salt from Anglesey, the UK's first and (as yet) only certified home-produced organic salt.

I've come to the conclusion, too, that this is one area where having so many imported foods is a good thing. Imported brands offer you something different, expand your taste buds; it's nice, for example, to be able to buy authentic roast peppers from organic co-operatives in Italy, or organic sauerkraut from Germany. Though supermarkets are beginning to stock organic condiments and what have you, to get the real flavour of what you can buy, visit an organic shop or supermarket when you can – not just because the range is so much larger but because most companies, especially the smaller ones, either choose not to sell to supermarkets or are simply not stocked by them.

The biggest change in the last couple of years has been the development of cook-in sauces available in jars; Go Organic, Seeds of Change, the Enjoy Organic Company and Meridian – who have brought out the first organic balti cook-in sauce – all have their own ranges. All kinds of salad dressings and salsa dips, and very good organic mayonnaises, plain and flavoured, follow close behind in popularity. There are now several brands of ketchup (my favourite is Seeds of Change because of its intense tomatoness) and Biona are currently developing the first organic Worcestershire sauce. With that other British must-have, baked beans, the choice ranges from Heinz's own-brand to the original wholesome Whole Earth's. Think Mediterranean lunch rather than beans on toast, and Biona and De Rit produce something a bit more special – fat, creamy cannellino beans cooked in a tomato sauce (in jars), just right for dressing with olive oil and dreaming of the sun. TerraSana's tasty, spicy Mexican refried beans are a third kind – try these as a dip, with olive oil drizzled over, to serve with crudités or bitter salad leaves. They make a good instant lunch, too.

The two products of which there is most choice are probably soups and chutneys (in tins and jars). You would simply not believe how many organic chutneys there are in the world today from Tasty Vittles spicy apricot chutney to good old-fashioned organic piccalilli.

Soups in jars are an import from the continent, where they are more popular than tins: it's a good idea – you can see what you are buying, and the jars are recyclable. For everyday soups, Go Organic's spiced parsnip is my personal favourite. For something special, Sierra Rica's gazpacho and their chestnut, apple and ginger soup from Andalucia lift processed soups out of the ordinary. Seeds of Change popular soups now come in modern stylish pouches, too. Tinned soups, especially those made from pulses such as Suma's dried-pea, are also good standbys; though as I've discovered while writing this book, when you're hungry, any kind of organic canned or instant soup can taste fine: Just Wholefoods and Marigold are two brands of instant cuppa soups – and like all organic soups, they come with no chemical tang.

You can get jars and tins of preserved and marinated vegetables, including favourites like Suma's new canned sweetcorn, as well as preserved fruits galore. Increasingly you can buy delicacies such as artichoke purée, and jars of Mediterranean vegetables preserved under oil, which make the perfect antipasto. Peanut butters and other nut butters are also popular – and very delicious. For vegetarians there are some excellent organic patés and spreads, such as Allos, Granvita's, Suma's, Shippam's, Nate and Tartex. Needless to say, the names get ever more inventive: Viana's range includes Casablanca, Temptation and Inca organic spreads.

There are also more organic wine and cider vinegars than ever before, including half a dozen different organic balsamic vinegars. There is more to balsamic vinegar than meets the eye. Cheaper brands like Aspall's and Marlett's are fine for cooking, but if you want the real thing, you need to pay more and go for an aged balsamic vinegar such as Clearspring's, or seek them out from specialist suppliers. If you prefer malt vinegar, Geo Organic has it, along with their pickled onions in malt vinegar, too.

Organic mustard also deserves a special mention. Two years ago, there was very little choice. That has changed, and you can now buy smooth, mild, grainy or flavoured organic mustards galore. Wiltshire Tracklement are the latest conventional company to produce their own organic mustards. The manager of Infinity Foods at Brighton reckons Delouis Fils Dijon is the best of the bunch.

Mustard may be a simple product, but making it well is not as easy as it sounds, as Andrew Duncan, MD of Gordon's Fine Foods – who have added very good English and Dijon organic mustards to their range – recently explained in *Organic Business* magazine. Much of its flavour comes from the chemical reaction between the enzymes and the volatile oils in the mustard flour and the other ingredients. Get it wrong, and the mustard will be bitter and have no heat. Mustard is good for your digestion, too: as Andrew Duncan notes, it's an unsung hero, 'not a product to be left on the side of your plate'. Don't forget you can cook with it, too: a simple mustard and cream sauce, for example, is classic with pork and chicken.

ABSOLUTE ESSENTIALS

I decided long ago that a store cupboard full of bottles and jars that I never use was not a good idea, and that a store cupboard of any lasting use would probably be better stocked with a few well-chosen ingredients, standbys and favourites, and not much else. An organic store cupboard is no different. Start with what you use most of, or find yourself needing when the urge to cook takes over, then add the perennial lifesavers. The usual dried goods apart, essential items for me, in no particular order, include:

Halen Mon sea salt: A truly delicious and sweet-tasting sea salt. A small family-run business, they produce two versions, plain and spiced, in attractive cartons. Available direct via mail order, online, or through fine food shops. So good, they cannot keep up with the demand, especially since Delia Smith discovered them: Tel: 01248 430871 to order, or visit their website: **www.seasalt.co.uk**.

Organic tomato purée and chopped tinned tomatoes: There are various brands and all are very good, with an extra intensity of flavour.

Marigold organic bouillon powder: However did I manage without it? An excellent seasoning, and the next-best thing to home-made. Another good stock cube brand is Kallo. A tip worth knowing: always use less rather than more of these kinds of seasoning, as a background enhancer rather than a full-on flavouring.

Tinned chickpeas and other cooked dried beans: Chickpeas for houmus and others for salads.

Tins or jars of soups: Just a few, just in case. Spicy and beany, for preference.
Bottled carrot juice: Usually Eden brand. I drink mine hot as instant soup.
Tahini: Essential for houmus. It comes in several kinds, light and dark and smooth and grainy. I still like Sunita's the best.
Organic cider vinegar: A must, and it's healthy, too. The original Aspall's, whose pedigree goes back fifty years, is the best. You can also get upmarket Breton cider vinegar.
Organic balsamic vinegar: A cheaper one for cooking, and a proper one for salad dressings. Clearspring's new apple version is excellent.
Organic olive oil: Meridian as my all-purpose olive oil, and a selection of others for salads, grilled fish, etc.
Archiamma, Seasoned Pioneers' and Chiman's spice blends: The easy way to spice up your cooking. Plus Seasoned Pioneers' organic cayenne, my current add-to-everything spice.
Hambledon Herbs organic saffron: The most fragrant and potent yet – indispensable for risottos.
Miso – light and dark: I eat mine out of the jar.
Organic capers: A must. I use Opie's capers in white wine vinegar, from Waitrose. Cereal Terra capers in olive oil are a treat.
Organic mayonnaise: my latest standby. I've tried several brands and none have disappointed me yet. For preference I go for Pollen Organics or similarly extra-thick minimally made mayos. Simply Organic and De Rit are also excellent.
Sacla organic pestos: Traditional Italian family firm, making authentic pestos. They even grow their own organic basil. Useful as instant salad dressings, and for French beans. Valentina Harris develops their recipes – no further recommendation needed.
A jar of something under oil: Roasted sweet peppers, etc. Useful to add to salads, or for instant pasta sauces.
Organic mustard: Another must, smooth and grainy.
Green & Black's hot chocolate: This, too, usually gets eaten straight out of the jar.
Organic chips and tortilla chips: Because I'm worth it, and so is he. Kettle brand for crisps, and various tortilla chips.

Brands

Brands producing a wide range of store-cupboard essentials include Epicure, Essential Foods, Suma, Granovita, Evernat, Martlett, Biona and De Rit. And here are two more that give a good idea of what organic brands are all about:

Probios: One of the high-quality artisan brands now being imported, whose products you will find in organic supermarkets and shops. Probios is an organic co-operative based in Florence, established twenty-four years ago, who seek out the best growers and producers. They have a high reputation in Italy, and their products are now on sale in the UK. Their organic range includes Italian rices and hand-made pastas, handmade Florentine cantuccini almond biscuits, grissini, various kamut and spelt bakery products and rice cakes, tomato pasta sauce, passata and tinned tomatoes, preserved roasted Mediterranean vegetables in extra-virgin olive oil, and *condimenti*, including the creamiest ever artichoke purée, plus vegan rice desserts, nut spreads and pure and simple fresh fruit compotes.

Meridian: A British company based in Corwen, Wales, founded in 1974 and specialising in natural foods. Their organic range has expanded considerably, and they are one of the many organic brands who do their best to maintain the highest integrity and a competitive edge. Their organic product range includes canned soups and veg mince bolognese, chilli and curry; dried pasta and pasta sauces, salad dressings, mayonnaise, cooking sauces, ketchup, brown sauce and seasonal cranberry sauce; peanut and other nut butters, tahini, oils, including their well-known Spanish olive oil; fruit spreads, and very good fruit juice concentrates. Available at independents. For more information, visit their excellent, heartwarming website: **www.meridianfoods.co.uk**, which includes recipes, info on special diets and a where-to-buy county search of their products. Or contact them direct on 01490 413151, or email: meridianfoods@enta.net.

CONVENIENCE FOODS

Just about everything you can buy in the conventional convenience food department you can now buy organic – from gourmet pizzas to jelly babies. It's not just that, but the choice of brands, from both organic and conventional manufacturers, has spiralled. The arrival of Heinz organic baked beans marked a watershed in the organic revolution. That there are at least nine other brands of organic baked beans, including Sainsbury's, Waitrose and Tesco own-brands, shows, I think, how far organic convenience foods have come. To deal with them all would take another book. Instead, I've covered the basics and given a brief taster of the main groups. I haven't included organic pet food, but you might like to know that your pet can eat organic, too – and that you can buy it in major supermarkets.

The Food Standards Agency's recent *Consumer Attitudes to Food* report stated that 80% of consumers eat convenience foods. The new Taylor Nelson Sofres report, commissioned for the *Grocer* magazine, meanwhile, has confirmed that we also want them to be free of additives and preservatives. Organic convenience foods offer the consumer that choice. Sales of convenience foods run into £billions. Every successful major brand of organic processed food means many more extra organic farms that would not have otherwise converted – a nice thought, when you open your next can of organic beans.

Why buy organic convenience foods, and what standards do they adhere to?

Organic convenience foods offer two major benefits. First, the ingredients have been grown by organic farmers, so choosing an organic cereal bar, for example, means supporting the wider benefits that organic farming brings. Second, organic convenience foods do offer a 'purer' and healthier option. Here, perhaps even more than with the other organic foods discussed in this book, it's what *isn't* in organic processed foods that counts. Suffice to say that only a handful of natural additives are permitted, instead of the 7,000 or so allowed in conventional food processing.

Processing standards are as strict as those for organic farming generally. Organic foods can be processed either in premises that are dedicated organic plants, or in conventional plants that fulfil organic processing requirements. Everyone processing organic foods must be inspected annually and certified by an approved body. To prevent substitution, all organic products must be transported either in their own packaging or in sealed containers. The recipes used, including a full list of ingredients, have to be certified too. Detailed records must be kept and organic ingredients must be kept separate at all times. Where organic and non-organic lines are being made on the same premises, all equipment has to be cleaned thoroughly and cleaning surfaces washed with potable water. The use of chlorine is prohibited. The current list of permitted additives and processing aids can be found on p. 388.

The audit trail of authenticity continues to the point of sale. To avoid any confusion with non-organic produce, most organic food is sold prepacked. Where there is no equivalent conventional produce being sold, or it is easy to differentiate between organic and conventional – for example, with different varieties of mushroom – produce may be sold loose, though proof of certification must be available. It's exactly the same with farmers' markets or farm shops selling their own organic produce. And as mentioned earlier, any shop, box scheme or home delivery service that repackages goods out of sight of customers, or cooks its own food and labels it 'organic', must have its own licence also.

Rather like organic farming itself, processing standards are constantly being reappraised, refined and adapted as the market develops. That some organic manufactured foods are clearly borderline – for instance, when derogations are manipulated so as to enable a manufacturer to produce a cheaper organic product by deliberately including cheaper permitted non-organic ingredients – causes disquiet and casts a shadow over the vast majority of organic foods, and needs to be dealt with.

Amongst the other more contentious issues under discussion is whether organic manufactured foods should always be made with purified or spring water (Suma's canned organic beans are), and whether the processing methods used should be stated explicitly on the labels, close to the product name. That such topics are under discussion at the Soil Association's standards committees is a very positive sign. Whereas in the conventional sector such issues tend to be discussed behind closed doors, in the organic sector things are much more transparent. That the door is always open, inviting consumers to engage in the debate about how to take organic food forward, is one of the most important safeguards we have for its continuing integrity. Above all, making our views heard *counts*.

A final point on organic processed foods. Many consumers believe passionately that such foods debase the organic ethos, founded as it is on providing what is natural, wholesome and healthy. Whether organic standards should have embraced processed foods is a matter of debate, but the fact remains that the existence of organic processed foods – which began in response to consumer demand rather than as a marketing opportunity – has meant that organic farming is now a force to be reckoned with worldwide.

How do I choose between brands?

This is the sixty-four-thousand-dollar question that I am constantly asked, and to which there is no simple answer. Every brand has its house style, reflected in the flavours, in the kind and quality of the ingredients used, in its packaging and in its price – and the only realistic way to find which brand suits you is by trial and error. The simplest – and only foolproof way – to judge whether an organic brand is likely to meet your expectations is to read the ingredients list – which remains the consumer's best ally and safeguard. This always clearly states what organic ingredients are used and their percentages, as well as any non-organic ingredients.

Generally speaking, the fewer the ingredients and the higher the percentage of the main ingredients, or of those that you like, the higher the quality or the more the product is likely to please you. If it's taste and quality you are looking for, premium organic brands or companies specialising in niche organic products made in small quantities are the ones to go for. There are some wonderful artisan organic foods, too, being imported from Italy, France, Spain and Germany that you will find in organic shops and supermarkets. And if you like mainstream brands, you will generally like their organic versions too. With some items – standard organic pastas, for example – there seems very little difference between brands, whereas there are often definite quality differences between brands of dried fruit – usually to be detected by sight.

Taste and quality

Let's be frank. Not all organic processed food is, or tastes, wonderful, and the eating quality of organic processed foods varies as much as between conventional processed foods, though I do personally think that as the market has developed, and they have become more mainstream, the overall taste of organic processed foods has improved generally. Part of the credit for this (whether their organic foods are to your liking or not) should go to conventional manufacturers and supermarkets who, after all, have had fifty years' experience in developing convenience foods. Some, like Heinz, go out of their way to make their organic option – in this case, their baked beans – taste exactly the same as their regular version. Others take a different view, believing that organic processed food should taste distinctive in some way. Often it does, simply because, for example, the instant flavour fixes that are available to the conventional food sector are not available to the organic sector.

Also, organic ingredients often have a slightly different flavour spectrum – which also comes through when those ingredients are processed. For instance, though the ingredients lists are the same (apart from the additives used) I find Sacla's new red organic pesto sweeter and mellower than their non-organic one – though which you prefer or think 'better' is a matter of personal taste. The other flavour difference to watch out for is the use of honey or apple juice instead of sugar – which you may find appealing or not.

The trendiest organic convenience food around, that has bags of Italian know-how, is ready-prepared, see-through, vacuum-sealed packs of seasoned risottos, produced by Probios. To cook, you add water. It makes a beautifully creamy risotto, though I suggest you make it in the usual way and fry the rice first with a finely chopped onion in plenty of butter and olive oil.

CHILLED, FROZEN AND READY-TO-GO

This is the fastest-growing sector of the market. Everything from salads and soups to freshly made award-winning organic custard (Joubère's); fresh organic ravioli, tortellini and cannelloni; ready-made fresh vegetarian, Indian and Chinese meals; quiches and Get-Real vegetarian lookalike pork pies from the freezer section; kids' organic meals, organic pizzas; tofu products galore (including Thai peanut tofu pizza); ready-made dairy and dairy-free desserts; organic apple pie and the Organic Pudding Company's must-have sticky toffee pudding (as served in Pizza Organic restaurants). From the deli counter you can buy organic houmus and dips and vegetarian pâtés, tapénade, falafel, aubergine tapas, caponata, tabbouleh, horseradish relish – and that's just for starters.

At the moment, the sector is dominated by small organic manufacturers and supermarket own-brands, though that is changing as more conventional manufacturers decide that they too want a slice of the organic ready-made pie. This means lots of choice, though not necessarily from brands you've heard of. Quality generally is good to excellent, especially from the small organic manufacturers aiming for the top of the market, such as Simply Organic, Tideford Foods and Pollen Organics – but don't go just by the name. *Time Out*, in a recent tasting of ready meals, gave the Finest Organics brand a definite thumbs down (though their frozen cakes are generally liked). Supermarket own-brand organic chilled and ready meals are made to exactly the same quality and taste standards as their conventional ones: if you enjoy these, you will enjoy their organic lines, too.

Market research shows that the most popular lines are soups, pasta (and pasta sauces) and frozen ready meals. As with convenience foods generally, you tend to get what you pay for: cheaper brands are likely to have more fillers or thickeners, or limit themselves to ingredients that are in ready supply and therefore cheaper. Because they're fresh (or frozen) and additive- and artificial-preservative-free, you can expect fresher, less processed flavours. Apart from the fact that rice can sometimes be cooked too soft for my liking, the only general complaint I have is that, except when the recipe actually needs it, I wish manufacturers would stop putting dried garlic in processed foods: organic or not, garlic does not freeze well, and always leaves a lingering unpleasant after-taste.

Ready-made meals do not compare with home-made: the vegetables are always softer than you would ideally want, and the meat is often dry. This is not a criticism, but the inevitable effect of food-processing. Spiced dishes and warming winter soups – and thick soups generally – seem to work particularly well. Stir-fries and soups that have thickening agents seem to be the least successful; but creamy sauces are a good bet any time, easily hitting the comfort zone.

To make summer complete and even more fun, organic iced fruit lollipops have made their debut: Waitrose, Sainsbury's and Tesco all sell them in packs, under their own-brand labels. Makes waiting at the check-out on a hot day much more bearable, too.

Three tips:

- If too thick, soups can always be diluted with water, water and milk, or extra vegetable stock or cooking liquid – and it makes them stretch further, too.
- For home-made appeal and an instant lift, add chopped fresh organic herbs.
- Always check the sell-by date and use any chilled or frozen ready-made meal as soon as possible.

A few manufacturers . . . to give you the flavour:

Clive's Organic pies and Lucie's Organic cakes (SA): A tiny organic bakery in Buckfastleigh, Devon, producing gourmet vegan chilled and frozen ready-to-eat creamy mushroom, Mexican chilli, Arabian chickpea and Hungarian goulash pies, made with their own rough-puff pastry; 'soyage rolls' made with okara, the highly nutritious soya bean skins, known as the 'honourable husk' in Japan; and two luxury gluten-free cakes, Choco Mocha and Almond Bliss, made with almonds instead of flour, which come in two sizes, individual and large. Available at independents, organic supermarkets and local healthfood shops. They recently started a mail order service for their cakes: tel: 01364 642279.

Evernat (SA, OFF and European certifiers): Owned by Brewhurst, who specialise in natural and whole foods, Evernat are a reliable mass brand with one of the widest ranges of organic food – over 90 products – including fresh organic sandwiches and frozen vegetables and ready meals, organic quiche and pizza, and chilled vegetarian savouries, crisps, tortilla chips, salsa dips, excellent Dijon mustard, plus yoghurts and desserts. Selected products are available at Sainsbury's and Waitrose. Note that not all their products are 100% organic, though all contain 95% minimum organic ingredients. Their customer care line is 01932 334501. For more information, click on the Evernat section of Brewhurst's website: **www.brewhurst.com**.

Get Real (SA): Something different and very tasty for vegetarians – high-quality organic sutaki and frozen Ambledown raised pies with inventive fillings, which began in Sue Gwilliam's Shropshire kitchen and are now available nationwide, including selected Waitrose and Sainsbury's stores. Watch out for their new range of traditional meat and gravy pies, such as organic steak and onion, made with lean steak, available chilled and frozen. For more information, including ingredients listings and stockists, visit their website: **www.get-real.co.uk** or email: info@get-real.co.uk.

Joubère (OFF): Specialise in high-quality chilled foods – their fresh organic stocks and custard have really caught on. The stocks contain minimum salt and are made in the home-cooked way, simmering for several hours, and the custard is made with milk, egg yolks and vanilla pods. Their seasonal organic soups (Classic and Gourmet range) include Californian tomato, bacon and blue cheese, and Thai chicken and coriander. Recently they have launched individual treat-yourself dairy desserts and ready-made porridge, which you can buy plain or with honey and cinnamon. Their products are available at major supermarkets such as Booth's, Sainsbury's and Waitrose, plus organic shops and supermarkets. For more information, visit their website: **www.joubere.co.uk**.

Organicindia (SA): The best of the organic Indian ready meals – read the ingredients list and you will see why. The family firm also owns a chain of Indian restaurants in London, Tandoori Nights, and for their ready meals they use the same authentic recipes as for their restaurants, high-quality ingredients and freshly ground spices. They buy whole chickens from Traditional Norfolk Poultry, and their lamb comes from Graig Farm organics and the Welsh Hook Meat Centre. They cut the meat themselves, seaming it in the French way, which means prime pieces every time. Their rice is excellent, and the flavour of the sauces is exceptionally good. Altogether recommended, their range includes Lamb Korma, Chicken Jalfrezi, Vegetable Spice and Saag Aloo. Attractively packaged, the shelf life is seven days, but the meals can be frozen. Readily available in London, including Cullen's, Debenham's, Europa Foods and organic supermarkets, or nationwide through Simply Organic. For more, visit their website: **www.organicindia.co.uk**. To find your nearest stockists, tel: 020 8805 2223.

Pollen Organics (SA): Superb fine food, made in small batches by a tiny company – you won't get much better flavour or quality than these. Their chilled products include soups, houmus, and basil and watercress pestos, and they offer a range of salad dressings, plus such delights as tomato pasta sauce, sundried tomato pesto and red onion marmalade. Their best-ever mayo is available through Simply Organic. Products sold at Milford, Arundel, Petersfield and Winchester farmers' markets. To find out more or to order direct, visit their website: **www.pollenorganics.com** or email: organics@pollen associates.com.

The Quiet Revolution Soups Company (SA): Mr Original Wonderful Organic Soups – trailblazer for fresh and organic. They produce in small batches, seasonally, in stylish packs and available at independent outlets. To find out more, visit their website **www.quietrevolution.co.uk**, which has a list of stockists. They now have 3 organic cafés (see p. 112).

Simply Organic (SA): Are simply excellent. This award-winning Scottish company, founded in 1998, is run by two food-loving women, each with a young family, not much time but a passion for all things organic. They produce a range of soups, dips, pasta sauces and baby food (under their Original Fresh Babyfood brand, see p. 306) – everything is 100% organic. Look out for them at Tesco, Safeway and Sainsbury's.

Swaddles Green (SA): Well-known organic pioneers, whose ready meals have consistently won praise. Their children's meals (see p. 351) are available nationwide.

The Enjoy Organic Company (SA): No one can fail to miss their bright, breezy packaging, designed to make you smile and feel good about organics. A small organic company, owned by RHM and run by the dedicated Harriet Rhys-Williams, this is another brand aiming for mass appeal. Their frozen organic pizzas (made by a small family firm in Italy) are the star of the show; their ready-frozen meals do not pretend to be in the gourmet league, but are nicely spiced and well judged (and their minced meat is finely minced). They have a fun website, with recipes, links and customer feedback: **www.enjoyorganic.com**.

Tideford Organic Foods (SA): A small organic company based in Totnes, Devon, whose chirpy award-winning seasonal soups, pestos and pasta sauces have caught on. My favourite winter soup is their organic borscht, for summer their minted-pea vichyssoise. Latest introductions are their large meal-in-one Super Soups including Moroccan Lamb and Country Potage, three Hurry-Curry chilled sauces, Korma, Madras and Green Curry, and the new chilled (Hey Pesto) watercress and rocket pesto. Their products are made in small batches, have a two-week shelf life and are on sale at Waitrose, organic supermarkets and shops, Cullens in London, and locally. They also make an organic Christmas pudding (in a crock bowl, wrapped in muslin) and brandy butter at Christmas time. To find your nearest stockist, tel: 01803 840555.

ORGANIC BREAKFAST CEREALS

An organic start to the day continues to be the best kind, especially given that most conventionally grown cereals are not only amongst the most heavily sprayed of crops but also amongst the most environmentally unsound – witness the dust bowls of America, or our own East Anglian and Wiltshire prairies.

But if you thought that organic breakfast cereals meant limiting yourself to seriously worthy mueslis, think again. The range has expanded even more – take, for instance, Good Morning's seven kinds of cereal puffs, the new Big Oz range of puffed cereals from Australia, and the malted wheat flakes, bran flakes and crunchies and mueslis by the score. Breakfast cereals are also one of the fastest-growing grocery lines – and for children, too (see p. 350). More unusual lines worth investigating include non-wheat cereals such as puffed amaranth, buckwheat millet and spelt; and amaranth, hempseed and rice mueslis.

The biggest development is that major conventional breakfast and muesli manufacturers have brought out organic versions – including Jordan's, now the number one organic brand – and even Weetabix have introduced their Nature's Own wheat squares and organic Weetabix. The Enjoy Organic Company, too, aim for mass appeal (for which read much sweeter than many), and are amongst the best-selling at Sainsbury's, who in turn have brought out four own-brand organic breakfast cereals. Tesco have five own-brands, Waitrose and M&S have their own muesli, Safeway their organic crunch, and so on. At the other end of the scale are the chic imported breakfast cereals made by dedicated artisan producers such as Céréco in Brittany, who produce several types under their Terres et Céréales brand, some without sugar, some using spelt; or, if you prefer, honey cornflakes and chocolate crunch, beautifully packaged and made with all the integrity you could wish for.

Taste-wise, there is something for everyone – from cereals that cry out for lashings of milk and sugar, such as plain puffed rice, to Evernat Tropical Krunchy, which you will find difficult to resist snacking on at any hour of the day or night. (One fan of honeyed puffed rice likens them to healthier Sugar Puffs.) There are several brands of cornflakes, each tasting slightly different from the next. They come in two broad types: those made from whole corn, such as Whole Earth's and Doves Farm, with a much higher fibre content – they contain natural B and E vitamins and minerals – and a delicious nutty flavour that everyone appreciates, including children; and those made from refined organic maize, which look and taste more like regular cornflakes. Two other tasty, moreish flakes that are distinctly different are Nature's Path Heritage Cereal, made from spelt, quinoa and kamut, and their equally nutty millet and rice flakes. This Canadian brand, which also produces five breakfast cereals for children, remains my favourite, and its products are now available in major supermarkets. They also have an excellent, albeit a bit slow, website: **www.naturespath.com**, which includes ingredients listings and nutritional profiles of all their products.

More and more people are turning to wheat- and gluten-free breakfast cereals. As a result, spelt and kamut are the up-and-coming alternatives, while organic cereal bars look ready to upstage mueslis. Incidentally, anyone interested in kamut, the ancient Egyptian grain, that is both delicious and more nutritious than wheat (it has 5% more protein, for example), can visit the Kamut Association of Europe and North America combined website, **www.kamut.com**. Breakfast flakes – rye, malted wheat, barley – can be bought loose; uninteresting on their own, they are for making your own muesli. Cornflake oats, available in supermarkets, are easy to cook and a popular favourite. Jordan's also have organic porridge oats. Any kind of organic crunchy I find difficult to resist; ditto Whole Earth's Swiss Muesli.

Too tired to make your own? The last word in organic breakfasts is surely Joubère's new ready-made thick, creamy individual pots of porridge, plain or flavoured with honey and cinnamon – look out for them in the chilled cabinets.

All of these are readily available, though for a really good range you will need to visit an organic shop or supermarket. Pricewise, organic breakfast cereals compare very favourably to 'healthfood' and upmarket brands of cereals – and are sometimes cheaper. In most cases, the extra cost per serving is minimal. It also pays to shop around, as prices do vary. Large bags of muesli, or breakfast cereals bought loose, are the most economical.

Mueslis

Organic mueslis contain full-of-goodness grains that have nourished mankind from the earliest times, and come in many different varieties – standard or deluxe, with or without added sugar, as a base for you to add your own extras, and so on. The latest from Schnitzer are probiotic organic mueslis, in two varieties, Amaranth and Fruit. Cottage Delight brand, based in Leek, Staffordshire, who also produce organic pastas and jams, go one better: their muesli range includes a probiotic, yoghurt-coated, mixed-berry variety.

You can buy mueslis prepacked, or they may be mixed by the wholefood shop and sold loose. Organic millers, for example Little Salkeld, Maud Foster (see p. 229) sometimes offer their own mueslis, and they are a popular item in mail order catalogues. The ingredients vary slightly from one mix to the next – so read the label carefully to see if it is to your taste. For instance, some include salt or milk powder. Boxed mueslis are more expensive than bagged ones.

Well-known organic brands to try include Alara, Doves Farm, the Enjoy Organic Company, Whole Earth (Swiss Muesli), Nature's Path, Essential, Suma, Infinity Foods, Community Foods, Evernat and Sundrum Organic's award-winning Tropical Muesli, as well as Jordan's organic muesli; and there are many more excellent imported mueslis.

The old and the new . . .
Eat your heart out for organic mueslis with these two brands:

Alara : Alara's organic mueslis receive universal praise. A small company, they were one of the first manufacturers to join the Soil Association and have been making their muesli for over twenty years. Their mission is to provide high-quality nutritious food that 'helps to restore harmony and balance to the environment'. They produce three – Tropical, Branberry (with pieces of strawberry to provide a cheery start to the day) and Organic Rich Muesli – all reasonably priced. To find out more, visit their definitive muesli website: **www.alara.co.uk**. As it's one of the top ten in the book, visit it anyway. It gives information on every ingredient used, including the farm it was grown on, quality specifications and nutritional analyses, plus an impressive search facility for your nearest stockist (which includes a really useful description of each shop and what it sells).

Pertwood Farm: The latest feel-good brand of organic wheat and dairy-free mueslis, made by Lower Pertwood Farm in Wiltshire, who use their own organic oats. Soon they plan to include their own rye and barley as well. Lower Pertwood Farm itself offers plenty for consumers to feel good about. They grow wheat, oats, barley, rye, spelt and triticale, raise pedigree Welsh Black and Hereford cattle, rare-breed Wiltshire Horned sheep, keep outdoor pigs and grow a range of organic vegetables for their local box scheme. The heart of the farm is 330 acres of ancient pasture, with remnants of a Celtic field system dating from 3,500 BC. Many rare species such as wild thyme, milkwort and green-winged orchid, Holly Blue butterflies, buzzards and serotine bats find refuge here. The cereals in Pertwood Farm mueslis are grown as part of a mixed rotation, deriving their nourishment from clover-rich leys and composted manure, enriched with watercress sludge from John Hurd. All the animals are built into the field rotation, providing extra fertility and helping to keep down the weeds. Their wheat is stoneground locally at N. R. Stoate's watermill to produce a range of premium organic flours. Beat that.

Their breakfast cereal range also includes porridge oats and two organic crunchies. Sainsbury's now stock their mueslis and porridge oats. For other stockists, call Chris Walford on 01747 820720, or email him on chris.walford@cwcom.net. For location, see directory.

ORGANIC CAKES AND BISCUITS

Organic cakes and biscuits have grown up; which is to say, they've become mass-market. You will find them in all the major supermarkets. Waitrose will bake you an organic birthday cake to order, Sainsbury's have their organic teddy-bear cake, Tesco their own organic fruit and chocolate-chip cake, and you can buy frozen cakes, too. Like all organic convenience fare, because they contain no artificial flavours or additives and virtually all chemical processing aids are prohibited in their making, they are nearer to home-made than many conventional ones. It hadn't occurred to me before but, also because most organic food is imported, as well as all the familiar British stalwarts and favourites (including, now, organic clotted-cream biscuits and Eccles cakes) you can buy European-style cakes and biscuits that you would normally only get to eat on holiday. Christmas specialities – cakes, mince-pies, organic plum puddings and Christmas puddings – are now part of everyday life, as are organic digestive and chocolate biscuits. These days, too, they come at prices to suit every pocket.

I do not have a sweet tooth, but apart from flapjacks, which I find problematic at the best of times, most organic cakes and biscuits I can happily munch away on all too easily. Most of the bakers mentioned in chapter 9 produce their own very good organic baked goods, including cakes and biscuits. Small companies like Respect and Lucie's Organic Cakes (see p. 318) – try, for instance, their gluten-free luxury cakes – are also emerging, and recently launched too is a range of handmade, upmarket fruit-cakes produced by Leeds-based manufacturer Anthony Stephens, which also come in individual portions. Mrs Muffin's Groovy Muffin Mixes are child's play and very good. Biona's handmade cookies are something out of the ordinary, too, baked from freshly stoneground flour every week in small batches. Biona BioDiet is a range of high-quality gluten-free cookies. Biona is one of several imported brands such as Molen Aartje, who specialise in high-quality biscuits offering something a little bit different.

The range is so vast that you would need to be a glutton or a mountain-climber to try them all: as with any convenience food, whether it's a brand you trust or whether you just feel like trying something new, be guided by the ingredients. There was a time when most organic cakes and biscuits catered primarily for the wholefood or vegetarian market rather than for either the general or the gourmet market. This has changed. As long as you remember that the eating appeal of any cake or biscuit is largely a personal matter, that tends to be based on what you're used to and how sweet a tooth you have, you won't go far wrong. As for my desert island cake, if I could only choose one it would still be the Village Bakery's chocolate and almond cake below (though I would probably sneak in a packet of their organic brownies, too).

TIP: The best and easiest way to store most cakes is in an airtight plastic box. And keep them cool. Otherwise, keep them well wrapped. Carrot and apple cakes, which have a high moisture content, do not store well; put them in the fridge and eat within two or three days.

ORGANIC CHOCOLATE

There is no excuse not to eat organic chocolate: better for you, better for the environment, and so much good organic chocolate and chocolate products to buy it would take months to try them all. Waitrose and Tesco have introduced their own brands; Sainsbury's will indulge you with a made-to-order, organic teddy-bear chocolate cake. The chic and handsomely packaged bite-sized luxury Petite Organique squares from Delvaux can be ordered online: **www.delvaux.co.uk**. Green & Black's remain my all-time favourite brand; and award-winning Booja Booja vegan truffles are my favourite indulgence. The latest indulgence, I guess, would be Rosengarten's chocolate-covered fruits soaked in alcohol, including rum pineapple and grappa raisins. Organic chocolate of all kinds can now be bought at all major retailers and the price is not exorbitant, so this is one treat you can feel wholly good about.

Why buy organic chocolate?

The UK is one of the biggest consumers of chocolate in the world and some £3 billion worth is eaten every year, three-quarters of it by women and children. But most cocoa production is heavily dependent on agrochemicals, and the health and working conditions of workers in cocoa plantations, many of whom in some countries are also female, give considerable pause for thought. One food-writer friend, who has visited cocoa plantations, described 'a fog of pesticides, and plants and cocoa pods sticky with residues'; it is these cocoa beans that go to make all conventional chocolate, including the high-quality kind. Monoculture leads to the destruction of the natural ecosystem, which means that plantations cannot function without pesticides, traces of which, especially the OC lindane, have cropped up frequently in tests. And cocoa production inflicts other environmental damage, such as deforestation and land erosion. In comparison, organic cocoa production is tiny, confined to small-scale plantations, employing traditional methods of cultivation and disease control, and is often fair-traded – and, incidentally, is said often to produce better-quality cocoa.

Comparing organic chocolate with your average bar of chocolate is to compare two quite different substances. Mass-produced chocolate contains up to 50% refined sugar, hydrogenated vegetable fats and artificial flavourings, and far less of cocoa-butter solids (the ingredient that makes chocolate chocolaty). Organic chocolate is up to twice as high in cocoa-butter solids, has less (unrefined) sugar and no hydrogenated fats, and contains only natural flavourings. It tastes delicious, and being high in cocoa solids, a little goes a pleasurable long way.

For anyone who enjoys chocolate, then, making the switch to organic, and fair-traded, chocolate makes sense; as the same friend who went to see for himself put it, it's better to feel good about eating less organic chocolate than bad about eating too much ordinary chocolate. The same applies to cocoa powder.

- Organic chocolate is made from cocoa beans, milk, sugar and natural flavourings, and must contain a minimum of 95% organic ingredients. The only permitted emulsifier is soya lecithin made from non-GM soya.
- Most organic chocolate typically contains double the amount of cocoa solids found in many conventional brands: dark, 55–70% instead of 30%; milk, 30% instead of 20% or less.

Chocolates and other chocolate products

Chocolate cakes, biscuits, spreads, ice-cream and drinks are becoming more and more popular; indeed, as far as chocolate is concerned the world is going green, organic and fair-traded fast, with an ever-growing selection of brands and products to choose from. To give you some idea, organic chocolate comes with nuts and all kinds of flavourings, in large bars and in small; you can buy chocolate mints, chocolate truffles, buttons, chocolate-covered raisins, chocolate Father Christmases and Easter eggs – and a lot more besides, including handmade chocolates. New brands are constantly being introduced to tempt you, and there is non-dairy organic chocolate, too. As with conventional chocolate, the flavour and 'mouth feel' of the different brands vary. To take two extremes, Evernat dark chocolate is grainy and earthy, while Green & Black's is smooth and satiny. Apart from UK top-of-the-choc-pops G&B's, other major brands include Allos, Bonvita, Bruno Fisher, Kaoka, The Cocoa Tree, Chocoreale, Choconat, Evernat, Kakoa (French chocolatiers), and Leissiter's Swiss organic chocolate, sold at Sainsbury's and Waitrose. Montezuma (p. 329) is the latest award-winning brand to watch.

Rapunzel produce the widest range of organic fair-traded chocolates. All their chocolate is sweetened with Rapadura (dried sugar-cane juice). Other brands include Oxfam's Organic Masca chocolate bars, made in Switzerland using Bolivian cocoa and mascobado sugar cane from the Philippines, and Traidcraft. A sign of the times, too, is Rainforest Exquisite's fair-traded organic choc-covered cocoa beans and Brazil nuts, imported from Bolivia; and Organica's milk chocolate caramel bar, the nearest we have to the you-know-what (Mars Bar, of course). The Stamp Collection produce excellent dairy-free chocolate-covered sultanas and sunflower seeds, and apricot centres, plus their new vegan Easter bunny; Plamil is the major non-dairy brand.

I am not a chocoholic, but do find all the organic chocolate I have tried very good: this includes Tesco's own-brand milk chocolate (which I secretly ate, along with everything else, while writing this book). The golden rule with chocolate, as with most other things, is to look at the ingredients: if fine chocolate is your tipple, you want maximum cocoa solids. Five other brands deserve a special mention: look out for them at organic retailers and independents.

Booja Booja organic truffles (SA): Award-winning handmade vegan chocolate truffles, made by a small chocolatier in Norfolk, high in cocoa solids, low in sugar, and made with deodorised coconut oil to give them that melt-in-the-mouth feel: if they sound unlikely, just trust me. Packed in stylish boxes, very delicious, and selling like hot cakes (and they now do Easter Eggs, too). Flavours include Around Midnight Express and cognac-flambéd banana. Their latest much-talked-about variety is their organic champagne truffles. To find your nearest stockist, or for mail order, tel: 01508 499049. Also sold at selected Sainsbury's stores, and available from online organic retailers also.

Duchy Originals Chocolate Thins (SA): Elegant, sophisticated thin rounds of delicious dark chocolate, plain or flavoured with natural oils – ginger, mint or tangerine. Made by Ackermans Chocolates in London, to their usual high standard. Ditto their chocolate-covered Mediterranean orange peel treats: the peel is prepared especially for them on a co-operative in Puglia, southern Italy, and is used in their equally delicious and equally elegant new chocolate orange biscuits.

Jeannette's Organic Chocolate (SA): The last word in luxury, a popular continental brand of handmade dark and milk chocolates, containing minimum sugar and maximum cocoa solids, made by a family firm of chocolatiers in Holland, certified by SKAL, available loose or boxed, with over twenty tantalising centres to choose from.

Gerbana (SA): The new fair-trade brand that is catching everyone's eye. These brightly coloured milk chocolate bars are made from chocolate-covered dried fruits: Banola – bananas; Mangola – mango; and Pineola – pineapple. The pack says 'for the good of humans and nature'. The production story is on the bar. They also produce a whole chocolate-covered dried banana bar, Bananita, and banana pralines.

Plus:

Montezuma's organic and handmade chocolate (SA): 15 Duke Street, Brighton, tel: 01273 324979, email: simon.pattinson@montezuma.co.uk. Organic chocoholics, look no further – here is the UK's first certified and now award-winning organic chocolate-bar manufacturer. A new, small company producing handmade chocolates, chocolate bars, truffles, drinking choc and just about everything else to satisfy a chocoholic's heart's desire, including chilli chocolate, all on sale in their shop. Special orders taken. Ring for the mail order catalogue. To find out more, or to order online, visit their excellent and mouth-watering website: **www.montezumas.co.uk**.

Cocoa spreads and drinks

These are now commonplace. As well as Green & Black's hot chocolate, hazelnut chocolate spread and cocoa powder, other good products include: cacao and chocolate powder (Rapunzel); chocolate spreads (Allos, Bio-Choco, Chocoreale, La Moretta, Rapunzel and Voegel); choco-cream and chocolate hazelnut spread (La Mokita, whose hazelnuts are grown in a village outside Rome, Martlett and Molen Aartje); chocolate drinks and hot chocolate (Granovita, Prewett's, Joannusmolen, Rapunzel, Tra'fo, Molen Aartje); and cocoa powder (Infinity Foods, Hambleden Herbs and Equal Exchange Fairtrade). Newest of all is new company Cocounique's organic chocolate-flake drink, which contains 55.5% cocoa solids. The flakes can also be used as a luxury topping to sprinkle on desserts and ice-cream, and in cakes – or on your organic cappuccino.

PROFILE: GREEN AND BLACK'S

Green & Black's award-winning chocolate, on sale just about everywhere, has become synonymous with high-quality chocolate that is also organic. Dedicated to the organic cause, they trade directly with organic cocoa producers in the Dominican Republic and elsewhere, who receive a premium for their cocoa beans. Green & Black's milk chocolate uses organic milk from farms in the Bavarian Alps. Their dark chocolate contains 70% cocoa solids; their milk chocolate, 34% cocoa solids and 27% whole-milk powder. All their chocolate carries the Soil Association symbol. Their Maya Gold was the first chocolate to carry the Fairtrade logo. Their range continues to grow and includes luxury bite-sized chocs, truffles, Easter eggs, chocolate-covered almonds, cooking chocolate, and the best white chocolate buttons ever. In addition, they produce hot chocolate, hazelnut chocolate spread and ice-cream – their latest wicked varieties are dark toffee and their raved-about organic white. Their chocolate is also used in Village Bakery products.

But that, in a sense, is just the start. I cheerfully admit to being overwhelmed with admiration for what they do and the way they do it: you simply cannot fault them. Visit their delightful website:

www.greenandblacks.com – one of the best there is – and you will probably agree. As well as their products, the website includes everything from the history of chocolate, growing chocolate organically, making chocolate and yummy recipes, to the email address of their resident chef and chocolate expert, Micah; all this, plus thought-provoking glimpses of the rainforests of Central America.

▲▲▲

ORGANIC DRIED BEANS AND OTHER PULSES, PLUS GRAINS

Organic grains, beans and other pulses can be bought from major supermarkets as well as from healthfood shops and organic retailers. It's worth remembering that organic soya beans and maize are the only kind of these crops that are guaranteed not to be genetically modified.

Pulses include everything from haricot beans, chickpeas, mung beans and split peas to the much-prized creamy pale-green flageolets and slate-grey Puy lentils. Most are imported from America and Canada, but some come from Slovakia, Turkey and elsewhere (it's worth noting that pesticide residues, even in conventionally grown pulses, are generally low). The selection of grains available is equally impressive: every kind of rice (Biona has a very good specialist range) including – at last – white risotto rices, whole grains such as wheat and rye, as well as millet, buckwheat, popcorn and couscous and bulgur wheat, plus excellent organic polenta from Italy (which you can now buy ready-made, too).

Extra-special from Probios (see p. 313) is Cascine Orsini vacuum-packed organic arborio rice, grown in Verona. There is only a limited production, which means it's only available for a few months (October–June) every year until stocks run out (Fresh & Wild and Harvey Nichols in London sell it, for example).

Unusual grains include those from South America, such as quinoa and amaranth seed; spelt, already mentioned in this book, which is useful for those with allergies to normal wheat; and kamut. All are pleasantly nutty, and will be enjoyed by those who appreciate whole grains; quinoa, especially, is becoming more popular. It is a highly nutritious, gluten-free seed, native to the Andes and a traditional staple since the Incas. It belongs to the beet (Chenopodium) family, is rich in protein, and contains all the essential amino acids, calcium and iron. Quinoa Real specialise in fair-traded quinoa products from an organic farming co-operative in Bolivia, cultivated 4,000 metres up in the Andes. Fair-trading also helps to prevent the drift towards producing coca (the plant from which cocaine is produced). Quinoa takes fifteen minutes to cook, expanding to become soft like millet, and has a mild, slightly nutty flavour. The Quinoa Real range comprises quinoa mueslis, pastas, a sandwich loaf, dried soups, plain and chocolate-covered rice; cakes, pretzels (salted crackers) and cookies. They also produce an excellent recipe leaflet.

The two major importers of organic pulses and grains are Infinity Foods and Suma, though smaller companies such as Community Foods and Essential deal in them also. All are wholesalers who sell on to retail outlets, either in bulk for the retailer to repack under his own label, or prepacked with their label. Country Harvest and Crazy Jack are two other well-known and respected brands. Epicure have brought out an excellent range of organic rices in stylish tubular cartons. Search the shelves of organic supermarkets and you will also find biodynamically grown rice from small co-operatives such as Azienda Agricola Cascine Orsine, while Rapunzel's range includes kamut and wood-dried green spelt.

Value for money

You can expect to pay around 10–25% more for organic pulses and grains, but since all are relatively cheap foods, the extra per portion is minimal. Organic supermarkets and shops often sell them loose which, as usual, is the most economical way to buy. Canned cooked organic beans, such as chickpeas, kidney beans, butter beans and mixed beans are excellent, and immensely useful. Suma can theirs in spring water – even better.

Cooking with organic pulses and grains

From the culinary point of view you can expect to find two main differences between organically grown and conventional dried pulses and grains. The first is appearance. Organic pulses are not uniformly shiny or cosmetically perfect; chickpeas, for example, are generally smaller and occasionally have a slightly wizened look, and you can expect variations in size, colour and shape in most beans. As any good gardener will tell you, this is perfectly natural. You will also find that, for instance, couscous, bulgur wheat and polenta are darker and coarser. This is a good sign because – and here is the second difference – when they look like this they tend to be nutty and more concentrated in flavour. My particular favourite, stoneground organic polenta, tastes very different from the normal bland kind. The flavour differences in organic pulses are much less marked than in organic grains, though generally they seem to have a slightly fuller flavour and a creamier texture than their conventional equivalents. Soaking and cooking times for organic and conventional pulses and grains are usually the same as for ordinary kinds, but note that brown risotto rice takes approximately twice as long as conventional risotto rice.

The fact that organic dried pulses and grains are not cosmetically perfect does not mean, of course, that they should get away with being substandard. Inspect the packets carefully; they should not contain many broken beans or chipped grains, any debris, or any other signs of inferiority.

Organic pulses and grains have the same shelf life as conventional ones; store in a cool, dark place.

Organic dried fruit

A full range of organic dried fruit is available, including Italian citrus peel sweetened with maize syrup, pitted French prunes and intensely flavoured tropical dried fruit – mango, pineapple, papaya and banana. As you would expect, their flavour is excellent. You will notice that organic dried fruit is darker; this is because none are sprayed with sulphur dioxide. To give you an idea of what else conventionally grown dried fruit may contain, one ready-to-eat brand of luxury mixed dried fruit I found to include glucose syrup, salt, glazing agents, vegetable oil, glycerine, potassium sorbate, sulphur dioxide and tartaric acid. Also, unlike most conventional dried fruit, the organic sort is coated not with mineral oil but with organic sunflower oil, and chopped organic dried fruit is coated with organic rice flour. No need to point out that pesticide residues in conventional dried fruit mirror those found in fresh fruit.

Like nuts, organic dried fruit is often sourced from different areas from conventional dried fruit, and this has a bearing not only on its quality but also on its price. Organic dates, for example, primarily come from Israel and are much plumper and juicier (and more expensive) than the usual non-organic Iranian ones, while all organic currants are the Vostizza brand from Greece, which are the best you can buy. Apricots are another case in point. Though organic dried fruit is generally expensive compared with the standard sort, compare, say, unsulphured non-organic apricots with organic ones and you will find there is only a 15–20% difference in price, yet the flavour is incomparably better. (Indeed, I could not live without them.)

Organic sultanas are a bargain – a few pence extra, at most. Quality is consistently improving, and you should find little or no quality difference between organic and conventional dried fruit of the same grade. Prices do vary according to outlet, so it's worth shopping around.

Packets of organic dried fruits – mango, papaya, pineapple, banana chips – make excellent snacks. Full marks to Traidcraft for their organic fair-traded kiddie packs of sundried mango.

ORGANIC NUTS AND SEEDS

A sign of the organic times are snazzy packs of organic nuts and seeds on supermarket shelves, including Crazy Jack's and supermarket own-brands. Organic pine nuts are more readily available, and organic macadamia nuts have arrived. Pollen Organic's honey-coated nuts – cashews, almonds and mixed nuts – are a winner. Ditto, treat of treats, Christmas bags of unshelled organic walnuts and Brazils at my local Waitrose. You will often find that these have a better flavour, partly because they are sometimes sourced from different countries and may be grown from different varieties. Organic almonds, for example, which come from Spain, are the prime example: they have a darker, thicker and more bitter skin but a far richer, more distinctive flavour than the conventional bland almonds from California, and are to be especially recommended; as are jumbo organic cashew nuts.

It's the same with certain seeds. The most noteworthy are organic pumpkin seeds – from Hungary, not China. The Rapunzel ones, for instance, are darker-skinned, larger, plumper and far more delicious than your average pumpkin seeds. I find the same with African organic sesame seeds; but having chomped my way through several bags, I can detect little noticeable difference between conventional and organic sunflower seeds. There is sometimes, as so often with organic crops, more cosmetic variation, so do not expect them to be all the same size, shape or colour.

It's well worth pointing out that, organic or not, nuts and seeds do not last for ever – around nine to twelve months at most – so check that the packs still have lots of life left in them. The higher the oil content – it is particularly high, for example, in hazelnuts, walnuts, Brazils, coconut and sesame seeds – the shorter the shelf life. Nuts have a shorter shelf life than seeds, and are particularly prone to rancidity. Both should be stored somewhere cool and dark – never in the light.

Since all organic nuts and seeds are grown without artificial fertilisers or synthetic pesticides, yields are lower. Nor are they treated with fumigants during shipment and storage, as is often the case with conventional nuts and seeds.

Because supplies are limited, they cost anything from 50% more than conventional nuts and seeds. For the best value, buy them loose when you can. As they are very light, the extra cost per portion of sesame, sunflower and pumpkin seeds is minimal, and these are good organic items to change to when you can. I personally couldn't go back to conventional almonds, either.

TIP: Toasted organic hazelnuts, walnuts and sesame seeds all make an excellent salad dressing for salad leaves, as well as for vegetables such as cooked green beans, beetroot, cauliflower and broccoli. Toast and crush one tablespoon or so of the nuts or seeds with a little salt with a pestle and mortar, stir in organic olive oil and drizzle over the salad or vegetables.

Organic chestnuts :Food for the gods. Quite how chestnuts are classified from a culinary point of view I'm not sure, but two new arrivals, both marketing certified organic chestnut products, are the French brand Primeal, who do dried and roasted chestnuts and fabulous chocolate, apple and cinnamon and vanilla chestnut spreads; and Sierra Rica from Andalucía, whose ancient chestnut groves produce superb chestnuts, available in jars, peeled and cooked or as sweet chestnut purée.

ORGANIC JAMS, SPREADS AND MARMALADE

Commercial organic jams, spreads and marmalades are often made from organic fruit and a natural organic sweetener, be it concentrated apple or other fruit juice, or honey, and natural fruit pectin. This means that, as well as being healthier, they do not taste like ordinary fruit and white-sugar jams, and so are not to everyone's taste. They tend to be more concentrated, and the use of apple juice can sometimes produce an aftertaste not found in ordinary jams. Organic fruit spreads consist of mainly fruit, have a thick, soft texture, are suitable for diabetics and typically contain less than half the calories of conventional jams. They can be used in many ways: as a filling for cakes and pancakes, mixed with organic yoghurt as an instant dessert, made into sweet-sour sauces, or thinned down with a little extra fruit juice and laced with a dash of brandy as a fruit sauce to accompany ice-cream. The varieties available continue to increase – from La Sirene's exotic organic lychee, banana, pineapple, mango and passion-fruit jams and vanilla and cinnamon jellies, and artisan French jams and jellies, such as Organic Breton's with extra-high fruit content, to reduced-sugar spreads.

The fruit content of organic jams and spreads varies, though most contain more than many conventional brands. The higher the fruit content, the fruitier the flavour and, generally, the higher the quality. Note, too, that the size of jars varies, and take it into account when comparing prices. There is an ever-growing choice, including own-brands, British brands, including conventional manufacturers such as Wilkins & Sons and Baxter's, and the well-known natural-foods brand Martlett, as well as imported brands such as these:

Achillea: Organic Italian preserves, made with 80% fruit, 10% malt and 10% apple juice concentrate. The range comprises apple, apricot, bilberry and chestnut. 300 g jars.

Allos: A range of high-quality tangy pure-fruit spreads, sweetened with neutral-flavoured agave syrup, which gives a fresh, vibrant flavour, and set with natural pectin and lemon juice. The range comprises organic apricot, blackcurrant, cherry, strawberry and wild blueberry. 250 g jars.

Crofter's Organic Conserves: A recently introduced American range, with 7 flavours including Golden Apricot, Sicilian Blood Orange and Wild Blackberry. 283 g jars.

De Rit: Produce a range of deluxe organic fruit conserves sweetened with a mild wild honey and set with natural lemon-rind pectin, some to Demeter standard. If you want a flavour most like conventional jams, try these. The range comprises apricot, strawberry and blackcurrant, Demeter-registered cherry and plum, Wild Forest and wild raspberry conserve, and marmalade. 400 g jars.

Ekoland: An extensive variety including apricot, blackcurrant, blueberry, blue plum, buckthorn, cranberry, elderberry, mixed-berry, morello cherry and orange marmalade spreads. 250 g jars.

More British brands:

All Natural Preserving Company (SA): A specialist preserve and chutney company, based in Dorset. Their organic range of conserves includes blackberry and apple and cherry.

Clearspring (SA):Produce a range of full-bodied, fresh-tasting organic fruit spreads, containing 50% (they say) fewer calories than conventional jams, and sweetened with fruit juices instead of sugar. Choose from prune, strawberry, blueberry, orange and sour cherry.

Meridian (SA): Manufacture high-quality all-fruit spreads, containing only organic fruit, sweetened with concentrated organic apple juice and set with lime pectin. The flavour is excellent, and they are delicious with yoghurt. The range comprises apricot, blackcurrant, morello cherry, strawberry, wild blueberry and Seville orange. Recipe leaflets available, 284 g jars.

Home-made organic jams and marmalades

(Or the next best thing.) Where preserves are concerned, the nearer you can get to home-made, often the fruitier and fresher the taste will be. A number of organic producers manufacture jams on a small scale. Seek them out when you can:

Botton Village, North Yorks (Demeter): Produce a range of jams, jellies and marmalades from organic fruit and organic raw cane sugar, for sale at the Food Centre shop on the estate, at local outlets, at Bumblebee wholefood shop in North London and at some Camphill Village Trust centres. The range comprises apricot, blackcurrant, superb gooseberry, redcurrant, rhubarb and ginger, and strawberry jam; blackcurrant and redcurrant jelly, and Seville orange and grapefruit marmalade. 340 g jars.

Duchy Originals (SA): Worth mentioning because of their excellent bursting-with-fruit-and-flavour organic raspberry preserve with lime (on sale at Sainsbury's). Their other preserves are their award-winning lemon curd and coarse-cut clementine marmalade (though it doesn't for me pack the tart punch of Seville marmalade). 340 g jars.

The Herb Stall (SA): You cannot possibly get nearer to home-made than Jo Fowler's preserves, because she makes them all herself. Her delicious lemon curd, made with local organic eggs and Castle Dairy's organic butter, is as good as you will ever make. She also makes organic strawberry, rhubarb, ginger and banana jam, 3 different marmalades, whole-grain mustard and tomato and mango chutney. Available at their farm and at their shop in Lancaster (see p. 451) and at organic shops.

Kitchen Garden Preserves (SA): This small company, run by Barbara Moinet, who began by making jams in her own kitchen, produces superb high-quality organic jams, chutneys and marmalades – still cooked like you and I would. They are made in small batches (around 12–30 jars at a time), in open pans on domestic stoves. Their range includes award-winning Seville marmalade, wild blueberry and apple jam, and Christmas lines such as organic brandy butter and cranberry jelly with whole cranberries. They buy local first, then UK organic fruit whenever possible, and sell through independents and farmers; markets, through Graig Farm Organics and **www.realfooddirect.com**, or direct by mail order. For nearest stockists and mail order, tel: 01453 759612. For more, visit their website: **www.kitchengardenpreserves.co.uk**.

Thursday Cottage (SA): Another speciality high-quality jam-maker, based in Lyme Regis. They make all their preserves in small quantities, around 20–30 jars at a time, and produce 4 organic marmalades and organic raspberry jam. To find out more, visit their website: **www.Thursday-cottage.com**.

Village Bakery (SA): Make their own high-quality blackcurrant, damson, gooseberry, plum and raspberry jams, and Seville orange and three-fruits marmalades from organic fruit and raw cane sugar. Available by mail order, 340 g jars.

ORGANIC JUICES

Organic juices, made from organic fruit and vegetables, are health drinks in their own right. They come fresh or concentrated, clear or thick, and range from the familiar apple, orange and carrot to exotic combinations. Almost all are imported and the most popular are now stocked by major multiples, but you will need to go to an organic retailer or healthfood shop to get an idea of the many brands and varieties available. Most are bottled, though a few brands, notably Libby's, come in cartons; and there are fresh pressed chilled juices such as the excellent Grove Fresh range (though mind the caps – they can be infuriating to screw back on again). Some supermarkets have their own-brand versions, for example Waitrose's fresh organic and apple pressés.

The juice market generally is a 'happening' market, as people become more health-conscious and want a non-alcoholic drink that will do them good. Libby's is one major conventional company to have brought out organic apple and orange juice, and is planning more. We can expect to see more mini and maxi organic juice packs, too. Though costs of popular juices vary from brand to brand, for the peace of mind you get from drinking organic juices the extra cost over comparable conventional juices – around 20% – is not unreasonable.

Once opened, bottled juices and cartons will keep in the fridge for three or four days, or longer for certain brands, though they are best drunk as soon as possible. Organic apple juice is cheaper than other organic juices, and some is made from named varieties of apples. The thick, pulpy juices pressed from the whole fruit are more like a food, and best taken in small glasses and savoured slowly – which is what juice therapists recommend for any juice. Prune juice is surprisingly good.

Organic fruit and vegetable juices can also be used in cooking. Eden, for example, have produced two recipe leaflets for sweet and savoury dishes, using their organic carrot, vegetable and beetroot juices, written by cookery expert Roz Denny; write to PO Box 1059, Pulborough, West Sussex, RH20 2YX.

Given the intensive use of pesticides on fruit, it's not surprising that residues are detected in some conventional fruit juices, including blackcurrant drinks, and in apple juice particularly. (In 1994, the last time they were sampled, the Working Party on Pesticide Residues report found that a quarter of UK-produced apple juice samples contained permitted fungicide residues and 10% contained multiple residues.) Statistics show that infants especially, and small children too who are all more susceptible to toxic chemicals than adults are, drink much higher quantities of juices, especially orange and apple. So try to give them organic when you can. The only preservative used in organic fruit and vegetable juices is vitamin C. Most come in large bottles (700, 735 and 750 ml) and 200 ml bottles are also available. Like conventional juices, these days some of the cheaper ones are made from concentrates, so check to see.

Most that I have tried have been excellent, with pure bursting-with-health flavours. Pasteurised chilled orange juice inevitably has that slightly flat flavour when compared with the freshly squeezed sort. Varietal apple juices from small producers are the tops and are really distinctive, and pear and apricot juices are uniformly delicious. Add plain or sparkling mineral water to thick fruit juices, and you have a thirst-quenching drink.

Bottled fruit juices are good for breakfast, or diluted as non-alcoholic alternatives when entertaining. Vegetable juices are good lunchtime revivers – easier than making soup – or can be taken instead of a meal if you're feeling too tired to eat. Both make delicious nutritional pick-ups. Carrot juice, reckoned to be the most cleansing and revitalising, is the one to try first, while tomato juice is noted for its blood-purifying properties. Vegetable cocktail juices vary slightly in flavour depending on the mix, but are predominantly carrot and tomato. Clear beetroot juice is nothing like as strong as you would imagine. Therapeutically, it's rated second-highest to carrot juice and, like carrot, is recommended extensively in alternative-cancer therapies. *Juice Therapy*, by Ray Hill, available from Sunshine Health Foods gives more information about the healing properties of organic juices and about how Biotta juices are made. Remember that mail order organic wine companies also stock them.

Major brands

Major brands, producing a range of bottled juices, include Achillea, La Bio Idea, Libby's, Biona, Biotta, Eden, Evernat, Jacoby (Demeter), Rabenhorst, Sunsweet, the award-winning Vitalia range of pure pressed juices, and Voelkel (Demeter); the well-known apple juice brand, James White, now do a range of organic juices, including apple and carrot and raspberry and pear. Should you get bored with all the rest, Biona have recently introduced an organic Ayurvedic gingko, ginseng and grape juice well-being drink, fermented with Kombucha. The other two flavours in this range are Harmony, with mango juice, and Relaxing, with pineapple juice.

This is how three well-known names produce their bottled juices:

Biotta: a family-run specialist Swiss company that has pioneered organic farming methods for over thirty years and has its own farms, plus others who grow specifically for it in Switzerland, Austria and Israel. All crops (and soils) undertake rigorous laboratory analysis for purity. The fruit is pressed in as natural a way as possible, and the juices preserved by adding lactofermented whey, a process that gives it nutritional extras and is said to benefit intestinal flora, making it easier to digest and absorb nutrients and helping to increase resistance to intestinal infections. Note that this gives a slightly sharp tang, for example, to their carrot juice. Their juices will keep for up to eight days in the fridge. They are regularly used in cure centres, and their specially formulated Breuss vegetable juice is used in cancer clinics and as a dietary tonic.

Eden: A popular brand. The juices are flash-pasteurised in the bottle, which minimises nutrient losses to 1–2%. The beetroot juice (clear and delicious) is fermented with lactofermenting bacteria, as described above. New flavours include an excellent red grape juice and tomato juice.

Voelkel: A high-quality Demeter-registered German brand run by a family firm involved in organic farming for generations. Their extensive range includes many mixed juices such as apple and pineapple; apple, blackcurrant and grape; and apple and mango; plus single-fruit juices, Seven Dwarfs (children's) and Vital-A.C.E. juice. The bottles – small, medium and large – are filled to order, and arrive in the shops eight days, at most, after bottling. Their juices are processed with the same attention to detail as Biotta's.

Other widely available brands include Achillea, La Bio-Idea, Biona, Evernat, Jacoby, Rabenhorst, Vitalia and Whole Earth.

Local brands

Organic apple growers, and those in conversion, are increasingly pressing their own fruit to make their own juices, sold at the farm gate, locally or through farmers' markets: all are excellent, so look out for them when you can. Other small producers are:

Crones (SA): apart from their cider (see p. 270) they produce award-winning single-variety organic apple juices and apple and pear blends, plus organic pink grapefruit juice.

Hermitage Farm (SA): Herefordshire apple growers who produce their own unfiltered apple juice (Cox and Red Pippin), available locally and at Sainsbury's in Herefordshire.

Luscombe Organic Drinks (SA): Apart from their Devon cider (see p. 271) this company produces a wide range of award-winning single-variety apple juices, pear and apple juice, plus ginger beer, Sicilian lemonade and elderflower bubbly.

Oakwood Farm (SA): Kentish apple growers, near Robertsbridge, who produce six single-variety organic apple juices from their own orchards, on sale at organic shops and independents in the south east, plus small bottles (using in-conversion apples) available locally and at Lewes farmers' market.

Sedlescombe Vineyard (SA): Their 1066 brand comprises apple, pear, English grape, apple and blackcurrant, apple and grape; widely available. For their full entry, see p. 261.

Three tips:

- Serve organic apple juice at room temperature or lightly chilled. Delicious as a base for fruit salads, punches and non-alcoholic fruit drinks, and to use on muesli instead of milk.
- Make fruit refreshers by diluting bottled fruit juices with fizzy mineral water. Add a twist of organic lemon or orange.
- Heat carrot juice with strips of fresh chilli (if you like them) and add chopped fresh mint for an instant lunch and pick-up (I live on this in winter).

OLIVE OIL

Thanks to recent research establishing the health benefits of the Mediterranean diet, the world's most ancient product has seen a spectacular revival and is now the oil *de rigueur* for modern cooks. Sadly, the image of olive oil as a 'pure' food, produced by natural or traditional methods, is no longer realistic. Most is produced from olives grown by modern methods dependent on chemical fertilisers and pesticides. By contrast, organic olive oil is pressed from olives grown naturally, using organic methods of cultivation.

Organic groves are often in mountainous regions, where pests are less prevalent anyway and where it is difficult to cultivate *except* by traditional methods. Where necessary, in order to qualify for organic certification, contamination by conventional olive groves is avoided by physical barriers such as a river, strips of non-agricultural land, mountains or even dense bands of trees.

The good news is that organic production has increased substantially and organic olive oil can now be found on most supermarket shelves – Waitrose, Tesco, Marks & Spencer and Sainsbury's have all recently introduced own-brand, as well as stocking the one that I use most, the excellent Meridian (also on sale at Safeway and Booth's). Olive oil is also being produced in Australia, New Zealand and Israel, who are pioneering new varieties. Though Spanish organic olive oils predominate, there are now more French, Italian and Greek ones, plus some from Portugal and even California, a good proportion of which are pressed in the traditional way. Currently, all organic olive oils are grown to the same standards throughout the EU. They are certified by one of the recognised organic certification bodies, which inspects the groves and the production procedures and whose code number or symbol should be present on the label.

Broadly, there are two types to choose from – everyday olive oils and premium ones. The everyday sort is readily available from all outlets, including home delivery and online retailers. Premium olive oils are available from high-class food shops and specialist wine merchants and by mail order. Waitrose stock the excellent Umbrian PaxJani organic olive oil, one of the first Italian oils to be certified and produced by David McTaggert, founder of Greenpeace International (a nice eco-touch to make you feel even better when you buy it). As Nature Intended stores in London stock an exemplary selection.

Everyday olive oils

Usually produced on a commercial scale in modern mills using organic olives from various growers. They are ideal for general cooking and for dressings. Apart from supermarket own-label, widely available brands include La Bio-Idea (Italian) and Sunita (Greek), plus Meadowsweet, Midsummer and Suma (no country of origin stated). Two other good-value ones are Provence Régime and Rapunzel. The most common brand, Meridian (Spanish), is exceptional value in that it is an award-winning premium oil but comes within the everyday price bracket, as does Bio Aras olive oil, both from Andalucía.

Premium olive oils

Most are produced by small growers using traditional methods, which include picking the olives by hand and pressing the oil in traditional mills. Supply is limited. They should be used for dips and dressings, for salads, hot vegetables, pasta and risotto, and to pour over grilled meats and fish as a final enhancement.

They include Mani (Greek); L'Estornell and Nuñez de Prado (Spanish); Romanico (Catalan); Oleificio Gabro, Campo, Il Casale, De Vito, Fattoria Roi, La Terra e il Cielo and Azienda Agricola S. Christiana (Italian); Ravida (Sicilian); Sadeg and Spectrum Organic (Californian); Mas de la Dame, Mas de Gourgonnier (Provençal) and Sphère (French). Fortnum and Mason in London sell the only Demeter-registered olive oil, from Fattoria Mose in Sicily, under their own label. Seggiano estate-bottled olive oil from a small group of growers near Siena in Tuscany is made from a unique and ancient variety of olivastro olive, which produces a mild, delicate oil.

Prices

Producing organic olive oil is a precarious, costly, labour-intensive business that requires dedication. Given this, and the fact that all organic olive oil is extra-virgin (the highest grade you can buy), prices are not extortionate – and increased supply means that they have recently come down. Everyday oils currently sell at 10–20% more than an equivalent conventionally produced oil. Premium oils, which are comparable to conventional estate-bottled oils, command a similar high price. Best-value oils are those available in 5-litre tins. Look out for introductory promotional offers, too. As with the conventional kind, Greek and Spanish organic olive oils represent the best value for money – watch out for more of both (Italian and French are usually more expensive). Latest news is that La Puglia, in southern Italy, one of the most important areas for olive oil in the world, with 30% of all Italian olive groves and over 4,000 organic growers, is gearing up to expand its production of organic olive oil and olives and to broaden its customer base.

Do organic olive oils taste different from conventional ones?

The flavour of all olive oils, whether organically produced or not, depend on the country of origin, the variety of olive, the climate, the acidity of the oil, how it is processed, and whether the oil is blended to suit a particular market. However, because organic olive oil is produced on a much smaller scale than the conventional kind, and often by small producers using traditional methods, many organic olive oils are individual oils with distinctive flavour notes.

Buying and storing

Olive oil is a matter of personal taste, so the first rule is to try different types to discover which ones you like. Remember that olive oils in dark bottles or in tins are protected from the light, which causes oxidation and makes the oils deteriorate.

The two guiding rules when buying olive oil are:

- Never buy oil that has been displayed under bright lights.
- Check the sell-by date; if possible, look for the harvest date – which will tell you when the oil was pressed – and buy the most recent vintage.

If stored correctly, olive oil has a shelf life of two or three years – though you will use it much sooner. As all organic olive oil is extra-virgin, neither processed nor heat-treated, you should store it carefully. Keep it somewhere cool as well as dark, and make sure you don't leave it on the table (again, to avoid exposing it to the light).

TIP:

Extra-virgin olive oil may become cloudy and solid in cold weather, and unfiltered oils will form a deposit in the bottom of the bottle.

Three suppliers worth knowing about:

The Oil Merchant Ltd, 47 Ashchurch Grove, London W12 9BU, tel: 020 8740 1335, fax: 020 8740 1319, email: The-Oil-Merchant@compuserve.com. The country's leading olive oil specialist, which stocks seven delicious organic olive oils, including extra-good value-for-money Nuñez de Prado in 5-litre tins. Catalogue available, and help and advice given.

Take It From Here Ltd, freephone order number 0800 137064, supply Roi Carte Noir and Roi Biologica.

The Organic Wine Company, tel: 01494 446557, supply four organic olive oils, including the award-winning Mas de Gourgonnier Provençal.

ORGANIC OLIVES

Organic table olives are grown in the same way as those used for organic olive oil. In addition, the vast majority are not subjected to treatment with caustic soda – common in conventional olive-curing – but are cured entirely naturally with salt and water only. Like the oil, they are now more readily available, and there's more choice of both green and black, plain and stuffed (with garlic, almonds or red pepper). You can buy them loose in organic supermarkets, and in jars and packs elsewhere, including some major supermarkets. They do vary in taste – some are sharper and some are more salty, so ask your retailer what they taste like first. Whether organic or not, the quality of olives varies enormously. The variety of the olive counts for a lot. If you find some organic niçoise olives – small and sweet – snap them up. Brands include Bio Aras, Community Isana, Bio Verde, Sunita and TerraSana. Pollen Organics' Kalamata olives in herbs and extra-virgin olive oil are excellent. Once opened, keep in the fridge. Alternatively, a good way to store them – and the best way for any loose olives you buy – is to drain off the brine and keep them in a small jar covered with olive oil.

Organic olive pastes, made from minced olives, olive oil and seasonings – for instance, Gaea organic green olive spread from Greece (you can buy it at Waitrose) and Olivella black Meditrinalia paste from Italy – are widely available. Use these to spread on croûtes, or to make your own tapénade, adding pounded organic capers, garlic and anchovies.

OTHER ORGANIC OILS

A complete range of other organic oils is available, including cooking oils, speciality oils such as delicious walnut and hazelnut, and, from the USA, the latest state-of-the-art health oils described on p. 293 (brands include Biona's new Oxyguard range). Bio Planète produce organic hazelnut, peanut and rapeseed oils as well as sunflower. All are cold-pressed, thereby preserving the maximum nutritional value, which is considerable, as well as the flavour. A cold-pressed organic sunflower oil, for example, rather than conventionally bland, will taste strongly of sunflower seeds, so allow for this in your cooking, keeping such oils for salad dressings rather than for frying. And because the flavours are so positive, you need very little as a flavouring agent. Organic grapeseed oil is excellent as a mild general-purpose oil, and for making mayonnaise.

The precautions to be taken when buying and storing olive oil apply to these oils too. There are many brands available. Rapunzel have the largest selection, all in dark-brown bottles so as to exclude the light, including hazelnut, pumpkin seed, walnut, soya, safflower, sunflower and sesame; and also organic coconut fat in jars, for your organic South East Asian cooking. Clearspring have recently brought out a complete range of all the cold-pressed organic oils you could wish for, produced to their usual high standards. And new in autumn 2001 is a range of flavoured oils such as mint, chilli and garlic to use for salad dressings, dips and so on, from Castle Aromatics in Ross-on-Wye.

ORGANIC PASTA AND NOODLES

Does anyone need another brand of organic pasta? I doubt it. Walk into any organic store anywhere in the world and you will find shelves stacked high with them, from classic Italian wheat pastas, plain or flavoured with everything from beetroot to seaweed, Asian rice noodles, silky-smooth traditional Japanese noodles, to every kind of non-wheat and gluten-free pasta, made from a variety of grains such as corn, millet and even soya. Today that list has expanded even more to include hemp pastas (an excellent non-wheat product) and several brands of chilled fresh organic pastas, plain and stuffed, ready to eat. Speciality pastas have gone crazy: Primeal, for example, produce organic spirulina pasta, chestnut and turmeric and poppy-seed tagliatelle, and lemon and saffron spirals. More down to earth, organic pastas for babies such as those made by Baby Organix, and Epicure's cute 'Pasta Pals' car and teddy-bear shapes for kids, have scored a definite hit.

Italian pastas still dominate. They come in all shapes and sizes, at prices to suit all pockets, and cook in exactly the same way as conventional pastas. Like conventional pastas, too, some are made by artisan craftsmen in the traditional ways, like the beautiful Terra de Puglia, or Antico Pastificio Umbro's egg pastas made in southern Italy with purified water and packed in see-through 250 gm packs, or Probios's handmade wholewheat flavoured gourmet pastas made in Florence; and others are made in modern factories for the mass market.

Because intensive farming methods dominate the production for the world's staple grains, especially wheat, this means that organic pastas and noodles, like bread, have an especially important role to play. Buying them helps support and develop sustainable grain-growing methods, and brings you pasta and noodles produced as nature intended. All major supermarkets now stock a selection of dried organic pastas, and most sell fresh or frozen pasta meals.

Remember that although organic wheat pasta (apart, perhaps, from the artisan handmade kind) cooks and tastes exactly the same as conventional pasta, organic non-wheat pastas, produced primarily for those allergic to wheat or gluten, taste entirely different – more like the grain they are made from – and most cook to a softer texture. Unless your dietary requirements say otherwise, it all depends on what you like. Food writer Annie Bell describes spelt pasta as pinkish in colour and quite fragrant and earthy; it works best, she says, with rich vegetable sauces such as ratatouille, spinach or aubergine – though try convincing my husband, who would not sacrifice traditional pasta for anything. All organic pasta is made with certified organic durum wheat or other grains, and any other ingredients, such as the tomato and spinach in flavoured pastas, are also certified organic.

Quality

Probably the most important variable is whether a particular pasta is made in the traditional way or using the modern extruding method. The finest pastas – such as those mentioned above – are cut using bronze dies and dried slowly at low temperatures. Research shows that pasta dried this way keeps the vitamin and protein content intact and cooks better. Many small Italian organic pasta manufacturers, such as the Campo and award-winning La Terra e il Cielo co-operatives, and the Barbagallo family in Fiumefreddo in Sicily, pasta-makers since 1911, use this technique. The Barbagallos grow their own organic durum wheat, and to preserve maximum flavour and vitality they grind it fresh in their own mill, and mix it with pure mountain water. The Sakuri family, who live in the foothills of the Japanese Alps, use the same method, air-drying their organic pasta (available from Clearspring) over bamboo rods for 30 hours. Seeds of Change is one major brand whose pastas are produced in the traditional way, cut with bronze dies and slowly air-dried. Biona, too, have brought out their own range of handmade, hand-rolled dried spelt and egg pastas.

Brands

Major British brands include the Enjoy Organic Company, Evernat and Seeds of Change. The Noodle Company produce spinach, chilli and garlic as well as plain noodles; Eco-Zone, seaweed pastas, and Mother Hemp (see p. 295), hemp pastas. Imported brands include Barbagallo, Biona, Bionaturae, Buonapasta, Campo, De Rit, Ecogrande, Eunature, Eu Vita, La Bio-Idea, La Terra e il Cielo and Rapunzel. Fresh pasta brands include Del Ugo, Marigold, Biona, Isana and Viana, and Everfresh's Giovanni range of pasta-spaghettini with turmeric, tagliolini with basil and tortellini stuffed with mushroom or smoked tofu. The pastas are egg-free and are not dried but vacuum-packed, which means that they cook like fresh pasta, in 3–5 minutes.

Japanese noodles are becoming quite chic. There are several to choose from, including soba (buckwheat), jinjeno soba (buckwheat and mountain yam), yomagi soba (buckwheat and mugwort), udon (brown wheat), genmai (brown wheat and brown rice) and ramen. They are all instant, and come with their own Japanese soup broth mix. The wonderful Clearspring is the major supplier.

Pasta sauces

Everyone, it seems, wants to make an organic pasta sauce. The range is almost as overwhelming as the range of organic pastas. I must confess that I am not the best judge, as my husband insists on the home-made kind but, organic or not, I'm rarely impressed by any. For my taste a chilled fresh pasta sauce has to be a better bet than those that come out of jars, but many people feel quite differently. The Go Organic range, for example, does not stint on the extra-virgin olive oil, which makes their pasta sauces immediately appealing. People I know speak highly of Seeds of Change sauces too, especially their tomato and roasted garlic. Those made by artisan co-operatives usually score well. If you like red peppers, for example (and who doesn't?), Sierra Rica's organic red pepper sauce, made from puréed peppers and olive oil and with just the right amount of chilli bite, is excellent, and can be used for potatoes and with grilled meat and fish also.

There are almost as many jars of organic pestos around. Pollen Organics's fresh pesto is a winner by anyone's standards. Tideford Organic Foods and Bio-verde also produce very good fresh pestos. Suma have brought out two new bottled vegan pestos, green and red (sundried tomato) pesto. Many a time a dollop of Sacla's organic red pesto, on the sly when no-one was looking, has saved my life as a dressing for salads. And I really like Mother Hemp's organic hemp-seed pestos.

Kids' food

Organic food for kids is growing up and moving on from Pasta Pals, to ready meals and other convenience foods. Designed for children aged from three upwards, a sound range is – at last – becoming more readily available. Its hallmarks are bright and cheerful packaging designed to appeal, and a strong emphasis on nutrition – not perfect, but a better start.

Children's food is a difficult area: there is a need to produce that which is fun, that they will like, that is nutritionally sound – and that will compete successfully with the junk that makes up an awful lot of children's fast food. Thus far the few organic food manufacturers, who have ventured into this area, have acquitted themselves well. Sainsbury's Blue Parrot Café range, developed in consultation with mothers, includes organic apple and strawberry and blackcurrant drinks, apple-juice lollies, jelly bears and mini jam tarts. The French company Vitagermine has just launched its Kalibio range of kids' organic cereal bars,juices, sandwich spreads, chocolate biscuits and snacks. Breakfast cereals – Whole Earth's Cocoa Crunch, Doves Farm Noughts and Crosses, Nature's Path Envirokidz, Amazon Frosted Flakes, Gorilla Munch, Koala Crisp and Orangutan – constitute one of the fastest-growing sectors. Organic kids can also buy their first organic super-nutrient tropical smoothie, Soma's Cool Banana, made from bananas, pineapple, passion fruit and acerola, a Brazilian cherry-like fruit and nature's richest source of vitamin C. You can't do better than that.

Brands to try:

Eastbrook Farms Organic Meat (SA): This company produces Helen Browning's fresh organic pork bangers with spices and honey, available at Sainsbury's and through their home delivery service (see p. 181). The packs include recipes for kids to cook themselves, such as organic bangers and creamy hedgehog mash with onion gravy; new products are being developed.

Pure Organics Ltd (SA): Determined to feed their own children food they could trust, the Pure Organics Company launched the very first range of frozen organic children's ready meals, For Georgia's Sake (named after their daughter), which have proved very popular with mothers. They produce children's sausages, chicken- and beefburgers, chicken nuggets, pork Hulas, premium beef mince, beef- and beanburgers and veggie pizza. They are currently working with the Allergy-Induced Autism Society to make sure that minor ingredients such as yeast extract are not included, and all their meat products are wheat- and dairy-free. The ingredients of all their products are posted in detail on their website, **www.organics.org**. Each product has an identifying batch code number, which when entered into their website enables you to track the ingredients right back to the farm of origin. Available at major supermarkets including Tesco, Sainsbury's and Booth's, and independents. For your nearest stockists, tel: 01980 626263.

Swaddles Green (SA): Already produce a large range of organic dishes suitable for children, available through their home delivery service (see p. 181). They have now launched a separate frozen high-quality children's range of meat product available at independents, including ketchup burgers, chicken nuggets, alphabet spaghetti with chicken sausages, and pork sausages with baked beans.

Sunshine Organics Ltd (SA): A new small organic company producing the Kids Organic Kitchen range of frozen, nutritionally balanced, complete ready meals, including Mincy Monster Mash, Cool Con Carne and Pasta Blasta. For more information, including detailed ingredients list, visit their website at **www.kidzorganickitchen.com**, or email: info@kidzorganickitchen.com. For your nearest stockist, tel: 01926 633086.

CONFECTIONERY AND SAVOURY SNACKS

Three years ago, I wrote that although there were plenty of fruit and nut/seed/chocolate organic bars of one kind or another, including many high-quality bars made without sugar or containing honey or agave syrup, there was very little organic confectionery. Today Sainsbury's sell everyone's favourite, Just Wholefoods delicious, award-winning, gelatine-free, vegan organic jelly babies (buy a packet, and you'll soon see why they are so popular), plus Confectionery Craft's organic lemon barley-sugars and mint humbugs, while at Tesco you can buy their own-brand organic mint humbugs and dairy toffees. Organic lollipops are commonplace, as are Fruit Fruits organic wine gums, all kinds of liquorice sweets (three brands to look out for are Tufty, the American Liquorice Company and Free's Laidback Liquorice sticks); and Tropical Source's Butterscotch Dreams and Raspberry Crush sweets, plus various other organic fruity snacks, such as Cool Fruits' Green Apple, Strawberry and Wild berry bars (as healthy and fruity as you can get). You can also buy organic chewing-gum in four different flavours produced by SpeakEasy, who make peppermints, spearmints, vanillamints and lemonmints as well.

Many are imported, and the vast majority are in packaging you cannot resist, especially Candy Tree sweetie packets – twenty-four sorts of organic sweets, toffees and lollies. A new UK gourmet brand to look out for, with plenty of eye and taste appeal, is Sweet Organics: handmade organic candy sticks and lollipops, plus gelatine-free fruit gums and chocolate beans. All those I have tried, including liquorice sweets, have been impressive: better flavour, less sickly, no artificial undertones, easier to digest than most sweets, and, in some cases, positively moreish.

The range of sweet organic snack bars, including ever more muesli bars, continues to grow (well over a dozen at the last count), including conventional brands like Jordan's. From Clearspring, three wholesomely good newcomers: sesame, sesame and raisin, and an irresistible crunchy organic almond bar, all stuck together with pure organic maple syrup. And how about Organic Earth's honeyed or saffron or chocolate-flavoured popcorn, and sweet rice cakes, too?

Savoury snacks

The range has similarly expanded. So much so, I've lost count of the number of different brands of organic crisps and tortilla chips. Both are addictive, and on sale in major supermarkets. Other savoury snacks include various crackers (watch out for Bioland's Dr Karg Family Bakers' flavoured crispbreads, one of the best yet), water biscuits, pizza crackers, mini pretzels, puffed spelt chips, and spelt pretzels and sticks.

Organic crisps are made with organic potatoes (skins left on), fried in unhydrogenated organic oil, seasoned with sea salt and natural flavourings, which these days include organic vinegar and garden herbs. They have a nutty flavour, and come crinkle-cut, too. Kettle organic handmade crisps, on sale at major supermarkets, are clear winners and compulsively good. No wonder. They're made from a particular variety of potato that remains a trade secret, and each batch is cooked in fresh organic sunflower oil. Tesco have their own brand. Others include Crucial, Gaston's, Stour Valley, Tasty Vittles and Trafo.

Now that GM corn is grown extensively in the USA, organic maize snacks have assumed a greater importance. Again, pesticide residues are frequently detected in conventional samples of maize-based snacks.

Organic tortilla chips come in white, yellow or blue; plain, and in a wide range of flavours, including spicy. Most brands of stoneground tortilla chips, such as Santa Cruz, Fiesta and Apache, are excellent. Taste and price vary, and some are saltier than others, so it's worth trying several. Other brands include Amaizin, Evernat, Garden of Eatin, Margaritas, Mexi-snax, Molen Aartje, Rapunzel and TerraSana. Flavours include natural, basil and tomato, black bean and garlic, Cajun, chilli, French onion, Mexicana hot and sesame. Other maize snacks include taco shells, corn puffs and organic popcorn.
NOTE: Mexi-snax produce both organic and conventional tortilla chips in virtually identical packs. Check the label – the organic version has the certification logo on the bottom of the packet.

Finally, don't forget organic Bombay Mix from Suma, and Organic Earth's irresistibly named Mr Hot Spicy Bombay Mix, or their Love and Movie fruit-and-nut mixes. Remember, you read about them here first.

ORGANIC SOYA AND OTHER NON-DAIRY PRODUCTS

Since the advent of GM soya, this benign bean has rarely been out of the headlines, and whether you are vegan or not the arrival of GM soya has sent what was already a blossoming sector of the market into overdrive. For anyone who does not want to eat GM soya products, or who wants a dairy-free alternative to conventional milk products, organic soya is the obvious solution.

Soya is one of the world's most perfect foods, enjoyed in the East – and a major staple of Japan, China and South East Asia – for many centuries. Soya beans are 35% protein, and like animal protein it contains all the essential amino acids that we need. Soya beans are also high in fibre and a good source of vitamins and minerals (especially calcium), are one of the few plant sources of the essential alpha-linolenic fatty acid, and contain health-protecting phyto-oestrogens (plant hormones that mimic oestrogen).

As a food, soya is impressively versatile. Soya milk can be used instead of cow's milk in exactly the same way for all your cooking, as can soya cream. Tofu (soya bean curd) is an alternative to meat, easy to digest, and can be used in all kinds of ways.

To give you an idea of the range, expanding daily, that one small bean can produce, organic soya products include (apart from soya milk and cream), soya ready meals, yoghurts, frozen desserts, margarine and oil; tofu – plain, smoked, marinated and fried and in the form of burgers, tasty schnitzels, pâtés, terrines, sausages and tempeh product; plus soy sauce, Japanese shoyu and tamari sauces, and miso. All are suitable for vegans. Many will be found in the chilled section. Many organic soya product manufacturers, such as Dragonfly and Paul's, are small concerns who make their tofu in the traditional way and their soya products in small batches.

GM Soya

Just so that you know: soya has become the world's most popular processing aid, and GM soya is now found in at least 60% of processed foods from pizzas to ice-cream, as well as 90% of animal feeds. Labelling laws require that GM derivatives such as lecithin need not be labelled if they contain no foreign DNA or protein, and GM animal feeds do not have to be labelled at all.

Soya milk and yoghurt

An alternative for those who cannot digest, or who don't wish to drink cow's milk, and for vegans. Available in 500 ml or 1 litre cartons in all major supermarkets, including in some cases (like Waitrose) their own brands. Major brands are Bonsoy, Granose, Granovita, Provamel, Unisoy and Vitasoy; some have added calcium. Recently, Provamel have introduced two fruit-flavoured soya milks, apple and pear and orange and pineapple, and Vitasoy offer Carob, Rich Cocoa and Vanilla Delite. Plain sweetened soya milk is also available, including wheat-sweetened (Provamel) and with organic malt (Sunrise).

There are now several brands of organic soya yoghurts, plain and fruit. Brands include Elms Dairy, Granovita, Provamel, Sojasun's (sold in glass jars) and fruity Soy Yofus by Vandemoortele UK. Also new are Feelgood's live Soya Culture drinks in four flavours, including cappuccino, which tastes like real coffee. I have become a convert – Sojasun's natural is my tipple.

Soya desserts

Fresh organic soya desserts are the latest addition. Most are fruity and some are exotic, such as Sojasun's raspberry and passion-fruit and apricot and guava soya desserts, or Provamel's excellent organic layered raspberry and chocolate soya desserts. Feelgood produce four live soya yoghurt desserts, including breakfast-in-a-tub banana and muesli flavour. Ice Delight offer a strawberry and chocolate Frozen Swirl. Others? Marinelli make Frozen Soya Supreme, Swedish Glace frozen non-dairy ice-creams and Lollytots (Swedish Glace on a stick), Biona produce three vegan crème desserts – vanilla, blueberry and strawberry – and Rapunzel make vegan chocolate and vanilla pudding powder, which makes up like custard.

Tofu

Tofu is sold fresh and frozen. The best is creamy and delicate, some brands can be rubbery. On its own it is bland, but its ability to soak up other flavours brings many advantages. There are more brands of organic tofu and tofu savouries than ever, including Bio-Appetite, Biona, Clear Spot, Cauldron Foods, Marigold, Soto and Viana; Clearspring produce plain organic tofu. In Edinburgh, the Engine Shed makes a range including tofu and onion pies and tofu fruit whip, available locally. Plain tofu has a fridge life of three weeks; marinated tofu, two weeks; and fried tofu, five days. You'll find tofu savouries and ready meals of all kinds, from lookalike bacon and sausages, to pâtes, fresh tofu ravioli, Greek-style tofu bites (Bio-Appetite), tofu fricassé and crispy tofu fingers in breadcrumbs (Biona). Organic tofuburgers are surprisingly yummy – another good convenience food to add to your list, whether you are vegetarian or not.

Tofu brands

Biona – Bio-Grill: Biona is one of the best imported brands, whose products can generally be trusted to please. They produce a range of fresh tofu savouries such as their excellent Wiener Schnitzels and lookalike tofu fish fingers in breadcrumbs (mentioned above).

Dragonfly (SA): A small company based in Devon with a mission to convert as many people as possible to the nutritional benefits of tofu, including children. Their award-winning plain tofu, tofu products and tofu Beany Burgers are delicious and widely available. They have recently introduced a selection of Sweet Beanys – chocolate, date, fig, apple, apricot and Fruity.

Paul's (SA): Another small outfit making tofu in the traditional way, whose excellent organic breads are also well known. They produce plain, marinated and fried tofu. Their wide range of savouries includes vegetable samosas, pasties, hot and spicy pies and mushroom and tofu rolls (with a fridge life of 5 days).

Taifun: A German brand with probably the largest range of tofu savouries and certainly the most inventive. Their products are very good and very tasty: plain, almond and sesame, smoked and marinated tofu; carrot and paprika terrine, smoked farmhouse terrine, and six different sausages, including frankfurters, cocktail, and the slicing sort.

TIPS:

- For delicious GM-free gravies, add a spoonful of organic tamari, shoyu or soy sauce. Here is my standard way to make gravy: make a roux with flour and the meat fat left in the roasting tin, add any meat juices plus vegetable cooking liquor or, if not, plain water. Simmer for a few minutes and flavour to taste with organic tamari, soy or shoyu.
- Cubes of ready-marinated, smoked or fried tofu are perfect for kebabs, stir-fries, oriental-style soups, noodles and vegetable casseroles.

Tofu-to-try

- Substitute tofu for cream-cheese when making dips, blend in a blender, and serve with organic crudités or crackers.
- Stir-fry with chopped garlic and ginger, splash with organic tamari, add stir-fried vegetables and serve.
- Marinate tofu cubes in organic tamari, lime or lemon juice, add chopped coriander or mint and add to rice, dried bean and cooked green bean salads.
- Serve baby organic spinach with tofu fried with sesame seeds, slices of mango and toasted coconut chips.
- Marinate cubes of tofu in organic lime or orange juice plus the finely grated rind, thread on to skewers with cubes of banana and pineapple, brush with oil and barbecue.

Other non-dairy drinks

Organic milk drinks and desserts made from grains are widely available from organic retailers and healthfood shops. The most popular is Rice Dream, original and vanilla-flavoured, a naturally sweet drink made from brown rice, imported by Clearspring. Lima make organic Rev Rice drink, and Probios produce an Italian drink called Rice Rice, made from organic brown rice, the first cold pressing of organic sunflower oil, water, and no added sugar. Evernat make a delicious almond milk; EcoMil, an almond, soya and cereal drink; Mill Milk, a vanilla oaty drink; and Oatley, an organic oat milk, available in some major supermarkets. Other non-dairy drinks include Granose banana and chocolate shakes and Perlemande's Alamandina organic almond drink.

You can also buy – at last – organic coconut milk under the Biona label. Omega Nutrition produce coconut fat for cooking.

Non-dairy organic margarines

There are now several brands, including Suma's organic sunflower margarine and reduced-fat soya spread; Krone's Bio margarine and Bio Olive margarine (with olive oil); Biona, Rapunzel, Munsterland and Fertillia margarines; Palmaline vegetable fat, and Pure Organic reduced-fat spread (on sale at Waitrose). All are made with non-hydrogenated fats and contain no artificial colourings or flavourings (to harden margarines naturally, you use a proportion of palm or coconut oil, which are solid at room temperature).

The way Rapunzel make their organic vegetarian margarine illustrates the difference between the organic and conventional approaches. Rapunzel's contains no hydrogenated fats, transfats, milk protein, milk sugar or other animal ingredients, salt, added water or flavourings. It is made from 60% organic sunflower oil, fair-traded organic palm and coconut fats to give the required spreading consistency, plus lemon juice, carrot juice as a natural colouring and soya lecithin as a stabiliser – and it has a pleasant flavour.

NOTE:

- Palm and coconut oil are naturally high in saturated fat – which makes them solid at room temperature. Though saturated fats are not good for you, there is mounting evidence to suggest that hydrogenated fats may be the more harmful.

15: Organics Online

Love it or hate it, anyone who wants to find out about organic food and farming, discover where to buy organic food, or check out the latest on the GM debate, or what's happening organically worldwide, can do so on the Web. Buying organic online is becoming as popular as traditional mail order and, increasingly, organic producers and manufacturers have their own websites – so you can see the farm and get a sense of the people and what they offer. Most websites also have links to other like-minded sites, building up an organic network that stretches on seemingly forever.

Whoever coined the term 'surfing the Web' should be awarded the world's first Internet knighthood. Surfing the Web is like negotiating a massive spider's web: you can so easily get caught up in it, and before you know it another day has passed staring at the screen. As any novice soon discovers, there are good and bad websites – those that are easy to use and tell you what you want to know; and those that are frustrating, or contain a lot of useless information, or consist mainly of free – or not free – ads (like many of the where-to-buy searches, for example). Here I aim to cut a path through the enormous number of websites and give you a basic resource directory, as well as covering the ins and outs of buying organic food online. As many producer and company websites as possible have been included throughout the book also.

Computer aids

Spending hours at the computer is neither good for your health nor good for your soul. Two eco-aids that you might want to consider are:

LifeEnergy Biolights: These fiercely bright bulbs (you'd need a pair of sunglasses to look directly at them), imported from America, are the latest in fluorescent technology; they give a full-spectrum light, replicating natural daylight at noon, thus bringing some of the benefits of real sunshine into your working environment. They give out a bluish but very clear light, and if you like it, you'll find it difficult to go back to an ordinary bulb; you may also think it's odd. They are said to be useful against seasonal affective disorder (SAD), for improving energy levels, well-being and sleep. They last for around 10,000 hours (or up to 5 years) if they are on for an average of 5 hours a day. I'm very pleased with mine. Can be ordered from Higher Nature, tel: 01435 882880.

Computer Clear: A software program on CD-ROM, based on tomorrow's Energy Medicine technology and designed to neutralise the effects of the stresses felt by people who need to spend long hours staring at the screen. The harmful electromagnetic radiations emanating from your computer are used, the manufacturers say, to carry a healing signal made up of a wide range of natural healing energies that have been stored digitally on CD-ROM. The signal reportedly relieves stresses caused by the radiation; reducing headaches, for instance, and increasing energy levels and concentration. Suitable for PCs but, alas, not yet for Macs, so I haven't been able to test it yet. Available from Life-Energies International plc, The Coach House, The Avenue, Odstock, nr Salisbury SP5 4JA, tel: 01722 340221, fax: 01722 349468, email: enquiries@lifeenergies.com. To find out more, visit their futuristic website: **www.life-energies.com**.

The Compu Dome: An alternative to the Computer Clear, which can be used for all computers, including Macs. A tiny disc, containing micro-crystals, that you attach to your computer, which reduces the effects of electromagnetic radiation. Available from Tools for Energy Balance & Health, tel: 07000 822496 or visit their website: **www.toolsforenergy.com**.

Before you start

A few points about surfing the Web generally and about buying organic online in particular, from my researcher, Jane Faulkes:

- One of the problems with websites is discerning how often the information is updated. Not all websites are dated, and those that are often display disappointing last-update dates. The image we all have of instant, real information is misleading. Many commercial operations have websites constructed by agents, friends or family, with varying degrees of success. Once running, they can be forgotten about, so you can be ordering a product only to find that the price given is last year's.

- Website addresses change and the new address carries all the up-to-date information. But the old one is still in existence, displaying out-of-date information.
- Supermarket websites are often the most professionally designed, but because they carry an enormous amount of information it can take ages to work your way past the latest price deals, say, on French wine in order to find the organic section. You often have to fight your way down the aisles anyway, only to discover that your local store is not one of the 'selected' ones carrying the organic mung beans that you're after.
- Mail order websites are generally the best, most informative and accurate. This is because the companies concerned are more dependent on the sales generated by their websites than is the case with your local organic farm (who may well also have their own website, but laden with pictures of contented cows and Beautiful Corner of Britain vistas).
- Where to buy: organic directories online are some of the more accessible Web resources out there. It is in the interest of the directories to get it right, as many of them charge their contributors as if they were placing an advertisement in a magazine.
- Anyone can create a website, and many people do, so as to create a forum for airing their personal views. So take some of the information you read with a pinch of salt. Since, currently, the World Wide Web is one of the least regulated publicity organs, some outlandish opinions are postulated as fact and you have no way of knowing, without cross-referencing the veracity of statements made. Beware of unsubstantiated sources. More than with any other medium, phrases like 'We endeavour to ...' give you no guarantee of organic authenticity. If you can't telephone and speak to a real person and ask questions, use another site that allows you to.

Search engines

Search engines do the searching for you and enable you (hopefully) to find whatever it is that you have been searching fruitlessly for. The major problem is that they contain so much that it is virtually impossible to sort through even a fraction of the information on offer. There is no quick way around this information overload. The best advice is always to use a specific site first, and resort to search engines when you feel in the mood – or when you are desperate.

It is imperative to be as specific as you can with your search words, or you will end up with literally thousands of matches that it will take you half the night to scroll through. The word 'organic', for example, will give you organic chemistry, compost, worms, medicines, and just about everything else you can think if. If you want an organic shop, specify the area, as in 'organic shops in Berkshire'. Make a point of entering UK in your search as well; otherwise, as Jane says, that really interesting box scheme will turn out to deliver on Tuesdays and Fridays to Richmond, Virginia.

Some of the better search engines are:

www.lycos.co.uk: customer-friendly
www.ukplus.co.uk: a good ShopSmart search, easy informative style
www.yahoo.co.uk: one of the best-known, which has now combined with:
www.google.co.uk: a mechanised search engine: enter your search words, and thousands of possible matches spill out instantly on screen – so be specific

ONLINE ORGANIC SUPERMARKETS

If you want to do a supermarket shop online, organic companies offer the best option and often the widest variety; and you don't have the extra complication or frustration of having to find the organic option first. All their sites are clear, easy to browse, interesting and generally a pleasure. Prices are mostly keener than you'd think, and the best advice is to surf around and take a look at all of them before deciding which is for you. The following companies offer a complete shopping basket; many offer non-food goods as well. They produce catalogues and do business via mail order, also.

Fresh Food Co – www.freshfood.co.uk

Tel: 020 8969 0351, email: organics@freshfood.co.uk

A great website, clearly presented, with no-nonsense directions on how to get the best out of your Web experience. Around 4,000 items are available, including fresh fruit and vegetables, meat from Pembrokeshire, fish from the Cornish coast, dairy, wholefoods, groceries; and eco-friendly cleaning and baby-care products. All their foods are organic or wild-harvested, and their organic fruit and vegetables, 70% of which are UK-produced, are supplied by Organic Connections International. Nationwide delivery on Thursdays only. There is a delivery charge of £5 on orders under £75, except for their fruit and vegetable boxes for which delivery is included. A weekly newsletter, containing news, views and recipes, is supplied with your order. They offer a no-quibble money-back policy, should your delivery not afford you full satisfaction.

Your order can be made using one of their box selections, to which you can then add your personal selection.

The Food Revolution Ltd – www.foodrevolution.com

Freephone/fax: 0800 169 66731, email: info@foodrevolution.com
Speciality online shopping for, as they say, 'people who care about food'. If you are a keen cook, you will enjoy this excellent so-easy-to-use website as well as their products – and the information about their meat, for example. Over 300 hand-picked items (all suppliers are visited personally), mainly, but not exclusively, organic: a full range of fresh meats and sausages from Organic Oasis, poultry from Sheepdrove Farm; smoked foods, dairy, groceries, including What on Earth gourmet pizzas and breads, Pollen Organic and Duchy Original products and hampers. Good recipes. Order over their secure server, or from their clear, attractive catalogue. Deliveries can be made Tues–Sat (some things may not be available). A delivery charge of £5 is levied on all orders.

Organics Direct – www.organicsdirect.co.uk

Tel: 020 7622 3003, email: info@organicsdirect.co.uk
Began as the first (and only) nationwide vegetarian box-scheme delivery company and now offers over 450 items including wines and beers, bodycare products, juicers, baby foods, organic cotton goods, plus a good recipe section. Clear, simple, no-fuss website. List also available by post. Order by phone, fax or email, or online on their secure server. Deliveries are made Tues–Fri by overnight courier. £5 delivery charge on all orders except vegetable and fruit boxes (delivery included), plus 25p per additional kilo on all orders that weigh in at over 20 kg.

Simply Organic Food Company – www.simplyorganic.net

Tel: 0845 100444
A friendly website, and easy to navigate around. They offer 1,750 organic products online, thoughtfully selected and including excellent brands such as Pollen Organics, Kinvara (smoked salmon), the Stamp Collection, Booja

Booja (chocolates) and Organic India (ready meals), not normally found. The range comprises fruit and vegetables, organic meats, fish, dairy produce, childcare products, wines and beers, plus eco-friendly personal and homecare products, cotton clothing and lifestyle goods – which means you can buy your clockwork radio from them, too. They supply a colourful nice-to-browse catalogue. Selection boxes available, on to which you can add your own personal selection. A newsletter and recipe suggestions, updated weekly, are included with every order. Nationwide delivery Tues–Sat, guaranteed by noon. Carbon Neutral delivers (they donate the organisation to Forest Trees, who use the cash to plant more trees) and offer a freepost service for returning the chilled boxes. The only delivery surcharge is for inaccessible places. Pay by card on their secure-payment server, or order using the order form in their catalogue. You can order by phone, fax, email or freepost also.

The Organic Shop – www.theorganicshop.co.uk

Tel: 0845 674 4000

A friendly, logical, no-frills site, easily navigable and giving explanatory information about their products. Affiliated to the HDRA Food Club. Meat, fruit and vegetable boxes, with add-on selection option. Meat is sourced from a family farm in Wales, and their produce from the Green Growers' Co-operative in Herefordshire. Good range of dairy products, wines and beers, and a wide range of groceries and household products. In total, 450 lines. Online catalogue, as well as catalogue available by post. Helpful drop-down help menu and secure ordering portal. Delivery charge of £4.95 on orders up to £50. Deliveries can be made Tues–Sat (check which day they deliver to your area) during the day or evening (extra £8 charge for evening or Saturday deliveries).

ONLINE CONVENTIONAL SUPERMARKETS

Major retailers are currently developing home delivery online shopping services, for which you need to register first. Remember, there is a minimum order and a delivery charge. All insist that their websites are very easy to use. We found them all frustrating in one way or another. For online buffs only. At the time of writing their organic portfolio shaped up like this:

ASDA – www.asda.co.uk

Defeated us, and the most boring of all those visited. ASDA do not have an organic icon on their website, nor do they promote organics, though they do give information about their environmental policy – sounds impressive. Home delivery is to selected areas, where they say a selected range of organic lines is available. No online shopping option.

Safeway – www.safeway.co.uk

As yet, no online shopping available, nor home delivery, but a useful and nicely designed site to browse: click on fresh food ideas on the home page, then click the organic icon. You can see their complete range as a list (currently over 500 organic lines, which are available at most of their stores), get meal ideas and recipes, the history of organic, organic food facts, and so on. There are plans to increase the spread and variety of organic food available throughout their stores.

Sainsbury's – www.taste.co.uk

Sainsbury's have two websites, their lifestyle website **www.taste.co.uk** and their general website, **www.sainsburys.co.uk**, which includes their online home delivery section, 'Sainsbury's To You'. Unfortunately, at the moment, 'Sainsbury's To You' is a nightmare to use, though is being completely overhauled. Their lifestyle website has an extensive organics section including news, views, guest interviews and a regular column by Jackie Gear, Executive Director of the HDRA; plus recipes, and a useful starter search for organic eateries, which has a link to 'Sainsbury's To You'. You can browse without registering first, but need to wait a few minutes for the shopping section to download. It does not have an organic icon, so you need to go to 'Shopping Trolley'. You then key in organics in the search slot. Thereafter, the best of luck. They have two easy lists, one for fresh organic produce and another that lists about 20 organic grocery items.

Tesco – www.tesco.com

Tesco have their own organic club and newsletter. Their website **www.tesco.com** is vast and it is not easy to get straight to their organic online aisle: you need to register first, which means you need to give name, full address, email and contact numbers, plus a password. If that sounds like hard work, you can phone their customer care line on 0845 7225533 (Mon–

Sat 9 am–11 pm; Sun 10 am–6 pm), where they are very user-friendly, will talk you through and give you an 9-digit customer ID number. You then need to key both your ID and password numbers in before you can finally browse the shopping section. Unfortunately, it's still not simple. There is no ready-made organic icon, so you need to key the word 'organic' in the find box. They offer a basic shop: the menu includes a selection of fresh produce, bread, cakes, dairy, tofu and a tiny amount of meat – around 100 items in all.

The website is linked in to **www.iVillage.co.uk** (an easy link, just click on the icon), which has its own organic lifestyle section, including recipes and a chat line with organic experts to answer your questions.

Waitrose – www.waitrose.com

The only multiple retailer to operate their own online organic box scheme, Waitrose Organics Direct (4 different boxes – salad, vegetables, fruit and mixed), ordered through their website **www.waitrose.com**. They are currently piloting Waitrose Deliver (visit **www.waitrose.com**, click on the WAITROSEdeliver link), which you can browse before registering.

Their website itself is clear and a dream to use, and the organic section is easy to find: click once on 'shopping', then click on 'organics direct' in the left-hand corner (there is no need to register first). It offers their full list of organic products and producers' recipes, information and features (including those from *Waitrose Food Illustrated*), and tells you how to buy the Soil Association's video *Organic Farming – Food for Life*. To buy their organic wines online, click on the Waitrose Wine Direct section, and key the word 'organic' in the find box. Around 20 organic wines are included. Their home shopping section seems as puzzling as the others, and, as with the others, defeated me.

ONLINE LOCAL

It had to happen next. Exciting new online organic ventures are bringing farmers' markets and local farm shops to your door: local organic food from a particular region, available nationwide, at competitive prices. Two examples:

Somerset Organics – www.somersetorganics.co.uk

Tel: 01749 870919, email: info@somersetorganics.co.uk

Award-winning movie-style website, brainchild of Somerset farmer Rodney Stoke. It works like this. The website acts as the showcase and marketing arm for local producers who work together and sell their products as a county brand. A full range of organic meats, poultry, cheese and cider is available. Their meat comes from traditional breeds such as Gloucester Old Spot and Saddleback pigs, Dorset Down lambs and Red Ruby cattle. Delivery charge is £4.95. The website contains much more: a tour of Somerset, lots of information, recipes and a 'ring me' link. You can also download their catalogue – but it takes around 20 minutes. Alternatively, ring or email direct.

Other county groups are currently being formed, and will each have their own county brand and website.

Westcountry Organics – **www.westcountryorganics.co.uk**

Tel: 01647 24724

Secure online shop selling organic meat, farmed salmon and trout, vegetables, dairy produce, vegetarian products, wines and beers. They have a network of over 25 farms, from Bath to Lands End, and supply mainly local food, including seasonal produce and meat, meat cut to your requirements, vegetable boxes with extensive add-on list option. Good product information and good-value meat boxes, single-species and variety packs, to suit different pockets. Orders welcomed by post, fax, phone, email and internet. Delivery charge £4 for orders over £35, and £5.50 for under £35. Saturday delivery surcharge. Delivery days Mon–Sat, Friday only for vegetables.

Plus:

Graig Farm Organics – **www.graigfarm.co.uk**

Too good a website to miss out. One organic Internet shop buff described it as 'a lovely website – full of stories and information, nice pics etc, easy to navigate, and a great retail site that takes you into the thick of the products immediately and enables very straightforward purchases rapidly'. I agree. Free delivery for orders over £45. For their full entry, see p. 180.

See also:

Taste of the Wild: www.tasteofthewild.co.uk
Northumbrian Meats:
www.northumbrian-organic-meat.co.uk
Pure Meat Direct: www.puremeatdirectonline.co.uk

USEFUL GENERAL ORGANIC SHOPPING AND LIFESTYLE WEBSITES

Surfing the web for where to buy organic food is a very useful tool to find out what's happening in your area, and to keep up to date with new ventures. Often the websites have additional information about organic food and farming, news items and generally what you'd like to know. Most have links to other organic sites. Lifestyle websites may or may not include suppliers, but often include recipes, tastings, and interviews.

Major websites for locating organic suppliers:

www.theorganicdirectory.co.uk

The Organic Directory on line. The contributors to this comprehensive organic directory are listed here in an easy-to-access format. Make your selection of area, name, or type of outlet, and find them all listed in easy-to-follow drop-down menu format. Useful links to farmers' markets, organic butchers, organic farms and the American super-extraordinary website, OrganicHub.com.

www.infolondon.ukf.net/organic

The London Organic Directory, and the website for Londoners interested in organic food, wines, eating out and much more. Excellent resource website, with comprehensive listings of organic suppliers. Easy-to-use map format, select your preferred category, e.g., restaurants or stores, then click on your most local region on their map. Link to **www.urbanbite.com**, which gives you your nearest restaurant that delivers to home or office, lets you browse the menu and order on line. As yet, limited to London.

www.organic-supermarket.co.uk

Useful where to buy website, includes map references, contact details, plus news features. Easy to use, select region (nationwide) and category desired.

www.greenguideonline.com

Green Guides website. Eco-lifestyle website for everything about sustainable living, including how to find an eco-joiner. Not organic but includes extensive nationwide resource directory, including food and drink, which features many organic suppliers.

www.networkorganic.com
New organic lifestyle website, still being developed, but includes kids' section and will include UK's first directory of local buyers that you can buy direct from.

www.organicmarketplace.co.uk
Good graphics and easy-to-use trade website, which includes organic news and events and links to well-known organic organisations. Retail shopping search facility, either by product or retailer to find your nearest organic supplier.

www.organicbutchers.co.uk
Handy site, regularly updated, holds information on companies specialising in organic meat who retail to the public. Contains a county guide, a mail order list, and an online ordering list. Select the category and county of your choice for list, then click on the 'go' for 'details' box for full contact details.

Local Authority websites

Most regions also have local authority sites, some easier than others to navigate, but which often include local food suppliers. Find them by entering **www.county.gov.uk** into your top address bar, e.g. **www.devonfoodlinks.org.uk** gives information on what's on in the Devonshire food world, including their organic scene. Devon, for example, gives their farmers' markets and organic box schemes and produces a newsletter. Monmouthshire has an excellent easy-to-use website: **www.monmouthshire.gov.uk/food**, listing all their farmers' markets, WI markets, with details on producers at the markets, and has a food directory listing that you can search by product or area.

Local and other speciality websites

www.BigBarn.co.uk
A must-visit virtual farmer's market, and excellent website, that literally puts local, fresh food on the interactive map. Type in your postcode or town name and see your area showing different icons, each representing a local producer and the type of goods they sell. Two thousand seven hundred producers are listed, including farm shops, box schemes, organic producers and markets;

plus recipes and specialist search facilities. Register with BigBarn for special offers from your local producers. For enquiries tel: 01234 871005, or e-mail: postmaster@bigbarn.co.uk.

www.eafl.org.uk
Website for East Anglia Food Links. Their 'Buying Good Food' section has details of local organic retailers, suppliers and farmers' markets.

www.farmgarden.org.uk
Federation of City Farms and Community Gardens website. Includes search to find your nearest and what they grow.

www.farmersmarket.net
National Farmers' Market Association website. Includes listings.

http://www.localfood.org.uk
For local food contacts, including organic, plus information about local food projects.

www.organicatcost.co.uk
Website for novel subscription farm scheme currently being set up, run by Richard Prince and Jill Fergusen. Members will eventually receive share of food produced.

www.organic-kosher.co.uk
Mail order and online provider of organic kosher approved meats and other foods. See p. 188.

www.rare-breeds.com
Rare Breeds Survival Trust. Includes locations of accredited butchers.

www.sheepdairying.com
Sheep are wonderful. This is the website for the British Sheep Dairying Association. All you ever wanted to know about sheep's milk and cheese, plus a useful search site for producers and farm shops, including organic. Good site for the producer, consumer and enthusiast.

www.speciality-foods.co.uk
Food producer search site, for regional foods, and 'Taste of' series of leaflets. Includes some organic food producers.

www.londonfarmersmarkets.com
Website for London's Farmer's markets. Includes up-to-date listings and info.

www.wimarkets.co.uk
Women's Institute website: cheerful, nice to use, includes listings and products.

Lifestyle websites

www.foodfirst.co.uk
New foodie website, which brings food lovers and the people who produce food together, plus produce calendar, interviews, recipes and interviews. Includes a good 'find organics' search directory – producers, wholesalers and retailers specialising in organic food and drink, by county or product: click on to the county and you see a range of local (mainly) organic suppliers at a glance.

www.greenpages-uk.net
Cheerful green lifestyle, no-nonsense, easy-to-use website, which includes organic food and drink suppliers.

www.greenpeople.co.uk
Organic lifestyle website of the excellent Green People skincare and bodycare products. Lots of interest, including information on health matters and how to detox, organic news and extensive links to organisations, shops, and box schemes dealing in organic or fairtraded goods. Online shop for their products, including their organic herbal elixir and seaweed supplements.

www.iVillage.co.uk
The purely-for-women lifestyle website, with its own organic section.

www.organicfood.co.uk
Organic Delivery Company's organic lifestyle magazine website, including

online chat. Also has a where-to-shop search facility, by name, county or post code.

www.organic-lifestyle.co.uk
Where to start, easy-to-use link site for anyone interested in the organic lifestyle, that gives you what you want in concise, easy-to-digest format, and includes retail listings. About to be revamped and will concentrate on organic smallholdings and gardening. Links to most of the major organic internet retailers, delivering locally or nationwide, across Britain, and contact details for those not on the net.

www.organicvegetarian.co.uk
Does not deal with where to buy organic food but has a good link site to various other organisations, including the *Organic Living* Magazine site, and the Organic Delivery Company site.

www.taste.co.uk
Lifestyle website, with its own organic section.

www.tasteofthewild.co.uk
Delightful and one of the most intelligently put together websites in the book. Nationwide, home-delivery internet company, specialising in organic and natural foods for special diets, green body care, and wildlife products and wildflower seeds, to encourage wildlife back to your garden. Gift boxes, all kinds of hampers, organic wines by the case, and good range of organic groceries, including sea vegetables, preserves and chocolates. Their shopping hall (no visuals, so no time wasted) lists all ingredients, and dietary status of each product. Excellent links section. Order by phone, also: 01189 542263.

www.timeout.com
Funky website, with shopping section, accessed either through the main website, or go direct to **www.shopping.timeout.com** where you can find all you wanted to know about food availability in London, including organic butchers, fairtrade suppliers, farmers' markets and organic home delivery. Select the category you want, entries are listed with contact details and a 'review' button, for a brief description of products and services on offer. Regular tastings also included.

www.vegveg.com
Online (free) global business directory for vegetarian, vegan and organic companies, with a mission 'to launch the definitive worldwide vegetarian and organic revolution'. Categories include food and drink, restaurants and dining, but be specific or you'll get suggestions from around the world.

ORGANIC EATING OUT AND WHERE TO STAY

There is, as yet, no one comprehensive specialist website for these. To recap, useful websites are:

www.greenguideonline.com
www.iVillage.com
www.Organicholidays.com
www.specialplacetostay.com
www.theorganicdirectory.co.uk
www.vegveg.com

ORGANIC INFORMATION WEBSITES

If it's hard information about organics and related topics you seek, these are some of the best websites to surf.

www.anth.org.uk/biodynamic
The website of the BDAA, which includes a list of biodynamic farms selling to the public.

www.efrc.com
Website of Elm Farm Research Centre, the UK's leading organic farming research organisation. News, views, advice, research information, topical issues, plus independent comment about organic farming and food and related topics.

www.ewg.org
Website of the American Environmental Working Group, who promote healthier food choices, pesticide-free foods and organic farming. Information on cutting-edge research on health and the environment, and on why pesticides are bad for you.

www.hdra.org.uk

Website of the Henry Doubleday Research Association: if it's organic gardening you are interested in, this is the website for you. Much on organic food and their research activities, plus link to their online HDRA Food and Wine Club and their organic seed catalogue.

www.ifoam.org

Website of the International Federation of Organic Agricultural Movements – good and informative, and should keep you organically occupied for ages.

www.linksorganic.com

International organic directory for just about everything, including restaurants and that lovely organic farmhouse in Italy where you want to spend your next holiday.

www.defra.gov.uk

New Department of Environment, Food and Rural Affairs website. Click on 'farming' button, then go to 'organic farming'.

www.organic.aber.ac.uk

Website of the Organic Centre Wales, research organisation for organic farming at the University of Wales. Visit this for the latest statistics and research information.

www.organicconsumers.org

An American grassroots website that campaigns for food safety, organic agriculture and sustainability. Find out what's happening in America, plus information on various topics including pesticides.

www.organic.cwc.net

Organic & Hydro UK is a one-man website designed to give practical support to all those interested in growing their own food organically and hydroponically. Good easy-to-use website, with practical information (especially on how to grow food in small spaces) and news; and it has good links.

www.organichub.com
An amazingly exhaustive and exclusively organic American website, billed as the largest online organic marketplace. Search for anything you want, including links to information websites and online organic magazines.

www.organic-research.com
This one is for organic buffs. Primarily for academics, it is a huge database of over 100,000 research papers on organic and associated life-science research, plus news and events; and a useful laws and regulations section which contains various sets of organic standards. The website is run by CAB International, based in Wallingford, Oxon, tel: 01491 83211, a long-established, not-for-profit intergovernmental organisation, which disseminates information about life sciences and human health.

www.organicTS.com
Excellent organic trade website, with an extensive fortnightly newsline service info@organics.com (now available on subscription). If you want to know what's happening organically in the UK and across the world, this is the one for you. It also has a search facility for producers etc, and UKROFS standards for organic farming.

www.ota.com
Website for the US Organic Trade Association. Learn all about American organics here, plus the latest on American organic standards.

www.rodaleinstitute.org
Website for the Rodale Institute and their organic farm systems trials.

www.soilassociation.org
The Soil Association website, the best one for an introduction to organic farming and the work of the Soil Association. It includes up-to-date reports on campaigns etc and an excellent library section which holds all their reports and briefings.

www.soilfoodweb.com
For soil buffs, Dr Elaine Ingham's fascinating Soil Foodweb website: a mine of scientific and general information on soils and composts.

www.sustainweb.org
Website for the organisation Sustain. Visit this for the latest on the Organic Targets Bill.

www.wwoof.org
Willing workers on organic farms.

Organic kids' websites

www.organics.org
Pure Organics, specially designed interactive website for kids.

www.yeovalley.com
Yeo Valley's website, including specially designed Yeo Kids section complete with twittering birds and cows that moo.

Green, GM and environmental websites

www.bananalink.org.uk
Banana Link. Information on social and environmental issues affecting the banana trade.

www.cat.org.uk
Centre for Alternative Technology.

www.cwf.co.uk
Compassion in World Farming.

www.climateark.org
Information on global climate, deforestation and alternative energy.

www.foe.co.uk
Friends of the Earth.

www.foodcomm.org.uk
The Food Commission, an independent organisation campaigning for safer, healthier food. They produce *The Food Magazine*.

www.genewatch.org
GeneWatch UK. The best GM website, which has a superb link section to most of the other sites associated with GM issues, including government bodies.

www.greenpeace.org.uk
Greenpeace.

www.msc.org
Marine Stewardship Council.

www.primalseeds.org
A grassroots biodiversity information site, opposing the intensification of farming and promoting seed-saving, seed-swapping, etc. An amazingly complex site map shows you the extent of the subjects covered; much on GM updates.

www.nationaltrust.org.uk
The National Trust.

www.btinternet.com/~nlpwessex
Natural Law Party GM website.

www.permaculture.org.uk
Permaculture Association UK.

www.rainforestfoundationuk.org
The Rainforest Foundation.

www.rspb.org.uk
Royal Society for the Protection of Birds.

www.theecologist.org
The Ecologist magazine.

www.wildlifeline.org
Wildlifeline.

www.wildlifetrust.org.uk
The Wildlife Trusts.

www.gn.apc.org/web
Women's Environmental Network (WEN)

www.wwf-uk.org
WWF The Global Environment network.

PESTICIDE WEBSITES

www.foodnews.org
Part of the Environmental Working Group (see p. 372), this devotes itself to pesticides in foods and will probably be able to answer most of your questions. Get an idea of the pesticides present in your daily diet here, but remember they are calculated using American data for food.

www.pan-uk.org
Pesticide Action Network. Authoritative website of a much-respected organisation. Find out what's happening worldwide here.

www.pesticides.gov.uk
Government Pesticides Safety Directorate website, including latest annual Pesticide Residues Committee report on residues in food. Click on 'committees', then 'Pesticides Residues Committee'.

FAIR-TRADE ORGANISATIONS' WEBSITES

www.fairtrade.org.uk/products.htm
Fairtrade Foundation.

www.traidcraft.co.uk
Traidcraft.

Also:

www.oxfam.org.uk

Appendix and Further Information

- Biodynamic farming
- The principles of organic farming
- Pesticides: A brief overview
- The worldwide standards web
- EU livestock regulations
- Organic poultry standards
- Organic tea, coffee and cocoa standards
- Main permitted additives and processing aids

BIODYNAMIC FARMING

Central to the biodynamic philosophy is that man, the earth and the universe are inextricably bound together, that cosmic forces have an effect on soil, plants and animals, and that each farm or garden is a unique entity in which the personality of the farmer or gardener shines through. Crops grown under the biodynamic system are said to be in tune with the whole universe and, when tested, are found to have a consistently high nutritional value – sometimes higher even than that of 'ordinary' organic crops, as well as more 'harmony' and vitality. Biodynamic farms actively support low external-input sustainable agriculture (LEISA). Wherever practicable farms are mixed, and always aim to be as self-sustaining as possible, growing as much of their own feed as they can and depending on their own manures and composts for fertility.

The first difference that sets biodynamic farming apart is its use of a small number of specialised therapeutic 'energising' preparations on soil, compost and crops. These are used as homoeopathic dilutions in the form of sprays, and have specific functions:

Preparation 500: a biofermented substance, prepared from cow's manure, applied to the soil usually in spring and autumn to promote earthworm and microbiological activity and to increase the availability of trace elements.
Preparation 501: prepared from biofermented ground quartz crystals and

applied to plants in the growing season to enhance photosynthesis, leading to improved nutritional quality, increased resistance to fungal diseases, sweetness of taste and longer keeping qualities.
Preparation 502–507: herbal preparations applied to composts and liquid manures to aid their fermentation, and exerting a catalytic effect on soil mineral processes.

The second difference between biodynamic farming and the rest is the use of a lunar calendar to determine the best time to sow, plant and harvest plants. There is a well-established scientific base for this: the moon's phases determine the gravitational pull of the earth, and sowing in a new moon, for example, when the gravitational pull is downwards, will help new roots to establish. The biodynamic calendar also attached particular importance to the moon's sidereal rhythm.

THE PRINCIPLES OF ORGANIC FARMING

The principles of organic agriculture are the bedrock on which the organic ethos, and organic practices, are built. They embrace every aspect of the production and manufacture of food, including working conditions, the encouragement and support of local lifestyles and of biodiversity, as well as wider issues of waste, pollution, recycling and energy conservation. No other system of agriculture offers such a complete package of benefits for people or the environment. They can be summed up like this (source: SA certification standards):

Agricultural principles

- the production of high-quality, healthy food which avoids the use of pesticides
- respect for natural eco-systems and cycles, from the soil to plants and animals
- the preservation, maintenance and increase in the long-term fertility and biological activity of the soil
- the ethical treatment of livestock, allowing all their behavioural needs to be expressed
- the development of extensive systems based on sustainable production methods

- respect for traditional practices and the recognition of regional, climatic, environmental and geographic differences

Environmental principles

- the encouragement of bio-diversity and the protection of sensitive habitats and landscape features
- the maximisation of renewable resources, and recycling
- the minimisation of pollution and waste

Food-processing principles

- minimum processing, consistent with the product in question
- the restriction of the number of permitted food-processing aids (to be constantly reviewed)
- the provision of maximum consumer information on processing methods and ingredients

Social principles

- the provision of fair working conditions and quality of life
- the development of ecologically responsible production, processing and distribution chains, emphasising local systems.

▲▲▲

PESTICIDES: A BRIEF OVERVIEW

At the last count, around 170 pesticides have been linked to major immune-system diseases such as cancer, allergies, infertility and foetal-development problems. They also cause an estimated 3 million acute poisonings, resulting in 220,000 deaths every year.

Despite the fact that pest populations have increased, that animals and plants continually develop resistance to pesticides, that pesticides once declared 'safe' are constantly withdrawn or banned and that many persist in the environment for decades, every year we continue to pour out about another 2.5 billion kg of them. And we still lose as many crops today as we did before pesticides were introduced. In the USA, insecticide use alone has increased tenfold, yet crop losses have almost doubled in that time.

Pesticides are present in the food we eat, are a major pollutant of drinking-water, and pervade the food chain at every level. The cocktail effect of regularly ingesting tiny amounts of different pesticides has never been investigated: what we do know is that the average daily UK diet now contains traces of thirty of them, and that residues on individual food samples vary wildly. As Peter Beaumont, former development director of the Pesticides Action Network, has said:

> ***'There are prices to be paid for pesticide use. Pesticides are toxic, intending to harm living systems, and the only toxic chemicals deliberately released into the environment. Every year British farmers spend £500 million to spray 24,000 tonnes of active pesticide ingredients. There are short- and long-term impacts on human health. One tablespoon of herbicide carelessly used near water can pollute the drinking-water for 200,000 people. It costs £100 million every year to remove pesticides from water. Wouldn't it make more sense to pay farmers not to put pesticides into water rather than to pay water companies to remove pesticides*** from ***water?'***

Though the principle that the polluter should pay is now generally accepted, the government has so far refused to do anything about it, and the tax bill for cleaning up the environment continues to rise. If you want to see the latest pesticide residues in food, visit Pesticides Safety Directorate website: **www.pesticides.gov.uk**. Click on 'committees', then 'Pesticide Residue Committee'. Reports for 2000–2002 are listed. To calculate the pesticide residues in your daily diet, visit the American website **www.foodnews.org**.

Pesticide residues in conventional food

Pesticide and other toxic residues concern everyone, the rise in polychlorinated biphenyls (PCBs) in farmed salmon bring the most recent worry. The problem is that it is impossible to give clear and unequivocal advice on which foods are likely to contain the highest residues, as these differ from year to year. The things we do know with certainty are that:

- Pesticide residues occur regularly, albeit usually below the official safety limits.
- Only a tiny fraction of the foods that we consume are tested for pesticide residues.
- Residues can vary considerably between one sample and the next.
- The average daily UK diet now contains traces of a cocktail of thirty different pesticide residues.

- The potential health implications for the 'cocktail effect' have never been systematically investigated but the occasional studies that have been done have shown that exposure to tiny amounts of just two chemicals at the same time can have an effect one thousand times greater than either chemical alone; one report in the *New Scientist* has suggested that the combination of two or three common pesticides found at low levels in the environment can be up to 1,600 times more powerful when found individually.
- The retiring chairman of the Pesticide Residues Committee (formerly the Working Party on Pesticide Residues (WPPR) has acknowledged that the multiple residues found in conventional fruit and vegetables need to be reduced. Their 2000 report, for example, found that though the overall levels of residues of the 2,300 samples tested were down, there was a significant increase in fresh vegetables and fruit, of which 43% contained traces of residues. Of all foods tested, 1.6% contained residues above the minimum recommended levels (MRLs), and around 1% contained residues of pesticides not permitted in the UK. Oranges, along with most of the celery tested, had the most residues of different kinds.

Pesticide residues in organic food

While eating organic food will keep your residue intake down to a minimum, organic food does not and cannot claim to be pesticide-free. Given the high level of background pollution and contamination, including spray drift from surrounding farms (97% of UK crops are routinely sprayed with pesticides), pesticides are endemic in the air, land, seas and water-courses. In order to minimise the residues that do occur in organic foods, the standards insist on hedges or windbreaks, and buffer zones. The Soil Association, for example, requires a minimum of 10–20 metres to separate organic orchards from possible sources of contamination.

Organic food samples are now included in the annual government pesticide residue surveys. Extensive tests conducted in Europe, for instance, show consistently that organic food has either no or minimal residues. In the UK, the Pesticides Safety Directorate (PSD) has now begun to monitor organic food. When residues are found, as part of their remit the PSD investigates such findings in order to determine whether the residues are unavoidable or the result of malpractice. Because all organic food is traceable back to the farm of origin, when residues are detected the records of even a single apple –

as was the case recently with an imported apple from the USA – can be checked. When investigated, contamination with non-organic ingredients or spray drift from nearby farms has usually been found to be the cause. For the pesticides that *are* currently permitted in UK organic agriculture see p. 40.

THE WORLDWIDE STANDARDS WEB

In the UK, the overall governing body is the independent UK Register of Organic Food Standards (UKROFS), which sets the basic standards to which all the various organic bodies and producers adhere. UKROFS standards in turn conform to the European Union's directive on organic production, regulation 2092/91. These standards are regularly updated, and are enforced by the certification bodies recognised by UKROFS set out on p. 79. Each certification body has its own symbol and EU code number. These are the symbols and codes you will find on organic products, and are visible proof that they have met the required UKROFS standards *and* any others set by that certification body.

Worldwide, there are several hundred independent certifying bodies, though national standards are still rare. The USA's nationally agreed organic standards, introduced in spring 2001, will be fully implemented by October 2002. Japan and Ireland are working towards theirs.

In the EU, each country has its own national organic certification authority, but certification is generally delegated to private accredited bodies, so that there may be several within each member state. Germany, for example, has 59, including Naturland, which is international, Austria 21 and Holland over 35. In other countries – such as Finland, Denmark and Spain – inspections are government-controlled, which means that in effect there is only one certification body. Any products imported into the EU must have certification standards equivalent to those in the EU and be approved by an EU certifying body, again ensuring basic harmonisation. Most certifying bodies also adhere to the International Federation of Organic Agricultural Movements' standards.

There are two basic routes via which food may be imported into the EU from outside. First, foods can be imported from a country recognised as applying standards and regulatory procedures equivalent to those of the EU: currently six countries, Australia, Argentina, the Czech Republic, Hungary, Israel and Switzerland meet this criterion, which means that their goods may pass freely into the EU, though each product must be certified by a registered certification body. The second route entails the individual importer applying to the member state concerned and providing proof that the product meets its standards, including certification inspection measures already taken in the country of origin; if satisfied, the EU certification authority will grant authorisation for it to be sold as organic.

In practice, this means that either a whole country may apply for EU recognition of its organic standards – as the six countries listed above have done – or, where national standards do not exist, importers may apply on behalf of specific organic producers, who will then be inspected in situ by one of the recognised certification bodies and subjected to annual inspections thereafter in the usual way. Storage facilities for any imported food must be open to inspection at all times.

What the regulation covers

The EU regulation 2092/91 began initially by covering unprocessed and processed food crops. Since then wild crops, mushrooms and livestock have been added; but wine has not, and nor have non-food crops such as cotton and herbal remedies. Standards for these have been drawn up independently by accredited organic certification bodies, which means that 'organic' in these cases means adherence to the standards of the particular certification body, but such standards have no national or international standing.

The new EU livestock regulation 1804/99, explained below, covers livestock and livestock products, including the inspection of permitted feedstuffs, and, for the first time, the prohibition of GMOs and their derivatives in organic farming. The livestock standards apply also to domesticated animals and insects such as bees, but exclude the hunting or fishing of wild animals. If you want to see what all the fuss is about, and what standards actually look like in practice, for the first time the newly revised UK Register of Organic Food Standards, including the EU livestock regulations, can be viewed on the Web at **http://www.organicTS.com/organic_info/ukrofs/standards.htm**. Alternatively, the printed version may be bought from the UKROFS Secretariat, c/o MAFF, Room 118, 17 Smith Square, London SW1P 3JR; a cheque for £20 should be made payable to MAFF.

EU LIVESTOCK REGULATIONS

The main principles enshrined in the livestock regulations, and which will shape the future production of organic meat in Europe, are:

- Livestock should be an integral part of the organic system.
- Livestock farming should be a land-related activity, based on free range.
- All livestock should be managed organically throughout their lives.
- Feed should be organically produced: the permitted ration of non-organic feed has been reduced, and all feed must be organic by 2005. Vitamins and minerals are allowed, but the use of synthetic amino acids as feed additives has been prohibited.
- The only preventive veterinary treatment permitted is vaccination, and courses of preventive treatment must not exceed three a year. The withdrawal period before slaughter for all veterinary treatments is twice the statutory withdrawal period.
- All manures produced by the farm must be spread on organic land, with a maximum limit of 170 kg of nitrogen per hectare per year (as for nitrogen-sensitive areas).

Because organic livestock farming systems differ in detail from one member state to another, the regulation also includes a range of derogations (permitted exceptions) for a limited period of time to allow everyone to comply with the new minimum standards. It is here that member countries and individual certification bodies are drawing up their own higher standards, where they feel they are necessary. The main derogations are:

- Free range is not required for pigs, which are allowed to be kept inside as long as they have an exercise area or open-air runs. Tethering (a common agricultural practice on the continent) is also permitted on existing units where it is already practised, until 2010 (and indefinitely for pigs raised on 'smallholdings'). It is now also possible to bring young piglets into organic units at weaning stage (4–5 weeks) from conventional farms, and sell the meat as organic. This is a very serious change, meaning that some imported organic pork in future will not be truly organic pork.
- At the moment in the UK, although a small percentage of non-organic stock may be brought in as replacements, except for chickens, only livestock born and reared on an organic holding may be sold as 'organic'. In Europe this is not the case. Beef animals, pigs and lambs born on

conventional farms may be brought into an organic holding when they are very young, raised organically, and then sold as organic meat. This practice is set to discontinue by 2003; thereafter, all livestock throughout the EU must be born and raised on an organic holding to qualify as organic.

ORGANIC POULTRY STANDARDS

Flock sizes

Flock sizes per housing unit for organic poultry are significantly lower than for most conventional poultry. For table birds they vary from 50 to 500 for small flocks and from 1,000–2,000 up to 4,800 for large flocks (this new limit, enforced in August 2000, replaced a previous limit of 8,000). Conventional commercial systems set no limit for flock size per house, and typically contain many more thousands of birds per unit. Organic regulations also set a maximum area of 1,600 sq m for poultry housing on any unit that limits the maximum size of flocks on a holding. The only other systems that do so are 'traditional' and 'total freedom' free-range.

The difference between organic and 'standard', 'traditional' and 'total freedom' free-range

At the moment no chicks are being produced to organic standards, which means that all organic producers must buy in conventional chicks. To qualify for organic status they must be raised for a minimum of ten weeks under organic poultry regulations, including access to organic pasture, with a minimum of 100 m range per bird. This is approximately 10 times more than standard free-range and 5 times more than 'traditional' and 'total freedom' free-range birds. For fixed housing, the stocking densities cannot exceed 21 kg (about 10 grown birds) per square metre. This compares with 27.5 kg for standard free-range, 25 kg/sq m for 'traditional' and 'total freedom' free-range systems, 30 kg/sq m for Freedom Foods, 34 kg/sq m for FAWC (the Farm Animal Welfare Council) and 34–38 kg/sq m for the farm-assured Red Truck label. Slow-growing, sturdier breeds are encouraged, as is the use of mobile housing wherever possible.

As the former MAFF website (**www.maff.gov.uk/foodrin/poultry**) explained, 'free-range', 'traditional free-range' and 'total freedom free-range' are special marketing terms (SMTs). As with the organic system, specific criteria must be met before any of these can be used on a label. Apart from all the differences that organic status brings with it (see chapter 8), the production differences are as follows:

Standard free-range: Compared with organic chickens, maximum stocking rates inside are higher (13 compared to 10), the birds have far less land to range on (1 sq m compared with a range of 100 metres) and their lives are approximately one-third shorter (56 days instead of 81 minimum).

Traditional free-range: The birds must be of recognised slow-growing strains. Compared with organic chickens, maximum stocking rates inside are higher (12 birds as against 10, or 20 as against 16 if housed in mobile houses), and they have around one-fifth of the amount of land to roam on (2 sq m compared with 100 metres). The maximum flock size per house, the maximum area of the poultry houses per holding and the minimum slaughter are the same.

Total freedom free-range: This is the best of the conventional systems. The criteria are exactly the same as for traditional free-range except that the birds must have continuous daytime access to open-air runs of unlimited area. Compared with standard organic chickens, therefore, they have more space to roam, though stocking densities inside the house are higher.

Soil Association poultry standards

The Soil Association operates more stringent standards (mainly suitable for small producers) than the other certification bodies, who all adhere to UKROFS standards, and can be said to be at the cutting edge of organic poultry standards. Any organic chicken producer will be happy to tell you how their birds are produced. To judge whether their standards meet yours, the following list is also a good checklist to ensure animal welfare and overall quality:

- Soil Association producers must be part of an integrated farming system, and not a specialist chicken production unit.
- Except where certain conditions are fulfilled, birds are kept in mobile housing.
- The maximum number of table birds per house allowed by the SA is 500

birds or, in exceptional cases, where certain conditions are fulfilled, 1,000 birds as compared to the new official limit of 4,800.

- The maximum stocking rate for laying birds is 1,000 per hectare under SA regulations, instead of 2,500; the maximum stocking rate for laying birds is 2,000 instead of 3,000.
- For laying stock, the purchase of debeaked chicks is forbidden. Though not common, it can be allowed under certain conditions under UKROFS regulations. (NOTE: The issue of debeaking is highly controversial. Because chickens can be cannibalistic in crowded conditions, RSPCA (freedom foods) allows the procedure. There is also intense debate as to how old chicks should be when debeaked.
- Birds must have access to permanent pasture for a minimum of two-thirds instead of one-third of their lives.
- Withdrawal times after medication are three times instead of twice the legal limit.

ORGANIC TEA, COFFEE AND COCOA STANDARDS

These are the guidelines set by IFOAM that all certification bodies affiliated to them must adhere to.

- Tea, coffee and cocoa should be produced as part of a sustainable farming system that observes conservation practices. The whole farm should be organic.
- Clearance of land must not adversely affect the environment or the local population. The demand for firewood, used as fuel for processing, must not lead to deforestation, and the use of fossil fuels and other non-renewable resources must be minimised. Any by-product – coffee and cocoa pulp, tea stalks – is to be recycled back into the fields.
- Only natural fermentation and mechanical and physical processes are allowed in the processing. As far as possible, processing and packing should be done in the country of origin.
- Crops should aim to be residue-free, and samples may be taken for residue analysis.

MAIN PERMITTED ADDITIVES AND PROCESSING AIDS

The following processing aids are allowed under organic standards regulations. Each one is under constant review (source: Soil Association).

Annatto (E160(B)): Vegetable dye extracted from the annatto tree. Allowed to be used only in Double Gloucester and Red Leicester cheese (where it is a mandatory ingredient).

Calcium carbonate (E170): Natural chalk. Used to reduce excess acid in wines.

Sulphur dioxide (E220): Preservative and antioxidant. Allowed only for use in wine and cider, to clean out unwanted microbes and to prevent discolouration. Levels allowed are about half to one third those used in conventional production.

Sodium nitrite (E250): Derived from sodium nitrite (chile saltpetre). Allowed to be used only in the curing of bacon and ham – it kills the botulinum bacteria and imparts a red colour to the meat.

Sodium nitrate (E251)
Potassium nitrate (E252): Mined mineral, saltpetre or chile saltpetre. Allowed to be used only in the curing of bacon and ham. Reduces to nitrite, which is the active ingredient in the curing process.

Lactic acid (E270): Naturally occurring from lactic bacteria. Used as a food preservative.

Carbon dioxide (E290): Natural gas. Used in carbonated water and soft drinks, also in modified atmosphere packaging to slow down respiration and ripening.

Malic acid (E296): Occurs naturally in apples. Used to increase acidity in cider (where low-acidity varieties are used) and in fruit-based foods.

Ascorbic acid (E300): Vitamin C. Antioxidant and preservative used in fruit juice; also used as a flour improver.

Tocopherol (E306): Vitamin E (only from natural concentrate, for example wheat germ, soya bean oil). Allowed to be used only as an antioxidant in fats and oils (such as margarine) to prevent them going rancid.

Lecithins (E322): Extracted from soya oil. Used as an emulsifier in chocolate, margarine and other foods.

Citric acid (E330)
Calcium citrates (E333): Naturally occurring in citrus fruits. Used as an antioxidant, acidifier and preservative in fruit products.

Tartaric acid (E334)
Sodium tartrates (E335): Naturally occurring in grapes. Used as an antioxidant and an acidity regulator.

Potassium tartrate (E336): Cream of tartare; used as a raising agent in flour.

Monocalcium phosphate (E341(A)): Derived from the mineral apatite. Allowed to be used only as a raising agent in self-raising flours.

Agar (E406): Derived from seaweed. Used as a thickening and gelling agent.

Carrageenan (E407): 'Irish Moss', which is derived from seaweed. Used as a stabiliser, thickener and gelling agent. Only 'un-degraded' carrageenan is allowed for use, as this is not carcinogenic.

Locust bean gum (Carob) (E410)
Guar gum (Cluster bean) (E412)
Arabic gum (Acacia) (E414)
Xanthan gum (fermentation product from corn syrup) (E415): All these are extracted from different natural products. They are used as gelling, stabilising and thickening agents. As they each have different properties, they are often used in combination to achieve the specific texture or qualities that are required, for example in sauces, dressings, ice-creams or jellies.

Pectin (E440(A)): Extracted from the pith of citrus fruits. Used as a gelling agent in jams and fruit preserves.

Sodium carbonates (E500)
Potassium carbonates (E501): Bicarbonate of soda. Used as a raising agent in flour and in the processing of sugar.

Ammonium carbonates (E503): Made by mixing chalk and ammonium sulphate. Recently approved as a raising agent in flour and baked products.

Calcium chloride (E509): Derived from natural salt brines. Allowed to be used only as a coagulation agent, for example in tofu.

Calcium sulphate (E516): Gypsum. Allowed only as a carrier, for example for the minerals and vitamins that are required by law in white flour, or as a coagulation agent, for example in tofu.

Nitrogen (E391)
Oxygen (E948): Natural gases. Used in modified atmosphere packaging.

Sodium chloride or potassium chloride: Natural salt. Used widely as a flavour enhancer and preservative. A flowing agent may be used where it can be proved to be necessary, to ensure even application in the manufacturing process.

Magnesium chloride: Otherwise known as nigari. Allowed to be used only as a coagulation agent, for example for tofu.

A–Z OF ORGANIC BRITAIN

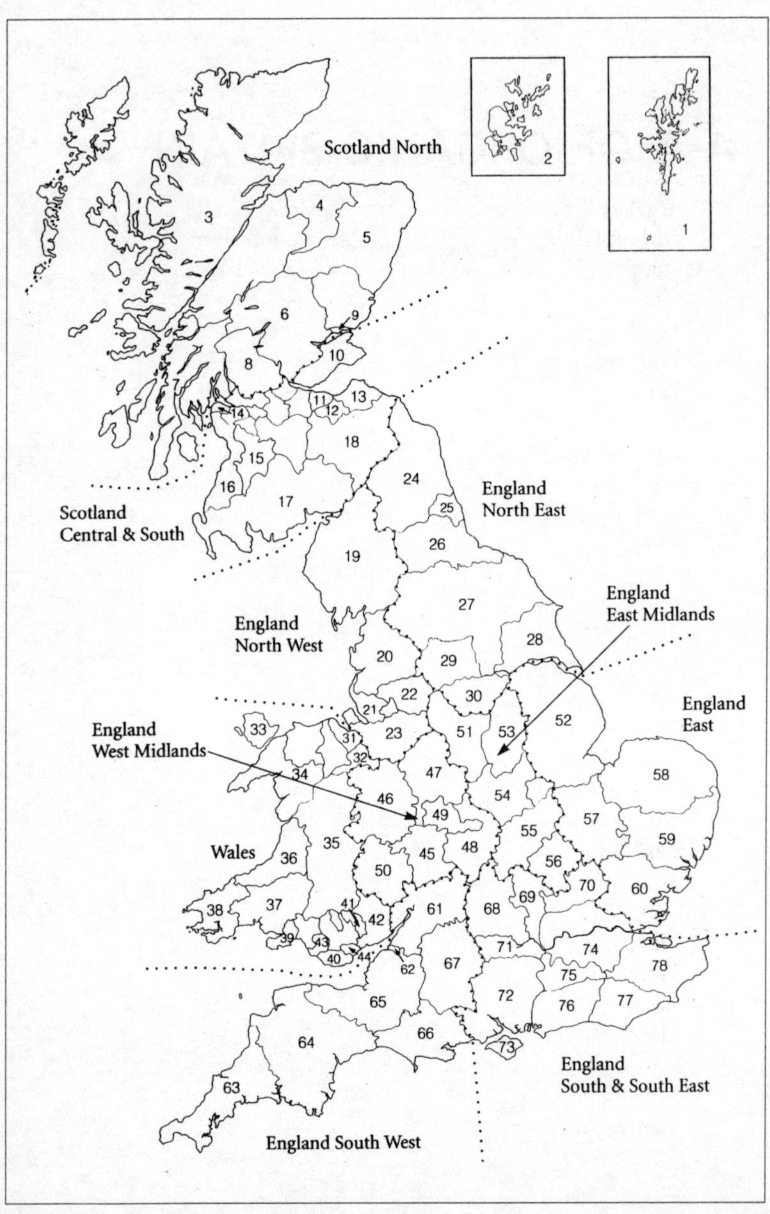
Scotland North
Scotland Central & South
England North East
England North West
England East Midlands
England East
England West Midlands
Wales
England South & South East
England South West
1
2
3
4
5
6
7
8
9
10
11
12
13
14
15
16
17
18
19
20
21
22
23
24
25
26
27
28
29
30
31
32
33
34
35
36
37
38
39
40
41
42
43
44
45
46
47
48
49
50
51
52
53
54
55
56
57
58
59
60
61
62
63
64
65
66
67
68
69
70
71
72
73
74
75
76
77
78

1 Shetland Islands
2 Orkney Islands
3 Highland
4 Moray
5 Aberdeenshire
6 Perth & Kinross
7 Argyll & Bute
8 Stirlingshire
9 Dundee
10 Fife
11 Edinburgh
12 Midlothian
13 East Lothian
14 Glasgow
15 East Ayrshire
16 South Ayrshire
17 Dumfries & Galloway
18 Borders
19 Cumbria
20 Lancashire
21 Merseyside
22 Greater Manchester
23 Cheshire
24 Northumberland
25 Tyne & Wear
26 Durham
27 North Yorkshire
28 East Riding of Yorkshire
29 West Yorkshire
30 South Yorkshire
31 Flintshire
32 Wrexham
33 Isle of Anglesey
34 Gwynedd
35 Powys
36 Ceredigion
37 Carmarthenshire
38 Pembrokeshire
39 Swansea
40 Vale of Glamorgan
41 Torfaen
42 Monmouthshire
43 Bridgend
44 Cardiff
45 Worcestershire
46 Shropshire
47 Staffordshire
48 Warwickshire
49 West Midlands
50 Herefordshire
51 Derbyshire
52 Lincolnshire
53 Nottinghamshire
54 Leicestershire
55 Northamptonshire
56 Bedfordshire
57 Cambridgeshire
58 Norfolk
59 Suffolk
60 Essex
61 Gloucestershire
62 Bristol
63 Cornwall
64 Devon
65 Somerset
66 Dorset
67 Wiltshire
68 Oxfordshire
69 Buckinghamshire
70 Hertfordshire
71 Berkshire
72 Hampshire
73 Isle of Wight
74 Greater London
75 Surrey
76 West Sussex
77 East Sussex
78 Kent

INTRODUCTION

The *A–Z of Organic Britain* directory has been compiled using information from various sources, including the websites of the excellent *Organic Directory* (**www.theorganicdirectory.co.uk**) and *Green Guide* (**www.greenguideonline.com**) and that of Big Barn (**www.bigbarn.co.uk**). All their regularly updated information can be readily accessed online. The *Organic Directory* and *Green Guide* include organic places for eating out and staying away.

Alastair Sawday's Special Places to Stay books (*British Bed & Breakfast* and *British Hotels, Inns and Other Places*) are one of the best sources for finding somewhere lovely to stay. There are nearly 200 entries where they use mainly organic ingredients. A specially selected list of his organic-minded bed and breakfast establishments starts on p. 536. For more, visit the excellent website, **www.specialplacestostay.com** that contains around 900 entries and has an exemplary links section:

For London, useful websites are **www.londonorganicfood.com** and **www.shopping.timeout.com**.

How to use the directory

To make it easy to use, our directory is organised on a regional basis. Within each of the British regions – they are the same as those used by the National Trust in its guide book – the entries are first subdivided into one of our six categories listed below. Within each of these categories they are further subdivided into the administrative region – county or unitary authority – where they are located. At this level entries are listed alphabetically by name, ignoring both the definite article and any initials.

For each entry contact details including address, phone number and, where appropriate, fax number, email address and website address are given. If the establishment is certified, for example by the Soil Association, this is indicated in brackets immediately after the address postcode.

By their very nature many of the establishments are in rural and sometimes quite remote places. To help you to find them, we have highlighted in a **bold** typeface the lowest level location (city, town, village or hamlet) of the address that is also listed in the *AA 2000 Gazetteer* and shown on its road maps. If this directory is used with this or a similar, comprehensive British gazetteer, it will make finding many of the establishments that much easier.

For each entry a short description of what you can expect to find or see is given. Within this description we have highlighted in **bold** towns and other specific geographic areas where the organisation's services are provided or can be found. This will help you quickly find products or services available in a specific place or area by scanning relevant parts of the directory.

Where, as is often the case, a single organisation is involved in more than one of our six categories, the main entry is usually listed in what we have assessed is the more important (but not necessarily the largest) of these activities. Under each other activity the establishment is listed at the end of the appropriate administrative area section after 'See also:'. Occasionally you will find entries for one organisation in two or more of our categories. These are also cross-referenced in the associated texts to help you find exactly what you are looking for as quickly as possible.

Finally, any other establishment mentioned in the text that also has its own entry is printed with its full name and, in a **bold** typeface, the place where it is located. The (abbreviated) administrative area in which its entry appears is also included if it is different to the section you are reading. The reference includes (in brackets) which of our six categories the organisation is listed under.

Our six categories are:

(A) **Box Schemes** Local/regional box schemes and/or home delivery services. Included are organisations providing both standard and customer-choice boxes for both pick up and delivery to either private addresses or pick-up points.

(B) **Shops** All shops except Farm Shops – see below – usually selling a minimum of 50% organic foods. They often also sell organic drinks, including wines and beers, and, sometimes, eco-friendly household or bodycare products. This is detailed in the accompanying text.

(C) **Farm Shops** Located at the producer, these range from small outlets selling just their own organic produce to some of the largest farm shops in the country, stocking 2,000 or more organic items.

(D) **Specialist Providers** Sellers and producers of specialist produce or products, including, for example, butchers, cheese-makers, fish farmers and millers.

(E) **Places to Eat and Stay** Cafés, bistros, restaurants, campsites and hotels. Also included in the main directory are cross-references to selected bed and breakfast establishments from Alastair Sawday's list.

(F) **Farm Gate** Producers offering sales at the farm gate, including those where an order has to be placed first.

For 'England Greater London', instead of a 'Farm Gate' section we have included a 'Farmers' and Organic Markets' section. It also contains some general comments on this growing area. The 'Specialist Providers' section for 'England Greater London' also contains separate 'Bakers' and 'Butchers' subsections.

Abbreviations

The following abbreviations (in brackets immediately after the address) have been used:

'Demeter': registered with the Biodynamic Organic Farmers Association
'OFF': registered with Organic Food Federation
'OF&G': registered with Organic Farmers & Growers
'SA': registered with the Soil Association
'SOPA': registered with the Scottish Organic Producers Association

The organic marketplace is a dynamic marketplace that is changing continuously with new entries and, unfortunately, some businesses closing and much data, such as opening times, subject to change. What was correct yesterday may well be different tomorrow. So please, to be sure, phone an establishment before making a long journey to visit it.

SOIL ASSOCIATION ORGANIC FARMS NETWORK

Seeing is believing. The nationwide Soil Association Organic Farms Network gives you the opportunity to do just that. Visiting a selection of these farms will allow you to see for yourself how organic farms are working towards a better quality of life and a more sustainable use of our natural resources.

The farms that you can visit range from those tucked away in idyllic countryside in Devon to a city farm in Yorkshire. Each has something special to offer, from lambing to hedge-laying, vineyards, orchards, woodlands, beetlebanks, farm trails and nature reserves. Many of the farms are open all the time and have special open days. Others, especially smaller working farms, are open by arrangement only. Check their opening times before you visit and if in any doubt contact the farmer. Many are also included in our directory.

You can also contact Rupert Aker at the Soil Association, tel: 0117 9142422, email: raker@soilassociation.org. For schools the Soil Association also provides the *Organic Experience* guidebook to all the farms in the network with activities and advice on arranging a visit.

The farms are listed below alphabetically within geographic region.

ENGLAND EAST MIDLANDS

Manor Farm

Long Whatton, Loughborough, Leicestershire, LE12 5DF
contacts: Graeme and Vivienne Matravers
T: 01509 646413 F: 01509 846644
e-mail: manorfarm.shop@btinternet.com
website: www.manororganicfarm.co.uk

A 300-acre mixed farm located in centre of seventeenth-century village. Involved in number of conservation projects, including tree planting, pond restoration and hedgerow management. Winners of 1998 Farming and Wildlife Advisory Group Award. Produce includes beef, sheep and poultry. Way-marked trail. **Farm Shop** – see main directory. Local box scheme. Granary visitor centre and classroom available to schools and groups by arrangement. Open: Thurs 9am–6pm, Fri 9am–7pm, Sat 9am–3pm.

ENGLAND NORTH EAST

Meanwood Valley Urban Farm

Sugarwell Rd, **Meanwood**, Leeds, West Yorkshire, LS7 2QG
contact: Sue Reddington
T: 0113 262 9759 F: 0113 239 2551

A city farm with organic market garden. Farm trail with disabled access. Demonstrates benefits of small-scale horticultural production promoting local, organic food for local people. Shop and café. New EpiCentre provides interactive educational arena on environmental issues. Education service provided to schools that meets National Curriculum criteria. Group visits by appointment. Coach access. See also main directory, **Specialist Providers**. Open: daily.

ENGLAND NORTH WEST

Howbarrow Farm

Cartmel, Grange-over-Sands, Cumbria, LA11 7SS
contacts: Paul Hughes and Julia Sayburn
T/F: 01539 536330
e-mail:
enquiries@howbarroworganic.demon.co.uk
website:
www.howbarroworganic.demon.co.uk

A 15-acre smallholding in the picturesque southern Cumbria fells. Grows fruit and vegetables and herbs. Rears chickens, turkeys, sheep and pigs. Farm trail open year round. Produce sold to consumers through **Farm Shop** – see main directory – box scheme and farmers' markets. Bed and breakfast provided. Also visits under the Willing Workers On Organic Farms (WWOOF) scheme. Holds open days. Farm tours and talks for groups year round by arrangement. Open: trail year round; otherwise Wed and Sat 10am–5pm.

ENGLAND SOUTH AND SOUTH EAST

Church Farm

Beale Park, **Lower Basildon**, Reading, Berkshire, RG8 9NH
contact: Clive Hill
T: 01189 845172

A 300-acre farm. Situated alongside River Thames and organically managed to preserve traditional flood meadows. New 40-acre native woodland. Hedge restoration programme underway. Farm trail. Open days and events. School and group visits by prior arrangement. Rears rare breeds of sheep and cattle. Open: farm trail at any time.

Elm Farm

Hamstead Marshall, Newbury, Berkshire, RG20 0HR
contact: Judith Towers
T: 01488 658298 F: 01488 658503
e-mail: elmfarm@efrc.com
website: www.efrc.co.uk

A 230-acre farm tucked away in a little known backwater and home of Elm Farm Research Centre. The Centre is the UK's foremost organic farming research establishment. Runs community composting project. Open access to farm trail passing conservation areas and research plots. **Farm Gate** sales – see main directory. Schools welcome by arrangement; education officer and materials available. Guided walks for groups by appointment. Open: trail open year round.

Luddesdown Organic Farms

Court Lodge, **Luddesdown**, Cobham, Kent, DA13 0XE
Contacts: Gerry and Jill Minister

T: 01474 813376 F: 01474 812 048
e-mail:
mailto:organic@luddesdown.u-net.com
website: www.luddesdownorganicfarms.co.uk

Inspirational 900-acre farm. Farm trail open all year. Annual open day with tractor and trailer tours. Other farm walks, guided tours and school groups by prior arrangement. Grows cereals and forage and thatching straws. Rears beef. Operates **Box Scheme** – see main directory. Open: please phone.

Scragoak Organic Farm

Brightling Rd, **Robertsbridge**, East Sussex, TN32 5EY
contacts: David and Karen Wenman
T/F: 01424 838420
e-mail: mail@scragoak.co.uk
website: www.scragoak.co.uk

Amazing organic market garden. Farm trail. Field-grown vegetables and polytunnels. Award-winning **Farm Shop** and **Box Scheme** – see main directory. School and group tours welcome by prior arrangement. Open: Tues–Sat 9.30am–5pm.

Sedlescombe Organic Vineyard

Cripp's Corner, **Sedlescombe**, Robertsbridge, East Sussex, TN32 5SA
contact: Roy Cook
T: 01580 830715 F: 01580 830122
e-mail: rcook91137@aol.com
website: www.englishorganicwine.co.uk

Remarkable 15-acre organic vineyard. The vineyard trail passes a sweet chestnut coppice and a stream. Produces award-winning English wine, cider and fruit juices. Vineyard **Farm Shop** – see main directory. Wine tasting. School and group tours by prior arrangement. Open: April–Dec 10am–5pm. Jan–March Sat–Sun only, 12am–5pm.

Sheepdrove Organic Farm

Lambourn, Berkshire, RG17 7UN (SA)
Contact: Jason Ball
T: 01488 71659 F: 01488 72677
e-mail: manager@sheepdrove.com
website: www.sheepdrove.com

Large 2,000-acre mixed farm on Berkshire downs. Crops include cereals. Rears sheep, cattle, pigs, turkeys, geese, ducks and chicken. Farm trail. Composting enterprise has to be seen to be believed; about 5,000 tonnes of green waste, coffee grounds and horse manure processed annually. Sales at **Farm Gate** – see main directory. Open days and special events. Schools and groups by appointment. Large library. Computer centre available to visiting teachers. Education officer. Plan for themed days linked to National Curriculum under development – check website for update. Classroom/conference room/visitor centre. Coach access. Open: trail year round, otherwise by appointment.

Step Farm

Lechlade Rd, Faringdon, Oxfordshire, SN7 8BH
contacts: Mr and Mrs Saunders
T: 01367 240558/240183 F: 01367 244324

A mixed 1,560-acre farm. Conservation is important aspect of activities. Studies have been conducted into skylarks and sparrows. Grows cereals. Rears beef and dairy cattle and sheep. Produce available at **Farm Gate** – see main directory. Special events held throughout year. Prearranged guided tours for groups of up to 40–50 people. Open: by prior arrangement.

Waltham Place Farm

White Waltham, Maidenhead, Berkshire, SL6 3JH
contact: Mary Healy
T: 01628 824605

A 140-acre estate. Organic farm with woodlands, orchards and beautiful landscaped and ornamental gardens (see p. **469**). Farm trail. Rears cattle, sheep, pigs, goats and chickens. Has kitchen garden. Regular open days. School visits welcome by arrangement. Has classroom facilities and education officer. Open: by appointment.

ENGLAND SOUTH WEST

Colham Farm

Castle Combe, Chippenham, Wiltshire, SN14 7HZ
Contact: Soil Association
T: 0117 9142422

Remarkable 600-acre organic farm. Three hundred acres of mature woodland, 50 acres of new, broadleafed plantations. Three Sites of Special Scientific Interest. Farm trail. Conservation is main focus. Rears suckler beef, pigs and sheep. Grows wheat. Open: trail open year round. Please keep dogs on lead.

Coswinsawsin

The Duchy College, **Rosewarne**, Camborne, Cornwall, TR14 0AB
Contact: Steve Roderick
T: 01209 722100 F: 01209 722159

A 63-acre holding farmed by the Duchy College. The farm converted to organic production in 2001. Grows a variety of field crops, including field-scale vegetables, sugar beet, potatoes and cereals. Educational visits, open days and farm walks are available by prior appointment. Open: by arrangement.

Eastbrook Farm

Bishopstone, nr Swindon, Wiltshire, SN6 8PW
Contact: Barbara Rayner
T: 01793 791460

A 1,350-acre mixed downland farm. One of country's best-known organic farms, tenanted by Helen Browning, chairman of Soil Association. Farm trail. Horticulture with cereals and beef, sheep, pigs and two dairy herds – must see the pigs! Schools and groups welcome by arrangement. Open: trail open year round.

Higher Hacknell Farm

Burrington, Umberleigh, Devon, EX37 9LX
Contacts: Tim and Jo Burden
T: 01769 560292 F: 01769 560909
e-mail: burden@hacknell.fsbusiness.co.uk
website: www.higherhacknell.co.uk

A 350-acre idyllic farm in mid-Devon, past winner of the Loraine Award for Nature Conservation and Organic Farming and featured in the *Mail on Sunday*'s *You* magazine. Woodlands, ponds and orchards provide excellent wildlife habitats. Farm trail. Has South Devon suckler beef herd and sheep. Grows cereals and potatoes. Organic meat sold at **Farm Gate** – see main directory – and by mail order. Public and school visits by appointment. Open: by arrangement.

Highfield Farm

Clyst Road, **Topsham**, Exeter, Devon, EX3 0BY
contact: Ian Shears
T/F: 01392 876388
website:
www.highfieldharvest.freeserve.co.uk

A 118-acre mixed farm bordering the River Clyst. Farm trail around meadows and nature reserve – look out for kingfishers, herons and even rare cirl buntings. Grows vegetables and rears cows, sheep, pigs and chickens. Award-winning **Farm Shop** – see main directory. School and group visits by prior appointment. Open: Tues–Sat 9am–6pm, Sun 10am–1pm. Closed: Mon.

Lower Pertwood Farm

Hindon, Salisbury, Wiltshire, SP3 6TA
contact: Mark Houghton-Brown
T/F: 01747 820499
website:
www.highfieldharvest.freeserve.co.uk

A 1,850-acre mixed farm with many archaeological sites, including field systems, earthworks and a stretch of Roman road. Its downland pastures are rich in wild flowers including many rare species. Produces Pertwood cereals (see p. **324**) from own organic oats. Also grows other cereal crops and vegetables. Rears beef and rare Wiltshire Horn sheep. Group visits by prior arrangement. Open: by prior arrangement only.

Organic Herb Trading Company

Court Farm, **Milverton**, Somerset, TA4 1NF
Contact: Gaye Donaldson
T: 01823 401205

A 35-acre idyllic farm, headquarters of Organic Herb Trading Company, owners of Hambleden Herbs, Britain's specialist organic herb company (see p. **253**). Produces herbs and beef cattle. Farm trail through parkland and woodland past ponds and hedgerows. Two-and-a-half acres of herb beds. Walled garden. Herb-drying and a tincture-making room. School and group visits by arrangement. Visitors' centre. Annual farm open day. Open: by prior arrangement only.

ENGLAND WEST MIDLANDS

Elmhurst Organic Farm

Bow Lane, **Withybrook**, nr Coventry, CV7 9LQ
Contacts: Rod and Ann Pattison
T: 01788 832233 F: 01788 832690

A famous 174-acre family farm near the Fosse Way. Has unspoilt wildflower meadows and network of new woodland belts. Past winner of Loraine Award for Nature Conservation. Featured in Soil Association video, *Organic Farming: Food for Life*. Farm trail. **Farm Shop** – see main directory. Grows cereals. Rears cattle, sheep and pigs. Group visits by arrangement. Visit shop and walk trail. Open: Mon–Sat.

Pimhill Farm

Harmer Hill, Shrewsbury, Shropshire, SY4 3DY
contact: Ginny Mayall
T: 01939 290342 F: 01939 291156
e-mail: info@pimhillorganic.co.uk
website: www.pimhillorganic.co.uk

Organic (since 1949) family run farm. Herd of 175 pedigree Holstein dairy cattle. Grows wheat, oats and vegetables and spring beans for cattle fodder. Wheat stone ground on farm to produce famous Pimhill flours. Farm trail. **Specialist Provider** – see main directory. See website for further information. Open: farm trail open all year – please phone first.

SCOTLAND

Wester Lawrenceton Farm Ltd

Forres, Moray, IV36 2RH
contacts: Nick and Pam Rodway
T: 01309 676566

A 65-acre mixed farm. Grows cereal crops.

Rears Ayrshire dairy cows, small flock of milking sheep – wool used for dyeing and knitting – milking goats and poultry. All milk used in farm dairy for cheese-making. Awarded Best Producer 2001, Radio 4's *Food Programme* Awards. Happily provides cheese-making demonstrations and tuition by arrangement. See **Specialist Providers** in main directory. Open: by arrangement.

WALES

Dolgoch

Brongest, **Newcastle Emlyn**,
Carmarthenshire, SA38 9EU
contact: Nick Fordham
T: 01239 851466

Organic dairy farm also growing cereals and carrots. Also has 20-acre woodland, archaeology site and two rivers. Farm is good example of a West Wales dairy farm. Demonstrates production of dairy milk hand in hand with nature conservation. Farm and woodland trail. School and other groups welcome by arrangement. Open: by arrangement.

TASTE OF ORGANIC BRITAIN: A–Z DIRECTORY

This listing is broken down geographically by region and then by administrative area. This breakdown is listed below but with counties or unitary authorities for which there is no entry omitted.

ENGLAND EAST

England East – Box Schemes

CAMBRIDGESHIRE

Naturally Yours

The Horse and Gate Farm, Witcham Toll, **Ely**, CB6 2AB (SA)
T: 01353 778723
e-mail: orders@naturally-yours.demon.co.uk
website: www.naturally-yours.demon.co.uk

Local home delivery and box scheme, supplying locally produced organic rare breed meats, poultry, cured meats, home-made pies and sausages, and customer choice vegetable boxes with added choice of groceries. Delivery to **Cambridgeshire**, **Bedfordshire** and **Hertfordshire**. Also nationwide by courier.

Waterland Organics

Quaystone Cottage, **Reach**, CB5 0HZ (SA)
T: 01638 742178
e-mail: waterland.organics@farming.co.uk
website: www.waterlandorganics.co.uk

Home-grown (95%) seasonal fruit and vegetables, available year-round through their local box scheme. Mail order for top fruit trees and soft fruit plants. Phone for catalogue, or visit their website.

ESSEX

Jenny Usher

Green Oaks, Threshers Bush, **Harlow**, CM17 0NS (SA)
T: 01279 444663

Well-known and respected organic grower. Sells mainly at the Organic Food Market, Old Spitalfields, London **E1**. Stalls at **Billericay** and **Hatfield** farmers' markets. Also runs a local box scheme in **Essex** (25% home-grown). Boxes also available from: Traders Fair World Shop, **Colchester** and **Harlow** (Shops); Writtle College Garden Centre, **Writtle** (Farm Shops).

LINCOLNSHIRE

Blyton Organics

Church Lane, **Blyton**, DN21 3JZ (SA)
T: 01427 628928

Seasonal selection fruit and vegetable box scheme (100% home-grown). Delivers to drop-off points in **Lincoln** and surrounding villages.

Eden Farms

Rectory Lane, **Old Bolingbroke**, Spilsby, PE23 4EY (SA)
T/F: 01790 763582
e-mail: organics@edenfarms.co.uk
website: www.edenfarms.co.uk/

Organic grower for 20 years. Founder member of Eastern Counties Organic Producers (ECOP). Grows extensive range of excellent vegetables. Operates value for money box scheme with customer choice. Supplies mainly home-grown vegetables (90% in summer), fruit, local organic eggs and breads from Paul's, **Melton Mowbray** (Leics) (Specialist Providers). Delivers to **Lincoln**, **Loughborough**, **Newark** and **Nottingham** areas. Stall at **Gainsborough**, **Lincoln**, **Newark**,

Nottingham and **Retford** farmers' markets. Nationwide delivery by courier.

B. M. Sadd
Birchwood Farm, Drawdyke, **Sutton St James**, PE12 0HP (SA)
T: 01945 440388
e-mail: bmsorganics@hotmail.com

Old-established seasonal selection fruit and vegetable box scheme (70% home-produced). Pick up from farm.

Woodlands Farm
Kirton House, **Kirton**, nr Boston, PE20 1JD (SA)
T: 01205 722491 F: 01205 722905
e-mail: info@woodlandsfarm.co.uk
website: www.woodlandsfarm.co.uk

Year round, value for money fruit and vegetable box scheme, 90% home-grown. Seasonal selection with some customer choice. Delivery within 50-mile radius, covering **LN** and **PE** postcodes, **Northampton** and **Rutland**. Also produces own much-praised Christmas organic Bronze Originals (OBO) turkeys, raised in small flocks to highest standards. Mail order but can also be collected from farm.
See also:
Holbeach Wholefoods, **Holbeach**; Spice of Life, **Bourne** (Shops)

NORFOLK

A. Hood
The Stables, **Gresham**, Norwich, NR11 8AD (SA)
T: 01263 577468

Small, local box scheme (May to Christmas) and farm-gate pick-up of home-grown seasonal fruit and vegetables.

Graham Hughes Organic Boxes
Eastview, 61 Fen St, **Old Buckenham**, Attleborough NR17 1SR (SA)
T: 01953 789 000

Delivery of seasonal selection fruit and vegetable boxes, customer choice options available (75% locally produced), to **Suffolk** and **Norfolk**. Boxes also available from: Fruits of the Earth, **Ipswich** (Suffk) (Shops); Green City Central, **Norwich** (Shops); Paradise Organics, **Poringland** (Box Schemes).

Organic Connections International
Riverdale, Town St, **Upwell**, nr Wisbech, PE14 9AF (SA)
T: 01945 773374 F: 01945 773033
e-mail: sales@organic-connections.co.uk
website: www.organic-connections.co.uk

Award-winning box scheme. Seasonal selection fruit and vegetables boxes with customer choice options. Also supplies wholefoods, petfoods, dairy, juices and breads. Delivery nationwide.

Paradise Organics
64 Glenn Rd, **Poringland**, Norwich, NR14 7LU
T: 01508 494260

Delivers seasonal selection fruit and vegetable boxes, eggs and wholefoods, supplied by Graham Hughes, **Old Buckenham** (Box Schemes), in and around **Norwich**.

The Really Real Food
The Old Chapel, Potash Farm, Potash Lane, **Hethel**, NR14 8EY (OF&G)
T: 01953 602125 F: 01953 601506
e-mail: reallyrealfood@aol.com
website: www.reallyrealfood.co.uk

Box scheme/home delivery and shop (location map on website). Also shop (Mon–

Sat 9.30am–5.30pm) outside Guildhall, **Norwich**. Sells home-produced lamb, plus beef, chicken, sausages and bacon and 100% organic fruit and vegetables, eggs, wholefoods, groceries and dairy. Free home delivery service (Tues–Sat) to **Norfolk** and **Suffolk**. Offers a selection of boxes, some including meat and dairy plus all their other products to order.

SUFFOLK

The Cambridge Organic Food Co.

Aston Organic Orchard, Welham Lane, Risby, nr **Bury St Edmunds**, IP28 6QS (OF&G)
T/F: 01284 811888
website: www.bigbarn.co.uk/cambridgeorganics

Local seasonal box scheme, with customer choice, supplying organic produce from local growers and HDRA's Audley End organic kitchen garden, plus their own organic apples. Also produces Earth's Crust apple pies sold in London and through their box scheme. Delivery to **Cambridge** city and **Saffron Walden**. For deliveries to **St Ives** and **Huntingdon**, contact Alpha Farms, T: 01480 831234 or visit their website: www.alphafarms.co.uk.

DJ Produce

Unit 1 G, Griffiths Yard, Gazeley Rd, **Moulton**, CB8 8SR (OF&G)
T/F: 01638 552709

Delivers seasonal selection fruit and vegetable box scheme and eggs, dairy and groceries to **Cambridge** area.

Greens Organic Foods

Milway Farm, **Palgrave**, IP22 1SN (SA)
T: 01379 652111 F: 01379 650408
e-mail: ester@greensorganic.co.uk
website: www.greensorganic.co.uk

Box scheme and home delivery. Customer choice fruit and vegetable boxes (30% home-grown) to **Norfolk** and **Suffolk**. Phone for product list, which includes dairy, local meat, bread, juices and wholefoods.

Hillside Nurseries

Hintlesham, Ipswich, IP8 3NJ (SA)
T: 01473 652682 F: 01473 652624

Delivers (65% home-grown) seasonal selection fruit and vegetable boxes, with eggs, meat and wholefoods to order, to **Ipswich**, **Woodbridge**, **Felixstowe** and to **Essex** border.

Water Lane Nurseries

Nayland, CO6 4JS (SA)
T: 01206 262880

Comprehensive seasonal selection fruit and vegetable box scheme. Produce mainly locally grown, including home-grown asparagus, soft fruit and medlars. Delivery to **Colchester** and **Sudbury** area.

Waveney Valley Foods

Mardelle High Common, Clerks Lane, **Barsham**, Beccles, NR34 8HN (Demeter)
T/F: 01502 714285

Seasonal selection fruit and vegetable box scheme with customer choice options plus, home-produced organic Large Black pork and homemade sausages. Delivery to **Cambridge**, **Suffolk** and **South Norfolk**.

England East – Shops

CAMBRIDGESHIRE

Arjuna Wholefoods

12 Mill Rd, **Cambridge**, CB1 2AD (SA)
T: 01223 364845

Vegetarian and vegan store (70% organic), selling wide range of fruit, vegetables, groceries, dairy, herbs and wines, beers and spirits.

Daily Bread Co-operative

Unit 3, Kilmaine Close, **Cambridge**, CB4 2PH (SA)
T: 01223 423177

Large, spacious, friendly warehouse style store (20% organic and growing) selling wide range of organic fruit and vegetables, wholefoods and groceries. Bulk buying available. Small snack bar serving drinks and cakes.

Wisbech Wholefoods

8 North St, Old Market, **Wisbech**, PE13 1NP
T: 01945 464468

Vegetarian shop (70% organic). Sells fruit and vegetables, groceries, dairy, juices, wines, beers and cider, and eco-friendly cleaning goods.

ESSEX

Pilgrim's Natural

41–43 High St, **Halstead**, CO9 2AA (SA)
T: 01787 478513

Also at: Pilgrims Natural, Unit 4, Portal Precinct, Sir Isaacs' Walk, **Colchester**, CO1 1JJ
T: 01206 763380

Wholefood store (50% organic) selling bread, meat, dairy, groceries and wholefoods. Pick-up point for Eden Farms, **Old Bolingbroke** (Lincs) (Box Schemes) boxes ordered through shop.

Sunrise

31 Spa Rd, **Hockley**, SS5 4AZ
T: 01702 207017
e-mail: sunrisehealth@hotmail.com

Healthfood shop (30% organic). Range includes bread, groceries, dairy and wholefoods. In conjunction with the local gardening club operates a chemical-free vegetable box scheme during the summer.

The Wholefood Store

25 High St, **Manningtree**, CO11 1AJ (SA)
T: 01206 391 200
e-mail: dyvig@hotmail.com

Vegetarian shop (40% organic). Sells mainly home-grown fruit and vegetables, dairy and dairy alternatives, breads, wholefoods and groceries.

Traders Fair World Shop

Tye Green Community Centre, Tilegate Rd, **Harlow**, CM18 6LU
T: 01279 540908
e-mail: jokey@compuserve.com
website: www.worldshops.org
Also at: Traders Fair World Shop, Unit 4, Portal Precinct, Sir Isaac's Walk, **Colchester**, CO1 1JJ
T: 01206 763380

Fair trade shop (25% organic). Sells wholefoods and groceries, also fair-traded and eco-friendly household products. Pick-up point for Jenny Usher, **Harlow** (Box Schemes) fruit and vegetable boxes ordered through shop.

LINCOLNSHIRE

Holbeach Wholefood

32 High St, **Holbeach**, Spalding, PE2 7DY
T: 01406 422149
e-mail: d.west@easynet.co.uk

Sells vegetarian and vegan foods (35% organic), bread, dairy and dairy alternatives, fruit and vegetables, wholefoods and groceries. Collection point for Paul's, **Melton Mowbray** (Leics) (Specialist Providers) box scheme.

Keep Yourself Right

4 Ravendale St, **Scunthorpe**, DN15 6NE
T: 01724 854236

Healthfood shop (50% organic) selling wholefoods, groceries, wines and beers.

Spice of Life

4 Burghley Centre, **Bourne**, PE10 9EG
T: 01778 394735 F: 01778 362939

Vegetarian shop (40% organic) selling bread, fruit and vegetables, groceries and wholefoods. Collection point for Paul's, **Melton Mowbray** (Leics) (Specialist Providers) box scheme.

NORFOLK

Arthur's Wholefoods

3a Wellington Rd, **Dereham**, NR19 2BP (SA)
T: 01362 697750

Wide range of organic foods (50% organic), including fruit and vegetables, (100% organic), wholefoods, bread, groceries and dairy. Refill service for herbs, spices, oils and vinegars.

Green City Central

42–46 Bethel St, **Norwich**, NR2 1NR
T: 01603 631007 F: 01603 666879

Eighty per cent organic shop. Range includes breads, wholefoods and dairy, plus organic bed linen, towels, and eco-friendly cleaning goods. Pick-up point for Graham Hughes, **Old Buckenham** (Box Schemes) boxes. Small café sells soups and snacks mostly made with organic ingredients.

The Natural Foodstore

Norfolk House Yard, St Nicholas St, **Diss**, IP22 4LB
T: 01379 651832

Healthfood shop (35% organic) selling 100% organic fruit and vegetables, a wide range of groceries, plus homemade cakes, bread and savouries made with organic flour.

Rainbow Wholefoods

16 Dove St, **Norwich**, NR2 1DE (SA)
T: 01603 625560 F: 01603 664066
e-mail: richard@rainbowwholefoods.co.uk

Sell over 1,500 organic products, including fruit and vegetables, bread, groceries, dairy, frozen ready meals and organic wines, spirits and beers.
See also:
Mangreen Creations, **Swardeston** (Specialist Providers)

SUFFOLK

Focus Organic Ltd

High St, **Southwold**, IP18 6DN (SA)
T: 01502 725299

One hundred per cent organic shop. Sells Pure Organic Foods' meat, vegetables, Metfield Bakery, **Metfield** (Specialist Providers) organic bread and takeaway savouries, wholefoods, babyfoods, dairy, groceries and wines and beers. Also at Halesworth – see below.

Focus Organic Ltd

14 The Thoroughfare, **Halesworth**, IP19 8AH (SA)
T: 01986 872899 F: 01986 872995

Wholefood shop (75% organic) selling organic vegetables, wines and beers and bread, wholefoods, dairy and groceries.

Fruits of the Earth

67 Upper Orwell St, **Ipswich**, IP4 1HP
T: 01473 211282

Vegetarian shop (80+% organic) selling wholefoods, groceries, soya products, breads and 100% organic fruit and vegetables. Operates local home delivery service to **Ipswich**, including Graham Hughes, **Old Buckenham** (Norfk)box scheme produce.

Hungate Health Store

4 Hungate, **Beccles**, NR34 9TL
T: 01502 715009

Sells wide range of organic foods (50% organic) including dairy, bread, wholefoods and groceries.

Loaves and Fishes

52 Thoroughfare, **Woodbridge**, IP12 1AL
T: 01394 385650

Natural food store (60% organic), selling fruit and vegetables, chicken, fish, deli meats, dairy, bread, wholefoods and wines and beers.

Natural Food Store

Norfolk House Yard, St Nicholas St, **Diss**, IP22 4LB (SA)
T: 01379 651832

Vegetarian wholefood store (50% organic) selling wholefoods, groceries, dairy, bread, fruit and vegetables and deli.

England East – Farm Shops

CAMBRIDGESHIRE

The Prospects Trust

Snakehall Farm, 50 Swaffham Rd, **Reach**, CB5 0HZ (SA)
T: 01638 741551

Farm shop selling home-produced organic vegetables, herbs and eggs. The Prospects Trust is a charity supporting people with learning difficulties.

ESSEX

Brooklynne Farm Shop

Chapel Rd, **Beaumont–cum–Moze**, nr Clacton, CO16 0AR (SA)
T: 01255 862184

Sell fruit and vegetables grown on their 8-acre organic holding, including organic herbs, salad crops, peppers and aubergines and home-grown conventional produce with a range of organic groceries, tea and coffee.

Hill Crest Farm Shop

Stock Rd, Stock, **Ingatestone**, CM4 9QZ (SA)
T: 01277 840727

Traditional family butcher's (10% organic) selling organic pork, beef, lamb, chickens and bacon.

Writtle College Garden Centre Farm Shop

Lordship Rd, **Writtle**, Chelmsford, CM1 3RR
T: 01245 422011 F: 01245 424250

Shop (20% organic) sells groceries, fruit and

vegetables and eco-friendly gardening equipment. Pick-up point for Jenny Usher, **Harlow** (Box Scheme) boxes.

LINCOLNSHIRE

Wolds Organic Foods Ltd

Haugham House, **Louth**, LN11 8PU (SA)
T/F: 01507 610686

One hundred per cent organic farm shop. Sells home-grown seasonal fruit (apples, pears, plums, strawberries and blackcurrants) and vegetables, plus other seasonal local organic produce, groceries, dairy and local organic eggs. Open Wed–Fri and Sun 10am–5pm.

NORFOLK

Ash Farm

Stone Lane, Dintree, **Dereham**, NR20 5NA (SA)
T: 01362 683228
website: www.ashfarmorganics.co.uk

Small farm shop selling home-produced organic beef, pork and chicken from the freezer and home-grown organic seasonal vegetables. Open Fri 10.30am–3pm, Sat 9.30am–12am.

SUFFOLK

Longwood Farm

Tuddenham St Mary, Bury St Edmunds, IP28 6TB (SA)
T: 01638 717120
e-mail: enquiries@longwoodfarm.co.uk
website: www.longwoodfarm.co.uk

Award-winning organic meat-producer, selling own beef, lamb, pork, chicken, Christmas turkeys and geese, homemade sausages and burgers and pheasant and wild duck through their shop, at local farmers' markets, by mail order and at **Spitalfields** Market, London **E1**. Farm shop (100% organic), open Fri and Sat, sells home-produced meats, dairy, fruit and vegetables, bread and a complete range of groceries. Delivery to **Cambridge** and surrounding areas. Extensive mail order list.

England East – Specialist Providers

ESSEX

Audley End Walled Organic Kitchen Garden

Saffron Walden, CB11 4JF (SA)
T/F: 01799 520444

Part of the Henry Doubleday Research Association (see Specialist Providers, Warks.). A magnificent restored Victorian display kitchen garden in the grounds of Audley End country house, with its own organic shop selling home-grown organic fruit and vegetables, groceries, dairy, drinks, snacks and ice creams, plus organic seeds and gardening sundries. Open Wed–Sun, from April to October.

Buntings

89 High St, **Maldon**, CM9 5EP (SA)
T: 01621 853271 F: 01376 561233
Also at: Buntings, 18 Church St, **Coggleshall**, CO6 1TU (SA)
T: 01376 561233

Accredited traditional butchers for Rare Breeds Survival Trust and food shop (25% organic). Sells local organic beef and poultry, organic lamb and pork and organic cheeses and condiments.

LINCOLNSHIRE

The Five Sailed Windmill

East St, **Alford**, LN13 9EQ (SA)
T: 01507 462136
e-mail: enquiries@fivesailed.co.uk

Produces a range of 11 organic stoneground flours and cereals, available from the mill shop and by mail order.

Maud Foster Mill

Willoughby Rd, **Boston**, PE21 9EG (SA)
T: 01205 352188

One of only 4 working, commercial windmills in country. Produces a wide range of stoneground organic flours available locally and in their own delightful vegetarian tea-room.

Mount Pleasant Windmill

North Cliff Rd, **Kirton in Lindsey**, nr Gainsborough, DN21 4NH (SA)
T: 01652 640177

Working windmill with tea-room, bakery and shop selling organic stoneground flours. Open Fri–Sun all year and weekdays in August and at bank holidays.

NORFOLK

Crone's

Fairview, Fersfield Rd, **Kenninghall**, NR16 2DP (SA)
T: 01379 687687 F: 01379 688323
e-mail: sales@crones.co.uk
website: www.crones.co.uk

Award-winning organic apple and pear juices available from the farm shop. See full entry p. **270**.

Diane's Pantry

8 Market Place, **Reepham**, Norwich, NR10 4JJ
T: 01603 871075

Small bakery and coffee shop, using organic ingredients where possible. Bread made with organic flour baked to order. Stocks range of organic products (25% organic), including wholefoods, groceries and dairy.

Garboldisham Windmill

Garboldisham, Diss, IP22 2RJ (SA)
T: 01953 681593

Mills and sells a wide variety of flours (75% organic), including wholewheat, gluten-free and oatmeals. Mill open for bulk sales Wed and Fri am. Flours available through retail outlets in **Norfolk** and **Suffolk**. Ring Adrian Colman for availability and outlets.

Harveys Pure Meat

63 Grove Rd, **Norwich**, NR1 3RL (OFF)
T: 01603 621908
website: www.puremeat.org.uk

Traditional butcher selling lamb, pork, beef (75% organic) and locally produced free-range chicken and eggs.

Letheringsett Water Mill

Riverside Rd, **Holt**, NR25 7YD (Demeter)
T: 01263 713153
website: www.bigbarn.co.uk (Insert 'NR25 7YD' in postcode box. Then click on their icon.)

Two-hundred-year-old working mill and popular tourist attraction open all year. Produces a variety of 100% stoneground flours (30% biodynamic, remainder conventional) available in their shop, throughout Norfolk and by mail order. Working demonstrations Tues–Fri 2pm–4.30pm. Camphill Community at Thornage Hall grow their biodynamic wheat for them locally.

Mangreen Creations Ltd

Mangreen, **Swardeston**, Norwich, NR14 8DD
T: 01508 570444 F: 01508 578899
e-mail: trust@mangreen.co.uk
website: www.mangreen.co.uk

Holistic education and visitor centre with its own small shop (90% organic). Sells fruit and vegetables, groceries, bread, wholefoods, eggs, tea and coffee, confectionery and snacks. Open 8am–6pm every day. Pay through honesty box when staff not available.

SUFFOLK

Metfield Bakery

Metfield Stores, The Street, **Metfield**, Harleston, IP20 0LB (SA)
T: 01379 586798

Small, friendly local bakery. Produces 5 certified organic breads and a range of savouries made with organic ingredients where possible. Other breads all made with organic flour. Sold through local shops including Focus Organic, **Southwold** and **Halesworth** (Shops). Phone for additional outlets.

England East – Places to Eat and Stay

CAMBRIDGESHIRE

Sascombe Vineyards

The Thrift, **Kirtling**, Newmarket, CB8 9JB
T: 01440 783100 (phone early am or evenings)
website: www.sascombe-vineyards.co.uk

New 12-acre organic eco-weekend 'get-away' site with vineyard, incorporating feng shui principles with solar, wind and other natural energy systems currently being developed. Offers cabin accommodation.

ESSEX

See:
Little Brockholds Farm, **Radwinter** (B & B List)

LINCOLNSHIRE

See:
Maud Foster Mill, **Boston** (Specialist Providers)

NORFOLK

The Ark Restaurant

The Street, **Erpingham**, NR11 7QB
T: 01263 76535

Restaurant serving home-grown vegetables and organic meat and fish where possible. Three double rooms offering bed, breakfast and evening meal.

See also:
Green City Central, **Norwich** (Shops)
Diane's Pantry, **Norwich** (Specialist Providers)
Highfield Farm, **Great Ryburgh**; Manor Farm Barn, **Tatterford** (B & B List)

SUFFOLK

Southwold Lodge

67 Southwold Rd, **Beccles**, NR34 7JE
T: 01502 676148

Comfortable bed and breakfast owned by proprietors of The Queens Head – see next entry. Guests receive 10% discount at the pub.

The Queens Head

The Street, **Bramfield**, IP19 9HT
T: 01986 784214 F: 01986 784797
e-mail: ghbfield@aol.com

Attractive pub, passionate about organic and local foods. Serves excellent traditional and modern pub fare, all home made. About 70%

of meat and 50% of dairy and vegetables used are organic. Several organic wines, Crone's, **Kenninghall** (Norfk) (Specialist Providers) cider and juices served. Descriptions of local suppliers included in menu. Owners run Southwold Lodge B & B establishment – see previous entry.

England East – Farm Gate

ESSEX

Farmer Kit

Little Bowsers, **Little Walden**, Saffron Walden, CB10 1XQ (OF&G)
T: 01799 527315

Farm-gate sales of home-produced eggs and strawberries.

Kelly Turkey Farms

Springate Farm, Bicknacre Rd, **Danbury**, CM3 4EP (SA)
T: 01245 223581
e-mail: info@kelly-turkeys.com
website: www.kelly-turkeys.com

Acclaimed poultry producer. Christmas Kelly Bronze(TM) organic turkey and organic 'special roast' chicken (Oct–April) available at farm gate.

LINCOLNSHIRE

Birchwood Farm

Draw Dyke, **Sutton St James**, Spalding, PE12 0HP (SA)
T: 01945 440388

Farm-gate sales of vegetables and salads. Phone for more details.

Bridge Farm Organic Foods

Snitterby Carr, **Snitterby**, Gainsborough, DN21 4UU (SA)
T: 01673 818272 F: 01673 818477

Home-produced, organic goats-milk cheese (soft and semi-hard) available from farm, **Brigg** farmers' market and selected local retailers. Limited range of seasonal vegetables available at farm gate.

Cottage Organics

The Cottage, Midville Lane, **Stickney**, Boston, PE22 8DW (SA)
T: 01205 480602

Farm-gate sales of home-grown fruit and vegetables, plus a range of groceries and breads, mainly to order.

Wilsford Organics

11 Main St, **Wilsford**, Grantham, NG32 3NS (SA)
T: 01400 230224

Farm-gate and local sales of home-produced vegetables and eggs.

NORFOLK

Bagthorpe Farm

Bagthorpe, nr Syderstone, PE31 6QY (SA)
T: 01485 578528 F: 01485 578151

Farm-gate sales of home-produced organic root vegetables, brassicas and strawberries in season. Phone first to order.

Church Barn Farm

Arminghall, Norwich, NR14 8SG (SA)
T: 01508 495574

Self-service farm-gate sales of home-produced seasonal fruit (apples, plums, raspberries) and vegetables (leeks, potatoes, broad beans). Summer PYO.

Cottage Farm

Sneeth Rd, **Marshland St James**, Wisbech, PE14 8EP (OFF)
T: 01945 430292

Farm-gate sales of home-produced organic top fruit, plums and eggs.

John Savory
Highfield Farm, **Great Ryburgh**, Fakenham, NR21 7AL (SA)
T: 01328 829249

Farm-gate sales of home-produced organic eggs. Phone first to order. See also B & B list.
See also:
A. Hood, **Gresham** (Box Schemes)

SUFFOLK

Domini Quality Foods
Village Farm, **Market Weston**, nr Diss, IP22 2NZ (SA)
T: 01359 221240

Long-standing inspirational organic family farm. Farm-gate sales of unpasteurised (green-top) milk, cream and butter from Jersey herd, grazing on 200-year-old pastures, plus their own meat (beef, lamb, pork and poultry), stoneground flour and eggs – all subject to availability. Also available by mail order and at Spitalfields Organic Food Market, London **E1**.

ENGLAND EAST MIDLANDS

England East Midlands – Box Schemes

DERBYSHIRE

Natural Delivery Wholefoods

The Old King's, Buxton Rd, **Bakewell**, DE45 1OA
T/F: 01629 814507
e-mail: orders@ndwholefoods.free-online.co.uk
website: www.bbr-online.com/n-d-wholefoods

Wholefood home delivery service and fruit and vegetable box scheme (via Goosemoor Organics (**Cowthorpe**, N Yorks)) to whole of **South Yorkshire** and **Derbyshire**. Order online or using their catalogue. Store (30% organic) sells comprehensive range of wholefoods, groceries, dairy, fruit and vegetables, bodycare and eco-friendly goods.
See also:
Wild Carrot, **Buxton** (Shops)

LEICESTERSHIRE

Chevelswarde Organic Growers

Chevel House, The Belt, **South Kilworth**, Lutterworth, LE17 6DX (SA)
T: 01858 575309
e-mail: john@chevel.freeserve.co.uk
website: www.chevel.freeserve.co.uk

Soil Association symbol holders since 1975, with their own 1-acre vineyard producing white wine. Operate a seasonal selection box scheme, delivering locally produced fruit and vegetables to drop-off points in **Leicester**, The Naturally Good Food Delivery Service, **Lutterworth** (see next entry), **Market Harborough** and The Wholefood Shop, **Rugby** (Warks) (Shops). Also available from their farm shop that is open every day. Shop sells their own wine, seasonal fruit and vegetables, ciders, apple and pear juices, breads, eggs, plus milk to order.

The Naturally Good Food Delivery Service

3 Rye Hill Avenue, **Lutterworth**, LE17 4AS (SA)
T: 01455 556878
e-mail: orders@goodfooddelivery.co.uk
website: www.goodfooddelivery.co.uk

Friendly, family–run, local vegetarian wholefood and organic home delivery service (90% organic). Supplies extensive range of organic groceries, dairy, chilled foods, local organic flour and Kim's Cakes, **Weddington** (Warks.) (Specialist Providers)), plus green bodycare and homecare products. Pick-up point for Chevelswarde Organic Growers, **South Kilworth** box scheme. Delivery within 10-mile radius of Lutterworth. Excellent website and nationwide mail order for non-perishables.

Bambury Farm

Peatling Magna, LE8 5UE (SA)
T: 0116 2478907
e-mail: bamburyfarm@btinternet.com

Local box scheme. Delivers mainly home-grown organic vegetables (around 70%) and seasonal UK fruit, plus additional fruit boxes, to **Leicester** and surrounding area. Supplies home-produced lamb, pork and eggs to order.

David Watts
Springfield Farm Bungalow, **Sapcote**, LE9 4LD (SA)
T: 01455 272840

Box scheme supplying vegetables and fruit (50% home-produced) in seasonal selection boxes. Enquiries welcome from the **Hinckley** area.
See also:
Paul's (bakery and tofu producer) **Melton Mowbray** (Specialist Providers)
Manor Organic Farm Shop, **Long Whetton**; Picks Organic Farm Shop, **Barkby Thorpe** (Farm Shops)

NORTHAMPTONSHIRE

Leafcycles
24 St Michaels Avenue, **Northampton**, NN1 4JQ
T: 01604 628956

Seasonal selection boxes – fruit and vegetables from Eden Farms, **Old Bolingbroke** (Lincs) (Box Schemes) – with monthly extras list to choose from. Deliveries to **Northampton** town by bicycle trailer.

NOTTINGHAMSHIRE

The Organic Man
27 Manton Crescent, **Lenton Abbey**, NG9 2GD (SA)
T: 0115 9134337
e-mail: johngriffiths11@ntlworld.com

Customised local box scheme and home delivery service dispatching fruit and vegetables, wholefoods, groceries, drinks, dairy products, Graig Farm Organics, **Dolau** (Powys) (Farm Shops) meat and fish to addresses within a 35-mile radius. All fruit and vegetables locally produced.
See also:
Trinity Farm, **Cossall** (Farm Shops)

England East Midlands – Shops

DERBYSHIRE

Beano's Wholefoods
Holme Rd, **Matlock Bath**, DE4 3NU
T: 01629 57130 F: 01629 57143
e-mail: sales@beanos.fsbusiness.co.uk

Well-established vegetarian store. Wide selection of organic foods, including fruit and vegetables, wholefoods, wines, beers and dairy. Also operates a year-round seasonal selection vegetable box scheme (60% locally produced); delivers within 10-mile radius of Matlock.

The Organic Shop
3 Sett Close, off Market St, New Mills, **High Peak**, SK22 4AQ
T: 01663 747550

One hundred per cent organic shop selling comprehensive range of organic foods and drinks, including meat, dairy, fruit and vegetables and groceries. Also sells organic clothes and environmentally friendly cleaning products.

Wild Carrot
5 Bridge St, **Buxton**, SK17 6BS (SA)
T: 01298 22843
e-mail: shop@wildcarrot.freeserve.co.uk
website: www.wildcarrot.freeserve.co.uk

Wholefood shop (50% organic) selling wide range of organic products including fruit and vegetables, bread, dairy, chilled and frozen foods, special diet and vegan foods and wines and beers. Also runs local box scheme with home delivery to **Buxton** area.

LEICESTERSHIRE

Currant Affairs

9a Loseby Lane, **Leicester**, LE1 5DR
T: 0116 251 0887

Natural food store (50% organic) selling wines and beers, bread, fruit and vegetables, eggs, dairy and wholefoods. In-house bakery using mainly organic ingredients to make savouries and cakes, to take away.

Leicester Wholefood Co-operative

Unit 3 Freehold St, **Leicester**, LE1 2LX (SA)
T: 0116 2512525

Fifty per cent organic shop selling wines, beers, locally produced organic meat, bread, fruit and vegetables, groceries, eggs, dairy, wholefoods and herbs.

NORTHAMPTONSHIRE

Daily Bread Co-operative Ltd

The Old Laundry, Bedford Road, **Northampton**, NN4 7AD (SA)
T: 01604 621531 F: 01604 603725
e-mail: northampton@dailybread.co.uk
website: www.dailybread.co.uk

Value for money 'people before profit' wholefood shop (25% organic). Organic range includes dried foods, groceries, and non-dairy products. No fresh produce but pick-up point for Leafcycles box scheme. Bulk buying also available.

NOTTINGHAMSHIRE

Inkskips Organics

16 Main Street, **East Bridgford**, NG13 8PA (SA)
T: 01949 21057
e-mail: inkskipsorg@aol.com

Village shop and post office selling home-grown fruit and vegetables in season, pork and eggs from their organic smallholding, plus a range of organic groceries, Graig Farm Organics, **Dolau** (Powys) (Farm Shops) meat and fish, dairy and local breads from Paul's, **Melton Mowbray** (Leics) (Specialist Providers).

Out of this World

Unit 1, Villa Street, **Beeston**, NG9 2NY
T: 0115 9431311 F: 0115 9225455
website: www.ootw.co.uk

Ethical and organic consumer co-operative with over 18,000 members. Sells over 4,000 organic products, including 100% organic fruit and vegetables and meat. Local foods include Demeter meat from Hungary Lane Farm, **Sutton Bonnington** (Leics) (Farm Gate), fresh produce and tofu and breads from Paul's, **Melton Mowbray** (Leics) (Specialist Providers). Also stocks eco-friendly household and garden products, body- and babycare. Open Mon–Sat, 9am–8pm, Sun, 10am–4pm.
Also at:
Gosforth (T & W) (Shops)
Head office: 106 High Street, **Gosforth**, NE3 1HB
T: 0191 2135377

Roots Natural Foods

526 Mansfield Road, **Sherwood**, NG5 2FR
T: 0115 9609014

Vegetarian and vegan foods (60 percent organic), including organic fruit and vegetables, dairy, groceries and babyfoods. Operates local home delivery service. Fresh produce supplied by Eden Farms, **Old Bolingbroke** (Lincs) (Box Schemes).

England East Midlands – Farm Shops

DERBYSHIRE

Meynell Langley Farm Shop

Meynell Langley, **Kirk Langley**, DE6 4NT (SA)
T: 01332 824815
e-mail: organic@meynell-langley.co.uk

Small shop selling home-produced Welsh Black beef and North Cheviot lamb (frozen or fresh to order), chickens, seasonal vegetables and eggs, plus local organic pork. Open Fri, 1–6.30pm, and Sat, 10am–2pm. Other times by arrangement. Please phone first.

LEICESTERSHIRE

Growing Concern

Home Farm, Woodhouse Lane, **Nanpantan**, Loughborough, LE11 3YG (OF&G)
T: 01509 239228
e-mail: info@growingconcern.co.uk
website: www.growingconcern.co.uk

All the inspiration you will ever need. The Bells rear the UK's only pure-bred Horned Hereford cattle herd, totally grass-fed, and one of only 50 accredited BSE free herds (which means they can slaughter at 42 months, 12 months longer than usual). They also rear traditional pork, Dorset Down lamb, chickens and eggs. The farm has its own mini butcher's, smoke-box, and delightful Beth's coffee and cake café-cum-farm shop, selling home-made cakes, puddings, bread, award-winning pork pie, pâtés, chutneys and frozen ready meals, plus organic fruit and vegetables, local cheese and groceries. Their meat, cakes and ready meals are available mail order or online via the most heart-warming website in the book. The farm also has a play barn, play area and woodland walk. Shop open Wed–Sun. Phone to check first. Also supply Christmas poultry – turkey, goose, duck and chicken – with cockerels available at Easter and Christmas.

Manor Organic Farm Shop

Manor Farm, **Long Whatton**, Loughborough, LE12 5DF (SA)
T: 01509 646413 F: 01509 846644
e-mail: manorfarm.shop@btinternet.com
website: www.manororganicfarm.co.uk

Inspirational organic farm situated in the centre of seventeenth-century village, with small farm shop selling their own organic beef, lamb, chickens (raised in free-ranging small flocks of 70 birds), fruit and vegetables, plus organic bread, dairy and wholefoods. Also operate local box scheme, delivering home-grown fruit and vegetables to **Loughborough**. See also SA Farm listing, England East Midlands.

Picks Organic Farm Shop

The Cottage, Hamilton Grounds, **Barkby Thorpe**, Leicester, LE7 3QF (OF&G)
T/F: 01162 693548

Organic farm shop, open 7 days a week, selling their own Dexter beef, lamb, pork and chickens, plus a full range of organic groceries, dairy products and fruit and vegetables (some home-grown). Operates a local box scheme and home delivery service within 20-mile radius.
See also:
Chevelswarde Organic Growers, **South Kilworth** (Box Schemes)

NOTTINGHAMSHIRE

Trinity Farm

Awsworth Lane, **Cossall**,
NG16 2RZ (OF&G)
T: 01159 442545

One hundred per cent organic, friendly farm shop selling wide range of fruit and vegetables (50% home-grown, specialising in rare varieties), their own pork and eggs, other meats, dairy, wholefoods and groceries. Seasonal selection box scheme and customised home deliveries to Derby and Nottingham areas. Delivery by their van doubling as a mobile shop carrying a full range of products. See also entry under Box Scheme.

England East Midlands – Specialist Providers

LEICESTERSHIRE

Great Claybrooke Flour

Hall House, Hall Lane, Ullesthorpe,
Lutterworth, LE17 5DD (SA)
T: 01455 202443 F: 01455 202553
e-mail: claybrooke.mill@pipemedia.co.uk

Watermill producing traditional stoneground flours (50% organic), including wholemeal, unbleached white and speciality flours. Available by mail order and in local shops. Visits and orders collected by prior arrangement.

Heards of Wigston

69 Long St, **Wigston**, Leicester, LE8 2AJ
T: 0116 2880444

Traditional butcher (95% organic) selling organic lamb, pork, beef and chicken, plus cheeses, jams and chutneys and sundries.

Stephen Morris Butchers

26–27 High St, **Loughborough**,
LE11 2PZ (Demeter)
T: 01509 215260

A find. Dedicated organic, traditional family butchers, (90+% organic) selling beef, lamb, pork and poultry from two local biodynamic farmers, plus home-cured organic bacon, hams, sausages, cooked meats, and home-made pies made with organic ingredients such as steak and ale and chicken and mushroom.

Paul's

66–68 Snow Hill, **Melton Mowbray**,
LE13 1PD (SA)
T: 01664 560572
e-mail: paul@soyfoods.freeserve.co.uk

Renowned artisan small bakers and tofu-producer (95% organic). Bakes an impressive range of delicious fresh breads and baked products, using flour from local miller, Nigel Moon, ionised water and sea salt. Products available from bake house, Melton Mowbray farmers' market, and widely throughout the country, including London and Manchester. They also operate a box scheme, delivering throughout the region, sourcing as much local and UK grown produce as possible. For more, see p. **220**.

Whissendine Windmill

Melton Rd, **Whissendine**,
LE15 7EU (OF&G)
T: 01664 474172

Produces wholemeal, brown and unbleached white organic flour; also organic oatmeal, barleymeal, ryemeal, maizemeal and bran. All available from the mill and selected retailers.

Michael F. Wood
51 Hartopp Rd, **Leicester**, LE2 1WG (SA)
T: 0116 2705194

Family butcher (25% organic) selling locally sourced organic beef, lamb, pork and chicken, plus organic bread and eggs.

England East Midlands – Places to Eat and Stay

DERBYSHIRE

Beechenhill Farm
Ilam, Ashbourne, DE6 2BD (SA)
T: 01335 310274
e-mail: beechenhill@btinternet.com

Organic farm offering self-catering accommodation and self-contained bed and breakfast that includes their own unpasteurised (green-top) milk. Their organic lamb (whole or sides) is available on request, butchered, to pick up from the farm.

Mimmo's
1 St Mary's Gate, **Wirksworth**, Matlock, DE4 4DQ
T: 01629 826724

Italian restaurant, sourcing locally produced organic food where possible, making pasta and rice dishes using organic ingredients.

New House Organic Farm
Kniveton, Ashbourne, DE6 1JL (OF&G)
T: 01335 342429

Family bed and breakfast, including meals made with organic ingredients as far as possible. Also farm-gate sales of Hereford beef, lamb, eggs and vegetables.
See also:
Mount Tabor House, **Crich** (B & B List)

LEICESTERSHIRE

See:
Growing Concern, **Nanpantan** (Farm Shops)

NOTTINGHAMSHIRE

Barn Farm Cottage
Kneeton Rd, **East Bridgeford**, G13 8PJ (SA)
T: 01949 20196

Award-winning bed and breakfast on organic holding, serving meals, including dinners, prepared with organic ingredients.

England East Midlands – Farm Gate

DERBYSHIRE

Liberty Farm
Findern Lane, **Burnaston**, DE65 6JG (OF&G)
T: 01332 523263

Farm-gate sales of organic eggs. Help yourself from the fridge, honesty box provided. Bulk sales also available.

Lower Hurst Farm
Hartington, Nr Buxton, SK17 0HJ (SA)
T: 01298 84900 F: 01298 84732
e-mail: sales@lowerhurstfarm.co.uk
website: www.lowerhurstfarm.co.uk

Online mail-order sales of pedigree Hereford beef, blast frozen to reach customers in perfect condition. Also supplies own organic lamb. Produce available from farm gate by prior arrangement.

Turlowfields Organic Farm Shop
Turlowfields Farm, **Hognaston**, nr Ashbourne, DE6 1PW (SA)
T: 01335 370834

e-mail: hunters@turlow.co.uk

Small farm shop, open Friday and Saturday, other times by arrangement, selling frozen home-produced organic Aberdeen Angus beef, pork, lamb and chickens.

LEICESTERSHIRE

Hungary Lane Farm
Sutton Bonnington, nr Loughborough, LE12 5NB (Demeter)
T/F: 01509 673897

Picturesque biodynamic farm. Their farm shop, open Saturdays from February to August, sells own beef, lamb, poultry, eggs, apples and pears, and winter vegetables. Their meat is also available through Stephen Morris Butchers and Out of This World.

Osbaston Kitchen Garden
Osbaston Hall, **Osbaston**, nr Nuneaton, CV13 0DR (SA)
T: 01455 440811

Walled kitchen garden producing organic fruit, vegetables and herbs. Available at the farm gate and at local farmers' markets.

ENGLAND GREATER LONDON

England Greater London – Box Schemes

Abel and Cole

8–13 MGI Estate, Milkwood Rd, **SE24** 0JF (SA)
T: 020 7737 3648 F: 020 7737 7785
e-mail: telesales@abel-cole.co.uk
website: www.abel-cole.co.uk

Stylish, popular, bespoke home delivery service, with excellent website, specialising in organic fresh produce and meat. Offers a range of fruit and vegetable boxes, plus individual packs. Has full range of organic meats and poultry and select range of organic groceries: breads, milk, eggs, olive oil, balsamic vinegar, apple juice, Rock's cordials and Llanllyr organic farm mineral water. Delivery by their own van to **Greater London** addresses; small/ standard boxes delivered throughout mainland England and Wales by overnight courier. Order by phone, fax or email.

Farm-a-Round Ltd

Offices B140–B143, New Covent Garden Market, Nine Elms Lane, **SW8** 5PA (OF&G)
T: 020 7627 8066 F: 020 7627 0069
e-mail: homedelivery@farmaround.co.uk
website: www.farmaround.co.uk

Established in 1994, well-known box scheme and home delivery service, which buys direct from UK and European growers. Impressive, friendly and informative website that tells you what you really want to know (includes recipes from Rose Elliot and weekly list of box contents). Offers range of fruit and vegetable boxes, packed in sturdy large paper bags, including 'mini' bags for singles, which usually contain unusual items to delight and surprise you, with some customer choice, plus a wide range of groceries and eco-friendly cleaning products. Regular newsletter, loyalty scheme and visits arranged to growers. Delivery originally within the M25 plus Surrey, and now nationwide. Order via website, phone or fax.

Just Organics

113 Wilberforce Rd, **N4** 2SP (SA)
T: 020 7704 2566

Supplies fruit and vegetable boxes, with customer choice. Evening deliveries to **Central, North, East and West London**.

Organic Delivery Company

70 Rivington St, **EC2**A 3AY (SA)
T: 020 7739 8181 F: 020 7613 5800
e-mail: info@organicdelivery.co.uk
website: www.organicdelivery.co.uk

Local vegetarian home delivery service, offering value-for-money fruit and vegetable boxes (from £9.99), plus wide range of groceries, breads, cheese, wines and beers by the case, eco-friendly cleaning products, organic clothing and bed linen, juicers and organic books. Delivery between 5pm–10pm to **London** postcodes and **Kingston** and **Twickenham** (daytime delivery to Central London homes and offices). Order online, by phone, fax or email. Nicely designed website.

Spring Green Organic Home Shopping

21 Purley Avenue, **NW2** 1SH (SA)
T: 020 8208 0855
e-mail: enquiries@spring-green.co.uk
website: www.spring-green.co.uk

Established vegetarian home delivery service supplying extensive range of organic foods including fruit and vegetables, breads, groceries, plus bodycare and eco-friendly household products. Delivery to **London** postcode area.
See also:
Greenwich Organics, **SE10**; Sense, **SW12** (Shops)
The Fresh Food Company; Organics Direct; Simply Organic

England Greater London – Shops

Alara Wholefoods

56–60 Marchmont St, **WC1**N 1AB
T: 020 7837 1172 F: 0207 833 8089

Large store selling wide range of organic wholefoods, groceries, fruit and vegetables, dairy and frozen foods (60% organic), plus new juice bar and takeaway counter for sandwiches and snacks using organic ingredients.

Alternatives Health Store

1369 High Rd, Whetstone, **N20** 9LN
T: 020 8445 2675

Vegetarian shop (50% organic). Organic range includes wholefoods, groceries, juices, dairy and frozen ready meals. Alternative therapy centre at back of shop.

As Nature Intended

Head Office: Unit 3 Roslin Square, Roslin Rd, South Acton, London **W3** 8DH
T: 020 8752 0468 F: 020 8752 0418
e-mail: enquiries@asnatureintended.uk.com
website: www.asnatureintended.com

New chain, 100% organic, all to be located within the M25, catering for all ages and all types. Friendly, spacious, good prices and products. Comprehensive range of foods and drinks, including fresh produce, babyfoods, wines and beers, plus snacks and sandwiches, and well chosen bodycare section.
Stores at:

As Nature Intended – Chiswick

201 Chiswick High Rd, Chiswick, **W4** 2DR
T: 020 8742 8838 F: 020 8742 3131

Five minutes from Turnham Green tube station. Park outside the door, also. Open Mon–Fri 9am–8pm; Sat 9am–7pm; Sun 11am–5.30pm.

As Nature Intended – East Sheen

272–274 Upper Richmond St, East Sheen, **SW14** 7JE
T: 020 8878 0627 F: 020 8878 6694

Around the corner from Mortlake station, on the main bus routes, a couple of doors from Safeway. Open Mon–Fri 9am–8pm; Sat 9am–7pm; Sun 11am–5.30pm.

Bluebird

The Food Market, 350 Kings Rd, **SW3** 5UU
T: 020 7559 1153 F: 020 7559 1111
website: www.bluebird-store.co.uk

Terence Conran's gastrodome – a gourmet supermarket, wine shop, flower stall, home and kitchen shop, restaurant, café and bar. Stocks a wide range of foods (25% organic) including groceries, organic meat and dairy products.

Bumblebee
30, 32 and 33 Brecknock Rd, **N7** 0DD
T/F: 020 7607 1936
T: (orders): 020 7607 1935
T: (information): mail
to:info@bumblebee.co.uk
T: (orders): delivery@bumblebee.co.uk
website: www.bumblebee.co.uk

Remarkable one-stop, friendly, vegetarian, natural food/organic independent retailer established for over 20 years. Comprises three separate shops: greengrocer and dairy; bakery and takeaway; wholefood and grocery. Stocks over 5,000 items (around 70% organic). Range includes over 30 organic olive oils, 100 wines, organic breads from best organic bakers, difficult to find items such as organic tapioca and chestnut flour plus eco-friendly household products and organic bed linen. Bulk buying at knock-down prices available. Also home delivery service to north London by van and nationwide by courier. Excellent website. Order via phone, fax, email or online.

Bushwacker Wholefoods
132 Kings St, Hammersmith, London,
W6 0QU (SA)
T: 020 8748 2061

One-stop shop (40% organic). Sells fruit and vegetables (100% organic), organic groceries, wholefoods, wide range of breads and baked goods, dairy products, savoury takeaways from Paul's **Melton Mowbray** (Leics) (Specialist Providers), plus eco-friendly lifestyle products.

Christopher's Delicatessen and Fine Organic Foods
103 Larriston Rd, Victoria Park, **E9** 7HJ
T: 020 8986 2466 F: 020 8985 4101
e-mail: chrispowney@aol.com
website: www.organiccatering.co.uk

One hundred per cent organic store open every day. Sells high-quality organic meats, Parma ham, Italian salamis, pâtés, cheeses, wholefoods and groceries, not to mention freshly made organic cappuccinos. Also outside catering.

Countryside Healthfoods
19 Fortyhill, **Enfield**, EN2 9HT
T: 0208 363 2933

Sells wholefoods, groceries and fruit and vegetables (50% organic). Mail order service for wholefoods and non-fragile items.

Dandelion
120 Northcote Rd, **SW11** 6QU
T: 020 7350 0902
e-mail: friedmanhiller@hotmail.com

Healthfood shop (80% organic). Sells 100% organic fruit and vegetables and breads, plus organic babyfoods, special diet foods, dairy and groceries. Nutritional advice available.

Food for Thought
4 Cameron Rd, Seven Kings, **Ilford**,
IG3 8LA
T: 020 8597 4388

Wholefood shop (50% organic). Sells fruit and vegetables, wholefoods, groceries, dairy and eco-friendly cleaning products.

Food for Thought
38 Market Place,
Kingston-upon-Thames, KT1 1JQ
T: 020 8546 7806 F: 01276 27282

Healthfood shop (65% organic). Sells wholefoods, groceries, dairy and babyfoods.

Fresh & Wild – (OFF)

e-mail: shop@freshandwild.com
website: www.freshandwild.com
Customer careline: 0800 9175 175

Funky, upbeat award-winning chain of organic and natural foods community stores (95% organic). Sells over 5,000 certified organic foods and 3,000 natural remedies, health and bodycare products. All stores have excellent food to go (prepared in their own kitchen), and except for the City Branch have a deli counter, juice bar, and eat in bar. Stores at:

Fresh & Wild – City
194 Old St, **EC1V** 9FR

One minute from Old Street tube station. Open Mon–Fri 9.30am–7.30pm, Sat 11.30am–5.30pm.

Fresh & Wild – Stoke Newington
32–40 Church St, Stoke Newington, **N16** 0LH
T: 020 7254 2332

No handy tube, but 76 bus stops outside. Open Mon–Fri 9am–9pm, Sat 8.30am–8.30pm, Sun 11am–8pm.

Fresh & Wild – Camden Town Branch
49 Parkway, Camden Town, **NW1** 7PN
T: 020 7428 7575

Two minutes from Camden Town tube station. Natural Products Europe 2000 Retailer of the Year award. Open Mon–Fri 8am–9pm, Sat 9.30am–9pm, Sun 11am–8pm.

Fresh & Wild – Lavender Hill Branch
305–311 Lavender Hill, **SW11** 1LN
T: 020 7585 1488

Two minutes from Clapham Junction station. Open Mon–Fri 9am–9pm, Sat 8.30am–7.30pm, Sun noon–6pm.

Fresh & Wild – Soho Branch
71–75 Brewer St, **W1**R 3FL
T: 020 7434 3179

One minute from Piccadilly Circus tube station. Open Mon–Fri 7.30am–9pm, Sat 9am–9pm, Sun 11.30m–8.30pm

Fresh & Wild – Notting Hill Branch
210 Westbourne Grove, **W11** 2RH
T: 020 7229 1063

Seven minutes from Notting Hill tube station. Open Mon–Sat 8am–8pm, Sun 10am–7pm.

Gaia Wholefoods
123 St Margarets Rd, **Twickenham**, TW1 2LH
T: 020 8892 2262

Stocks a wide range of organic foods (60% organic), including breads, groceries, fruit and vegetables, dairy, vegan and macrobiotic foods.

Greenwich Organics
86 Royal Hill, Greenwich, **SE10** 8RT (SA)
T: 020 8488 6764
e-mail: info@greenwichorganic.co.uk
website: www.greenwichorganics.co.uk

One hundred per cent organic shop with 1,500 lines, including fruit and vegetables, meat and poultry, dairy, wholefoods, groceries, juices and babyfoods, plus bodycare and eco-friendly cleaning products. Operates box scheme and home delivery (brochure available) of all products to south and east London in environmentally friendly gas-fuelled van. Superb, friendly, informative website with online ordering, recipes, restaurant reviews and links section.

The Harvey Nichols Food Market
Harvey Nichols, Knightsbridge, **SW1**X 7RJ
T: 020 7235 5000 F: 020 7245 6561
e-mail: foodmarket@harveynichols.co.uk

Well-known fine food emporium with excellent selection of organic foods (25%), including fruit and vegetables, dairy, breads, groceries, meat from their butchery counter and ready meals (fresh and frozen).

Haelan Centre
41 The Broadway, Crouch End, **N8** 8DT
T: 020 8340 4258 F: 020 8292 2232

Celebrating their 30th anniversary, natural foods supermarket (80% organic) stocking over 2,000 organic lines including fruit and vegetables, groceries, wholefoods, bread, babyfoods, dairy, a huge range of dried herbs and spices and a new wine and drinks section. Alternative health centre upstairs.

Here
Chelsea Farmers' Market, 125 Sydney St, London **SW3** 6NR
T: 020 7351 4321 F: 020 7351 2211

100% organic, stylish, neighbourhood mini-supermarket, specialising in value for money. Full range of organic food and drink, around 4000 organic lines. Excellent butchery counter, food to go, home delivery. Open Mon–Sat 9.30am–8pm, Sun 10.30am–6.30pm.

Just Natural
304 Park Rd, **N8** 8LA
T: 020 8340 1720 F: 020 8348 2599
e-mail: natural@virgin.net

Friendly, community one-stop, 100% organic shop run by mother and daughter. Open every day. Sells fruit and vegetables, local breads, meat and fish, dairy, babyfoods, chilled goods, extensive range of groceries, wines, beers and spirits, eco-friendly household products, plus homemade pesto salad dressings, salads, fresh juices, and takeaway lunches, made with all-organic ingredients. Local home delivery and mail order service.

Kelly's Organic Foods
48 Northcote Rd, **SW11** 1PA (OF&G)
T: 020 7207 3967

One hundred per cent organic food store. Sells comprehensive range, including fruit and vegetables, dairy, wheat-free breads, meat, groceries, deli, wines and beers, plus homemade take-away salads and quiches made with organic ingredients.

Oliver's Wholefood Store
5 Station Approach, **Kew Gardens**, Richmond, TW9 3QB (SA)
T: 020 8948 3990 F: 020 8948 3991
e-mail: info@oliverswholefoods.co.uk

Award-winning, bright, friendly, community organic and natural health store (90% organic). Sells full and varied range of fresh and ambient organic foods, including biodynamic products, organic sandwiches, salads and cakes to take away, wines and beers and eco-friendly products. Has resident food therapist/nutritionist and holds regular evening lectures.

Peaches Health Foods
143 High St, Wanstead, **E11** 2RL
T: 020 8530 3617

Vegetarian store (40% organic). Organic range includes wholefoods, groceries, juices, breads and wines.

Planet Organic
42 Westbourne Grove, **W2** 5SH (SA)
T: 020 7727 2227 F: 020 7727 8547
e-mail: renee@planetorganic.com
website: www.planetorganic.com

Four minutes from Bayswater and Royal Oak tube stations, an award-winning one-stop organic supermarket. Sells wide range of fruit and vegetables, dairy, groceries and wholefoods, with excellent fresh fish and organic meat counters. Serves fresh juices at

juice bar. Open Mon–Sat 9.30am–8pm, Sun noon–6pm. For deliveries and mail order hamper service phone 020 7221 1345.
Also at:

Planet Organic
22 Torrington Place, **WC1**
T: 020 7436 1929 F: 020 7436 1992
Two minutes from Goodge St tube station. Has chic, state-of-the-art, food-to-go counter and juice bar.

Selfridges
400 Oxford St, **W1**A 1AB
T: 020 7629 1234 F: 020 7495 8321
website: www.selfridges.com

Selfridges' food hall sells organic fruit and vegetables, a range of organic groceries, dairy products, bread, poultry and a small range of wines and beers.

Sense
45 Balham High Rd, **SW12** 9AN (SA)
T: 020 8675 2002 020 8675 0202
e-mail: shop@senseorganic.com

One hundred per cent organic, must-visit, one-stop stylish shop, with its own organic juice bar and organic café. Stocks around 2,000 organic products, including groceries, wholefoods, fruit and vegetables, dairy, special diet products, breads, meat, salmon, babyfoods and wines. Eat-in or takeaway, friendly café with daily menu, all home cooked, including salads galore, fish pies, risottos and lasagnes. Operates local box scheme.

Temple Health Foods
17 Temple Fortune Parade, Golders Green, **NW11** 0QS
T: 020 8458 6087 F: 020 8209 0059
e-mail: info@templehealth.co.uk
website: www.templehealth.co.uk

Popular health-food store (40% organic) established for over 50 years. Organic range includes wholefoods, groceries, confectionery, drinks and frozen meals, plus eco-friendly cleaning products. Home delivery.

Today's Living
92 Clapham High St, **SW4** 7UL
T: 020 7622 1772 F: 020 7720 2851

Health food store (75% organic). Sells wholefoods, groceries, dairy and frozen ready meals.

Villandry Foodstore & Restaurant
170 Great Portland St, **W1**N 5QB
T: 020 7631 3131

Well-known fine-food store, open every day, with its own restaurant that often features organic meat. Shop sells range of organic foods (30%) including fruit and vegetables, meat, groceries, breads and dairy foods.

Well Bean Health Store
9 Old Dover Rd, Blackheath, **SE3** 7BT
T: 020 8858 6854

Health food shop (80% organic). Sells extensive range of organic products, including specialist breads, wholefoods, groceries, dairy and dairy alternatives, babyfoods, and frozen foods.

Wholefood Ltd
24 Paddington St, **W1**M 4DR (SA)
T: 020 7935 3924 F: 020 7486 2756

One of the early pioneering organic shops, organic since 1960. Stocks over 2,500 organic items, including comprehensive range of groceries, babyfoods, dairy, meat and poultry, chilled foods and frozen ready meals. Will prepare orders for collection.

England Greater London – Specialist Providers

Please note that there are separate listings of both 'Bakers' and 'Butchers' at the end of this section.

Aroma Herbs and Spices

9 Leigham Court Rd, **SW16** 2ND (SA)
T: 020 8769 2108

Specialist organic herb and spice shop. Sells extensive range, including many unusual items. Also sells organic wholefoods, groceries, condiments and teas and coffees (100% organic).

Aveda Institute

174 High Holborn, **WC1**V 7AA
T: (general): 020 7759 7350
T: (salon and lifestyle store): 020 7759 7355
T: (café): 020 7836 5407
e-mail: avedacoventgarden@aveda.co.uk
website: www.aveda.com

New, must-visit, eco-chic Aveda Institute combines lifestyle salon and spa with environmental store, the London Hair Academy, herbal sanctuary and Quiet Revolution Organic Café. Offers total well-being experience, including complementary comforting organic tea on arrival.

The Beer Shop

14 Pitfield St, **N1** 6EY
T: 020 7739 3701
e-mail: sales@pitfieldbeershop.co.uk
website: www.pitfieldbeershop.co.uk

Retail shop for the Pitfield Brewery. Sells extensive range of organic beers, lagers, wines and ciders. For full entry see p. **268**.

The Cooler

67 Stoke Newington Church St, **N16** 0AR
T: 020 7275 7266 F: 020 7923 7870
e-mail: greatfood@thecooler.co.uk
website: www.thecooler.co.uk

A cook and foodie's delight. Community minded, child-friendly, stylish delicatessen, passionate about food, selling range of fine foods (20% organic), including excellent selection of organic of babyfoods plus some organic groceries and wines and beers. Has own café.

Deli' Organic

60 Northcote Rd, **SW11** 1PA (OF&G)
T: 020 7585 0344 F: 020 7585 0399
e-mail: deli@deliorganic.co.uk
website: www.deliorganic.co.uk

Stylish, fashionable, totally yummy, must-visit, high-quality deli (100% organic) with child-friendly café, catering and home delivery services and the cutest website in the book. Deli sells cheeses, breads, charcuterie, dried pulses, preserves and olive oil, plus takeaway Mediterranean style homemade soups, meals, snacks, salads and excellent range of their own fresh and frozen babyfoods. Café serves breakfast, organic juices and all-day snacks and meals, and has children's menu. Also provides year-round seasonal organic hampers, including Mother and New Baby, delivered direct. Open every day. Phone or email for catering menu.

Organic Kosher Ltd

OK Foods, PO Box 3079, **Barnet**, EN5 4ZD
T: 0800 4585674 F: 0800 9806198
e-mail: sales@organickosher.co.uk
website: www.organicxpress.com

Specialist provider of organic kosher products, including chicken, lamb, smoked salmon, gravadlax and hot roast smoked salmon. All animals certified organically grown (SA or Naturland – German organic certification body) and all produce certified kosher by a Kashrut authority.

Organic Xpress

'Caterers Who Care', 26 Morrish Rd, **SW2** 4EH
T/F: 020 8674 6941
e-mail: info@organicxpress.com
website: www.organicxpress.com

A first. A 100% organic catering company using as much fair-trade and local foods as possible. A sister company to Patisserie Organic, dedicated to the organic ethos. Caters for all events for 15–20 people upwards from parties to corporate. Provides great food, wine and people. Meals prepared in Patisserie Organic kitchens include special menus using all UK-sourced foods.

Organic World

Friar Stile Rd, **Richmond**, TW10 6NH
T: 020 8940 0414

Friendly butcher (100% organic) also selling some deli, organic fish, game, cooked meats and dried goods. Full range of SA organic meats sourced direct from farmers and hung and butchered at shop.

The Tea and Coffee Plant

170 Portobello Rd, Notting Hill, **W11** 2EB (OF&G)
T: (mail order): 020 7221 8137
e-mail: coffee@pro-net.co.uk.
website: www.coffee.uk.com

Organic tea and coffee specialist. Has stall at Spitalfields Organic Food Market (**E1**). For full entry, see p. **438**.

Neal's Yard Dairy

17 Short's Gardens, Covent Garden, **WC2**H 9UP
T: 020 7645 3550
T: (shop): 020 7240 5700
T: (mail order): 020 7645 3555
e-mail: (mail order):
mailorder@nealsyarddairy.co.uk

Also at: 6 Park St, **SE1** 9AB (Corner of Stoney St and Park St, opposite Borough Market)
T: 020 7645 3554

A mecca for anyone who loves real cheese. Their extensive range includes several organic cheeses. Uses organic milk from September Organic Dairy, **Almeley** (Herefs).
See also:
Clarke's, **W8**; Monmouth Coffee Shop, **WC2** (Places to Eat and Stay)

Bakers

The following bakers produce organic breads that are widely available throughout London in organic shops and in supermarkets, food halls and other independents.

The Celtic Baker

West Hendon, **NW9** (Demeter and SA)
T: 020 8202 2586

Organic baking pioneer. Produces wide range of delicious and richly flavoured traditional hand-made breads using flour, minimum yeast, salt, water and long fermentation. Breads are widely available including at own Spitalfields (**E1**) stall and The Organic Shop, **Stow-on-the-Wold** (Gloucs) (Shops).

Cranks

Popular vegetarian restaurant chain. Sells organic breads. SA certified, made for them by a traditional bakery in London and another small bakery in Devon. The bread is used in their restaurants and widely distributed in major supermarkets and organic/wholefood/health food shops and delicatessens in London and the southeast and locally around Brixham, Devon.
Restaurants at:
Canary Wharf, **E14**

T: 020 7513 0678
Tottenham St, **W1**
T: 020 7631 3912
St Christopher's Place, **W1**
T: 020 7495 1340 .
8 Adelaide St, **WC2**
T: 020 7836 0660
Great Newport St, **WC2**
T: 020 7836 5226

Flour Power City

238 Hoxton St, **N1** 5LX (OFF)
T: 020 7729 7414

Specialist organic bakers with superb range of organic breads and baked goods made with organic ingredients. Open every day except Mondays. Stall at Borough Market, **SE1** (London, Organic and Farmers' Markets). Aso available at: Fresh & Wild, **EC1**, **N16**, **NW1**, **SW11**, **W1** and **W11**; Sundance Market, **SW3** (Shops); Neal's Yard Dairy, **WC2** (Specialist Providers). Also at Flour Power City, **Tunbridge Wells** (Kent) (Specialist Providers).

Natural Rise

21 Bernward Rd, Tottenham, **N15** 4PE (SA)
T: 020 8808 2007

Traditional bakery, wholesale only, specialising in much-praised natural (slow) rise yeasted and sourdough yeast-free breads.

Neal's Yard Bakery

6 Neal's Yard, **WC2** 9DP (SA)
T: 020 7836 5199 F: 020 7379 1544

Wonderful bakery, one of the early 'real bread' shops. Bakes a range of organic breads and some biscuits (including sugar/wheat/dairy-free oat biscuit). Organic ingredients are used in their products, including cakes and pastries, wherever possible. All breads are made with filtered water. Available from the bakery and from Portobello Wholefoods, 266 Portobello Rd, London **W10**. Also supplies Fortnum & Mason's.

The Old Post Office

76 Landor Rd, **SW9** 9PH (SA)
T/F: 020 7326 4408

Produces mainly organic yeasted and sourdough breads, plus baked goods, including pizzas made with organic flour. Sells direct, open Mon–Fri.

Butchers

The following London butchers sell a wide range of organic meats. Also Pure Organic Foods (see p. **192**) and Black Mountain Foods (see p. **193**) supply independent butchers and are happy to tell you the name of your nearest supplier. Planet Organic (**W2**) in London has an exceptional butchery department. The following London shops also sell fresh organic meat on their butchery counters: Bluebird, **SW3**; Harvey Nichols, **SW1**, Selfridges, **W1**.

C. Lidgate Ltd

Holland Park Avenue, **W11** 4UA
T: 020 7727 8243 F: 020 7229 7160

Acclaimed high-quality Q Guild butcher, one of London's best (10–30% organic), selling full range of organic meats and poultry, including Highgrove beef, lamb and pork when available, organic hams, homemade pies made with organic meat, sausages made with all organic ingredients, plus a wide range of organic groceries. Delivery to area including and bounded by **W5**, **W4**, **SW6**, **SW10**, **SW3**, **SW1**, **WC1**, **NW1**, **NW3**, **NW11**, **NW2** and **NW10** postal areas. Mail order on request.

Miller of Kensington

14 Stratford Rd, Kensington, **W8** 6QD (SA and Demeter)
T: 020 7937 1777

Another find. One hundred per cent organic butcher and French traiteur selling full range of organic and biodynamic meats and poultry, including Thanksgiving turkeys, and occasional veal, sourced direct from Pure Suffolk Foods and other producers. Every day they produce homemade dishes, such as organic boeuf bourguignon, and will also cook your leg of lamb for you. Catering menu available. Local deliveries to **Kensington**, **Knightsbridge**, **Park Lane** and **Holland Park**.

M. Moen & Sons

24 The Pavement, Clapham Common, **SW4** 0JA
T: 020 7622 1624 F: 020 7622 1628

Described as 'The Harrods Food Hall of South London', a high-quality butcher (40% organic) stocking full range of organic meats and poultry, plus homemade sausages made with organic pork.

Randalls

113 Wandsworth Bridge Rd, Fulham, **SW6** 2TE
T: 020 7736 3426

High-quality Q Guild butcher (25% organic) selling organic beef, pork, lamb, including from Highgrove when available, plus organic chicken, bacon, ham and homemade sausages made with organic pork.

G. G. Sparkes Organic Butchers

24 Old Dover Rd, **SE3** 7BT (SA)
T: 020 8355 8597
website: www.ggsparkesorganicbutchers.com

A treasure. Run by father and daughter, a traditional butchers (90% organic) with a welcoming shop front, selling full range of organic meats, Devon Red chickens, Christmas turkeys, all bought direct from producers, plus homemade organic Italian, Toulouse and Merguez sausages. Their deli counter sells organic eggs, Italian cheeses, including parmiggiano, and a range of groceries, preserves and soft drinks. Free delivery (minimum order applies) to **London** (within M25), **Kent**, **Sussex** and **Surrey**. Also mail order. Nice website too.

Stenton Butchers

55 Aldersley Rd, Hammersmith, **W6** 9PL
T: 020 8748 6121

Traditional butcher (75% organic). Sells full range of organic meats and poultry sourced primarily direct from producers, plus organic ham, bacon, eggs and homemade sausages and burgers made with organic meat.

Thorogoods Organic Meat Specialists

113 Northfields Avenue, Ealing, **W13** 9QR
T: 020 8567 0339 F: 020 8566 3033

Traditional butchers, (75% organic) with dedicated organic meat counter. Sells SA certified beef, pork, lamb and chicken, sourced from Black Mountain Foods (see p. **193**) plus homemade sausages made with organic pork and James White organic apple juice. Free local delivery, plus mail order to mainland UK.

England Greater London – Places to Eat and Stay

The capital has a range of organic eateries, and many cafés and restaurants and juice bars now either use some organic ingredients or offer dishes made with organic ingredients. For more on organic eating out generally see p. **107**.

Clarke's

124 Kensington Church St, **W8** 4BH
T: 020 7221 9225 F: 020 7229 4564

Revered restaurant owned by Sally Clarke. Offers supremely simple and perfectly cooked food that celebrates seasonality. Uses primarily British organic fresh produce. Open Mon–Fri. A joy to visit, their next-door bakery, specialist fine food shop and tiny café sell seasonal organic produce, organic dairy and groceries, plus Penelope Sachs' acclaimed organic herbal teas from Australia. They produce a selection of delicious breads and baked goods using organic flour. Their homemade soups and fresh pasta sauces are usually made with mainly organic ingredients.
Clarke's and River Café (**W6**) (q.v.) are two restaurants owned and run by female chefs, who have written their own cook books, serve delicious food, and have had enormous influence on changing the British food scene. Both are committed supporters of organic food and farming, use organic produce, and are dedicated to championing high-quality food produced by small, local producers, and source direct from them.

Coffee Matters

4 Southampton Row, **WC1**B 4AA
T: 020 7242 9090

Coffee shop serving fair trade and organic tea, coffee and cocoa, organic juices and salads and sandwiches made with organic ingredients.

The Crown

223 Grove Road, Victoria Park,
E3 5SN (SA)
T: 020 8981 9998

See next entry for The Duke of Cambridge.

The Duke of Cambridge

30 St Peter's St, Islington, **N1** 8JT (SA)
T: 020 7359 3066

Owned and run by Geetie Singh and Esther Boulton, and awarded best pub of the year 2000 by *Time Out* magazine. One hundred per cent organic, seasonal menu, changes daily lunch and evenings. Their two other pubs are The Crown (**E3**) and The Pelican (**W11**) (q.v.). Also for full entries see p. **112**.

fresh! The organic café

3 Princes St, Hanover Square,
W1B 2LD (OF&G)
T: 0207 495 7346
e-mail: info@fresh-go-organic.com
website: www.fresh-go-organic.com

Also at: fresh! The organic café, 8 Elliott Road, Chiswick, **W4** 1PE
T: 020 8742 0766

fresh! The organic café

78 Park Road, Regent's Park, **NW1** 4SH
T: 020 7724 1102

Modern, upbeat 100% organic café serving sandwiches, rolls and baps, casseroles and soup. Daytime salad bar. Closes 7pm. See p. **112** for full entry.

Manna Vegetarian Restaurant

4 Erskine Rd, Primrose Hill, **NW3** 3AJ.
T/F: 020 7722 8028

Serves a daily organic option: starter, main course and dessert. Stocks organic wines, beers and juices and uses organic wholefoods and dairy products in all their meals. Open for evening meals every night and lunchtime Sat and Sun.

Monmouth Street Coffee Shop
27 Monmouth St, **WC2**H 9EU
T: 020 7379 3516

Superb coffee shop, established in 1978, around the corner from Neal's Yard Dairy (Specialist Providers). Serves organic espresso and single estate coffees and uses organic farmhouse Jersey milk for all their drinks. Coffee roasted on premises and then freshly ground for each cup. Can be bought as beans or freshly ground.

Hugo's Café-Bar
25 Lonsdale Rd, Queens Park, **NW6** 6RA
T: 020 7372 1232
Also at: Hugo's Café-Bar, 51 Princes Gate, Exhibition Rd, Kensington, **SW7** 2PH
T: 020 7596 4006

As good as it gets. Owned and run by the remarkable Carol Charlton and her family. Modern, inventive, approachable seasonal menus, mainly organic, changed daily.

Pause
11 New Inn Yard, EC2A 3EY
T: 020 7729 1341

Vegetarian and vegan café and juice bar using 95% organic ingredients. Daily changing menu offering light and main meals.

The Pelican
45 All Saints Road, **W11** 1HE (SA)
T: 020 7792 0936

See entry for The Duke of Cambridge above.

Pizza Organic
20 Old Brompton Rd, **SW7** 3DL (SA)
T: 020 7589 9613
Also at: Pizza Organic, 100 Pitshanger Lane, Ealing **W5** 1QX (SA)
T: 020 8998 6878

Part of the Pizza Piazza chain. Serves pizza and pasta dishes and grill meals all made with organic ingredients. Open for lunch and evening meals. Also at **Beaconsfield** (Bucks) and **Walton-on-Thames** (Surrey).

The Quiet Revolution
49 Old St, **EC1**V 9HX (SA)
T: 020 7253 5556
Also at: 62 Weymouth Street, **W1**M 3PF
T: 020 7487 5683
174 High Holborn, Covent Garden, **WC1**
T: 020 7836 5407

One hundred per cent organic café serving homemade daytime meals from a daily changing menu. See p. **112** for full entry.

Ransome's Dock Restaurant
35–37 Parkgate Rd, **SW11** 4NP
T: 020 7223 1611 F: 020 7924 2614
e-mail: mailto:chef@ransomesdock.co.uk
website: www.ransomesdock.co.uk

Well-known local restaurant (40% organic). Serves modern European country-style flavoursome food. Owners are keen supporters of organic foods and passionate about quality and provenance of ingredients. Use UK seasonal organic produce, organic and speciality meats, plus organic dried foods. Selection of organic wines served.

Relax
65–67 Brewer St, Soho, **W1**F 9UP
T: 020 7494 3333 F: 020 7494 3399
e-mail: info@relax.org.uk
website: www.relax.org.uk

The latest organic experience. 'Let yourself go' neck, back and body off-the-peg massage centre, next door to Fresh &Wild (Shops), with its own small organic café providing breakfast, salads, sandwiches, juices and drinks. No need to book; just walk in for your instant 10-minute reviver at reasonable prices.

River Café
Thames Wharf, Rainville Rd, Hammersmith, **W6** 9HA
T: 020 7381 8824 F: 020 7386 4201
e-mail: info@rivercafe.co.uk

Fashionable and phenomenally busy Italian restaurant, owned by Rose Gray and Ruth Rogers. Uses organic fish and meat, organic UK fresh produce and dairy products. Pre-booking essential but limited to one month in advance to give more people a chance to eat there. See also note at end of entry for Clarke's above.

Roussillon
16 St Barnabas St, **SW1** 8PB
T: 020 7730 5550 F: 020 7824 8617
e-mail: tanner@roussillon.co.uk
website: www.roussillon.co.uk

Michelin one-star restaurant dubbed 'the garden gourmet'. French chef, Alexis Gauthier, produces seasonal cuisine with special emphasis and passion for vegetable dishes. Use 60–70% organic ingredients including fruit and vegetables and meat. Open lunchtime and evenings.

St Paul's Steiner Café
1 St Paul's Rd, Highbury, London, **N1** 2QH
T: 020 7359 3322

Attached to St Paul's Steiner School, an organic and biodynamic vegetarian café, open Tues–Sat, 10am–4pm. Run by volunteers. Serves coffees, teas and cakes all day, with a full lunch menu, including dairy/wheat/sugar-free options, all homemade, using around 95% organic and biodynamic ingredients.

Sauce Barorganicdiner
214 Camden High St, **NW1** 8QR (SA)
T: 020 7482 0777

Child-friendly stylish bar/diner and all day eatery. For full entry, see p. **113**.

The Source Café–Bar
43 Hereford Rd, Notting Hill Gate, **W2** 5AH. (SA)
T: 020 7792 3369

One hundred per cent organic café diner. Serves modern English 3-course menu or light snacks, lunchtime through to evening meals. Full organic wine list. Beers (50% organic).
See also:
Fresh & Wild, **EC1**, **N16**, **NW1**, **SW11**, **W1** and **W11** (organic juice bars and deli); Planet Organic, **W2** and **WC1** (organic juice bar, breakfast bar, and food-to-go); Sense, **SW12** (juice bar and café); Sundance Market, **SW3** (restaurants and noodle bar); Villandry, **W1** (restaurant) (Shops)
Aveda Institute, **WC1** (café); Deli' Organic, **SW11** (delicatessen and café) (Specialist Providers)
Cranks, **E14**, **WC1** and **WC2** (restaurants) (Specialist Providers – Bakers)

England Greater London – Organic & Farmers' Markets

Borough Market
Borough High St, London Bridge, **SE1**
T: 020 7407 1002
website: www.boroughmarket.org.uk
Fri: 12am–6pm. Sat: 9am–4pm

Not exclusively organic, but lovely market with some excellent organic produce, including the Flour Power City, **N1** (Specialist Providers – Bakers) amazing bread stall. Neal's Yard Dairy, **WC2**

(Specialist Providers) has a shop just outside. Excellent website lists current food providers.

Camden Organic Market

54 Camden Lock Place, off Chalk Farm Rd, Camden, **NW1** 8AL.
T: 020 7485 3459
Sat and Sun: 9am–6pm.

Fruit and vegetables, herbs, breads and cheese.

Greenwich Organic Market

off Stockwell St, Greenwich**, SE10**.
Sat: 10am–4pm.

Fruit and vegetables, meat, breads and cheese.

Portobello Road Organic Market

Portobello Rd, London, **N10**
Thurs: 11am–6pm.

Small market with around half a dozen regular stalls. Fruit and vegetables, meat, breads, pickles and conserves.

Spitalfields Organic Food Market

Old Spitalfields Market, Brushfield St, **E1** 6AA.
T: 020 7377 8909
website: www.spitalfields.co.uk
Sun: 10am–5pm.

Established in 1992, this is London's largest organic market. It is part of Spitalfields larger market, housed under a listed 3-acre glass-covered Victorian building. Around a dozen organic stalls sell fruit and vegetables, meat, dairy, breads, cheese, tofu, tea and coffee and wines. Raw Health (see p. **287**) demonstrates here. Longwood Farm has a permanent shop for meat, and the shop next door, Unwin's Organic Provisions, sells dairy, groceries and dried goods. (Note that the website is not about the market itself, but the Spitalfields' area, its development plans – not all good – and the history of the market.)

See also:
Jenny Usher, **Harlow**, Essex (Box Schemes)
Longwood Farm, **Tuddenham St Mary**, Suffolk, (Farm Shops)
The Celtic Baker, **NW9**; Global Organic Markets, **Brimscombe**, (Gloucs) (Specialist Providers)
Domini Quality Foods, **Market Weston**, Suffolk (Farm Gate)

London Farmers' Markets

These are producers-only markets, run by the indefatigable Nina Planck and her colleagues. The produce all comes from a region within 100 miles of the M25. There are currently about a dozen, though the situation is always changing. For the latest news/update contact:
T: 020 7704 9659 F: 020 7359 1938
e-mail: info@lfm.demon.co.uk
website: www.londonfarmersmarkets.com

Blackheath

Blackheath Railway Station Car Park, Blackheath Village, **SE3**
Sun: 10am–2pm
Rail: Blackheath

Ealing

Leeland Rd, **West Ealing**. (Next to Barclay's Bank, West Ealing.)
Sat: 9am–1pm
Tube: West Ealing.

Islington

Essex Rd, **N1**. (Opposite Islington Green.)
Sun: 10am–2pm
Tube: Angel Islington. Buses: 19, 30, 38, 73, 341.

Notting Hill

Notting Hill Gate, **W8**. (Car park behind Waterstone's. Access from Kensington Place.)
Sat: 9am–1pm.
Tube: Notting Hill Gate

Palmers Green
Palmers Green Railway Station Car Park, **N13**
Sun 10am to 2pm
Rail: Palmers Green.

Peckham
Peckham Square, Peckham High St, **SE15**. (Next to Peckham Library.)
Sun: 9.30am–1.30pm
Rail: Peckham Rye or Queens Road. Buses: 12, 36, 171, 345.

Swiss Cottage
O2 Centre Car Park, Finchley Rd, **NW3** (Near Homebase.)
Wed: 10am–4pm
Tube: Swiss Cottage. Buses: 268, 187 go into car park. 13, 82, 113 pass close by.

Twickenham
Holly Road Car Park, Holly Rd, off King St, Twickenham, **TW1**
Sat: 9am–1pm
Rail: Twickenham.
Buses: 33, 110, 267, 281, 290, 490, H22, R68, R70. Stop: King St

Uxbridge
Civic Centre Square, High St, Uxbridge, **UB8**. (Opposite Chimes shopping centre.)
Sun: 10am–2 pm.
Tube: Uxbridge.

Wandsworth
5 Garratt Lane (Spread Eagle Pub), **SW18**. (Opposite Arndale shopping centre. Two hours' free parking at Sainsbury's.)
Sat: 9am–1pm.
Tube: East Putney. Rail: Wandsworth Town

Wimbledon Park
Wimbledon Park First School, Havana Rd, **SW19**
Sat: 9am–1pm.
Tube: Wimbledon Park

ENGLAND NORTH EAST

England North East – Box Schemes

DURHAM

Organic Growers of Durham Ltd

Lower Walworth Market Garden,
Walworth, Darlington, DL2 2NA
T: 01325 362466

Vegetable and herb box scheme supplying home-grown, or locally produced, organic fruit and vegetables to drop off points within 5-mile radius of **Darlington**.

Down to Earth Organics Ltd

Stainton Grove, **Barnard Castle**,
DL12 8UG (SA)
T: 01833 695317

Versatile home delivery and box scheme selling organic vegetables (70% UK grown), meats, dairy and wholefoods within 50-mile radius.

NORTHUMBERLAND

North East Organic Growers

Earth Balance 2000, **Bomarsund**,
Bedlington, NE22 7AD (SA)
T: 01670 821070 F: 01670 821026
e-mail: neog@care4free.net
website: www.neog.co.uk

Local traditional box scheme supplying home-grown and local produce wherever possible to delivery drop-off points in **Northumberland** and **Tyne and Wear**. Their produce is grown on the Earth Balance 2000 site, volunteers welcome. Also runs courses on growing fresh produce to organic standards. See also: Earth Balance 2000 (Specialist Providers).

Cropped Up

Dilston College of Further Education,
Corbridge, Hexham, NE45 5RJ (SA)
T: (Sue Hicks): 07947 856641
F: 01434 633721

Local traditional vegetable box scheme, operates June–Christmas, supplying mainly home-grown vegetables to pick-up points in **Dilston**, **Allendale** and **Hexham**.

YORKSHIRE EAST RIDING

Arthur Street Trading Co. Ltd

Unit 2, 23 Arthur St, Hull, HU3 6BH (SA)
T: (workshop): 01482 76374
T: (evenings): 01482 212437/212871
e-mail: arthursorganics@hotmail.com
website: www.come.to/arthursorganics

Local box scheme and home delivery workers' co-operative. Supplies fruit and vegetables from Slater's, small range of wholefoods from Suma, wines and beers from Vinceremos and Bio-D locally produced eco-friendly products. Delivery in solar-powered, electric milk float. Also produce widely available hummus, veggie and hemp burgers.

YORKSHIRE NORTH

Goosemoor Organics

Warfield Lane, **Cowthorpe**, Wetherby,
LS22 5EU (SA)
T: 01423 358887
e-mail: vegebox@goosemoor.org.uk

website: www.goosemoor.org.uk

Well-known and respected organic growers operating regional box scheme supplying organic bread, salads, fruit, vegetables, eggs, dairy and wholefoods. Delivers to box scheme collection points in **Yorks**, parts of **Durham**, **Lancs**, **Derbys**, **Lincs** and **Notts**.

Nature's World

Ladgate Lane, **Acklam**, Middlesbrough, TS5 7YN (SA)
T: 01642 594 895
e-mail: mail@naturesworld.org.uk
website: www.naturesworld.org.uk

Vegetable subscription scheme. Prepay, on a half or full season basis, and collect vegetables you want from the farm direct.
See also:
The Organic Shop, **Clapham** (Shops)
Standfield Hall Organic Farm Shop, **Pickering** (Farm Shops)

YORKSHIRE SOUTH

See:
Beanies Wholefoods Co-Op, Crookesmoor, **Sheffield** (Shops)

YORKSHIRE WEST

Valley Garden Organics

7 Victoria Buildings, **Cragg Vale**, Hebden Bridge, HX7 5TJ (OFF)
T/F: 01422 886032

Organic growers operating local fruit and vegetable box scheme. Fixed boxes and customer-choice specials supplying as much seasonal, home-grown, local and UK produce as possible. Delivery to **Calderdale** area. Recently opened own 100% organic shop at 14 Market St, **Hebden Bridge**, selling complete range of organic foods plus eco-friendly household products. Open every day.

England North East – Shops

DURHAM

Molly's Wholefood Store

11 Front St, **Framwellgate Moor**, DH1 5EJ
T: 0191 3862216

Friendly wholefood shop (35% organic) selling organic bread, fruit and vegetables, wines and beers, frozen food, dairy and wholefoods. Pick-up point for Goosemoor Organics, **Cowthorpe** (N Yorks) box scheme. Café serves organic teas and coffees.

NORTHUMBERLAND

The Green Shop

30 Bridge St, **Berwick-upon-Tweed**, TD15 1AQ
T: 01289 305566

Sells environmentally friendly, and fair-traded items only. Ninety per cent organic foods, including meats, chilled products and wines, plus organic clothes, linen and seeds.

TYNE AND WEAR

Out of this World

Gosforth Shopping Centre, High St, **Gosforth**, NE3 1LZ (SA)
T: 0191 2130421 F: 0191 2130429
e-mail: info@ootw.co.uk
website: www.ootw.co.uk

Ethical, organic consumer co-operative with over 18,000 members. Sells over 4,000 organic products, many fair-traded, including

100% organic fruit and vegetables and meat. Vegetables produced by North East Organic Growers, **Bomarsund** (Box Schemes) and meat by Northumbrian Quality Meats, **Hexham** (Farm Gate). Also has deli counter and sells natural healthcare, eco-friendly household and garden products and fair-trade crafts. Mail order catalogue. Also at:
Beeston (Notts) (Shops)
Head office: 106 High Street, **Gosforth**, NE3 1HB
T: 0191 2135377

Seasons and Reasons
Livingstone View, **Tynemouth**, NE30 2PL (Demeter)
T: 0191 2964041

Friendly 100% organic shop selling meat, fruit and vegetables, wholefoods, groceries and dairy. Stocks as much local produce as possible. Delivery to **Tynemouth** area. Also runs meditation classes.

YORKSHIRE EAST RIDING

Hull Food
79 Princes Avenue, **Kingston-upon-Hull**, HU5 3XQ (SA)
T: 01482 446929

Wholefood shop (60% organic) including 100% organic fruit and vegetables, plus organic bread and dairy.

YORKSHIRE NORTH

Alligator
104 Fishergate, **York**, YO3 7LL
T: 01904 654525 F: 01904 647136

Wholefood shop selling organic produce where possible. Most of the fruit and vegetables are organic, with an organic option available on most other lines. Range includes bread, wholefoods, groceries and dairy.

The Organic Shop
Clapham Nurseries, **Clapham**, via Lancaster, LA2 8ER (SA)
T/F: 01524 251723
e-mail: orders@growingwithgrace.co.uk
website: www.growingwithgrace.co.uk

Vegetarian (100% organic) shop with local box scheme. Sells home-grown vegetables, salads and herbs plus fruit, dried foods, bread, groceries, eggs, chilled foods, vegan and fair trade products. 'Growing with Grace' box scheme delivery within 20-mile radius provides 15% home-grown fruit, vegetables and salads plus bought-in local and UK produce. Customer choice and set boxes. Home delivery and post office collection scheme.

The Green House
5 Station Parade, **Harrogate**, HG1 1UF
T: 01423 502580 F: 01423 505439

Popular shop (60% organic). All vegetables, fruit, wines and beers are organic, plus organic bread, groceries, wholefoods, eggs and dairy. Pick-up point for Goosemoor Organics, **Cowthorpe** (N Yorks) box scheme. Wild Ginger Vegetarian Bistro (Places to Eat and Stay) situated at the back of shop.

Shepherd's Purse
95 Church St, **Whitby**, YO22 4BH
T: 01947 820228 F: 01947 601670

Stylish, busy, well-known local wholefood shop with comprehensive range of wholefoods, breads, groceries, vegetables and cheeses. Every non-organic food item has an organic alternative available. Also offers bed and breakfast accommodation serving organic ingredients where possible.

YORKSHIRE SOUTH

Beanies Wholefoods Co-Op

205–207 Crookes Valley Rd, Crookesmoor, **Sheffield**, S10 1BA (SA)
T: 0114 268 1662

Best Community Retailer in Organic Food Awards 2000. Organic, vegetarian and vegan goods, (50% organic) including fruit and vegetables, wholefoods, dairy, special diet foods and wines. Operates a fruit and vegetable bag scheme to local areas.

Fishlake Fine Foods

Millfield Rd, **Fishlake**, Doncaster, DN7 5LF
T: 01302 846293

Friendly shop (80% organic) selling home-produced vegetables, salads and fruits grown using organic methods (not cert.). Also sells Graig Farm Organics (**Dolau** (Powys, Wales) (Farm Shops)) meat, dairy, groceries and homemade cakes and prepared meals using organic ingredients. Home delivery within 50-mile radius.

YORKSHIRE WEST

Beano Wholefoods

36 New Briggate, **Leeds**, LS1 6NU (SA)
T: 0113 243 5737
e-mail: info@beanowholefoods.co.uk
website: www.beanowholefods.co.uk

Well-known vegan and vegetarian wholefood co-operative stocking wide range of products (50% organic) including bread, dairy, wholefoods, cereals and eco-friendly household products. Tries to offer organic alternative to everything. Fresh produce supplied by Goosemoor Organics, **Cowthorpe** (N. Yorks) (Box Schemes).

Food Therapy

11 Northgate, **Halifax**, HX1 1UR
T: 01422 350826 F: 01422 362106
e-mail: kevin@foodtherapy.freeserve.co.uk
website: www.foodtherapy.co.uk

One of the best healthfood stores, established 20 years, stocking expanding range of organic foods (40% organic). All fruit and vegetables organic. Specialises in dietary and nutritional advice. Pick-up point for Valley Garden Organics (**Cragg Vale**) box scheme.

Natural Choice

72 Westbourne Rd, **Marsh**, Huddersfield, HD1 4LE (SA)
T: 01484 513162

Wholefood shop (60% organic) selling wide range of organic foods including bread, fruit and vegetables from Goosemoor Organics (**Cowthorpe**, N Yorks (Box Schemes)), groceries and dairy. Box scheme (self selection) and home delivery service available.

Offshoots

18–20 Cavendish St, **Keighley**, BD21 3RG
T: 01535 606589

Healthfood shop (50% organic) selling organic bread, dairy, wholefoods and a large range of groceries. Pick-up point for Goosemoor Organics (**Cowthorpe**, N Yorks) fruit and vegetable box scheme.

ORG

79 Great George St, **Leeds**, LS1 3BR (SA)
T: 0113 234 7000
e-mail: shop@org-organics.org.uk
website: www.org-organics.org.uk

Leeds first organic shop and juice bar and food-to-go, selling over 700 organic products including meat, fish, fresh produce, wines and beers, wholefoods, frozen ready meals and groceries. The deli bar sells hot and cold lunchtime food. The juice bar offers juices and smoothies. Caters for children's parties and business lunches.

Valley Garden Organics
14 Market St, **Hebden Bridge**, HX7 6AA

See entry for Valley Garden Organics, **Cragg Vale** (Box Schemes)

Your Nuts Healthfood
Springfield Mill, Norman Rd, **Denby Dale**, Huddersfield, HD8 8TH
T: 01484 864902
Also at: Your Nuts Healthfood, 14a Towngate, **Holmfirth**, HD7 1HA
T: 01484 680126

Friendly wholefood stores (70% organic). Range includes dairy and organic vegetarian ready meals.

England North East – Farm Shops

TYNE AND WEAR

Rising Sun Farm Shop
Kings Rd North, **Wallsend**, NE28 9JL (SA)
T/F: 0191 2340539
e-mail: douglashanks@risingsunfarm.co.uk

Friendly farm shop (90% organic) selling a wide range of products, including organic fruit and vegetables, eggs and homemade organic jams. Their café serves light meals and snacks, most of which are prepared exclusively with organic ingredients. Café open Mon–Fri, 9am–3pm. Phone to check shop opening times.

YORKSHIRE NORTH

Botton Village Store
Camphill Village Trust, Botton Village, **Danby**, Whitby, YO21 2NJ (Demeter)
T: 01287 661270
e-mail: botton@camphill.org.uk
website: www.camphill.org.co.uk

Inspirational biodynamic farm and food centre, part of the Camphill Communities network, selling home-produced fruit and vegetables in season, bread, baked goods and award-winning cordials and jams. Bakery and creamery open to visitors, who can observe and buy produce.

Smithy Farm Shop
Baldersby, Thirsk, YO7 4PN
T: 01765 640 676

Busy farm shop (60% organic) selling Graig Farm Organics, **Dolau** (Powys) (Farm Shops) meat, wholefoods, fruit and vegetables, bread and dairy.

Standfield Hall Organic Farm Shop
Westgate Carr Rd, **Pickering**, YO18 8LX (SA)
T: 01751 472249

One hundred per cent organic farm shop. Has been organic since 1982. Sells own beef, local lamb and pork and home-grown and local vegetables plus a wide range of groceries, 17 different organic cheeses and homemade bread, cakes and frozen vegetarian organic meals. Also operate a local box scheme delivering within 20-mile radius.

YORKSHIRE WEST

Brickyard Farm Shop

Badsworth, nr Pontefract, WF9 1AX (SA)
T: 01977 617327

Dedicated organic farm shop selling home-grown organic fruit and vegetables and salads in season. Local box scheme offering customer choice. Delivers to **Wakefield** and **Leeds**.

England North East – Specialist Providers

DURHAM

Eggleston Hall Gardens

The Cottage, Eggleston Hall, **Eggleston**, Barnard Castle, DG12 0AG
T: 01833 650115 F: 01833 650378

Organically grown seasonal fruit and vegetables and herbs sold from the gardens.

NORTHUMBERLAND

The Barn Bakery

Lee Moor Farm, **Rennington**, Alnwick, NE66 3RL (SA)
T: 01665 577155
e-mail: the-barn-bakery@beeb.net

Organic bakery producing bread and rolls, tea-cakes, scones, spiced buns, flapjacks and pizzas. Delivery to **Northumbria**, **Tyneside** and **Edinburgh**. Also sold at local farmers' markets, markets and shops.

Earth Balance 2000

West Sleekburn Farm, **Bomarsund**, Bedlington, NE22 7AD
T: 01670 821000 F: 01670 821026

Visitor centre and 260-acre SA certified organic farm – see North East Organic Growers (Box Schemes) – featuring sustainable energy systems. Visitor centre shop sells organic groceries, local crafts and fair-traded goods. Micro-brewery, recycled textile centre, and Sleekburn horticultural training unit that sells organically grown plants. Open daily except Christmas. Phone for opening times.

TYNE AND WEAR

The Head Chef Bakery

130 Brighton Grove, Arthur's Hill, **Newcastle-upon-Tyne**, NE4 5NT
T: 07900 677547

New one-man artisan bakery, run by Mark Barfot, not certified, but uses Doves Farm organic flours for all breads and organic ingredients where possible. Breads include spelt, sesame, vegan pizza, pain de campagne and focaccia. Open Mon-Thurs, 12am–6pm; Fri–Sat, 10am–6pm.

YORKSHIRE NORTH

Larchfield Community

Hemlington, Middlesbrough, TS8 9DY (Demeter)
T: (office): 01642 593688

Camphill Community selling surplus home-produced biodynamic vegetables at farm gate, with own popular organic bakery, butchery and coffee shop serving organic teas and coffees. The bakery produces organic breads, scones and biscuits also sold through local shops. The butchery sells own biodynamic beef, pork, lamb and 100% pork sausages, burgers and dry-cured bacon plus occasional poultry from Hungary Lane Farm, **Sutton Bonnington** (Leics) (Farm Gate). Bakery and coffee shop open 10am–1pm, Mon–Fri; butchery open Thur–Fri, 9am–5pm.

Sunflours

The Hutts Mill, **Grewelthorpe**, Ripon, HG4 3DA (SA)
T: 01765 658534
e-mail: info@sunflours.com
website: www.sunflours.com

Range includes organic wholewheat, wholemeal, strong white and nutty wheatbran flours available direct from mill. Will mill coarser or finer flours on request.

Wensleydale Dairy Products

Gayle Lane, **Hawes**, DL8 3NR (SA)
T: 01765 658212 F: 01765 658732
e-mail: creamery@wensleydale.co.uk
website: www.wensleydale.co.uk

Produces organic cheeses as part of their range sold nationwide, wholesale. They include Cheddar, Red Leicester, Cheshire, Wensleydale and Double Gloucester. Cheese shop on site sells a constantly updated range of own cheeses.

York Beer Shop

28 Sandringham St, Fishergate, **York**, YO1 4BA
T: 01904 647136

Specialist shop selling range of organic beers, wines, ciders and cheeses alongside non-organic range.

Yorkshire Garden World

Main Rd, **West Haddlesey**, nr Selby, YO8 8QA
T: 01757 228279
e-mail: carole@yorkshiregardenw.f9.co.uk
website: www.yorkshiregardenworld.co.uk

Delightful gardens and tourist attraction. Specialist growers of organic herbs. Design and plan herb gardens and display gardens. Stock over 2,000 organic plants and have gift shop and tea-room. Not certified organic but recommended by SA. Attractive website.

See also:
Botton Village Store, **Danby** (bakery and creamery) (Shops)

YORKSHIRE SOUTH

The Earth Centre

Denaby Main, Doncaster, DN12 4EA
T: 01709 512000
e-mail: info@earthcentre.org.uk
website: www.earthcentre.org.uk

Rapidly growing sustainable development education and conference centre. Organically maintained 26-acre gardens. Wetlands and other projects under development. Ninety-five per cent organic restaurant serves gourmet and children's meals using locally produced meat and vegetables where possible.

Potts Bakers Ltd

Stanley Rd, Stairfoot, **Barnsley**, S70 3PG (SA)
T: 01226 249175

Specialist organic breads available at farmers' markets and by carrier.

YORKSHIRE WEST

Meanwood Valley Urban Farm

Sugarwell Rd, **Meanwood**, Leeds, LS7 2QG
T: 0113 262 9759 F: 0113 239 2551

A city and demonstration farm with organic market garden, shop, café and new environmental EpiCentre that promotes benefits of local, organic food for local people. The farm provides an education service to schools. Trail with disabled access. Coach access. Open every day. See also SA Farm listing, England North West.

England North East – Places to Eat and Stay

NORTHUMBERLAND

See:
Rising Sun Farm Shop, **Wallsend** (café) (Farm Shops)
High Buston Hall, **High Buston** (B & B List)

TYNE AND WEAR

See: Rising Sun Farm Shop, **Wallsend** (Farm Shops)

YORKSHIRE NORTH

El Piano

15–17 Grape Lane, **York**, YO1 7HU
T: 01904 610676

Vegetarian restaurant. Uses organic dried staples, tofu and dairy products (50% organic).

Wild Ginger Vegetarian Bistro

5 Station Parade, **Harrogate**, HG1 1UF
T: 01423 566122
e-mail: info@wild-ginger.co.uk
website: www.wild-ginger.co.uk

Friendly vegetarian bistro located at the back of The Green House (Shops). Serves breakfast, lunch, soups, snacks, homemade cakes and puddings using some organic ingredients. Also serves organic tea, coffee, seltzers, fruit juices, hot chocolate, wines and beers. Open Mon–Thurs 10am–4pm and Fri and Sat 10am–9pm. Funky website.

See also:
Shepherd's Purse (bed and breakfast), **Whitby** (Shops)
Potto Grange, **Potto** (B & B List)

YORKSHIRE SOUTH

See:
The Earth Centre, **Denaby Main** (Specialist Providers)

YORKSHIRE WEST

See:
ORG, **Leeds** (Shops)
Meanwood Valley Urban Farm, **Meanwood** (Specialist Providers)

England North East – Farm Gate

NORTHUMBERLAND

Northumbrian Quality Meats

Monkridge Hill Farm, West Woodburn, **Hexham**, NE48 2TU (SA)
T: 01434 270184 F: 01434 270320
e-mail:
enqs@northumbrian-organic-meat.co.uk
website:
www.northumbrian-organic-meat.co.uk

A rare gem. Inspirational venture supplying highest quality, organically produced Aberdeen Angus cross beef and Blackface lamb from the unspoilt uplands of Northumberland, with unique traceability system. Pick-up from the farm by arrangement (so isolated it includes complimentary lunch at a local hotel. For full entry, see p. **184**.

YORKSHIRE NORTH

Brunswick Organic Nursery

Appleton Rd, **Bishopthorpe**, York, YO2 1RF (SA)
T: 01904 701869

Farm-gate sales of seasonal organic vegetables, apples, plums and herbs.

Burniston Farm Shop
Highlands Farm, **Burniston**,
YO13 0DL (SA)
T: 01723 870048

Home-produced organic lamb and free-range chickens, turkeys and geese. Available from farm shop on Fridays and at local farmers' markets. Please phone first.

Stark Farm
Sykes Lane, **Tollerton**, YO6 2HE (SA)
T: 01347 838169

Farm-gate sales of seasonal greenhouse vegetables.

YORKSHIRE SOUTH

Yorkshire Organic Earth
33 Devonshire Drive, Hallbalk, **Barnsley**,
S75 1EE (SA)
T: 07785 901215
e-mail:
stuartallen@yorkshireorganicearth.fsnet.co.uk

Farm-gate sales of award-winning organic eggs also sold by Harrods, plus summer seasonal vegetables. Please phone first.

ENGLAND NORTH WEST

England North West – Box Schemes

CHESHIRE

Cheshire Organics

5 Booths Hill Rd, **Lymm**, WA13 0DJ (SA)
T: 01925 758575 F: 01925 758043
e-mail: jackie@cheshireorganics.co.uk
website: www.cheshireorganics.co.uk

Box scheme supplying mainly local organic fruit and vegetables and wide range of groceries, dairy, bread, John Bryan organic meat, wines and beers, bodycare and eco-friendly household products from their catalogue. Delivery throughout **Cheshire**.

Oakcroft Organic Gardens

Cross O'Th'Hill, **Malpas**, SY14 8DH (SA)
T: 01948 860213

Fruit and vegetable seasonal selection box scheme, 90% home-grown. Delivers throughout **Cheshire**. Also supplies organic breads, cheese and eggs on request.

CUMBRIA

See:
Howbarrow Farm, **Cartmel** (Farm Shops)

Lancashire

Growing with Nature

Bradshaw Lane Nursery, **Pilling**, PR3 6AX (SA)
T/F: 01253 790046

One of the UK's top producer-owned local box schemes. Year-round seasonal selection with varied customer choice options. Delivers home- and locally grown vegetables to **Lancashire**. Collection at Kan Foods, **Kendal** (Cumb) (Shops). Regular newsletter.

Lyncroft Farm

Butchers Lane, Aughton Green, **Ormskirk**, L39 6SY (SA)
T: 01695 421712 F: 01695 422117
e-mail: office@organicveg.co.uk
website: http://www.organicveg.co.uk/

Produces organic vegetables, available through their box scheme (65% home-grown). Delivery within 20-mile radius. Organic fruit also available at their small farm shop, open Thurs pm. Please phone before visiting.

MANCHESTER, GREATER

FoodLife Doorstep Deliveries

68 Buckingham Road, **Cheadle Hulme**, Cheadle, SK8 5NA (SA)
T/F: 0161 4861173
e-mail:
anna@foodlife-doorstepdeliveries.co.uk

Friendly local box scheme and home delivery service supplying fresh produce sourced from local and northern growers wherever possible, plus Graig Farm Organics (**Dolau** (Powys, Wales) (Farm Shops)) meat, bread, dairy and groceries. Regular newsletter with recipes. Delivery to **South Manchester**, **Stockport** and **Macclesfield** areas.

Home Farm Deliveries Ltd

Studio 19, Imex Business Park, Hamilton Rd, Longsight, **Manchester**, M13 0PD (SA)
T: 0161 2248884 F: 0161 2248826
e-mail: info@homefarm.co.uk
website: www.homefarm.co.uk

Regional organic box scheme and home delivery offering fruit and vegetables (100% UK vegetables, 50% UK fruit of which around 50% locally produced), Graig Farm Organics (**Dolau** (Powys, Wales) (Farm Shops)) meat and poultry, salmon (kosher approved) groceries, wholefoods, dairy, bread, wines and spirits, chocolates and eco-friendly cleaning products. Phone or email to order. Delivery to **Cheshire**, **Lancashire** and **Manchester** and nationwide by courier.

Limited Resources

53 Old Birley St, **Hulme**, Manchester, M15 5RF (SA)
T: 0161 2264777 F: 0161 2263777

Customised box scheme, plus various standardised fruit and vegetable boxes and additional range of wholefoods, bread, eggs, etc.

MERSEYSIDE

Organic Direct

57 Blundell St, **Liverpool**, L1 0AJ (SA)
T/F: 0151 707 6949

Wide range of organic vegetables (40% UK produced) and organic bread and wholefoods, all available through customised box scheme throughout **Merseyside**, **St Helens** and **Wirral**.
See also:
Windmill Organic Wholefoods, **Liverpool** (Shops)

England North West – Shops

CHESHIRE

The Organic Stores

Brooklyn Farm, Sealand Rd, **Chester**, CH5 2LQ (SA)
T: (shop): 01244 881209
T: (office): 01352 740075

See full entry under Flintshire, Wales.

CUMBRIA

Alston Wholefoods Ltd

Kings Arms Lane, Front St, **Alston**, CA9 6HU
T: 01434 381588

Sells wide range of organic foods, including fruit and vegetables, cheeses, breads, snacks, herbs, spices, and ice cream (45% organic).

Kan Foods

9 New Shambles, **Kendal**, LA9 4TS
T: 01539 721190

Wholefood shop specialising in products for special diets (50% organic). Collection point for Growing with Nature, **Pilling** (Lancs) (Box Schemes) boxes.
See also:
The Village Bakery, **Melmerby** (Specialist Providers)

Lancashire

E. H. Booth & Co Ltd

4,5 and 6 Fishergate, **Preston**, PR1 3LJ
T: 01772 251701 F: 01772 204316

Independent, family run, high-quality supermarket chain, with strong commitment to locally produced and organic foods. Stores throughout Lancashire. Phone for nearest branch.

The Herb Stall

1 King Street, **Lancaster**, LA1 1JN (SA)
T/F: 01524 32916
website: www.theherbstall.co.uk

One hundred per cent organic shop, selling home-grown herbs and vegetables, homemade preserves, wholefoods, groceries and meat to order. Home delivery to **Lancaster** area. Order from the website, by fax or phone. See also: The Herb Stall, **Carnforth** (Farm Shops).

Single Step Co-operative Ltd

78a Penny Street, **Lancaster**, LA1 1XN
T: 01524 63021
Vegetarian co-operative selling 100% organic fruit and vegetables and bread and a range (30% organic) of wholefoods, groceries and dairy.

MANCHESTER, GREATER

Chorlton Wholefoods

64 Beech Rd, **Chorlton-cum-Hardy**, M21 9EG
T: 0161 881 6399
e-mail: georgereynolds@yahoo.co.uk
website: www.chorltonwholefoods.com

Busy well-stocked shop. Sells extensive range of products (75% organic), including organic fruit and vegetables, bread, dairy, groceries, takeaway and drinks. Home delivery service and mail order.

Health and Vegetarian Store

229 Oldham Rd, **Failsworth**, M35 0AY
T: 0161 683 4456
Friendly shop. Sells wide range of produce (50% organic), including organic bread, dairy, fruit and vegetables, wholefoods, groceries and chocolates.

On the Eighth Day Co-operative Ltd

107–111 Oxford Road, **Manchester**, M1 7DU
T: 0161 2734878
T: (café): 0161 273 1850 (Mon–Sat)
F: 0161 2734878
e-mail: mail@eighth-day.co.uk
website: www.eighth-day.co.uk
Also at: On the Eighth Day Co-operative Ltd, 49 Old Birley Street, **Hulme**, Manchester
T: 0161 2278848 F: 0161 2734878

Large, friendly, vegetarian healthfood shop with more than a thousand organic foods for sale, including bread, groceries, dairy, wholefoods, wines and beers and chilled and frozen convenience foods. Mail order. Bright, spacious vegetarian (non-organic) café. Good website. (Relocating to temporary building at Sugden Sports Centre around corner in Sidney Street while old building is demolished and replaced). Catering service from Hulme branch. Not certified.

Organix Wholefoods

Unit 6, Sevendale House, 7 Dale Street, **Manchester**, M1 1AJ
T: 0161 228 0220

Healthfood shop (70% organic). Range includes bread, wines and beers, fruit and vegetables, groceries and drinks, eggs and dairy to order. Not certified.

Unicorn Grocery

89 Albany Road, **Chorlton-cum-Hardy**, M21 0BN (SA)
T: 0161 8610010 F: 0161 8617675
e-mail: office@unicorn-grocery.co.uk
website: www.unicorn-grocery.co.uk

Large popular well-known co-operative. Extensive range of products (50% organic), including wholefoods, fruit and vegetables, beers and wines.

MERSEYSIDE

Windmill Organic Wholefoods

337 Smithdown Road, **Liverpool**, L15 3JJ (SA)
T: 0151 7341919
e-mail: windmill@windmill.abelgratis.co.uk

Shop (70% organic) selling range of vegetarian and vegan wholefoods and fruit and vegetables. Organic vegetable box scheme with customer choice, local produce where possible, with optional organic wholefood extras available. Delivery throughout **Liverpool**.

England North West – Farm Shops

CHESHIRE

Ravens Oak Dairy

Burland Farm, Wrexham Rd, **Burland**, Nantwich, CW5 8ND (SA)
T: (shop): 01270 524502
T: (dairy/office): 01270 524624
F: 01270 524724
website: www.ravensoakdairy.co.uk

New, must-visit one-stop organic Portakabin, run by dairy farmer and cheese-maker Sandra Allwood and family. Probably the best organic cheese in the country. Features around 20 different cheeses, including own delicious, award-winning cheeses, including Ravens Oak soft cheese and Burland Green mould-ripened organic cow's milk cheese made from own milk. Also a complete range of organic foods, including fresh produce, local bread and organic meat from Howbarrow Farm (**Cartmel** (Cumbria) (Farm Shops)), Graig Farm Organics, **Dolau** (Powys) (Farm Shops) and Providence Farm, **Holsworthy** (Devon) (Farm Gate). Passionate about quality, freshness and local foods. Awarded Best New Shop, Organic Food Awards 2001.

CUMBRIA

Castletown Farm Shop

Floriston Rigg, **Rockcliffe**, Carlisle, CA6 4HG (SA)
T/F: 01228 674400
e-mail: info@castletownfarm.co.uk
website: www.castletownfarmshop.co.uk

Attractive farm and coffee shop situated on the Castletown Estate. Sells organic and local non-organic foods. Produce available includes own organic beef, lamb, pork and home-grown potatoes, summer green vegetables, soft fruit and apples, game, dairy, preserves, plus a wide range of home-cooked ready meals using some organic ingredients. Coffee shop sells organic tea and coffee and home-baked cakes. Open every day.

Howbarrow Farm

Cartmel, Grange-over-Sands, LA11 7SS (SA)
T/F: 01539 536330
e-mail:
enquiries@howbarroworganic.demon.co.uk
website:
www.howbarroworganic.demon.co.uk

Must-visit small organic farm shop, local box scheme, and exemplary small, idyllic, organic farm. Produces own chicken, Berkshire pork, Jacob sheep lamb, Christmas turkeys, fruit and vegetables, herbs and eggs, all sold very reasonably in farm shop open all year round. Their eggs and chicken have been highly commended in the Organic Food Awards. Farm shop also stocks organic wholefoods and groceries. Offers bed and organic breakfast; makes UK's only organic sticky toffee pudding, available locally and

nationally. See also SA Farm listing, England North West.
See also:
Hawkshead Trout Farm, **Hawkshead** (Specialist Providers)

LANCASHIRE

The Herb Stall

Ferrocrete Farm, Arkholme, **Carnforth**, LA6 1AU (SA)
T/F: (orders): 01524 21965
T: (inquiries): 01524 32916
website: www.theherbstall.co.uk

Farm shop selling home-grown herbs and vegetables, home-produced jams, award-winning lemon cheese, piccalilli and chutneys, wholefoods, groceries and meat to order. Home delivery to **Lancaster** area. Order from the website, by fax or phone. Best Retailer award in Radio 4's Food Programme Awards 2001. Runs own shop – see The Herb Stall, **Lancaster** (Shops).

Minefleet Farm Shop

Moorend Farm, Back Lane, Stalmine, **Poulton-le-Fylde**, FY6 0LN
T: 01253 700229

Busy farm shop selling 100% organic foods. Produce includes prepacked organic meat, bread, dairy, fruit, local vegetables (seasonally available from the farm), wholefoods, wines and beers and groceries, plus own additive-free pork and local chickens. Also has tea-room with meals made using organic produce from the shop. Not certified.

MERSEYSIDE

Church Farm Organics

Church Lane, **Thurstaston**, CH61 0HW (SA)
T: 0151 6487838 F: 0151 6489644
e-mail: sales@churchfarm.org.uk
website: www.churchfarm.org.uk

A find. Remarkable organic farm and must-visit farm shop (95% organic). Overlooks River Dee with registered caravan and camping site. Operates a local box scheme. Grows organic vegetables, asparagus and PYO strawberries. Produces organic Oxford Sandy and Black pork, Shropshire lamb, and Christmas turkeys. Organic eggs available from home-reared hens, roaming freely in small flocks. Church Farm honey; coffee shop and organic bed and breakfast. Sells their own Christmas trees, and holds children's parties at the weekend that include tour of farm.

Farm shop, open every day, stocks their own and local organic produce, plus organic groceries, breads, dairy, babyfoods, chilled and frozen foods, and wines and beers. Coffee shop serves homemade organic snacks, salads, quiches, and cakes made with 100% organic ingredients. Their box scheme supplies fixed box of fruit and vegetables (80% home-grown in summer), plus customised orders for other goods. Best Farm Shop, Organic Food Awards 2001. Deliveries made throughout the **Wirral**. Easy to use website.

England North West – Specialist Providers

CHESHIRE

The Cheese Shop

116 Northgate St, **Chester**, CH1 2HT
T: 01244 346240 F: 01244 314559

Artisan shop selling farmhouse cheeses, chutneys and wines, with as much organic as possible. Produce available in sister restaurant – see Elliots, **Chester** (Places to Eat and Stay).

See also:
Ravens Oak Dairy, **Burland** (cheese)
(Farm Shops)

CUMBRIA

Hawkshead Organic Trout Farm
The Fisheries, The Boathouse,
Hawkshead, LA27 0QF (SA)
T: 01539 436541
e-mail: organicfish@edirectory.co.uk
website: www.edirectory.co.uk/organicfish

Pioneering idyllic organic trout farm, their unique pink lake trout are available mail order or from their lakeside shop.

Little Salkeld Watermill
Little Salkeld, Penrith, CA10 1NN (SA, Demeter)
T: 01768 881523 F: 01768 881047
e-mail: njbj@aol.com
website: www.organicmill.co.uk

Attractive water-powered mill, one of the best, producing excellent flours. Has own mill shop and gallery, exhibiting work of local artists. A friendly organic tea-room provides delicious homemade breads, soups, salads, quiches, puddings etc. using as many local organic ingredients as possible. Open Mon–Fri 10.30am–5pm. Nice website. Their flours, a range of wholefoods, teas and coffees and herbs and spices may be ordered online and by mail.

Muncaster Water Mill
Ravenglass, CA18 1ST (SA)
T: 01229 717232
e-mail: mill@muncaster.co.uk
website: www.muncaster.co.uk

Watermill in lovely unspoilt spot of Cumbria. Produces range of organic stoneground flours including excellent creamy-white flour. Mill and tea-room open from Easter to October. Flour available by mail order.

The Village Bakery
Melmerby, Penrith, CA10 1HE (SA)
T: 01768 881515 F: 01768 881848
e-mail: admin@village-bakery.com
website: www.village-bakery.com

A place not to be missed. The country's best-known, award-winning organic bakery, situated in the tiny village of Melmerby that attracts thousands of visitors every year and has its own award-winning restaurant. Sells full range of breads and baked goods.

LANCASHIRE

R. M. Cornmell Organic Food Specialists
459 Halliwell Rd, **Bolton**, BL1 8DE
T: 01204 846844

Well-known traditional butcher established for over 20 years. Sells wide range of organic foods, including cheese, bread, wholefoods, home dry-cured bacon and ham, homemade sausages and beef burgers as well as full range of meat and poultry from Fordhall Farm, Market Drayton (tel: 01630 638255). Though not registered, no chemicals have been used at Fordhall Farm for over 60 years and their beef and sheep are raised in the traditional way on permanent pastures. Stall at **Altrincham** Market (Gt Man) Thurs 9am–4pm.

Roy Porter Butchers
9 Bridge Rd, Chatburn, **Clitheroe**,
BB7 4AW (SA)
T: 01200 441392

Small village shop (20% organic) selling organic beef, lamb, pork and poultry, home-produced sausages, bacon and ham. Pick-up point for 'Growing with Grace' box scheme – see The Organic Shop, **Clapham** (N Yorks) (Shops).

MANCHESTER

See:

R. M. Cornmell Organic Food Specialists, **Bolton** (Lancs) who have a stall at **Altrincham** Market Thurs 9am–4pm.

England North West – Places to Eat and Stay

CHESHIRE

Elliots

2 Abbey Green, **Chester**, CH1 2JH
T: 01244 329932
e-mail: carol@chestercheese.co.uk

Friendly restaurant serving a daily organic option for starter, main course and pudding. Organic wines from the selection at their sister shop – see The Cheese Shop, **Chester** (Specialist Providers).

CUMBRIA

See:

Little Salkeld Watermill (tea-room), **Little Salkeld**; Muncaster Water Mill, **Ravenglass**; The Village Bakery (restaurant), **Melmerby** (Specialist Providers)
Low Fell, **Bowness-on-Windermere** (B & B List)

LANCASHIRE

Whale Tail Café

78a Penny Lane, **Lancaster**, LA1 1XN
T: 01524 845133

Welcoming vegetarian/vegan café, excellent value for money menu with lots of choice, including organic options and main meal on Fridays. Single Step wholefoods shop downstairs.

See also:

Minefleet Farm Shop tea-room), **Poulton-le-Fylde** (Farm Shops)

MANCHESTER

See:

On The Eighth Day Co-operative (café) **Hulme** and **Manchester** (Shops)

MERSEYSIDE

See:

Church Farm Organics (café, B & B and camping and caravan sites), **Thurstaston** (Farm Shops)

England North West – Farm Gate

CUMBRIA

Whiteholme Farm

Whiteholme, **Roweltown**, Carlisle, CA6 6LJ (SA)
T: 016977 48058

Farm-gate sales of home-produced organic beef, lamb and pork. Butchery on site. Delivery to North England. See also SA Farm listing, England North West.

LANCASHIRE

Bank House Farm

Silverdale, **Carnforth**, LA5 0RE (OF&G)
T: 01962 760219

Produces organic chickens available at local farmer's markets and from farm gate by arrangement. Please phone first.

Cliftons Farm

Silk Mill Lane, Inglewhite, **Goosnargh**, Preston, PR3 2LP (OF&G)
T: 01995 640564

Farm-gate sales of eggs, Jersey cream, seasonal fruit and potatoes.
See also:
Lyncroft Farm, **Ormskirk** (Box Schemes)

MERSEYSIDE

Abbotts Organic Vegetable and Herb Garden

Lower Thingwall Lane, **Thingwall**, CH61 1AZ (SA)
T: 0151 6084566

Home-grown organic seasonal vegetables, herbs and herb plants available from the farm.

ENGLAND SOUTH AND SOUTH EAST

England South and South East – Box Schemes

BERKSHIRE

Tolhurst Organic Produce

West Lodge, Hardwick Estate, **Whitchurch**, nr Pangbourne, RG8 7RA (SA)
T/F: 01189 843428
e-mail: tolhurstorganic@yahoo.co.uk

Year-round seasonal selection box scheme. One of UK's foremost traditional schemes run by one of the country's most experienced organic growers, Iain Tolhurst. All produce except mushrooms home grown. Delivery to pick-up points in **Reading** and **Oxford**. Bi-monthly newsletter includes recipes. Annual open day.

BUCKINGHAMSHIRE

Fieldfare Organic and Natural Ltd

The Barns, Springfield Farm, **Wendover**, HP22 6BG (SA)
T: 0845 6013240 F: 01296 622245
e-mail: office@fieldfare-organics.com
website: www.fieldfare-organics.com

Recently expanded regional home delivery and box scheme. Latest catalogue features 2,000+ items. Delivers complete range of organic foods, including Welsh Hook Meat Centre, **Haverfordwest** (Pembks) (Shops) organic meat, fruit and vegetables, dairy, wines and beers, plus bodycare and eco-friendly household products. Delivers to **Bedfordshire**, **Buckinghamshire**, **Hertfordshire**, **London** and **Middlesex**. Order by phone, fax or online.

Organic Trail

10 St Pauls Court, **Stony Stratford**, Milton Keynes, MK11 1LJ
T/F: 01908 568952
e-mail: jim@organictrail.freeserve.co.uk
website: www.organictrail.freeserve.co.uk

Simple local and nationwide no-fuss delivery service. Offers weekly or fortnightly mixed box of 10 different UK seasonal vegetables from Eden Farms, **Old Bolingbroke** (Lincs).

HAMPSHIRE

Green and Organic Ltd

Unit 2, Blacknest Industrial Estate, **Blacknest**, nr Alton, GU34 4PX (SA)
T: 01420 520838 F: 01420 23985
e-mail: info@greenandorganic.co.uk
website: www.greenandorganic.co.uk

Good value green and organic one-stop home delivery company with fruit and vegetable box scheme. Commended Home Delivery section, Organic Food Awards 2001. Has retail outlet – see below. Delivery to **Hampshire** and **Surrey** and nationwide by courier. Stocks 3,000 certified organic lines including fruit and vegetables, Graig Farm Organics, **Dolau** (Powys) (Farm Shops) meat, fish, babyfoods and wines, beers and spirits, plus organic clothing, skin- and bodycare and eco-friendly products. Caters for special diets and allergies, and buys as much local, fresh produce as possible. Order from their catalogue via the website, phone, fax or email. Orders can be picked up from their shops and from pick-up points in **Fareham** and **Bishop's Waltham**.

Shop: The Organic Warehouse. Address and phone number as above. Open to the public Wed–Fri 10am–4pm. Pick up pre-ordered selections and add to them from available stocks.

Northdown Orchard

South Litchfield, Basingstoke, RG25 3BP (SA)
T/F: 01256 771477
e-mail: northdownorchard@ukonline.co.uk
website: www.northdownorchard.co.com

Year-round box scheme delivering home-grown and local, where possible, organic vegetables in seasonal selection boxes to the **Basingstoke** and **Winchester** area.

Warborne Farm Organic Box Scheme

Warborne Farm, Boldre, **Lymington**, SO41 5QD (SA)
T: 01590 688488
e-mail: warborneveg@aol.com

Friendly, local, year-round vegetable box scheme supplying 100% home-grown produce and home-produced organic beef and lamb to order. Delivers to a 5-mile radius of Lymington. Highly Commended in Organic Food Awards 2001.
See also:
Godshill Organics, **Godshill**, (IOW) (Shops)
Park Farm Shop, **Heckfield**; Sunnyfields Organic Farm, **Totton** (Farm Shops)

HERTFORDSHIRE

The Organic Wholefood Network

33 Alexandra Rd, **Watford**, WD17 4QX
T: 01923 490526 F: 01923 490659

Seasonal selection box scheme delivering Riverford Farm (**Buckfastleigh** (Devon) (Box Schemes)) fruit and vegetables to **South Buckinghamshire** and **Hertfordshire**.
See also:
Cook's Delight, **Berkhamsted** (Shops)

KENT

Dabbs Place Organic Farm

Cobham, Gravesend, DA13 9BL (SA)
T: 01474 814333
e-mail: sferm@globalnet.co.uk

Year-round seasonal selection vegetable and fruit box delivering to the **Medway**, **Maidstone** and **Gravesham** areas (60% home-grown).

Perry Court Farm

Garlinge Green, **Chartham**, Canterbury, CT4 5RU (Demeter)
T: 01227 738449

Biodynamic farm adjacent to a Rudolf Steiner school. Runs a subscription vegetable box scheme (pick-up only) and produces its own stoneground wheatflour and bread that can be bought at their farm shop on Fridays. The farm also produces beef for sale at the farm. Also has stalls at **Faversham**, **Rochester** and **Wye** farmers' markets.

Ripple Farm

Godmersham, nr Canterbury, CT4 7EB (SA)
T: 01227 730898 F: 01227 730748

Year-round seasonal selection vegetable box scheme, delivering home-grown vegetables within a 10-mile radius.

Luddesdown Organic Farms

Court Lodge, **Luddesdown**, Cobham, DA13 0XE (SA)
T: 01474 813376

T: (box scheme): 01474 815044
e-mail: organic@luddesdown.u-net.com
website: www.luddesdownorgnicfarms.co.uk

Well-known, award-winning, farm. Operates year-round local box scheme (75% home-grown) with separate vegetable and fruit boxes. Also produces organic beef, available vacuum packed and frozen, in 5 or 10 kg boxes to order or from farm gate. See also SA Farm listing, England South and South East.
See also:
Harvest Supplies, **Chuck Hatch** (E Susx) (Shops)
Honeybrook Organics, **Burwash** (E Susx); Wingham Country Market, **Shatterling** (Farm Shops)

OXFORDSHIRE

Chipping Norton Organics (Serena Howard)

22 Worcester Rd, Industrial Estate, **Chipping Norton**, OX7 5XW (SA)
T/F: 01608 642973
website: www.chippingnortinorganics.co.uk

Year-round box scheme and home delivery of fruit and vegetables, eggs, bread and dairy (local and UK and some imported produce). Customer choice options. Delivery within 15-mile radius. Pick-up from Nature's Harvest, **Banbury** (Shops) and Ruperts, **Shipston-on-Stour**.

Ellis Organics

5 Lea Rd, **Sonning Common**, nr Reading, RG4 9LH (SA)
T: 01189 722826
e-mail: ellis-organics@clara.net
website: www.eatorganic.co.uk

Local box scheme and home delivery service. Supplies over 400 product lines, including fruit and vegetables (one-third home grown). Also comprehensive range of meats, poultry, wholefoods, dairy and groceries. Contact point for True Food Club, buying co-operative which operates at RISC centre, **Reading**.

North Aston Organics

3 Somerton Rd, **North Aston**, Bicester, OX6 4HP (SA)
T: 01869 347702

Delivers 70% home-grown fruit and vegetables to 200 homes in **Oxford**, **Cropredy** and villages surrounding **Bicester**. Seasonal boxes, with customer likes and dislikes catered for.

Veg in Clover

Sandy Lane Farm, Sandy Lane, **Tiddington**, OX9 2LA (OF&G)
T: 07931 109623
e-mail: VeginClover@aol.com

Supplies seasonal selection vegetable 'Veg in Clover' boxes, all year round, to around 100 households in **Thame**, **Oxford** and area in between. Seventy per cent home-produced, rest certified organic produce from Covent Garden. Holds farmers' market at farm Thurs 2.30pm–6.30pm.
See also:
Frugal Food, **Abingdon** (Shops)
Brook Cottage Farm, **Charney Bassett**; Corner Farm, **Horton-cum-Studley** (Farm Shops)

SURREY

Sunshine Organics

2 Knowle Cottages, Knowle Lane, **Cranleigh**, GU6 8JL (OF&G)
T: 01483 268014
e-mail:
amanda@sunshineorganics.demon.co.uk
website: www.sunshine-organics.co.uk

Run by one of the nicest ladies in the business. Offers home delivery of fresh organic fruit and vegetables and bread as well as Ecover cleaning products. Whenever possible supplies local vegetables from Lower Barrihurst Farm – see Cranleigh Organics, **Cranleigh** (Farm Shops).

SUSSEX EAST

Ashurst Organics
The Orchard, Ashurst Farm, Ashurst Lane, **Plumpton**, BN7 3AP (SA)
T: 01273 891219 F: 01273 891943

Year-round, seasonal selection fruit and vegetable box scheme (75% locally produced). Delivery to **Lewes**, **Brighton and Hove** and surrounding areas and drop-off points or collect from farm.

Barcombe Nurseries
Mill Lane, **Barcombe**, Lewes, BN8 5TH (SA)
T: 01273 400011

Seasonal selection fruit and vegetable box scheme (25% home-grown). Delivery to **Lewes** , **Haywards Heath** and **Brighton**.

Beans and Things
Harvest Home, Church Hatch, **Hartfield**, TN7 4EN (OF&G)
T/F: 01273 477774
e-mail: beans@attitude1.co.uk

One hundred per cent organic home delivery service with over 1,000 items available, including fruit and vegetables, wholefoods, groceries, dairy, bakery products, chocolate, eco-friendly cleaning products, garden products and compost. Delivery along Sussex coast between **Shoreham-by-Sea** and **Seaford** and to **Lewes** and surrounding villages. Order from catalogue first half of week for delivery during second half.

Holly Park Organics
Hollypark North Lane, **Guestling**, Hastings TN35 4LX (Demeter)
T: 01424 812229 F: 01424 812025

Bespoke home delivery and fruit and vegetable box scheme, providing mainly home-grown biodynamic vegetables, wholefoods and salads, plus their own eggs and award-winning goat's milk and cheeses. Delivery within 10-mile radius of **Hastings**. Full range available in the farm shop, open Thurs–Fri 9am–5pm, and through farmers' markets in Sussex.

Real Food Direct
Unit 4, Level 3, New England House, New England St, **Brighton**, BN1 4GH (SA)
T: 01273 621222 F: 01273 626226
e-mail: info@realfood-direct.com
website: www.realfood-direct.com

Online local box scheme/home delivery service (85% organic), providing seasonal selection fruit and vegetable boxes, with add-ons from extensive list, including meat, fish, bread, dairy, wines and beers, groceries and wholefoods. Delivery to **Brighton and Hove**. Phone, fax or order online.

Scragoak Organic Farm
Brightling Rd, **Robertsbridge**, TN32 5EY (SA)
T/F: 01424 838420
e-mail: mail@scragoak.co.uk
website: www.scragoak.co.uk

Award-winning year-round box scheme delivering throughout **South East England**, (60% home-grown). See also Scragoak Organic Farm, **Robertsbridge** (Farm Shops). Pick-up available at Trinity Wholefoods, **Hastings** (Shops).

See also:
Boathouse Organic Farm Shop, **Ringmer**; Honeybrook Organics, **Burwash** (Farm Shops)

SUSSEX WEST

Veg Out

72 Orchardside, **Hunston**, Chichester, PO20 6PQ (SA)
T: 01243 781438

Operates a year-round seasonal selection box scheme (60% home-grown). Delivery to **Arundel**, **Chichester**, **Bognor Regis** and **Havant** area.

Wayside Organics

Wayside, **Oving**, Chichester, PO20 6BT (SA)
T/F: 01243 779716
e-mail: bart.ives@talk21.com

Seasonal selection box scheme (90% home-grown). Delivery to **Chichester** and **Bognor Regis**. Open for farm-gate sales on Friday. Stall at Organic Food Market, Old Spitalfields, London **E1**.

Willow Nursery

44 Hill Lane, **Barnham**, PO22 0BL (SA)
T/F: 01243 552852
e-mail: willownursery@yahoo.co.uk

Year-round, family run, local fruit and vegetable box scheme supplying 50–60% home-grown vegetables (all home-grown in summer), plus local and UK organic produce where possible. Offer 8 sizes of boxes with some customer choice. Delivery within 25-mile radius.

England South and South East – Shops

BERKSHIRE

Garlands

6 Reading Rd, **Pangbourne**, RG8 7LY (SA)
T: 01189 844770 F: 01189 844220

Bright and welcoming shop (95% organic) selling complete range of organic foods, including wholefoods, meat, dairy produce, fruit and vegetables. During the summer most of the fruit and vegetables are produced on their organic holding in Upper Basildon. Range of specialist British farmhouse cheeses, many of which are organic.

The Swan Inn and Swan Inn Farm Shop

Inkpen, Hungerford, RG17 9DY (SA)
T: 01488 668 326

A must-visit, unique organic double. One hundred per cent organic farm shop attached to the picturesque seventeenth-century village inn, owned by local beef farmers. The farm shop sells over 1,500 organic products, including meat, wholefoods, groceries, wines, dairy produce and fruit and vegetables. They make their own bacon and other cured meats, including bresola on site. All the beef is home-produced; lamb, pork and poultry come in from local certified organic farms. The inn is an AA 4-star hotel, restaurant and pub (CAMRA pub of the year 2000) with 10 en-suite bedrooms. Meals made with organic ingredients including their own beef. Wines exclusively organic. Selection of organic beers and draft organic beer.

Brockhill Farm Organic Shop

Warfield, Bracknell, RG42 6JU (not cert)
T: 01344 882 643

One hundred per cent organic shop, selling over 1,200 lines, including wholefoods, meat, extensive selection of fruit and vegetables, groceries, wines and dairy. Local delivery. Open Wed–Sat.

BUCKINGHAMSHIRE

Healthright
48c Friars Square, **Aylesbury**, HP20 2SP (SA)
T: 01296 397022
Also at: Healthright, 27 High St, **Chesham**, HP5 1BG
T: 01494 794551

Vegetarian shop (50% organic) range includes wholefoods, gluten-free, dairy-free and vegan.

Healthy Stuff
11 Liston Court, High St, **Marlow**, SL7 1ER
T: 01628 473684 F: 01628 473760

A welcome first in Marlow: a shop (90% organic) specialising in special diet/ gluten-free foods. Sells wholefoods, babyfoods, soya products, juices, preserves, tea and coffee, chilled and frozen foods, including Cream O'Galloway ice creams and Get Real vegetarian pies and ready meals. They also sell Swiss organic baby clothes. Has upstairs therapy room. Also my excellent Chinese herbalist and acupuncturist, Sigyta Hart.

HAMPSHIRE

Naturally Health Foods
5 Waterloo Court, Shaws Walk, **Andover**, SP10 1QJ
T: 01264 332375 F: 01264 392689

Sells wide range (75% organic) including fruit and vegetables, wholefoods, groceries and dairy.

Scoltocks Health Foods
1 Market Place, **Ringwood**, BH24 1AN
T: 01425 473 787

Sells range of healthfoods, wholefoods, groceries and eco-friendly cleaning products (40% organic). Pick-up point for Sturts Farm, **Ferndown** (Box Schemes) boxes.
See also:
Green and Organic, **Blacknest** (Box Schemes)

HERTFORDSHIRE

Cook's Delight
360–364 High St, **Berkhamsted**, HP4 1HU (SA)
T: 01442 863584 F: 01442 863702
e-mail: info@cooksdelight.co.uk
website: www.cooksdelight.co.uk

Remarkable award-winning dedicated organic shop with one of the best selections of organic products in the UK, including biodynamic foods. Sells wide range of fruit and vegetables, macrobiotic foods, wines and beers, bread, groceries, dairy, wholefoods and herbs. Mail order available, please phone. Regular newsletter and easy to use website with limited online shop.

Fairhaven Wholefoods
27 Jubilee Trade Centre, **Letchworth**, SG8 1SP
T: 01462 675300 F: 01462 483008
e-mail: sales@fairhaven.co.uk
website: www.fairhaven.co.uk

Family run shop (50% organic) selling large range of groceries, bread, dairy, fruit and vegetables, wholefoods and herbs. Delivery available to Hertfordshire, Bedfordshire and Buckinghamshire. Easy parking.

Harmony

53 High St, **Tring**, HP23 5AG
T: 01442 822311

Healthfood shop, (50% organic) selling groceries, wine, bread and gluten-free products, dairy and wholefoods.

ISLE OF WIGHT

Godshill Organics

Yard Parlour, Newport Rd, **Godshill**, PO38 3LY (SA)
T: 01983 840723

Do not miss this 100% organic shop and the Isle of Wight's only organic smallholding that grows an extensive range of vegetables and some soft and top fruit for sale in the shop. All lines are certified. They also operate an excellent, good value box scheme and home delivery service.

KENT

Canterbury Wholefoods

10 The Borough, **Canterbury**, CT1 2DR (SA)
T: 01227 464623 F: 01227 764838
e-mail: info@canterbury-wholefoods.co.uk
website: www.canterbury-wholefoods.co.uk

Sells over 3,000 lines (60% organic) including fruit and vegetables (100% organic), wholefoods, wines, beers, dairy and breads.

Especially Health

119 High St, **Sevenoaks**, TN13 1UP
T: 01732 741181 F: 01732 740719

Healthfood store (50% organic). Range includes vegetables (100% organic), dairy, wholefoods and groceries.

Organic Health Canterbury

Unit 22, SCATS Country Store, Maynard Rd, Wincheap Estate, **Canterbury** CT1 3RH (SA)
T: 01227 472774

One-stop organic shop selling over 3,000 organic lines, including meat (beef, lamb, pork, mutton, turkey), fruit and vegetables, dairy, groceries, wines, beers and ciders, special diet (gluten-free, wheat-free, dairy-free), wholefoods, biodynamic foods and Fair Trade foods. Open Tues–Fri 9am–5pm, Sat 9am–12am.

OXFORDSHIRE

Frugal Food

17 West Saint Helens St, **Abingdon**, OX14 5BL
T: 01235 522239

Delightful small shop (50% organic) selling wide range of foods, including wholefoods, groceries, dairy and organic wines. Pick-up point for Kissing Bridge vegetable box scheme – see Brook Cottage Farm, **Charney Bassett** (Farm Shops).

The High (Health Foods) Ltd

41 Market Place, **Henley-on-Thames**, RG9 2AA
T: 01491 573764

My local, friendly, caring healthfood shop (40% organic), small but well stocked. Ever expanding range of organic wholefoods and groceries, including breakfast cereals, special diet breads, designer health oils, bottled juices and soya yoghurts plus full range of Ecover products.

Nature's Harvest

4a Church Lane, **Banbury**, OX16 8LR (SA)
T: 01295 253208 F: 01295 278621

Healthfood shop (40% organic) selling gluten-free foods, groceries, loose select-your-own wholefoods, dairy and dairy alternatives. Pick-up point (Thurs) for Chipping Norton Organics, **Chipping Norton** (Box Schemes) organic fruit and vegetables box scheme.

Uhuru Wholefoods
48 Cowley Rd, **Oxford**, OX4 1HZ
T: 01865 248249

Sells 100% organic fruit and vegetables, locally produced where possible, bread, dairy, wholefoods, wines and beers (75% organic).

SURREY

Body and Soul
1 Parade Court, Okham Road South, **East Horsley**, KT24 6QR (SA)
T: 01483 282868 F: 01483 282060
e-mail: bodyandsoul@organic-gmfree.co.uk
website: www.organic-gmfree.co.uk

One hundred per cent organic shop. Stocks over 2,000 certified organic lines, including fruit and vegetables, meat, dairy, groceries, special diet foods, groceries, alcoholic drinks and eco-friendly products. Home delivery to **Surrey** and **South West London**. Advice on special diets, allergies and for mums-to-be.

Octavia's Organics
7 Prices Lane, **Woodhatch**, Reigate, RH2 6BB
T: 01737 244155 F: 01737 244123

One hundred per cent organic shop. Full range of organic foods, including fruit and vegetables, bread, groceries, meat, fish, wholefoods, wines and beers and eco-friendly cleaning products. Local home delivery service.

SUSSEX EAST

Harvest Forestry
1 New England St, **Brighton**, BN1 4GT
T: 01273 689725
website: www.harvestforestry.co.uk

Unusual one-stop vegetarian organic food shop selling fruit and vegetables, dried foods, groceries and dairy, combined with a wood yard selling local hardwood timber, furniture, wooden crafts, organic paints and organic seeds. Tree surgery and forest management advice also available.

Harvest Supplies
Harvest Home, **Chuck Hatch**, Hartfield, TN7 4EN (OF&G)
T: 01342 823392 F: 01342 825594

One hundred per cent organic shop with over 1,000 items available, including fruit and vegetables, wholefoods, groceries and eco-friendly cleaning products. Operates box scheme with delivery in **Brighton** area and pick-up points in **Eastbourne** and **Tunbridge Wells**. Catalogue available.

Infinity Food Shop and Bakery
25 North Rd, **Brighton**, BN1 1YA (SA)
T: 01273 603563 F: 01273 675384
website: www.infinityfoods.co.uk

Long-established 75% organic, vegetarian wholefood store. Sells organic fruit and vegetables, groceries, dairy, vegan and gluten-free products, a range of organic breads, including rye, speciality breads and mini pizzas, baked daily on the premises, and wines and beers.

Montezuma's Organic and Handmade Chocolate
15 Duke St, **Brighton**, BN1 1AH (SA)
T: 01273 324979
e-mail: simon.pattinson@montezumas.co.uk
website: www.montezumas.co.uk

Don't miss the UK's first organic chocolate shop. Over 250 different handmade chocolate lines, over half certified organic. Mail order catalogue and online ordering. For full entry, see p. **329**.

Mother Hemp

22 Gardner St, North Lanes, **Brighton** BN1 1UP
T: 01273 818047

UK's first hemp shop selling hemp foods (all organic), bathroom products, clothes and accessories.

Seasons Forest Row Ltd

10 Hartfield Rd, **Forest Row**, RH18 5DN
T: 01342 824673 F: 01342 826119

Busy inspirational organic one-stop shop (95% organic) and wholesaler with strong emphasis on biodynamic foods, including groceries, dairy, and biodynamic meat and fresh produce from 3 local biodynamic farms. Fantastic selection of organic fruit and vegetables, plus breads, gluten-free products, wholefoods, organic cosmetics, bodycare, organic cotton clothing and eco-friendly cleaning products.

Trinity Wholefoods

3 Trinity St, **Hastings**, TN32 5SA (SA)
T: 01424 430473

Workers' co-operative shop (75% organic). Range includes beers and wines, vegetables, wholefoods, dairy and gluten- and dairy-free foods. Pick-up point for box scheme Scragoak Organic Farm, **Robertsbridge**.

Wealden Wholefoods

High St, **Wadhurst**, TN5 6AA
T: 01892 783 065

Well-established workers' co-operative shop (75% organic) selling fruit and vegetables, wines, beers and ciders, wholefoods, juices and dairy. Café serves meals made with mainly organic produce.

SUSSEX WEST

Down To Earth

12 The Mint Market, Grange Rd, **Midhurst**, GU29 9LT
T: 01730 815133

One hundred per cent organic shop selling fruit and vegetables, wholefoods, groceries, juices and dairy alternatives. Home delivery to Midhurst and surrounding areas.

The Organic Oasis

42–44 South Rd, **Haywards Heath**, RH16 4AL
T: 01444 459596 F: 01444 473338

A find. Fine food deli (95% organic) with its own kitchen, resident chef and butchery department. Specialises in homemade fare made with organic ingredients – soups, pâtés, quiches, meals, puddings and cakes, many wheat-free – and local organic foods, including meat, poultry and fresh produce. Also sells organic groceries, dairy, bread, special diet foods and wines. Meat is hung properly and raised pies a speciality. Their motto: 'If we won't eat it, we won't sell it.' Outside catering, food club for members, open evenings.

England South and South East – Farm Shops

BUCKINGHAMSHIRE

Fullers

Purveyors of Fine Organic Foods, Manor Farm, **Beachampton**, Milton Keynes, MK19 6DT (OF&G)
T: 01908 269868 F: 01908 262285

Farm shop (90% organic) selling home-produced meat (beef, pork, lamb, poultry), home-made sausages and dry cured bacon. Also sells 100% organic fruit and vegetables, dairy, frozen meals, bread and groceries.

HAMPSHIRE

Harroway Organic Gardens
Kingsclere Rd, **Whitchurch**,
RG28 7QB (SA)
T: 01256 895346

Farm shop, open Thurs–Sun, selling home-grown organic vegetables and fruit.

Park Farm Shop
Heckfield, **Hook**, RG27 0LD (SA)
T/F: 01189 326650
e-mail: alison@parkfarmorganics.co.uk
website: www.parkfarmorganics.co.uk

Farm shop, box scheme and home delivery service supplying home-produced beef, pork, lamb and chicken and home-cured organic bacon and sausages. Farm shop also sells organic fruit and vegetables, groceries and dairy. Year-round box scheme offers standard boxes plus meat, groceries etc. to order. Delivers locally to 20-mile radius, including **Surrey**.

Sunnyfields Organic Farm
Jacobs Gutter Lane, **Totton**, Southampton, SO40 9FX (SA)
T: 02380 871408 F: 02380 871146
e-mail: (inquiries): info@sunnyfields.co.uk
(sales and orders): orders@sunnyfields.co.uk
website: www.sunnyfields.co.uk

Well-established friendly 99% organic farm shop, home delivery and box scheme. Stocks over 2,500 organic items, including meat from Owl's Barn Farm, seasonal home-grown fruit and vegetables, wholefoods, groceries, special diet foods, baby foods, bread, dairy and wines and beers. Extensive home delivery list and box scheme (fixed box or customer choice). Delivers to **Hampshire**, **Dorset**, **South** and **West London**.

KENT

Ivy House Farm
Sandhills, **Ash**, nr Sandwich,
CT3 2NG (SA)
T/F: (farm): 01304 812437
T/F: (shop): 01227 720567

Farm shop (25% organic) with a dedicated organic area. Sells home-grown and local vegetables, wholefoods, groceries, some dairy, frozen Graig Farm Organics (**Dolau** (Powys, Wales) (Farm Shops)) meat and frozen home-produced chickens. Also sell home-baked organic bread, fresh daily.

Wingham Country Market
Shatterling, Canterbury CT3 1JW (SA)
T/F: 01227 720567

Farm shop and garden centre (30% organic). Sells 800 organic lines, including bread, eggs, home-produced organic chickens, Graig Farm Organics, **Dolau** (Powys) (Farm Shops) meat, dairy, fruit and vegetables, groceries, wholefoods and herbs. Seasonal selection box scheme to **Thanet** area (90% home-grown).
See also:
Perry Court Farm, **Chartham** (Box Schemes)

OXFORDSHIRE

Brook Cottage Farm
Charney Bassett, Wantage,
OX12 0EN (SA)
T: 01235 868492

Farm shop and local seasonal 'Kissing Bridge' vegetable box scheme (90% home-grown, remainder local). Delivery within 5 miles and pick-up from Frugal Food, **Abingdon** (Shops). The farm shop sells own frozen organic beef and chicken, eggs, vegetables and occasional seasonal fruits. Open Saturdays and by arrangement. Phone for details.

Corner Farm

Oakley Rd, **Horton-cum-Studley**, OX33 1BJ (SA)
T: 01865 358933 F: 01865 358806

Organic farm shop, home delivery and customer choice box scheme. Delivery to **Oxfordshire**, **North** and **South Buckinghamshire**. Shop (90% organic) sells organic fruit and vegetables, bread, meat, dairy, grocery and wholefoods. Also sells home-produced Oxford Downs lamb and seasonal free-range Bronze turkeys.

SURREY

Cranleigh Organic Farm Shop

Lower Barrihurst Farm, Dunsfold Rd, **Cranleigh**, Surrey, GU6 8LG (SA)
T: 01483 272896 F: 01483 273486
e-mail:
organicfarmshop@netscapeonline.co.uk

Farm shop (100% organic). Sells home-produced duck, chicken, eggs, pork and vegetables, locally produced beef and lamb, plus organic fish and wholefoods. Open Thurs–Sat 9am–5pm, otherwise by arrangement.

SUSSEX EAST

Boathouse Organic Farm Shop

The Orchards, Uckfield Rd, **Ringmer**, Lewes, BN8 5RX(SA)
T: 01273 814188
e-mail: shop@boathouseorganic.co.uk
website: www.boathouseorganic.co.uk

Enterprising, friendly farm shop (95% organic). Sells home-produced beef, mutton, lamb and home-grown vegetables and stoneground flour from home-grown wheat. Also sells chilled and frozen ready meals home made from organic ingredients as well as groceries and dairy. Operates local, year-round vegetable box scheme using home-grown seasonal vegetables when available. Pick up from the farm shop.

Glynde Kitchen Gardens

The Street, **Glynde**, Lewes, BN8 6NS (OF&G)
T: 01273 858148

Specialists in organic gourmet mixed leaf salads. Farm shop open weekends and special occasions (please phone for details). Sells home-grown salads and herbs and pot herbs, flowers and gifts. Mail order of gourmet pickles for the festive season.

Hidden Spring Vineyard and Organic Orchard

Vines Cross Rd, **Horam**, TN21 0HF (SA)
T: 01435 812640
e-mail: hidden-spring@eastbourne.org
website: www.hiddenspring.co.uk

Farm shop selling home-produced organic wines, and home-grown organic apples and pears. Also home-produced pickles, marmalades, honey and chutneys made mainly with organic ingredients. Wines available nationwide by mail order.

Honeybrook Organics

High St, **Burwash**, TN19 7HD (SA)
T: 01435 882951 F: 01435 883964
e-mail: honeybrookorganics@supernet.com

A find. Farm shop (95% organic) selling home-produced vegetables, beef, lamb, pork, chicken, milk, cream (unpasteurised to order), butter, yoghurts, ice cream and eggs, plus a wide range of groceries, fruit and wholefoods and wine, beer, champagne and port. Also operates year-round box scheme/ home delivery service supplying fruit and vegetable boxes (80% home grown), dairy, fish and freezer boxes. Delivery in **Kent/ Sussex** within 40-mile radius. Local milk delivery round supplying Channel Islands unpasteurised (green-top) milk.

Old Plaw Hatch Farm

Plaw Hatch Lane, **Sharpthorne**, RH19 4JL (Demeter)
T: (office): 01342 10652
T: (shop): 01342 810201 F: 01342 811478
e-mail: oldplawhatchfarm@hotmail.com

Acclaimed, award-winning biodynamic farm shop (100% organic) open all week. Sells own award-winning biodynamic unpasteurised milk, cheeses and yoghurts plus own fruit and vegetables, pork and occasionally beef and locally produced bread and eggs.

Old Spot Farm Shop

Old Spot Farm, **Piltdown**, Uckfield, TN22 3XN (SA)
T: 01825 722894 F: 01825 723623

Farm shop (70% organic). Sells locally produced, 100% organic fruit and vegetables and locally produced beef, pork, lamb and poultry plus organic dairy products and groceries and home-made sausages, bacon and hams made from free-range pork.

Scragoak Organic Farm

Brightling Rd, **Robertsbridge**, TN32 5EY (SA)
T: (shop): 01424 38454
T: (box scheme): 01424 838420
F: 01424 830420
e-mail: mail@scragoak.co.uk
website: www.scragoak.co.uk

One of the South's best known, award-winning, friendly 100% organic farm shops. 'If it's organic and it's good, we stock it.' Sells over 1,000 lines, including freshly picked, home-grown vegetables, local fruit, meat, fish, babyfoods and groceries. Clear, simple website includes online newsletter 'talking shop'. Operates award winning box scheme (q.v.).

Sedlescombe Organic Vineyard

Cripp's Corner, **Sedlescombe**, Robertsbridge, TN32 5SA (SA)
T: 0800 980 2884
T: (from outside UK): +44 (0)1580 830715
F: 01580 830122
e-mail: sedorganicwines@netscapeonline.co.uk
website: www.englishorganicwine.co.uk

Award-winning producers of English wines, ciders and fruit juices. Farm shop sells own wines, cider and fruit juices. Vineyard and nature trail. Mail order available online or by phone or fax. See also SA Farm listing, England South and South East.

Tablehurst Farm

off London Rd, **Forest Row**, RH18 5DP (Demeter)
T: 01342 823173 F: 01342 824873
e-mail: tablehurstfarm@talk21.com

Biodynamic and organic farm and local food treasure. Farm butchery shop prepares, matures and sells all their own meat and other produce, namely biodynamic beef and lamb, organic pork, chicken, Christmas turkeys and geese. Also eggs, homemade organic sausages, bacon and ham; biodynamic apples, field vegetables and home-milled flour. Recently planted new apple orchard (30,000 trees). Open Thurs–Sat 9am–5pm.

See also:
Holly Park Organics, **Guestling** (Box Schemes)

SUSSEX WEST

The Acorn Farm Shop and Coffee Shop

Brinbury College, **North Heath**, Pulborough, RH20 1DL (SA)
T/F: 01798 873533
e-mail: linfield@compuserve.com

Part of the Aldingbourne Trust, a training centre for people with learning difficulties. Farm shop sells freshly harvested vegetables grown by the students, plus organic dried foods and preserves.

England South and South East – Specialist Providers

BERKSHIRE

Waltham Place

Church Hill, **White Waltham**, SL6 3JH (SA)
T: 01628 825517
e-mail: walthamplace@fsnet

Organic estate, part of National Gardens Scheme, open to public April–Sept. Wonderful gardens including productive kitchen garden. Homemade organic tea and cakes available. Fresh produce also sold at local farmers' markets. Phone for details.

HERTFORDSHIRE

Broughton Pastures Organic Fruit Wines

The Old Brewery, 24 High St, **Tring**, HP23 5AH (SA)
T: 01442 823993
e-mail: organicfruitwine@aol.com

The UK's premier producer of organic fruit wines, including ginger, mead, elderberry, elderflower, blackberry and blackcurrant. Available by mail order and through selected retailers and local farmers' markets. Can also be purchased from warehouse.

Eastwoods of Berkhamsted

15 Gravel Path, **Berkhamsted**, HP4 2EF (SA)
T: 01442 865012 F: 01442 877212
website: www.eastwoodsofberkhamsted.co.uk

Renowned, award-winning, Q-Guild butcher's shop (80% organic). Sells beef, pork, lamb and chicken, home-produced bacon, sausages, burgers and pies, plus specialities such as Highgrove organic meat and salt-marsh lamb. Best specialist shop Organic Food Awards 1999, and winner for their organic hamburgers 2001. Free local delivery and mail order.

Redbournbury Watermill

Redbournbury Lane, **St Albans**, AL3 6RS (SA)
T: 01582 792874
e-mail: redbrymill@aol.com

Stoneground wholemeal 100% organic flour available direct from mill.

KENT

Artisan Bread

Unit 16–17 John Wilson Business Park , **Whitstable**, CT5 3QZ (Demeter)
T: 01227 771881 F: 01227 278661
e-mail: artisanbread@aol.com
website: www.artisanbread.ltd.uk

First biodynamic bakery in Britain. Baker Ingrid Greenfield mills her own grain. She produces superb artisan bread baked without yeast, using Kentish Hills spring water.

Flour Power City
19 Vale Rd, **Tunbridge Wells**,
TN1 1BS (OFF)
T: 01892 547456

Also at Flour Power City, London **N1** (Specialist Providers – Bakers). Sells range of fabulous organic breads, cakes made with organic ingredients, plus local non-organic preserves. Open Thurs–Fri noon–6pm, Sat 10am–6pm.

Wincheap Butchers
26 Wincheap, **Canterbury**
CT1 3QZ (Demeter)
T: 01227 462938

High-quality butcher (40% organic) selling lamb, beef, pork, poultry, sausages and cured meats.

Yalding Organic Gardens
Benover Rd, **Yalding**, nr Maidstone,
ME18 6EX (SA)
T/F: 01622 814650

Part of HDRA and popular sister garden to Ryton Organic Gardens. Extensive organic display gardens including gardening through the ages. Small shop sells gardening gifts, books, organic seeds, dried foods, breads, soft drinks, jams and biscuits. Café serves organic vegetarian meals.
See also:
Perry Court Farm, **Chartham** (bakery) (Box Schemes)
Pittsfield Farm, **Tunbridge Wells** (cheese) (Farm Gate)

OXFORDSHIRE

M. Feller
Son and Daughter, 54–55 Covered Market,
Oxford, OX1 3DY (SA)
T: 01865 251164 F: 01865 200553
e-mail: mfeller@mfeller.co.uk
website: www.mfeller.co.uk

Excellent, award-winning butcher's (90% organic) selling organic beef, lamb, pork and poultry, gammon, homemade sausages and home-cured bacon. Also sells organic salmon and trout. Free home delivery within Oxford ring road.

F. W. P. Matthews Ltd
The Cotswold Flour Millers, Station Rd,
Shipton-under-Wychwood,
OX7 6BH (SA)
T: 01993 830342 F: 01993 831615
e-mail: sales@fwpmatthews.co.uk
website: www.fwpmatthews.co.uk

Family-run mill. Produces organic wholemeal and white flours. Callers can buy direct. Mail order and online ordering available. Mill visits arranged on request.

SURREY

Lifestyle Natural Health Centre
4 The Centre, Hersham Green,
Walton-on-Thames, KT12 4HL
T: 01932 254624 F: 01932 228385

Therapy centre with food store (70% organic). Sells bread, groceries, wholefoods and herbs.

SUSSEX EAST

Choice Cuts
95 Preston Drove, **Brighton**, BN1 6LD
T: 01273 381616

Popular, small, cosy butcher's shop (60+% organic). Sells organic beef, pork and some organic lamb, homemade organic sausages, and free-range, additive-free poultry.
Next-door deli, Choice Deli, sells wide range of foods (50% organic), including groceries, bread, cheeses and cooked meats.

Sedlescombe Organic Vineyard

Cripp's Corner, **Sedlescombe**,
Robertsbridge, TN32 5SA (SA)
T: 0800 980 2884
T: (from outside UK): +44 1580 830715
F: 01580 830122
e-mail:
sedorganicwines@netscapeonline.co.uk
website: www.englishorganicwine.co.uk

Popular tourist attraction with own farm shop. See full entries under **Farm Shops** and in SA Farm listing, England South and South East.

Sussex High Weald Dairy Products

Putlands Farm, **Duddleswell**, Uckfield,
TN22 3BJ (SA)
T: 01825 712647 F: 01825 712474
e-mail: mhardy@agnet.co.uk
website: www.speciality-foods.com

Specialist cheese and dairy farm shop. Sells own soft and hard organic cow's-milk cheeses, including award-winning Ashdown Foresters. Also sheep's milk and sheep's-milk cheeses, sheep's-milk yoghurts and fromage frais. Hard cheeses available by mail order.

SUSSEX WEST

Hidden Spring Vineyard and Organic Orchard

Vines Cross Rd, **Heathfield**, Horsham,
TN21 0HF (SA)
T: 01435 812640
e-mail: hidden-spring@eastbourne.org
website: www.hiddenspring.co.uk

Farm shop selling home-produced wines and home-grown organic apples and pears. Also home-produced pickles, marmalades, honey and chutneys, made mainly with organic ingredients.

West Dean Gardens

West Dean College, **West Dean**,
Chichester, PO18 0QZ
T: 01243 818210
e-mail: gardens@westdean.org.uk
website: www.westdean.org.uk

A must for any kitchen garden enthusiast. A restored Victorian walled demonstration kitchen garden and ornamental fruit garden, part of West Dean Arts, Crafts and Gardening College, complete with Victorian glasshouses. Features include extensive variety of pears, apples, plums, tomatoes and chilli peppers and HDRA heritage seed varieties. Plants and some produce available from West Dean shop, and can be eaten in their restaurant. Open April to October (phone for times).

England South and South East – Places to Eat and Stay

BUCKINGHAMSHIRE

Pizza Organic

54 London End, **Beaconsfield**,
HP9 2JH (SA)
T: 01494 677758

Part of the Pizza Piazza chain. Serves pizza and pasta dishes and grill meals all made with organic ingredients. Open for lunch and evening meals. Also at **Walton-on-Thames** (Surrey), Ealing **W5** and **SW7**.

KENT

Harbour Street Café

48 Harbour St, **Whitstable**, CT5 1AQ
T: 01227 772575
website: www.harbourstreetcafe.co.uk

Eclectic, popular, modern café run by mother and daughter, Gillian and Josephine Reckitt.

Global menu changes every two months. Includes plenty of vegetarian, vegan and gluten-free options. Uses some organic and local ingredients. Everything homemade, including baked beans. Cakes made with organic ingredients. All dried foods and drinks, including tea and coffee, are organic. Open every day and Friday and Saturday evenings.

Sainsbury's (restaurant)
Otford Rd, **Sevenoaks**,
TN14 5EG (OF&G)
T: 01732 742561

A first for a supermarket. In-store restaurant serves hot organic ready meals all day from 11.30am. Menu includes toasted ciabatta with various fillings, including camembert, wild rocket and dried apricot, with organic salad garnish, toasted bagel with smoked salmon and cream cheese with simple snacks, desserts and drinks. Prices are reasonable. Staff, sporting their organic 'try me' aprons, have been specially trained. All organic pukka, as Jamie would say.

See also:
Yalding Organic Gardens, **Yalding**
(Specialist Providers)

SURREY

Pizza Organic
14 Bridge St, Walton-on-Thames,
KT12 1AA (SA)
T: 01932 220153

Part of the Pizza Piazza chain. Serves pizza and pasta dishes and grill meals all made with organic ingredients. Open for lunch and evening meals. Also at **Beaconsfield** (Bucks), Ealing **W5** and **SW7**.

SUSSEX EAST

Coriander
5 Hove Manor, Hove St, **Hove**, BN3 2DF
T: 01273 730850
e-mail: katrinesmale@aol.com

Small, informal, jolly restaurant with infectious enthusiasm for all things organic and sustainable. Owned and run by the chef, David Smale, and his wife Katrine. Global menu (90% organic). Produce sourced from local growers and suppliers. Extensive range of organic soft and alcoholic drinks, including over 25 wines. Live sustainable lifestyle, recycling everything, using eco-friendly cleaning products and manual washing up. Open Tues–Sat 7pm–11pm.

The Full Moon
8 Boyces St, **Brighton**, BN1 1AN
T: 01273 328797 F: 01273 728294
e-mail: info@the-full-moon.co.uk
website: www.the-full-moon.co.uk

Snug back-street pub. Wide selection of organic beers and other drinks. Simple, tasty, reasonably priced all-organic weekend menu. For more, including menu, drinks list, reviews and special events, visit website.

Granville Hotel
124 Kings Rd, **Brighton**, BN1 2FA
T: 01273 326302 F: 01273 728294
e-mail: granville@brighton.co.uk
website: www.granvillehotel.co.uk

Comfortable, stylish, luxurious, 'green' and eco-friendly hotel serving good food. Described as an 'organic feast'. Vegetarians, vegans and special diets catered for. Around 80% of the food served is organic.

Infinity Foods Café

50 Gardner St, **Brighton**, BN1 1UN
T: 01273 670743

New, fun vegetarian café. Part of the Infinity Foods workers' co-operative. Serves breakfasts, lunches and afternoon teas made mainly with organic ingredients.

Kai Organic Café

52 Gardner St, **Brighton**, BN1 1UN (SA)
T: 01273 684 921
website: www.kaicafe.co.uk

New, up-tempo spacious sandwich bar, food-to-go and licensed organic café using only organic ingredients. Open 7 days a week until 5 pm. Modern menu with very reasonable prices features freshly prepared soups, salads, sandwiches, cakes (including gluten- and wheat-free), drinks, etc.

Paskins Town House

18–19 Charlotte St, **Brighton**, BN2 1AG
T: 01273 60203 F: 01273 621973
e-mail: welcome@paskins.co.uk
website: www.paskins.co.uk

Something different. Grade 2 listed, attractive, green and eco-friendly restored Regency townhouse, in heart of conservation area. Offers bed and fabled enormous breakfast (twice nominated AA 'best breakfast') using local and mainly (80%) organic foods and ingredients, including vegetarian/ vegan options. Really good website.

Seasons of Lewes

199 High St, **Lewes**. BN7 2NS
T: 01273 473968

Family-run vegetarian and vegan restaurant. Serves morning coffee, lunch and tea (85% organic). Innovative menu changes daily.

Terre à Terre Vegetarian Restaurant

71 East St, **Brighton**, BN1 1HQ
T: 01273 729051

Much raved about vegetarian restaurant. Modern inventive cooking using seasonal organic produce and many organic ingredients. Organic wines and other drinks served. Booking essential. Open 12am–10.30pm, closed Mon.

Trogs

124 Kings Rd, **Brighton**, BN1 2FA
T: 01273 204655 F: 01273 728294

Situated in the basement of the Granville Hotel. Modern upbeat vegetarian café bar (12am–11pm) and restaurant (6pm–9.30pm, last orders), with enticing eclectic menu. Open every day. Café bar (75% organic ingredients) serves light bites. Restaurant uses 100% organic ingredients where possible. Vegans and special diets catered for.

See also:
Wealden Wholefoods, **Wadhurst** (Shops)
West Dean Gardens, **West Dean** (Specialist Providers)
Little Orchard House, **Rye** (B & B List)

SUSSEX WEST

The Avins Bridge Restaurant and Rooms

College Rd, **Ardingly**, Haywards Heath, RH17 6SH
T: 01444 892393
e-mail: enquiries@theavinsbridge.co.uk
website: www.theavinsbridge.co.uk

Quiet restaurant with five rooms. Offers varied evening menu using predominantly (80%) organic ingredients sourced locally where possible, plus good selection of organic wines.

St Martins Organic Tea Rooms
St Martin St, **Chichester**, PO19 1NP
T: 01243 786715
website: www.organictearooms.co.uk

Remarkable eighteenth-century cosy tea-room and cottage garden that has been using organic ingredients for 14 years. Emphasis on healthy eating. Serves simple, delicious homemade fare including soups, sandwiches, light meals and cakes, to eat in or takeaway. Ninety-five per cent organic ingredients including 100% organic fresh produce. Open Mon–Sat, 9am–6pm.

England South and South East – Farm Gate

BERKSHIRE

Elm Farm Research Centre
Hamstead Marshall, Newbury, RG20 0HR (SA)
T: 01488 658298 F: 01488 658503
e-mail: elmfarm@efrc.com
website: www.efrc.co.uk

UK's foremost organic farming research establishment. Holds open days. Farm-gate sales of home-produced organic beef and seasonal lamb, sold from the freezer or fresh to order. See also SA Farm listing, England South and South East.

Sheepdrove Organic Farm
Lambourn, RG17 7UU (SA)
T: 01488 71659 F: 01488 72677
e-mail: manager@sheepdrove.com
website: www.sheepdrove.com

Organic Food Producer of the Year, Organic Food Awards 2001. Produce includes lamb, mutton, turkeys, geese, duck, chicken, beef, pork and sausages and burgers. Also meat vacuum-packed for home delivery. Arrange to collect from farm gate, by mail order or online. Delivered locally every Friday in own chiller van or despatched nationwide overnight by courier. See also SA Farm listing, England South and South East.

HAMPSHIRE

Broughton Organics
The Anchorage, Salisbury Rd, **Broughton**, nr Stockbridge, SO20 8BX (SA)
T: 01794 301234

Home-produced fruit, vegetables, poultry and eggs available at farm.

Meadow Cottage Farm
Churt Rd, Headley, **Bordon**, GU35 8SS (SA)
T: 01428 712155
e-mail: weydown@netscapeonline.co.uk
website: members.netscapeonline.co.uk/weydown

Farmhouse dairy with small farm shop. Sells their delicious unpasteurised (green-top) organic milk and cream from their pedigree Weydown Jersey herd. Also sells their special homemade ice creams made exclusively from organic milk and cream. Open every day.

Period Plants
Rhode Island, Knights Lane, **Ball Hill**, nr Newbury, RG20 0NW
T: 01672 811735
e-mail: zundel@periodplants.freeserve.co.uk

Nursery producing old-fashioned and rare plants and herbs typically grown in English gardens up to 1700. All stock propagated using only organic compost and fertiliser. Send 4 x 2nd class stamps for mail order list and information on opening times and special events.

W. H. Rimes Organic Growers

Hill View, Church Lane, **West Meon**, Petersfield, GU32 1JB (SA)
T: 01730 829208

Farm-gate sales of home-grown organic vegetables, potatoes and soft fruit when in season.

Upton Redheads Organic Poultry

Upton House Farm, **Wonston**, Winchester, SO21 3LR (OF&G)
T: 01962 760219 F: 01962 761419

Farm-gate sales of organic chicken and chicken portions to order, fresh and smoked. Chickens are reared in small flocks in mobile houses moved to fresh grass every 10 days. Hung for 1 week after slaughter and processed on site. Also available at farmers' markets in **Hampshire** and surrounding counties.

KENT

Burscome Cliff Farm

Egerton, Ashford, TN7 5BB (SA)
T: 01233 756468

Farm-gate sales of home-produced beef, lamb, pork, sausages and bacon and some fruit. Attends **Wye** and **Lenham** farmers' markets.

Elmstone Organic Farm

Grafty Green, Maidstone, ME17 2AJ (SA)
T: 01622 858970
e-mail: julian@elmstone.freeserve.co.uk

Farm-gate sales of home-grown apples and pears, limited seasonal vegetables, some plums and cobnuts.

Pitfields Farm

Blackham, **Tunbridge Wells**, TN3 9UB (SA)
T/F: 01892 740302

Produces organic sheep's-milk cheese from own sheep. Together with fruit and vegetables sold at farm and farmers' markets in **Kent** and **Sussex**.
See also:
Luddesdown Organic Farm, **Luddesdown**; Perry Court Farm, **Chartham** (Box Schemes)

OXFORDSHIRE

Step Farm

Lechlade Rd, **Faringdon**, SN7 8BH (SA)
T: 01367 240558/240183 F: 01367 244324

Farm-gate sales of home-produced beef and lamb. Available by the cut or by the side, frozen except by special arrangement.

SUSSEX EAST

Little Warren Farm

Fletching Common, **Newick** BN8 4JH (SA)
T: 01825 722545

Farm-gate sales of organic beef and 'veaux de lait élevé sous la mère' – veal raised by their mothers for six months, fed entirely on their milk and allowed to range. Available fresh or frozen. Also available in local shops, including Old Spot Farm Shop, **Piltdown**. For more on organic veal, see p. **186**.

SUSSEX WEST

See:
Wayside Organics, **Oving** (Box Schemes)

ENGLAND SOUTH WEST

England South West – Box Schemes

BRISTOL

Arcadia Organics

Clover Nursery, Streamcross, **Lower Claversham**, BS49 4QA (SA)
T: 01934 876886

Box scheme delivering home-produced vegetables in seasonal selection boxes, year-round, to households in **North Somerset**.

The Better Food Company

Unit 1, Wallis Estate, Mina Rd, **Bristol**, BS2 9YW (SA)
T: 0117 904 1191 F: 0117 904 1190
e-mail: betterfood@compuserve.com
website: www.betterfood.co.uk

Excellent local home delivery service to 30-mile radius; £10 minimum order. Passionate about organic and locally produced foods. Extensive catalogue (90% organic); includes fruit and vegetables, meat, poultry, eggs, dairy, bread, wholefoods, groceries and wines and beers. Saturday market on site, select from their entire range.

The Green Wheel

45 Sherbourne St, St George, BS5 8EQ (OF&G)
T: 0117 955 9264

Seasonal selection fruit and vegetable boxes (90% locally grown) and eggs. Delivers year-round to households in **Bristol**.

CORNWALL

R. and M. Ashworth

PO Box 88, Truro, TR3 7YJ
T: 01872 865874

Box scheme and home delivery supplying fruit and vegetables from Riverford Farm (**Buckfastleigh** (Devon) (Box Schemes)) and organic wholefoods to **South West Cornwall**.

Cusgarne Organic Box Scheme

Cusgarne Wollas, **Cusgarne**, nr Truro, TR4 8RL (OF&G)
T: 01872 865922
e-mail: cusgarme@freenet.co.uk

A producer-owned box scheme, winner of Organic Food Awards 2000 and highly commended in 2001 awards. Organic family farm produces extensive range of vegetables, beef and eggs. Box scheme operates 52 weeks a year, supplying organic 'hampers' (90% home produce), plus local organic chickens. Delivery area covers **Truro**, **Falmouth** and **Redruth** and is expanding. Christmas geese available to order for farm pick-up.

Keveral Farmers Ltd

St Martins by Looe, PL13 1PA (SA)
T: 01503 250215

Local seasonal box scheme providing organic fruit and vegetables, either home-grown or from Riverford Farm, **Buckfastleigh** (Devon) (Farm Shops), proportions depending on season.

Leswidden Box Scheme
Leswidden Barn Farm, The Barn,
Leswidden, TR19 7RU
T: 01736 787953

Local box scheme supplying home-grown seasonal vegetables, plus their own pork, sausages, home-cured bacon and ham, available from the farm direct.

Tree of Life
Scala-nija, Mithian, **St Agnes**, nr Truro,
TR5 0QE (SA)
T/F: 01872 552661

Friendly local box scheme, with limited customer choice, supplying home-grown vegetables, salad crops including peppers and aubergines, soft fruit, herbs and organic eggs, plus some from other local organic growers. Delivery within 15-mile radius of Truro, plus pick-up points at the Mustard Seed, (**Perannporth**), Carley's (**Truro**) and Country Store Healthfoods (**Redruth**).

Tregannick Farm
Drakewalls, **Gunnislake**, PL18 9ED (SA)
T: 01822 833969 F: 01822 834285

Local box scheme and home delivery service to **East Cornwall** supplying vegetables from Riverford Farm, **Buckfastleigh** (Devon) (Box Schemes) and home-produced organic lamb and eggs.
See also:
Pure Meat Direct, **Northcott** (Box Schemes – Devon)

DEVON

Golland Farm
Burrington, Umberleigh, EX37 9JP (SA)
T/F: 01769 520263
e-mail: golland@btinternet.com
website: www.golland.btinternet.co.uk

June–March small local traditional box scheme. Delivers excellent range of delicious home-grown vegetables within a 5-mile radius. Home-produced delicious organic chicken, lamb and pork also available. Please phone first.

Holsworthy Organics
c/o Little East Lake Farm, East Chilla,
Beaworthy, EX31 5XF (SA)
T: 01409 254450 or 221417

All-year-round box scheme with seasonal vegetables, fruit, herbs (culinary and medicinal) and both hens and ducks eggs. Mostly home-grown, some bought in from other local SA certified producers. Delivery to **North** and **West Devon** and **North Cornwall**.

Linscombe Farm Vegetable Boxes
New Buildings, **Sandford**, Crediton,
EX17 4PS (SA)
T: 01363 84291
e-mail: linscombefarm@netscapeonline.co.uk

A treat. Small and very local box scheme operating from June to April. Farm grows an extensive range of vegetables and salad crops, specialising in different, rare and unusual varieties, including around 15 varieties of potatoes. Delivery to **Crediton** area (5-mile radius). Joint winners of Box Scheme award, Organic Food Awards 2001. At **Crediton** farmers' market first Sat of month.

Little Ash Eco Farm
Throwleigh, **Okehampton**,
EX20 2QJ (SA)
T: 01647 231394

Diverse environmental centre, producing organic beef, lamb, wheat, dairy produce and vegetables, which are available through their **local**, seasonal box scheme (deliveries by horse and cart) and **nationwide** mail order.

Lower Turley Farm
Cullompton, EX15 1NA (SA)
T: 01884 32234

Gourmet's box scheme. Operates June to February supplying fresh, home-grown seasonal vegetable boxes. Emphasis on fresh, flavourful produce and unusual varieties. Specialise in unusual varieties of potatoes. Lamb available by arrangement. Collect from farm. Also home-made felt from sheep's wool.

Marshford Organic Produce
Churchill Way, Northam, **Barnstaple**, EX39 1NS (SA)
T: 01237 477160 F: 01237 477148
e-mail: enquiries@marshford.co.uk
website: www.marshford.co.uk

Award-winning growers, who operate year round bespoke box scheme/home delivery service, and excellent nursery farm shop – see Marshford Organics, Northam, **Barnstaple** (Farm Shops) – and retail shop – see Marshford Organics, **Barnstable** (Shops). Box scheme supplies home-grown and local produce (70%, but all home-grown in summer), including vegetables, soft fruit, salads and herbs, plus full range of groceries etc. Delivery to **North Devon**.

NB Boxes
Christow, Exeter EX6 7PG (SA)
T: 01647 252915
Also at:
NB Boxes, **Shillingford Abbot**, Exeter. EX2 9QQ (SA)

Small co-operative box scheme, run by Northwood Farm and The Barton, operating from July to March. Northwood Farm was one of the original and best pioneering local box schemes, which became a role model for local food for local people. With an emphasis on freshness and quality, over 60 varieties of vegetables and salads are grown and delivered within a 3-mile radius. Customer likes, dislikes and special requests are catered for.

Old Cumming Organic Farm
Colston Rd, **Buckfastleigh**, TQ11 0LP (SA)
T: 01364 642672
e-mail: cummingorganic@lineone.net

Family-run organic farm supplying tailor-made fruit and vegetable boxes (80% home-grown) within a 20-mile radius.

Pure Meat Direct
Home Place Farm, **Northcott**, nr Launceston, PL15 9RQ (SA)
T/F: 01409 211127
e-mail: enquiries@puremeatdirectonline.co.uk
website: www.puremeatdirectonline.co.uk

Situated on **Devon/Cornwall** border, **nationwide** home delivery meat company selling organic and high animal welfare beef, lamb, pork and chicken (50% local), that also runs year-round local seasonal selection box scheme (50% home-grown, 90% in summer) delivering to **Dartmouth**. Meat orders can also be picked up at farm direct by prior arrangement.

Riverford Organic Vegetables
Wash Barn, **Buckfastleigh**, TQ11 0LD (SA)
T: 01803 762720 F: 01803 762718
e-mail: mail@riverford.co.uk
website: www.riverford.co.uk

One of the best-known Devon growers and box scheme. Winners of Fresh Produce Award, Organic Food Awards 2001. Ninety per cent of produce grown at Riverford or on associated supplier farms. Supplies over 4,000 households per week, locally and throughout south of England. Produce also sold locally and at Riverford Farm Shop, **Staverton** (Farm Shops). Offers five standard vegetable boxes, plus extras including fruit, fruit juices, Riverford Farm organic milk and cream, organic eggs, bread, Pertwood cereals (p. **324**), wines by the case and Churchtown Farm, **Lanteglos by Fowey** (Cnwll) (Farm Gate) organic beef and lamb. Also offers three standard meat boxes. Boxes also available from: R. & M. Ashworth, **Ponsanooth** (Cnwll); Kevarel Farm, **St Martins by Looe** (Cnwll); Noah's Ark Boxes, **Poole** (Dorset); The Organic Network, **Watford** (Herts); Tregannick Farm, **Gunnislake** (Cnwll) (Box Schemes).

Rod and Ben's

Bickham Farm, **Kenn**, Exeter,
EX6 7XL (SA)
T: 01392 833833 F: 01392 833832
e-mail: RodandBen@rodandbens.com
website: www.rodandbens.com

Year-round local vegetable box scheme (85% home-grown – 50 different types). Also honey from own beehives and eggs from two flocks of maran hens. Standard small and large boxes or customer choice from weekly availability list. Delivery to twelve drop-off points (or to your home for a small extra charge) in **Exeter** and **Exmouth** areas. Also free-range organic poultry including Bronze turkeys to order. Holds farm open days. Visit website or phone for latest information.

DORSET

Cannings Court Organics

Cannings Court, **Pulham**, Dorchester,
DT2 7EA (SA)
T: 01258 818035 F: 01258 817210
e-mail: john.cannings-court@care4free.net

New organic grower. Operates local box scheme end of June to February, providing home-grown organic vegetables, organic and free-range eggs , plus small amount (5%) of other certified organic produce. Delivery to pick-up points in **Pulham**, **Stalbridge** and **Sherborne**. Farm shop open spring 2002.

Gold Hill Organic Farm

Child Okeford, **Blandford Forum**,
DT11 8HB (SA)
T: 01258 860293 F: 01258 861413

Inspirational award-winning local box scheme and farm shop supplying home-grown organic fruit and vegetables to drop-off points in **Blandford**, **Shaftesbury** and **Wimborne**. Farm shop, open at the weekend, sells their own fruit and vegetables, eggs, frozen British White beef, homemade jams made with organic fruit, plus organic milk and bread.

Longmeadow Organic Vegetables

Godmanstone, Dorchester,
DT2 7AE (SA)
T: 01300 341779

Seasonal box scheme supplying home-grown vegetables to **Yeovil**, **Sherborne** and **Dorchester** from the end of June to mid-February. Also pick-up from Ceres Natural and Organic Foods, **Yeovil** (Shops). Their own farm shop, open Wed–Sat 9am–6pm, sells vegetables (80% home-grown), locally produced eggs and apples.

Noah's Ark Organic Boxes
33 Church Rd, **Poole**, BH14 8UF
T: 01202 747849

Local delivery of Riverford Farm (**Buckfastleigh** (Devon) (Box Schemes))organic boxes (fresh produce/ meat/dairy) plus organic juices within a 5-mile radius of **Bournemouth** and **Poole**.

Tamarisk Farm
West Bexington, DT2 9DF (SA)
T: 01308 897784
e-mail: organicfarm@tamariskfarm.co.uk
website: www.tamariskfarm.co.uk

Year-round local box scheme supplying home-grown organic vegetables. Farm-gate pick-up and **local** delivery of home-produced beef, lamb, mutton and sausages. Produced organically, their meat is not certified, as they use a local, non-certified abattoir for animal welfare reasons. Home-grown, stoneground wheat and rye flours also available.
See also:
Sturts Farm, **Ferndown** (Farm Shops)

GLOUCESTERSHIRE

Camphill Village Trust
Oaklands Park, **Newnham**, GL14 1EF (SA/ Demeter)
T: 01594 516063

Seasonal selection box scheme, supplying home-grown fruit, vegetables and herbs to the **Forest of Dean** area.

Duchy Home Farm Organic Vegetables
Broadfield Farm, **Tetbury**, GL8 8SE (SA)
T/F: 01666 504287

Local traditional box scheme operating June–March, supplying wide range of seasonal vegetables, salads and herbs grown on Prince Charles's organic farm. Delivery to 10-mile radius. Stall at **Cirencester**, **Stroud** and **Tetbury** farmers' markets. Also sold at Bath Organic Farms, **Weston** (Somset) (Farm Shops).

Slipstream Organics
34a Langdon Rd, **Cheltenham**, GL53 7NZ (SA)
T: 01242 227273 F: 01242 227798
e-mail: info@slipstream-organics.co.uk
website: www.slipstream-organics.co.uk

Award-winning seasonal selection box scheme delivering locally grown organic vegetables to **Cheltenham**, **Gloucester** and **Stroud**.

SOMERSET

Arcadia Organics
Clover Nursery, Stream Cross, **Lower Claverham**, BS49 4QA (SA)
T: 01934 876886

Local seasonal selection box scheme, delivering 95% home-grown vegetables to **North Somerset**.

Galingale
3 Victoria Gardens, **Henstridge**, BA8 0RE (SA)
T: 01963 362702
e-mail: Galingaleorganic@aol.com

Small and very local box scheme, operating May to January, supplying 100% home-grown vegetables, salad crops, soft fruit, herbs and free-range eggs to **Henstridge**. Has stall at Henstridge Market (Sat). Pick up from farm. Please phone first

Leigh Court Farm
Abbots Leigh, BS8 3RA
(SA)
T/F: 01275 375756
e-mail: mail@leighcourtfarm.org.co.uk

Local vegetable box scheme delivering home-grown vegetables. Stall at **Bristol** farmers' market. Runs horticultural courses.

Magdalen Farm
Magdalen Cross, **Winsham**, Chard, TA20 4PA (SA)
T: 01460 30277 F: 01460 30144

Local seasonal selection vegetable box scheme (95% home-grown). Delivery to collection points in **Chard** and **Crewkerne**. Operates July to February. Occasional farm-gate sales of home-produced frozen pork.

Merricks Organic Farm
Park Lane, **Langport**, TA10 0NF (SA)
T/F: 01458 252901
e-mail: simon@merricksorganicfarm.co.uk
website: www.merricksorganicfarm.co.uk

Award-winning local box scheme for lovers of fine food, renowned for its quality and variety. Customer choice, 100% home-grown, operating end-May to end-February. Rare breed pork to pick up frozen from the farm. Delivery within 12-mile radius of farm to drop-off points, also at Wessex WI, **Somerton** Market (Sat am). Joint winners Box Scheme Award, Organic Food Awards 2001.

Radford Mill Farm
Timsbury, BA2 0QF (SA)
T/F: 01761 472549
e-mail: farm@radfordmill.co.uk
website: www.radfordmill.co.uk

Small local box scheme/home delivery service. Supplies own organic plain and fruit yoghurts, soft cheese, seasonal fruit, vegetables and herbs, plus their lamb, beef, pork. Christmas turkeys to order. Delivery within 10-mile radius. Stalls at **Glastonbury** market and **Bath**, **Bristol** and **Frome** farmers' markets.

Stone Age Organics
Stone Age Farm, **Cothelstone**, Taunton, TA4 3ED (SA)
T: 01823 432488
e-mail: keith@stoneageorganics.co.uk
website: www.stoneageorganics.co.uk

Delivers seasonal selection vegetable boxes (75% home-produced) to collection points in **Somerset** and **Bristol**. Home-produced lamb also available from farm.
See also:
Trading Post, **South Petherton** (Shops)

WILTSHIRE

Coleshill Organics
59 Coleshill, **Swindon**, SN6 7PT (SA)
T/F: 01793 861070

Box scheme delivering seasonal selection fruit and vegetable boxes (60% home-grown) to drop-off points and addresses within a 20-mile radius. Farm shop (100% organic) sells fruit and home-grown vegetables and herbs, local eggs, plus small range of groceries. Open Wed–Sat. Phone first to check hours.

Pertwood Organics Co-op Ltd
The Old Barn at Lord's Hill, Lower Pertwood Farm, **Longbridge Deverill**, Warminster, BA12 7DY (SA)
T: 01985 840646
e-mail: mail@pertwood-organics.co.uk
website: www.pertwood-organics.co.uk

Box scheme and home delivery service providing fruit and vegetable boxes, with customer choice, home-produced beef, lamb and pork, Pertwood breakfast cereals and flours (see p. **324**), plus organic bread, dairy and wholefoods. Home delivery and pick-up points to **Wiltshire** and surrounding counties. Also attends **Wiltshire** and **Somerset** farmers' markets.

Purton House
Purton, Nr Swindon, SN4 9EB (SA)
T: 01793 770219 F: 01793 772750

Vegetable box scheme, home delivery and farm-gate sales. Sells a wide range of vegetables (80% home-grown) and home-produced free-range and organic eggs. Delivers to **Cirencester** and **Swindon** areas. Phone for details.

S. & J. Organic Growers
The Walled Garden, **Castle Combe**, SN14 7HH (SA)
T: 01249 783294 F: 01249 783427
e-mail: sjorganics@btinternet.com

Box scheme/home delivery providing year-round seasonal selection vegetable and fruit boxes (75% home-produced) and local lamb, beef, pork and cured meats, Providence Farm, **Holsworthy** (Devon) (Farm Gate) chickens and ducks, Hobbs House Bakery, **Chipping Sodbury** (Glos) (Specialist Providers) breads and wholefoods from order list. Delivery to **Bath** and **Wiltshire**.

Tallywacker Farm
50 The Ridings, **Kington St Michael**, Chippenham, SN14 6JG (SA)
T: 01249 750035
e-mail: sales@tallywackerfarm.co.uk
e-mail: (local box scheme): veg@tallywackerfarm.co.uk
e-mail: (hampers): hampers@tallywackerfarm.co.uk
e-mail: (worms): worms@tallywackerfarm.co.uk
website: www.tallywackerfarm.co.uk

Seasonal selection vegetable box scheme (50% home-produced), with some customer choice. Delivery to **Tetbury**, **Malmesbury**, **Chippenham** and **Corsham** area. Also offers UK-wide mail-order food hamper service – see website for contents of Breakfast, Kitchen Basics and Deluxe Hampers. Has Dendrabaena worm farm supplying both local and mail order customers with worms for home composting and general soil improvement.

England South West – Shops

BRISTOL

Harvest Natural Foods
224 Cheltenham Rd, **Bristol**, BS6 5QU
T: 0117 9425997

Wholefood store (50% organic). Range includes fruit and vegetables (100% organic), wholefoods, groceries, breads (including gluten-free), ice cream and snacks.

Stoneground
5 The Mall, **Clifton**, BS8 4DP
T: 0117 9741260

Vegetarian healthfood one-stop shop (45% organic), selling extensive range, including wholefoods, wines, beers and breads, fruit and vegetables (100% organic), babyfoods, dairy and dairy substitutes.

CORNWALL

Carleys

34–36 St Austell St, **Truro**, TR1 1SE (SA)
T: 01872 277686

Cornish organic mecca selling over 3,000 organic products, including meat, groceries, eggs, wines, fruit and vegetables, dairy, herbs and wholefoods. Pick-up point for Tree of Life box scheme.

Country Store Healthfoods

3 Bond St, **Redruth**, TR15 2QA
T: 01209 215012

Vegetarian store selling wide range (50%) of organic foods, including wholefoods, groceries, dairy, bread baked for them by the local baker, and local organic eggs. Pick-up point for Tree of Life box scheme.

Jilly's Organic Wholefoods

Biscombe's Lane, **Callington**, PL17 7LB
T: 01579 384356

Ninety per cent organic shop. Extensive range includes wholefoods, groceries and dairy.

The Natural Store

16 High St, **Falmouth**, TR11 2AS
T: 01326 311507 F: 01326 565848.
Also at: The Natural Store, The Parade, Trengrouse Way, Helston, TR13 8RT

Ninety-five per cent organic wholefood shop; extensive range includes fruit and vegetables, meat, dairy and wholefoods.

DEVON

The Ark Wholefood Shop

38 East St, **Ashburton**, TQ13 7AX
T: 01364 653020.

Small shop but wide range (75% organic) of products, including 100% organic fruit, vegetables and dairy, plus wholefoods, groceries and frozen foods.

Chops Away

1 Ticklemore Court, Ticklemore St, **Totnes**, TQ9 5EJ
T: 01803 864404
e-mail: noni@chopsaway.com
website: www.chopsaway.com

Organic and biodynamic producers' co-operative. Shop sells their produce, including organic meat, herbs, plants and seeds. Café serves organic tea, coffee and cakes.

The Courtyard

76 The Square, **Chagford**, Newton Abbot, TQ13 8BY
T: 01647 432571

Shop and café selling wide range of produce (80% organic) including wholefoods, dairy, fruit and vegetables. Around half of the food served in the café is made with organic ingredients.

Gourmet Organix

3–4 Queen St, **Lynton**, EX35 6AA (SA)
T: 01598 752228 F: 01598 752221
website: www.gourmetorganix.com (site currently under development)

Chic, spacious, award-winning 100% organic fine food shop. Meat and poultry sourced locally where possible, locally produced fruit and vegetables, plus exotics, full range of groceries and drinks, and delicatessen counter.

The Green House

2a Lower Pannier Market, **Crediton**, EX17 2BL
T: 01363 775580

Wholefood store with strong organic ethos (75% organic) with small café serving organic teas and coffee. Sells wholefoods, grocery, fruit and vegetables, dairy and frozen ready meals.

Greenlife

11–13 Fore St, **Totnes**, TQ9 5DA
T: 01803 866738 F: 01803 866538

Wholefood shop selling wide range of organic foods and drink (70% organic). All fruit and vegetables are organic and locally produced.

Marshford Organic Produce

14A Butcher's Row, **Barnstaple**, EX31 1BW (SA)
T: 01271 322855

Small retail outlet for Marshford Organic (**Barnstaple**, Farm Shops). Best Small Shop, Organic Food Awards 2001. Full range of organic foods includes home-grown fresh produce. Vegetables, soft fruit and salads picked daily. See also their box scheme (**Barnstaple**, Box Schemes). Also organic trout from Rye Farm (**Loxhore**, Specialist Providers).

Orgasmic Organics

20 Bedford St, **Exeter**, EX1 1LE (SA)
T: 01392 494449

One hundred per cent vegetarian organic shop selling comprehensive range of organic foods and drink, including frozen meals and special diet foods. Pick-up point for Rod and Ben's box scheme. (See p. **480**.)

Rocombe Farm Organic Ice Cream

123 Union St, Castle Circus, **Torquay**, TQ1 3DW (SA)
T: (shop): 01803 293996
T: (mail order and inquiries): 01626 834545
F: 01626 835777
e-mail: info@rocombefarm.co.uk
website: www.rocombefarm.co.uk

Supplies luxury organic ice-cream, sorbets, and frozen yoghurts through shop, and nationwide through retailers. Shop sells ice cream, drinks, snacks and soups (85% organic). Ice cream available nationwide by mail order, packed with dry ice.

Sacks

80 High St, **Totnes**, TQ9 5SN (SA)
T: 01803 863263

Healthfood shop selling a full range of organic products (75% organic), including herbs, wholefoods and dairy, also organic fruit and vegetables from Riverford Farm, **Staverton** (Farm Shops).
See also:
The Market Fish Shop, **Dartmouth** (Specialist Providers)

DORSET

Down to Earth

18 Princes St, **Dorchester**, DT1 1TW
T: 01305 268325

Specialist fine food shop (75% organic). All meat, dairy and fruit and vegetables are organic.

The Health Ministry

4 The Fountain, High St, **Christchurch**, BH23 1AE
T: 01202 471152 F: 01425 672075

Healthfood shop selling a range of organic foods (60% organic), including wholefoods, snacks and groceries.

GLOUCESTERSHIRE

Cheltenham Nutrition Centre

133 Bath Rd, **Cheltenham**, GL52 7TL
T: 01242 514150
Also at:
Cheltenham Nutrition Centre 28 Winchcombe St, **Cheltenham**, GL52 2LX
T: 01242 529934
Tewkesbury Nutrition Centre, 98 High St, **Tewkesbury**, GL20 5TZ
T: 01684 299620

Healthfood shops, (40% organic) selling bread, dairy, frozen foods, groceries and wholefoods.

Health-Wise

27 North Walk, **Yate**, BS27 4AP
T: 01454 322 168

Vegetarian shop (75% organic) selling wholefoods, groceries, dairy alternatives and vegetables.

La Bodega

Taurus Crafts, The Old Park, Lydney Park Estate, **Lydney**, GL15 6BU
T: 01594 844841 F: 01594 845636

One hundred per cent organic shop within a craft centre selling locally produced organic foods including meat, fruit, vegetables and herbs, plus groceries, deli and wines and beers.

Mother Nature

2 Bedford St, **Stroud**, GL5 1AY
T: 01453 758202 F: 01453 752595
e-mail: watertacks@cwcom.net

Wholefood shop and delicatessen (90% organic). Sells meat, dairy, wines and beers, herbs, wholefoods and groceries.

The Natural Grocery Store

142 Bath Rd, **Cheltenham**, GL53 7NG (SA)
T: 01242 243737 F: 01242 238872
e-mail: triple8.trading@virgin.net

Sells wide range (85% organic) of foods including meat, fish, fruit and vegetables, bread, wholefoods, groceries and wines, beer and cider.

The Organic Shop

The Square, **Stow-on-the-Wold**, GL54 1AB
T: 01451 831004

Pioneering organic shop (80% organic). Complete range of organic foods including meat, fresh produce and wines. Also makes its own soups, prepared meals, pasties, quiches, pies, cakes and flapjacks using organic ingredients – all available from the takeaway counter.

Out of this World

6–8 Pittville St, **Cheltenham**, GL52 2LJ
T: 01242 518300
e-mail: info@ootw.co.uk
website: www.ootw.co.uk

Shop, café and craft gallery operated by ethical, organic consumer co-operative with over 18,000 members. Sells over 4,000 organic products, many fair-traded, including 100% organic fruit and vegetables and meat. Also has deli counter and sells natural healthcare, eco-friendly household and garden products and fair-trade crafts. Mail order catalogue. Open Mon–Sat, 9am–6pm.
Also at:
Beeston (Notts); **Gosforth** (Tyne and Wear) (Shops)
Head office: 106 High Street, **Gosforth**, NE3 1HB
T: 0191 2135377

Pumpkin Organic
Jardinerie Garden Centre, Bath Rd, **Haresfield**, nr Stonehouse, GL10 3DP (SA)
T: 01452 725775 F: 01452 722445
e-mail: pumpkinorganic@talk21.com

Winner of best new shop Organic Food Awards 2000, this is a shop to be seen! Built with recycled wood, this friendly stylish one-stop shop sells over 2,000 lines of organic food, including excellent range and display of organic produce, groceries, dairy, wines etc. Large community notice board, local foods and local delivery service.

Sunshine Health Shop
25 Church St, **Stroud**, GL5 1JL (SA)
T: 01453 763923

Vegetarian shop, (75% organic) selling bread and cakes baked daily in own Sunshine Organic Bakery, **Stroud** (Specialist Providers) . Also sells fruit and vegetables, wholefoods, groceries, dairy and dairy-free foods, plus extra comprehensive range of bottled juices. Also at **Evesham** (Worcs) (q.v.).

Thornbury Organic Co-op
9 Crossways Rd, **Thornbury**, GL35 2YL
T: 01454 415345

Not a shop but a novel informal organic food co-op established for over twenty years and serving local community. Please phone for more details.

Wyedean Wholefoods
4 Forest Vale Rd, Cinderford, GL14 2PH
T: (head office): 01594 826639

Small chain of one-stop wholefood shops. Several branches in Gloucestershire, Herefordshire and Monmouthshire, including **Gloucester**, **Cinderford**, **Coleford**, **Lydney**, **Newent**, **Ross-on-Wye** and **Monmouth**. Sells over 700 organic products in all branches. Organic products include fruit and vegetables, wholefoods, dairy and groceries with meat in Cinderford and Lydney stores. Phone office for details of local outlet.

SOMERSET

Ceres Natural and Organic Foods
9–11 Princes St, **Yeovil**, BA20 1EN (SA)
T: 01935 428791 F: 01935 426862

Well-established, popular shop (35% organic). Expanding range of organic foods includes groceries, wholefoods, wines and beers, bread, dairy, eggs and Hambleden Herbs herbs and spices. Pick-up point for Longmeadow Organics, **Godmanstone** (Dorset) vegetable box scheme. Planning to introduce online shopping. See also Ceres Bakery (Specialist Providers) at 40 Princes St.

Frome Wholefoods
8 Cheap St, **Frome**, BA11 1BN
T: 01373 473334

Popular store (50% organic) selling bread, wholefoods and groceries, including 100% organic dairy, fruit and vegetables and wines, beers and spirits.

The Good Earth
4 Priory Rd, **Wells**, BA5 1SY
T: 01749 678600

Wholefood shop (50% organic). Range includes wholefoods, groceries and locally produced dairy.

Harvest Natural Foods
37 Walcot St, **Bath**, BA1 5BN (OF&G)
T: 01225 465519 F: 01225 401143

Shop selling 100% organic fruit and vegetables and bread plus 75% organic groceries, dairy, beers, wines and spirits and wholefoods.

High Street Organics
57 High St, **Bruton**, BA10 0AA (SA)
T: 01749 813191

One-stop, 100 percent organic shop with buy-local-first policy. Stocks full range of organic foods, including fruit and vegetables, dairy, frozen children's meat products, soft drinks and eco-friendly non-food products.

Trading Post
The Old Filling Station, Lopenhead, **South Petherton**, TA13 5JH
T/F: 01460 241666

Four-and-half-acre market garden, plant nursery and shop selling full range of organic foods (80%), including local organic fresh produce, breads and meat, plus wholefoods, groceries and dairy. All their own produce, including herbaceous plants, is grown organically though not certified. Operates local box scheme, pick up from the shop, plus delivery within 20-mile radius. New café open 2002.

WILTSHIRE

Malmesbury Wholefoods
29 Abbey Row, **Malmesbury**, SN16 0AG
T: 01666 823030 F: 01666 823475

Sells local vegetables, fruit, eggs, dairy, wholefoods, bread, Shipton Mill flour (see Shipton Mill, **Long Newnton** (Gloucs) (Specialist Providers)) and juices (50% organic). Will order in anything in any quantity.

Swindon Pulse Wholefoods
27 Curtis St, **Swindon**, SN1 5JU
T: 01793 692016

Vegetarian and vegan shop (60% organic). Organic products include bread, local vegetables, wines and beers, food for special diets, herbs and spices, eco-friendly health and bodycare and cleaning products. Discounts for bulk orders. Pick-up point for Purton House (**Swindon**) box scheme.

England South West – Farm Shops

BRISTOL

Windmill Hill City Farm Shop
Philip St, **Bedminster**, BS3 4EA
T: 0117 9633233 F: 0117 9633252
e-mail: info@windmillhillcityfarm.org.uk
website: www.winmillhillcityfarm.org.uk

Farm shop (50% organic) selling organic and locally produced foods, including wholefoods and fruit and vegetables and free-range beef, pork and lamb raised on the farm using organic principles. On-site café (not organic), open Tues–Sun, uses their own meat and vegetables from City Farm allotments.

CORNWALL

Higher Redwood Farm
Cornish Organics, Golberdon Rd, **Pensilva**, nr Liskeard, PL14 5RL
T/F: 01579 363275

New farm shop (90% organic) open every day, selling their own poultry and Black Rock speckled organic eggs, local organically reared beef, organic vegetables, groceries, dairy, chilled products, plus weekend chicken/vegetable boxes. Their organic poultry (layers and table birds) are raised in small flocks, kept in mobile houses and are totally free-ranging, with land rested for 12 months between flocks. Table birds are slow growing breeds, killed at 80 days minimum. Poultry and eggs are available at Riverford Farm shop, **Staverton** (Devon) and throughout **Devon** and **Cornwall**. Organic turkeys are available at Christmas.

Stoneybridge Organics
Tywardreath, **Par**, PL24 2TY
T: 01726 813858

Sell home-grown, organically produced fruit and vegetables, herbs and organic meats. Non-certified.

DEVON

Great Cummins Farm
Tedburn St Mary, nr Exeter, EX6 6BJ (SA)
T: 01647 61278

One hundred per cent organic farm shop selling home-produced organic lamb, fruit and vegetables and eggs and organic poultry and sausages.

Highfield Harvest Organic Farm Shop
Highfield Farm, Clyst Rd, **Topsham**, EX3 0BY (SA)
T/F: 01392 876388
website: www.highfieldharvest.freeserve.co.uk

Delightful award-winning 100% organic farm shop. Sells extensive variety of excellent freshly picked home-grown vegetables and soft fruit in season, plus own pork and eggs. Full range of other organic foods and drink, including 40 organic wines. Pretty courtyard, farm trail and camp and caravan site. Home delivery to **Exeter** and **Topsham**. Closed Mon. See also SA Farm listing, England South West.

Marshford Organic Produce
Churchill Way, **Northam**, nr Bideford, EX39 1NS (SA)
T: 01237 477160 F: 01237 477148
e-mail: enquiries@marshford.co.uk
website: www.marshford.co.uk

Wonderful, well-stocked organic farm shop attached to the nursery with a buy-local-first policy. Home-grown produce picked daily. Local organic beef, lamb, chicken, eggs, bread, cheese and mushrooms, a full range of groceries, plus wines and beers. Produce also available from sister shop (Marshford Organic Produce, **Barnstable** (Shops).

Riverford Farm Shop
Staverton, Totnes, TQ9 6AF (OF&G)
T: 01803 762523 F: 01803 762571
e-mail: rrfshop@netscapeonline.co.uk

Devon's best-known, award-winning farm shop, (75% organic). Large and spacious with own bakery and butchery counter, ample parking and friendly staff. Sell Riverford Farm, **Buckfastleigh** (Devon) (Box Schemes) organic vegetables, milk and cream, their own pork and bacon (not organic), award-winning beef and lamb from Churchtown Farm, **Lanteglos by Fowey** (Cnwll) (Farm Gate), eggs and chickens from Higher Redwood Farm, **Pensilva** (Cnwll) (Farm Shops), plus extensive range of wholefoods, groceries, chilled foods, wines and beers. Nationwide mail order delivery of meat on request.

Riverford at Kitley
Yealhampton, nr Plymouth, PL8 2LT (OF&G)
T: 01752 880925
e-mail: rffshop@netscapeonline.co.uk

Daughter shop of Riverford Farm Shop, **Staverton**, selling organic and locally grown produce (75% organic), including vegetables, meat, wholefoods and dairy. Café sells food made with organic produce, and garden centre offers organic seeds, composts and worm bins.

DORSET

Becklands Farm

Whitchurch Canonicorum, Bridport, DT6 6RG (SA)
T: 01297 560298
e-mail: becklands.farm@wdi.co.uk

One hundred per cent organic farm shop. Sells home-produced beef, pork, eggs, homemade jams. Bed and organic breakfast available in a charming thatched cottage.

Owls Barn Organic Farm Shop

Derritt Lane, Sopley, **Christchurch**, BH23 7AZ (SA)
T/F: 01425 672239
e-mail: mailto:shop@owlsbarn.com
website: www.owlsbarn.com

Attractive, spacious and friendly organic farm in the heart of the New Forest. Sells home-produced beef, Poll Dorset lamb, pork and sausages, local free-range chicken, local organic vegetables, cheeses and groceries, plus seasonal genuine wild New Forest venison and homemade venison products. Excellent cheese counter too..

Pampered Pigs Pantry

2 The Green, **Tolpuddle**, DT2 7EX (SA)
T/F: 01305 848107
T: (mobile): 0976 277185
e-mail: k.a.crocker@farmersweekly.net
website: www.organic-pork.co.uk

New organic farm shop in picturesque village. Sells home-produced saddleback pork and beef, locally reared lamb, local free-range chickens, vegetables and a full range of organic groceries. Friendly website with online ordering. Meat also sold at local farmers' markets. Free local delivery.

Sturts Farm

Three Cross Roads, West Moors, **Ferndown**, BH22 0NF (Demeter)
T: 01202 870572 01202 894292 (shop)

Camphill Community organic market garden and 100% organic farm shop, open Mon–Sat 9.30am–12.30pm. Sell home-grown biodynamic fruit and vegetables and organic wholefoods and groceries. Fruit and vegetable box scheme, 80% home-grown, delivered to local area. Pick-up points include Scoltocks Health Foods, **Ringwood** (Shops).
See also:
Gold Hill Organic Farm, **Child Okeford**; Longmeadow Organic Vegetables, **Godmanstone** (Box Schemes)

GLOUCESTERSHIRE

Kolisko Farm Shop

Wynstones Drive, **Brookthorpe**, GL4 0UN (Demeter)
T: 01452 812322

One hundred per cent organic shop selling home-produced biodynamic beef, lamb, eggs, vegetables and dairy. Also wide range of groceries and wholefoods.

The Organic Shop

Abbey Home Farm, Burford Rd, **Cirencester**, GL7 5HF (SA)
T: 01285 640441 F: 01285 644827
e-mail: cargofco@aol.com

One of the best organic farm shops (winner Organic Food Awards 2000). Bright, cheerful, with its own organic café serving excellent homemade soups, simple meals, cakes, etc. Dew-fresh home-grown vegetables, herbs and flowers, own lamb, eggs and milk, local breads and full range of organic groceries, etc. Farm trail and children's play area.

See also:
Ruskin Mill, **Nailsworth** (Specialist Providers)

SOMERSET

Alvis Bros Ltd Farm Shop

Lye Cross Farm, **Redhill**, BS40 5RH (SA)
T: 01934 862320 F: 01934 862213

Producer of the well-known Lyecross range of organic cheeses, available direct from farm shop. Also stock organic dairy and home reared (non-organic) beef and pork.

Bath Organic Farms

6 Brookside House, High Street, **Weston**, BA1 4BY (SA)
T: 01225 421507
e-mail: robinsonp@btconnect.com
website: www.bathorganicfarms.co.uk

New organic farm shop on outskirts of Bath. Dedicated to quality, value for money, seasonality, local foods and serving local community. Owned by broadcaster, organic farmer and president of Soil Association, Jonathan Dimbleby, and his partner and fellow organic farmer, Paul Robinson. Sells organic Hereford beef, lamb, pork, chicken and eggs from their nearby farms plus homemade sausages and burgers, ham and bacon and dairy. Meat is well hung in the traditional manner. Seasonal specialities include turkeys and game and locally grown vegetables from Duchy Home Farm, **Tetbury** (Glous) (Box Schemes). Clear, easy-to-use website with online shop offering variety of meat hampers.

Gilcombe Farm Shop

Gilcombe Farm, **Bruton**, BA10 0QE (SA)
T: 01749 81 825

Farm shop and butchery (25% organic) selling full range of local organic meats, their own unpasteurised organic milk, plus dairy, jams and pickles. Part of Somerset Organics (see p. **365**).

The Green Grocer

The Old Dairy, Poolbridge Rd, **Blackford**, Wedmore, BS28 4PA (SA)
T: 01934 713453
e-mail: greengrocer@madasafish.com

Small farm shop selling home-produced organic fruit and vegetables and eggs.

Norwood Farm

Bath Rd, **Norton St Philip**, BA3 6LP (SA)
T: 01373 834356 F: 01373 834884

Farm butcher's shop selling home-produced organic lamb, chicken, beef, pork and sausages (some rare breeds). Farm is a rare breeds conservation centre.

WILTSHIRE

Purely Organic Deverill Trout Farm

Longbridge Deverill, Warminster, BA12 7DZ (SA)
T: 01985 841093

On hundred per cent organic farm shop. Sell own organic spring-water, reared rainbow trout, trout products including fishcakes and smoked trout pâté and other homemade organic specialities that are also sold at local farmers' markets. Also sells wholefoods, groceries, dairy, meat, fish, fruit and vegetables, seeds and John Hurst's watercress (their trout farm is on his land). Nationwide delivery, free over £70.
See also:
Coleshill Organics, **Swindon** (Box Schemes)

England South West – Specialist Providers

CORNWALL

Cornish Fish Direct

The Pilchard Works, **Tolcarne**, Newlyn, TR18 5QH
T: 01736 332112 F: 01736 332442
e-mail: dee@cornishfish.com
website: www.cornishfish.com

Last family business to salt pilchards in traditional way. Also supply fabulous, freshly-caught fish landed at Newlyn. Fish prepared to customer requirements and packed in chilled, polystyrene boxes with information and recipe leaflet. Orders, accepted up to Tues 4pm, dispatched by overnight courier Thurs. Alternatively buy direct and visit award-winning pilchard museum and factory. For further information visit website or phone Mon–Fri, 8.30am–5.30pm.

DEVON

The Market Fish Shop

Victoria Road, **Dartmouth**, TQ6 9SE
T/F: 01803 832782

Shop run by Jenny Mackesy who also supplies local restaurants. Specialises in local caught seafood, including dived scallop, crab, lobster and John Dory in season. Also sells homemade fishcakes and fish pies. Customised mail-order service at shop prices with carriage fee of around £10. Fish prepared to customer requirements – gutted, filleted, etc. – vacuum packed in chilled polystyrene boxes for next-day delivery. Shop that I use; both fish and service splendid.

Otterton Mill Centre

Otterton, nr Budleigh Salterton, EX9 7HG
T/F: 01395 568521
e-mail: ottertonmill@ukonline.co.uk
website: www.ottertonmill.co.uk

Restored mill, powered by water, traditional bakery, restaurant, craft centre and workshop, and popular tourist attraction. Sells own stoneground wholemeal organic flour and a variety of home-baked breads and cakes made with organic flours. Their licensed Duckery restaurant uses vegetables, soft fruit and herbs grown using organic methods from their own garden, and offers organic lemonade and ginger beer. Menu includes light snacks, lunchtime and evening meals, cakes and cream teas. Open all year, they also hold regular exhibitions and events.

Rye Farm

Loxhore, Barnstaple, EX31 4ST (SA)
T: 01271 850642

Organic trout farm. Produce sold at Brian Ford's Discount Store and Marshford Organic Produce, **Barnstaple** (Shops)

Tamar Organics

The Organic Garden Centre, Tavistock Woodlands, Gulworthy, **Tavistock**, PL19 8JE (SA)
T: 01822 834887 F: 01822 834284
e-mail: tamarorganics@aol.com
website: www.tamarorganics.co.uk

Small organic growers and vegetable/herb/wildflower seed and garden supplies company specialising in mail order. Their new garden centre sells everything for the organic gardener, including plants, plus organic fruit and vegetables and groceries. Or visit their stall at Tavistock Friday Market, where they sell organic fruit and vegetables, groceries and gardening products

in season. Online ordering and clear, easy to use website.
See also:
Middle Campscott Farm (cheese), **Lee** (Farm Gate)

GLOUCESTERSHIRE

The Authentic Bread Company

Strawberry Hill Farm, Strawberry Hill, **Newent**, GL18 1LH (SA)
T: 01531 828181 F: 01531 828151
website: www.authenticbread.co.uk

Award-winning traditional bakers baking staple and specialist organic breads, pasties, cakes, *pain au chocolat* etc. Available locally and by mail order.

Global Organic Markets

Unit 5, Canal Ironworks, Hope Mill Lane, **Brimscombe**, Stroud, GL5 2SH (Demeter)
T: 01453 884123

Amazing award-winning market stall at Stroud Market on Fridays. Also at Spitalfields Organic Market, London **E1**, on Sundays. Sells huge range of organic fruit and vegetables, eggs, fresh herbs, plus biodynamic produce where possible, including that from local growers. Best specialist shop, Organic Food Awards 2001. .

Hobbs House Bakery

39 High St, **Chipping Sodbury**, BS37 6BA (SA)
T: 01454 321629 F: 01454 329757
Retail shop at: Hobbs House Bakery, 2 North Parade, **Yate**, BS37 5AH (SA)
T: 01454 320890

Traditional, high-quality family bakers making a name for excellent breads, including organic white and wholewheat loaves and rolls. Winner Organic Food Awards 2001 with their wild rye bread. Products widely available in shops in **Bath**, **Bristol** and **South Gloucestershire** and through S. & J. Organic Growers, **Castle Combe** (Wilts) (Box Schemes).

Ruskin Mill

Old Bristol Rd, **Nailsworth**, GL6 0LA (Demeter)
T (office): 01453 837500
T (café): 01453 837514
T (shop): 01453 837510 F: 01453 837512

Remarkable college for young adults with special needs, based on the teachings of Rudolf Steiner and John Ruskin. Specialises in land and craft skills with its own biodynamic market garden and farm, café and shop open to the public. The vegetarian café serves snacks and lunches made with produce from the farms. Their 100% organic and biodynamic shop, Living Earth Produce Vegetable Shop, sells home-grown produce, organic milk and bread together with crafts by local craftsmen and students. Developing own organic trout farm. Arts and crafts exhibitions held regularly.

Severn and Wye Smokery

Chaxhill, Westbury-on-Severn, GL14 1QW (OF&G)
T: 01452 760190 F: 01452 760193

Traditional smoke-house run by family involved in fishing for 40 years with line-caught sea bass boat. Sells full range of smoked products. Supplies local fresh and smoked wild salmon as well as fresh and smoked Glenarm organic salmon and organic trout. Their salmon is supplied to customer requirements – whole, steaks, filleted, etc. Best value for fresh salmon is to buy a whole fish and ask them to prepare and vacuum pack it.

Shipton Mill Ltd
Long Newnton, Tetbury, GL8 8RP (SA)
T: 01666 505050 F: 01666 504666
e-mail: jlister@shipton-mill.com
website: www.shipton-mill.com

Inspirational enterprise producing wide range of stoneground organic flours in their water-powered mill. Available mail order, from the mill door and from Malmesbury Wholefoods, **Malmesbury** (Wilts) (Shops). Visitors always welcome.

Sunshine Organic Bakery
The British School, Slad Rd, **Stroud**, GL5 1QW (SA)
T: 01453 752952

More than 30 certified organic lines baked daily. On sale at own shops – Sunshine Health Shop, **Stroud** and **Evesham** (Worcs) (Shops)) and other local retailers.

Colin Tyler (Amberley Vale Foods)
Down Barn, **Tetbury**, GL8 8SH (SA)
T: 01285 841480

Not a shop but a highly praised local butcher/home delivery enterprise (80% organic). Sells beef, lamb, pork and poultry, homemade sausages, burgers and pies. Delivery service within 25-mile radius.

SOMERSET

Avalon Vineyard
The Grove, East Pennard, **Shepton Mallet**, BA4 6UA (SA)
T: 01749 860393
e-mail: pennardorganicwines@mail.com
website: www.pennardorganicwines.co.uk

An organic vineyard and fruit farm, producing traditional cider and fruit wines, mead and English white wine made from their own fruit. Available by the case nationwide by mail order and through the farm shop. See p. **261**.

Ceres Bakery
40 Princes St, **Yeovil**, BA20 1EQ (OFF)
T: 01935 424558 F: 01935 411558

Traditional bakery producing about 25 organic breads, buns, cakes, savouries and Christmas pudding. Breads include crusty white sourdough widely available in the South West (30% organic). See also Ceres Natural and Organic Foods (Shops) at 9–11 Princes St.

B. H. Stacey
The Butchery, West St, **Somerton**, TA11 7PR (SA)
T: 01458 272285

Family-run local butcher (30% organic). Sells organic beef, pork and lamb and free-range chicken. Buy all stock locally, and slaughter in own abattoir.
See also:
Radford Mill Farm, **Timsbury** (cheese and yoghurt) (Box Schemes)

WILTSHIRE

Rushall Mill
Devizes Rd, **Rushall**, Pewsey, SN9 6ET (SA)
T: 01980 630335 F: 01980 630095
e-mail: info@rushallorganics.co.uk
website: www.rushallorganics.co.uk

Remarkable millers, milling exclusively home-grown organic grain. Bulk sales of stoneground organic wholewheat flour available at farm shop that also sells own meat, homemade breads and baked goods as well as local produce.

N. R. Stoate & Sons

Cann Mills, **Shaftesbury**, SP7 0BL (SA)
T: 01747 852475 F: 01747 851936
e-mail: michaelstoate@lineone.net

Water-powered mill grinds stoneground organic flours (six varieties of wheatflour plus ryeflour and maltstar), supplied in minimum quantity of 8 kilos. Pick up from the mill or from retailers in South-West.
See also:
Purely Organic, Deverill Trout Farm, **Longbridge Deverill** (Farm Shops)

England South West – Places to Eat and Stay

BRISTOL

Café Maitreya

89 St Marks Rd, **Easton**, BS5 6HY
T: 0117 951 0100

New well-being vegetarian eatery specialising in simple, delicious vegetarian, vegan and special diet foods, using mainly organic ingredients. Open-plan kitchen, organic juice bar, BYO and licensed, light, bright and cheerful.

Quartier Vert

85 White Ladies Rd, **Bristol**, BS8 2NT
T: 0117 973 4482 F: 0117 974 39193
e-mail: quartiervert@netscapeonline.co.uk

One of the best well-known restaurants with great food and atmosphere; serves lunch and evening meals. Uses mainly organic and local ingredients, including meat and organic or line-caught fish. Wine list includes many organic wines. Their new cookery school runs courses and workshops for children and adults.

The Severnshed

The Grove, **Bristol**, BS1 4RB
T: 0117 925 1212
e-mail: info@severnshed.co.uk
website: www.severnshed.co.uk

New restaurant (90% organic) using only organic meat, organic fruit and vegetables, organic and line-caught fish. Innovative café and restaurant menus. Café serves light meals all day, the restaurant menu offers three-course meals, lunch and evening. Extensive wine list (30% organic).
See also:
Windmill Hill City Farm, **Bedminster** (Farm Shops)

CORNWALL

Heskyn Mill

Tideford, Saltash, PL12 5BG
T: 01752 851481

Restaurant in restored mill offering meals prepared with organic and locally grown produce where available. Between 5 and 40% of the ingredients used are organic, depending on seasonality and availability.

Jopes Park

Luckett, Callington, PL17 8LG
T: 01579 370770 F: 01579 370807
e-mail: natpartner@aol.com
website: www.jopespark.co.uk

Bed and breakfast in peaceful 300-year-old cottage offering organic breakfast using local produce.

Lansallos Barton Farm

Lansallos, Looe, PL13 2PU (SA)
T: 01503 272293
e-mail: russell@churchtownfarm.com

Organic farmhouse cream teas, open April to September. Home-produced organic beef and lamb. Please phone out of season.

Making Waves
Vegan Guest House, 3 Richmond Place, **St Ives**, TR26 1JN
T: 01736 793895

Peaceful guest house serving breakfast and evening meals (80% organic).
See also:
Churchdown Farm, **Lanteglos** (Farm Gate)
The Old Rectory, **Mawgan**; Penellick, **Pelynt** (B & B List)

DEVON

Twitchen Farm
Challacombe, Barnstaple, EX31 4TT
T: 01598 763568
e-mail: holidays@twitchen.co.uk
website: www.twitchen.co.uk

Charming bed and breakfast, with optional evening meals. Simple, imaginative seasonal menu, with local and organic produce used extensively.

Wigham Farm Ltd
Wigham, **Morchard Bishop**, EX17 6RJ (SA)
T: 01363 877350
e-mail: info@wigham.co.uk
website: www.wigham.co.uk

Thirty-acre organic farm and picturesque thatched organic guest-house (one of *Which*'s top 3 farmhouses) serving organic food, much of which is home-produced, including their own lamb, pork, poultry, bacon, sausages and eggs. Limited amounts of frozen meat available for guests to buy.

Willow Vegetarian Garden Restaurant
57 High St, **Totnes**, TQ9 5PB
T: 01803 862 605
e-mail: kimndani@aol.com

Vegetarian restaurant serving food prepared with local, organic ingredients where possible. Organic wines and beers available.
See also:
Chops Away, **Totnes**; The Courtyard Café, **Chagford** (Shops)
Easdon Cottage, **Manaton**; Faye Down, **Upton**; Manor Mill House, **Bampton**; Mount Tavy Cottage, **Tavistock**; Woodhayne Barton, **Culumstock**; The Yeoman's Country House, **Collaton** (B & B List)

DORSET

The Bottle Inn
Marshwood, DT6 5OJ
T: 01297 678254

Friendly, informal pub, with a varied menu, serving good-value, homemade fare, featuring primarily organic, vegetarian and vegan dishes, plus organic wines, ales and lagers. Featured in CAMRA guide.

Terra Firma
Mustons Lane, **Shaftesbury**, SP7 8AD
T/F: 01747 858883

Modern, simple and stylish local restaurant serving unfussy and delicious food, using mainly (85+%) organic ingredients, sourced from local suppliers whenever possible, including their organic breads. Menu takes its inspiration from around the world. Ample portions, reasonable prices and friendly staff, who are happy to tell you exactly which ingredients are organic on the menu. Restaurant also provides focus for local community and organises musical events, yoga classes etc.
See also:
Becklands Farm, **Whitchurch Canonicorum** (Farm Shops)
Heritage Prime Earnestly British Meats,

Bridport; West Hembury Farm, **Askerswell** (Farm Gate)
The Old Forge, **Compton Abbas**, (B & B List)

GLOUCESTERSHIRE

Gilberts
Gilberts Lane, Brookthorpe, **Gloucester**, GL4 0UH
T: 01452 812364
e-mail: jenny@gilbertsbb.demon.co.uk

Bed and breakfast on organic smallholding. Most of the ingredients in the breakfast served are home-grown or organic.

Mad Hatters Restaurant
3 Cossack Square, **Nailsworth**, GL6 0DB
T: 01453 832615

Remarkable value, organically minded restaurant using almost totally organic ingredients, sourced locally where possible. Short modern menu, all freshly prepared. Open Tues–Sat for lunch and dinner. Pre-booked, fixed-price Sunday lunch. Bed and breakfast is recommended in Alastair Sawday's *Special Places to Stay*.

Woodruffs Organic Café
24 High Street, **Stroud**, GL5 1AJ (SA)
T: 01453 750898

The UK's first totally organic – and very good value – vegetarian/vegan café. Open all day Mon–Sat, 9am–5pm. Only organic ingredients are used, right down to the salt and pepper. Breakfast, inventive set menu, plus soup of the day (usually vegan), two daily specials, desserts, etc. All food is freshly prepared using local organic ingredients where possible. Special diets catered for. Upstairs tea-room, family room, cake-making service and outside catering.

See also:
Out of This World, **Cheltenham** (Shops)
The Organic Shop, **Cirencester** (Farm Shops)
Ruskin Mill, **Nailsworth** (Specialist Providers)
Crooked End Farm, **Ruardean** (Farm Gate)
Grove Farm, **Newnham** (B & B List)

SOMERSET

Higher Riscombe Farm
Exford, nr Minehead, TA24 7JY (SA)
T: 01643 831184
e-mail: rona@higherriscombefarm,co.uk
website: www.higherriscombefarm.co.uk

Bed and breakfast on organic farm, serving organic breakfast made with home-produced organic eggs. Guests free to explore the farm.
See also:
Trading Post, **South Petherton** (café) (Shops)
Lower Farm, **Shepton Montague**; Parsonage Farm, **Over Stowey** (B & B List)

WILTSHIRE

See:
Bullocks Horn Cottage, **Charlton**; Ebblesway Courtyard, **Salisbury** (B & B List)

England South West – Farm Gate

BRISTOL

Jekka's Herb Farm
Rose Cottage, Shellards Lane, **Alveston**, BS35 3SY (SA)
T: 01454 418878 F: 01454 411988
e-mail: farm@jekkasherbfarm.com
website: www.jekkasherbfarm.com

UK's best-known organic herb grower/mail order specialist, best-selling author and Chelsea Flower Show gold medallist (1995–2001), Jekka McVicar grows over 400 different organic herbs. Extensive mail order catalogue for plants includes native wild flowers and seeds. Excellent website includes the shows she attends where you can buy her plants. Orders can be collected from the nursery by prior arrangement.

CORNWALL

Churchtown Farm

Lanteglos by Fowey, PL23 1NH (SA)
T: 01726 870375
e-mail: russell@churchtownfarm.com

Model organic National Trust farm, winners of best beef and lamb at Organic Food Awards 2000. Home-produced beef and lamb, locally produced chicken and free-range pork available from the farm. Phone to order. Farmhouse holiday self-catering flat. Meat available nationwide by mail order via Riverford Farm Shop, **Buckfastleigh** (Devon).

South Torfrey Farm

Golant, Fowey, PL23 1LA (SA)
T: 01726 833126 F: 01726 832625
e-mail: southtorfreyfarm@macace.co.uk

Organic chicken producer raising very small flocks (about 100 birds) in mobile houses, completely free-ranging, killed at 81 days in a local SA-registered abattoir, resulting in delicious chicken with a yellow skin and firm texture. Supplies selected retailers in Cornwall and South-West including Carley's and West Country Organics, and River Café and other top London restaurants and butchers. Available direct from the farm. Please phone first.

DEVON

Dittisham Farm

Capton, Dartmouth, TQ6 0JE (SA)
T/F: 01803 712452

PYO organic blackcurrants, gooseberries and herbs, and farm-gate sales of home-produced organic eggs and Berkshire pork, plus their own honey. Phone first.

Heron Valley Juices and Ciders

Crannacombe Farm, Hazelwood, **Loddiswell**, nr Kingsbridge, TQ7 4DX (SA)
T/F: 01548 550256

Farm-gate sales of a variety of organic apple juices and sparkling cider. For full entry, see p. **271**.

Higher Hacknell Farm

Burrington, Umberleigh, EX37 9LX (SA)
T: 01769 560292 F: 01769 560909
e-mail: budden@hacknell.fsbusiness.co.uk
website: www.higherhacknell.co.uk

Inspirational small-is-beautiful organic farm. Farm-gate sales of award-winning organic beef, lamb, chicken, pork and Christmas turkeys. Also nationwide by mail order. Phone for order form for cuts and selection boxes. See also SA Farm listing, England South West.

Lackworthy Farm

Petrockstowe, Okehampton, EX20 3HQ (SA)
T: 01837 810691

Organic chickens (slow-growing breeds), Christmas turkeys and geese. Available at farm gate by arrangement and at farmers' markets and by mail order.

Middle Campscott Farm
Lee, Ilfracombe, EX34 8LS (SA)
T/F: 01271 864621
e-mail: mcampscott@aol.com

Lovely cheese-maker producing award-winning Campscott organic hard-pressed sheep's-milk cheeses, plain and flavoured with cumin, plus their speciality cheese (hard in summer, soft in winter). They also supply organically produced wool and blankets. Their cheeses are available at local **Bideford** and **Barnstaple** pannier markets, from farm gate and by mail order.

Providence Farm
Crosspark Cross, **Holsworthy**, EX22 6JW (SA)
T: 01409 254421
e-mail: info@providencefarm.co.uk
website: www.providencefarm.co.uk

Farm-gate and mail-order sales of superb award-winning home-produced organic lamb, chicken, duck, seasonal fowl (including geese), bacon, sausages and eggs. Meat also available at Raven's Oak Dairy, **Burland** (Ches) (Farm Shops).

Robert Owen Foundation
Lower Sharpham, Barton Farm, **Ashprington**, Totnes, TQ9 7DX (SA)
T: 01803 732502

Organic unpasteurised (green-top) milk, free-range eggs, lamb and beef. Delivery around **Totnes**, or available from farm gate. Foundation provides training on farm for adults with learning difficulties.

Wixon Farm
Chulmleigh, EX18 7DS (SA)
T: 01769 580438

Farm-gate sales of organic chickens and Aberdeen Angus beef. Both also available at farmers' markets in **Devon** and **Dorset**.

DORSET
Enford Farm, Durweston, **Blandford Forum**, DT11 0QW (SA)
T/F: 01258 455117

Newly registered organic farmers supplying fresh organic lamb and organically raised beef (French breed, Saler). Sold at farm gate and local farmers' markets.

Heritage Prime Earnestly British Meats of Rare Quality
Shedbush Farm, Muddy Ford Lane, Stanton St Gabriel, **Bridport**, Dorset, DT6 6DR (Demeter)
T: 01297 489304 F: 01297 489531

Remarkable biodynamic farm producing exceptional meat, available by mail order. Sells own knitwear and blankets. Offer bed and breakfast by arrangement. For full entry see p. **184**.

Manor Farm
Godmanstone, Dorchester, DT2 7AH (SA)
T: 01300 341415 F: 01300 341170
e-mail: enquiries@manor-farm-organic.co.uk
website: www.manor-farm-organic.co.uk

Farm-gate sales from award-winning farm of their Manor Farm organic milk and cream; home-produced Clun lamb and unpasteurised (green-top) milk, available to order.

Rectory Farm
East Chaldon Rd, **Winfrith Newburgh**, nr Dorchester, DT2 8DJ (SA)
T: 01305 852835

Farm-gate sales of dairy products from their pedigree Jersey herd: organic butter, cream (unpasteurised on request), curd- and cottage-cheeses, and ice cream made with their own organic cream, milk, eggs, organic sugar and natural flavourings. Occasional home-produced beef and pork.

Sea Spring Farm
Lyme View, **West Bexington**, Dorchester, DT2 9DD
T: 01308 897892

No longer certified, but chilli specialists who grow a wide range of fabulous, organically-grown chillies from sweet and mild to ferociously hot. Available from August to November by mail order (Peppers By Post) or from farm gate by arrangement. (Orders can be picked up twice a week.)

West Hembury Farm
Askerswell, Dorchester, DT2 9EW (SA)
T: 01308 485289 F: 01308 485014
e-mail: hunt@westhembury.com
website: www.westhembury.com
website: www.whitepark.org.uk

Farm-gate sales of home-produced White Park beef (Britain's oldest breed) either in mixed 10 kg boxes or by cut when available, plus Southdown lamb (mutton to order) and eggs from Light Sussex chickens. Very reasonable price list. Self-catering accommodation on and near farm in converted barns and cottage.
See also:
Tamarisk Farm, **West Bexington** (Box Schemes)

GLOUCESTERSHIRE

Adeys Farm Organic Meats
Adeys Farm, Breadstone, **Berkeley**, GL13 9HF (SA)
T: 01453 511218

Farm-gate sales of home-produced organic lamb, beef and pork, butchered to customer specification.

Crooked End Farm
Ruardean, Forest of Dean, GL17 9XF (SA)
T: 01594 544482

Farm-gate sales of home-produced beef, lamb, pork and eggs and seasonal vegetables. Self-catering holiday cottage available.

Severn Bank Organics
Camaroy Farm, **Broadoak**, Newnham, GL14 1JB (SA)
T: 01594 516367

Farm-gate sales of home-grown vegetables and salad crops.

SOMERSET

The Bell and Bird Table
Runnington, Wellington, TA21 0QW
T: 01823 663080

Growing organically for several years though not certified. Home-grown vegetables (including 47 varieties of tomatoes), soft fruit and free-range Maran eggs and Oxford Sandy and Black pork.

Court Farm
14 Chapel Lane, **Winford**, BS18 8EU (Demeter)
T: 01275 472335

Farm-gate sales of award-winning, delicious home-produced yoghurt, unpasteurised (green-top) milk and double cream from their Jersey herd. Occasionally beef and pork for the freezer.

The Elms Organic Dairy
Friars Oven Farm, **West Compton**, Shepton Mallet, BA4 4PD (OF&G)
T: 01749 890371

Farm-gate sales of home-produced goat cheese, cow milk, yoghurt, butter, cream and cheese, beef, pork and lamb. Also sells soya milk. See p. **159**.

Lyng Court Organic Meat
Lyng Court, **West Lyng**, Taunton, TA3 5AP (SA)
T: 01823 490510

Farm-gate sales of fresh and frozen home-produced lamb and beef.

Olive Farm (Babcary Ltd)
Babcary, Somerton, TA11 7EJ
T: 01458 223229

Guernsey herd, not organic, but raised extensively and with minimal chemical inputs. Wonderful unpasteurised (green-top) milk and cream and own butter and free-range quail eggs. Sells at farm gate and farmers' markets including **Guildford** (Surrey) and **Henley-on-Thames** (Oxon) as well as Islington, **N1** (London Farmers' Markets). Phone for up-to-date list of markets attended.

Orgarden Produce
Border Farm, **Yeovil**, BA22 9SZ (SA)
T: 01935 872483 F: 01935 873736

Award-winning grower. Produces wide range of vegetables, including cherry tomatoes, peppers and aubergines. Available from farm gate. Phone first with order.

Swaddles Green Farm
Hare Lane, **Buckland St Mary**, Chard, TA20 3JR (OF&G)
T: 01460 234387 F: 01460 234591
e-mail: organic@swaddles.co.uk
website: www.swaddles.co.uk

Award-winning nationwide meat home delivery service. Order by fax, email, phone or on their website. Orders can be picked up at farm. See p. **181**.
See also:
Magdalen Farm, **Winsham**; Stone Age Organics, **Cothelstone** (Box Schemes)

WILTSHIRE

Bratch Farmhouse
Wood Lane, **Fonthill Gifford**, SP3 6PX
T: 01747 870048 F: 01747 870059
e-mail: rosking@freenetname.co.uk

Tiny 1-acre holding, not certified organic, but grows fruit and vegetables organically, makes preserves from home-grown fruit and raises Wiltshire Horn lamb, available from farm gate. Breeder of rare and pure breed poultry, waterfowl and geese.

Furze Cottage
Telfont Magna, nr Salisbury, SP3 5QU (SA)
T: 01722 716285

Farm-gate sales of home-grown vegetables, herbs, soft and top fruit, available June to March, with back-up of vegetables and eggs from local organic growers. Phone to order, which is then made up ready for collection.

Kit Farm
South View, **Little Cheverall**, nr Devizes, SN10 4JJ (SA)
T: 01380 818591

Farm-gate sales of beef. Phone for further details.

Lakeside Eggs
Lakeside Stables, **Steeple Langford**, Salisbury, SP3 4NH (SA)
T: 01722 130786

Farm-gate sales of home-produced organic eggs.

Temple Farming

Rockley, Marlborough, SN8 1RU (SA)
T: 01672 514428 F: 01672 514116

An exciting new find. An organic venture dedicated to raising 'veaux de lait élevé sous la mère' to the highest standards. The calves (Simmental x Friesian/Simmental), born mid-Jan–mid-Mar, are reared exclusively on their mothers' milk and wild herbs from mineral-rich downland pastures. From March they range the downs freely and are not slaughtered until 7–8 months old. Their meat, tender and full of flavour, is available in limited quantities only in autumn and is sold only in hampers containing a range of vacuum-packed cuts. Phone to place order.

Willow Farm

Inglesham, Highworth, SN6 7QZ (SA)
T: 01367 252163

Sells home-produced beef and lamb from individual joints to freezer packs. Phone to order.

See also:
Purton House, **Purton** (Box Schemes)

ENGLAND WEST MIDLANDS

England West Midlands – Box Schemes

HEREFORDSHIRE

Abundance Produce

Glenthorpe, **Little Birch**, Hereford, HR2 8BD (Demeter)
T/F: 01981 540181

Biodynamic and organic fruit, vegetable and herb seasonal selection local box scheme delivering year-round within a 5-mile radius of **Hereford**.

Fern Verrow Vegetables

St Margarets, nr Peterchurch , HR2 OQF (Demeter)
T: 01981 510288
e-mail: fernverrow@talk21.com

The local box scheme and home delivery service everyone wants. Grows a mouth-watering selection of biodynamic vegetables, salads and herbs plus their own organic pork, homemade sausages and dry cured bacon and hams (and biodynamic beef from autumn 2001). Customers select from a weekly seasonal list and boxes are made up individually. Delivery service to **Central London**.

Flights Orchard Organics

Flights Orchard, Falcon Lane, **Ledbury**, HR8 2JN (SA)
T/F: 01531 635929

Year-round seasonal organic vegetable box scheme. Ninety per cent home-grown, rest from an adjacent holding. Delivery to **Ledbury** area. Pick-up point at Ledbury Wholefoods, **Ledbury** (Shops).

SHROPSHIRE

Hopesay Glebe Farm

Hopesay, Craven Arms, SY7 8HD (Demeter)
T: 01588 660 737
e-mail: hopesay.organics@barclays.net

Family holding in idyllic setting produces vegetables, eggs and pedigree Lleyn lamb, which are available through their box scheme, at the farm gate and at local shops. Also offers bed and breakfast with organic breakfast.

Organic by Order

Bentley House, **Clungunford**, Craven Arms, SY7 0PN (SA)
T: 01588 660747 F: 01588 660126

Seasonal selection vegetable and fruit box scheme, offering wide customer choice. Deliveries to **Shropshire**, **North Hereford**, **West Staffordshire** and **Powys**. Pick-up point at Broad Bean, **Ludlow** (Shops)
See also:
Pimhill Farm, **Harmer Hill** (Specialist Providers)

STAFFORDSHIRE

Stourton Farm

Stourton, Stourbridge, DY7 5BD (SA)
T: 01384 396384

Delivers organic fruit and vegetables, eggs and beef locally. Phone only, no visits.

WARWICKSHIRE

GAIA (Leamington Spa) Ltd

Worker's Co-operative, 7 Regent Place, off Bath St, **Leamington Spa**, CV31 1EH (SA)
T/F: 01926 338805
e-mail: shop@gaialeam.freeserve.co.uk

Local box scheme and home delivery service (three times a week) supplying fruit and vegetables, wholefoods, dairy, bread from Paul's, **Melton Mowbray** (Leics) (Specialist Providers) and eco-friendly cleaning products. Local deliveries by bicycle. Also deliver to **Coventry** and **Kenilworth**.
See also:
Down to Earth Organic, **Coventry**; Purely Organic Foods, **Leamington Spa**; The Wholefood Shop, **Rugby** (Shops)

WEST MIDLANDS

Hopwood Organic Farm

Bickenhill Lane, **Solihull**, B92 0DE (SA)
T: 0121 711 7787 F: 0121 704 4033
e-mail: info@hopwoodorganic.co.uk
website: www.hopwoodorganic.co.uk

Friendly, local, flexible box scheme and home delivery service supplying home-grown vegetables and some seasonal fruit to **Warwickshire** and **West Midlands**. Standard boxes or customer choice. Their farm shop (open Wed–Sat) sells own produce plus Graig Farm Organics, **Dolau** (Powys) (Farm Shops) meats, groceries, bread and dairy. Phone or email for free brochure.
See also:
Leverton and Halls, **Harborne** (Shops)

WORCESTERSHIRE

Oxton Organics

Broadway Lane, **Fladbury**, nr Evesham, WR10 2QQ (SA)
T: 01386 860477
e-mail: oxtons@hotmail.com

Local seasonal box scheme operating June to end February, with customer choice, supplying mainly home-grown (70–80%) organic vegetables, plus own strawberries, plums and apples. Home delivery and drop-off collection points for some areas from **Worcester** to **Cheltenham**.
See also:
Greenlink Organic Foods, **Malvern** (Shops)

England West Midlands – Shops

HEREFORDSHIRE

Hardwicke Organics

80 The Homend, **Ledbury**, HR8 1BX (SA)
T: 01531 633058

First organic growers with their own high street organic shop. Sells complete range of organic foods, including 32 different seasonal varieties of organic apples from local growers.

Hay Wholefoods and Delicatessen

Lion St, **Hay-on-Wye**, HR3 5AA
T: 01497 820708

Well-stocked shop (60% organic) selling a wide range of organic foods, local where possible, and wines.

Ledbury Wholefoods

82 The Homend, **Ledbury**, HR8 1BX
T: 01531 632889

Sells wide range (40% organic), including

wholefoods and groceries. Pick-up point for Flights Orchard Organics, **Ledbury** (Box Schemes) vegetable boxes.

Nitty Gritty Wholefoods
24 West St, **Leominster**, HR6 8ES
T: 01568 611600

Friendly shop (50% organic) selling wide range of organic foods including local organic bread, flour, eggs, cakes made from organic ingredients; also extensive range of locally grown fruit trees, herbs and perennials.

Oat Cuisine
47 Broad Street, **Ross-on-Wye**, HR9 7DY
T: 01989 566271

Health emporium including a shop, takeaway and café (35% organic) using organic ingredients, and homemade bread.

Organic Options
15a Broad Street, **Leominster**, HR6 8BT (SA)
T: 01568 612154
e-mail: gunson@gn.apc.org

One-stop, 100% organic shop selling a comprehensive range of organic foods, including meat, fish, dairy, bakery and local fruit and vegetables and herbs from Hillside Herb Farm in Leominster.

SHROPSHIRE

Broad Bean
60 Broad St, **Ludlow**, SY8 1NH
T: 01584 874239

Wholefood shop (20–30% organic). Organic range includes meat, wholefoods, and wines. Pick-up point for Organic By Order, **Clungunford** (Box Scheme) vegetable boxes..

Food for Thought
4 The Square, **Much Wenlock**, TF13 6LX (SA)
T: 01952 728038 F: 01952 726575
e-mail: organicfoodcentre@hotmail.com

Dedicated organic store selling complete range of organic foods, including Graig Farm Organics, **Dolau** (Powys) (Farm Shops) meat, local fruit and vegetables, wholefoods and groceries, plus bodycare and eco-friendly household products. Local deliveries.

Harvest Wholefoods
Lydham, Bishops Castle, SY9 5HB
T: 01588 638990 F: 01588 630298

Stocks a wide range of organic foods (50% organic) including 100% organic fruit and vegetables. Aims to offer an organic alternative for most items. Also sells bodycare, eco-friendly household products and organic seeds and garden products.

Honeysuckle Wholefood Co-op Ltd
53 Church St, **Oswestry**, SY11 2SZ (SA)
T: 01691 653125

Wholefood shop (50% organic). Sells wide range of organic foods including fruit and vegetables, chilled and dairy-free foods.

Myriad Organics
22 Corve St, **Ludlow**, SY8 1DA (SA)
T: 01584 872665 F: 01584 879356
website: www.myriadorganics.co.uk

Wholefood store (60% organic). Sells a complete range of organic food and drinks, including fresh produce from their own market garden.

Wild Thyme Wholefoods
1–2 Castlegates, **Shrewsbury**, SY1 2AQ
T: 01743 364559

Wholefood shop (60% organic). Range

includes fruit and vegetables (100% organic), wholefoods, dairy, groceries and beverages.

STAFFORDSHIRE

Boots Herbal Store
39–41 Merrial St,
Newcastle-under-Lyme, ST5 2AE
T/F: 01782 617463
e-mail: keith.woolley@btinternet.com

Range (75% organic) includes fruit and vegetables, wholefoods, groceries, dairy and bread. Pick-up point for The Good Food Shop – see next entry – vegetable bag scheme.

The Good Food Shop
1–2 Andrew Place,
Newcastle-under-Lyme, ST5 1DL
T/F: 01782 710234
website: www.thegoodfoodshop.co.uk

Specialist fine foods shop (80% organic) undergoing registration. Sells organic wholefoods, fruit and vegetables, meat and fish, juices, breads, groceries, dairy and artisan cheeses and wines, spirits and beers. Operates vegetable box scheme – see next entry. For pick-up point see previous entry. Open am Mon–Wed, all day until around 8pm Thurs–Sat.

The Real Food Company
50 Sandbach Rd South, **Alsager**,
Stoke-on-Trent, ST7 2LP
T: 01270 873322
e-mail: realfoodco.alsager@virgin.net

Wholefood shop (60% organic) including fruit and vegetables (100% organic), groceries, dairy, meat and fish. Operates vegetable box scheme through The Good Food Shop, **Newcastle-under-Lyme** – see above.

WARWICKSHIRE

GAIA (Leamington Spa) Ltd
7 Regent Place, off Bath St, **Leamington Spa**, CV31 1EH (SA)
T/F: 01926 338805

Local box scheme and home delivery service (three times a week) supplying fruit and vegetables, wholefoods, dairy, bread from Paul's, **Melton Mowbray** (Leics) (Specialist Providers), and eco-friendly cleaning products. Local deliveries by bicycle. Also deliver to **Coventry** and **Kenilworth**.

Purely Organic Foods
31–33 Oxford St (off Warwick St),
Leamington Spa, CV32 4RA (SA)
T/F: 01926 431744

Pat Gallimore's (Pat Archer in Radio 4's *The Archers*) favourite local 100% organic shop selling locally produced meat, fruit and vegetables, wholefoods, grocery, dairy, babyfoods and eco-friendly household products. Vegetable box scheme to **Leamington** area.

Warwick Health Foods
40a Brook St, Warwick, CV34 4BL
T: 01926 494311

Ninety per cent organic shop. Extensive range includes 100% organic fruit and vegetables, Graig Farm Organics, **Dolau** (Powys) (Farm Shops) meat, wholefoods, breads, dairy, groceries and special diet foods.

The Wholefood Shop
St Andrew's Church Hall, Church St,
Rugby, CV21 3PT
T/F: 01788 567757

Shop (80% organic) selling organic wholefoods and fruit and vegetables plus eco-friendly cleaning products. Local delivery service and collection point for Chevelswarde Organic Growers, **South Kilworth** (Leics) box scheme.

WEST MIDLANDS

Down to Earth Organic

96a Earlsdon St, **Coventry**, CV5 6EJ (SA)
T: 02476 677500
e-mail:
downtoearthorganic@compuserve.com
website: www.downtoearthorganic.co.uk

Shop (100% organic) selling fruit and vegetables, fish, meat, dairy and dairy alternatives, breads and gluten-free products, Kim's Cakes, **Weddington** (Warwks) (Specialist Providers), wholefoods and groceries. Operates local seasonal selection fruit and vegetable box scheme (65% locally produced).

One Earth Shop

54 Allison Street, **Digbeth**, B5 5TH
T: 0121 6326909
e-mail: rickards@lineone.net

Vegan wholefood shop (80% organic) selling grocery, chilled foods, and dairy substitutes. Pick-up point for Paul's, **Melton Mowbray** (Leics) (Specialist Providers) vegetable box scheme.

Sage Wholefoods

148 Alcester Rd, **Moseley**, B13 8HS (SA)
T: 0121 449 6909

Vegetarian shop (70% organic). Range includes fruit and vegetables (100% organic), wholefoods, groceries, dairy, teas and coffees and eco-friendly cleaning products.

The Small Green Company

25 Clark St, **Stourbridge**, DY8 3UF (SA)
T: 01384 396384

Deliveries of organic fruit and vegetables, eggs, bread and groceries to within 20-mile radius of Stourbridge.
See also:
Leverton and Halls, **Harborne** (Shops)

WORCESTERSHIRE

Beewell

4 Royal Arcade, Broad St, **Pershore**
WR10 1AG
T: 01386 556577

Foodstore and café (70% organic) stocking a wide range of organic foods, including fruit and vegetables, meat and groceries. Café serves morning coffees, mainly vegetarian lunchtime menu and afternoon teas, and uses as many organic ingredients as possible.

Greenlink Organic Foods

9 Graham Rd, **Malvern** WR14 2HR (SA)
T: 01684 576266
T: (deliveries): 01531 640140

Well-stocked, friendly one-stop shop (90% organic), selling local produce, Graig Farm Organics, **Dolau** (Powys) (Farm Shops) meat, dairy, breads and wholefoods. They operate a local box scheme and have a take-away counter and coffee shop.

Sunshine Health Shop

3 Vine St, **Evesham**, WR11 4RE
T: 01386 443757

Sells wide range of foods (75% organic), including organic breads and cakes from own Sunshine Organic Bakery, **Stroud** (Gloucs) (Specialist Providers), an excellent range of juices, wholefoods, groceries, dairy, special diet foods, babyfoods and eco-friendly household products. Also at **Stroud** (Gloucs) (Shops) (q.v.).

England West Midlands – Farm Shops

HEREFORDSHIRE

Green Acres Farm Shop

Green Acres, **Hope under Dinmore**, Hereford, HR4 8ED (SA)
T: 01568 797045

Set in middle of an organic cider orchard, converted barn-cum-organic farm shop (85% organic) selling home-grown soft fruit and vegetables, home-produced beef, lamb and pork (available frozen), local organic chickens and free-range ducks, organic farmed salmon and trout, plus range of organic groceries, local organic ciders and fruit juices. Local home delivery service.

Meadowland Meats

Phocle Farm, **Phocle Green**, nr Ross-on-Wye, HR9 7BF (SA)
T: 01989 780711 F: 01989 780722
e-mail: enquiries@meadowlandmeats.ltd.uk
website: www.meadowland.com

A rather special farm shop and butchery that hangs, butchers and sells Herefordshire organic and other free-range meats and poultry produced to the highest standards. All meat is sourced locally. The farm shop also sells organic vegetables, dairy, preserves and juices. Regional deliveries to **Birmingham**, **London**, **Bristol** and **Cardiff**. To find out more visit their website. Order online.

SHROPSHIRE

Ellesmere Road Organic Nursery

Cockshutt, Ellesmere, SY12 0JH (SA)
T: 01939 270270

Farm shop selling wide range of seasonal, home-grown soft fruit, vegetables and salads plus organic fertilisers. PYO Jun–Aug. Open May–Sept.
See also:
Pimhill Farm, **Harmer Hill** (Specialist Providers)

WARWICKSHIRE

Elmhurst Farm Shop

Bow Lane, **Withybrook**, nr Coventry, Warwickshire, CV7 9LQ (SA)
contacts: Rod and Ann Pattison
T: 01788 832233 F: 01788 832690

Inspirational organic farm. Farm shop sells home-produced beef, pork, lamb, poultry and eggs. Their chickens are slaughtered and butchered on site.

WEST MIDLANDS

Organic Roots

Crabtree Farm, Dark Lane, **King's Norton**, B38 0BS (SA)
T: 01564 822294 F: 01564 829212
e-mail: info@organicroots.co.uk
website: www.organicroots.co.uk

Farm shop (100% organic) selling home-grown vegetables, herbs and soft fruit, other local organic produce, plus complete range of organic foods including bread, dairy, groceries, convenience foods, frozen meats, poultry and beer and wines. Local delivery service, online ordering and nice website.

Leverton and Halls

14 Lonsdale Road, **Harborne**,
B17 9RA (SA)
T: 0121 428 2699

One hundred per cent organic shop selling fruit and vegetables, wholefoods, groceries, Graig Farm Organics, **Dolau** (Powys) (Farm Shops) meat, dairy, beers and wines and (Fri–Sat) fresh fish. Year-round box scheme, seasonal selection and customer choice. Delivery to the **West Midlands**. See also:
Hopwood Organic Farm, **Solihull** (Box Schemes)

WORCESTERSHIRE

Kites Nest Farm

Broadway, WR12 7JT (SA)
T: 01386 853320 F: 01386 853621

Famous organic farm, farming to highest organic standards possible, producing high quality richly flavoured beef (no longer certified, as they use local non-registered abattoir). Their animals live in family groups, roam freely, graze natural pastureland, and are fed only home-grown feed. The herd is accredited BSE-free. Meat available fresh and frozen from the farm shop, which also sells spun wool from own sheep. Please phone first.

England West Midlands – Specialist Providers

HEREFORDSHIRE

Legges of Bromyard

51 High Street, **Bromyard**, HR7 4AE (SA)
T: 01885 482417

Well-known local butcher (25% organic). Sells organic beef, lamb, pork and poultry, vegetables, salads and eggs from their own farm and other local free-range meats, plus organic pastas, condiments etc.

September Organic Dairy

Newhouse Farm, **Almeley**, nr Kington,
HR3 6LJ (SA)
T: 01544 327561
e-mail: september@ereal.net
website: www.september.ereal.net

Small, inspirational family-run dairy, making totally organic ice creams, using milk, eggs and cream produced on the farm. Farm shop open 7 days a week. Sells own ice creams, beef and pork raised to SA standards and organic cordials and preserves. Their milk is used in Neal's Yard Dairy, **WC2** (Specialist Providers) yoghurts, crème fraîche and Finn cheese.

SHROPSHIRE

The Cottage Herbery

Mill House, **Boraston**, nr Tenbury Wells,
WR15 8LZ (SA)
T: 01584 781575 F: 01584 781483

Delightful organic garden and herb, wildflower and cottage plant organic nursery, on the Shropshire border. Organic growers for over 25 years. Farm-gate sales of extensive range of plants including culinary, medicinal and native herb plants, available early April to end October. Advance orders taken. Show garden open May to June, every Sun 11am–5 pm. Attends major shows such as *Gardener's World* and produce own organic coir-based compost, 'Fertile Fibre', sold by mail order.

Pimhill Farm

Harmer Hill, Shrewsbury, SY4 3DY (SA)
T: 01939 290342 F: 01939 291156
e-mail: info@pimhillorganic.co.uk
website: www.pimhillorganic.co.uk

Located off A528, south of Harmer Hill, one of the original pioneering organic farms and member of the SA for over 50 years. Renowned for their home-grown and milled flours and oats. Produce available in local shops and in bulk direct from the farm by appointment. Bulk quantities of their potatoes. Please phone first. See also SA Farm listing, England South West.

STAFFORDSHIRE

See: Staffordshire Organic Cheeses, **Acton** (Farm Gate)

WARWICKSHIRE

Charlecote Mill

Hampton Lucy, CV35 8BB (SA)
T: 01789 842072
website: www.charlecotemill.vt9.co.uk

Stoneground organic wholemeal flour from water-driven mill.

Henry Doubleday Research Association

Ryton Organic Gardens,
Ryton-on-Dunsmore, Coventry,
CV8 3LG (SA)
T: 02476 303517 F: 02476 639229
e-mail: enquiry@hdra.org.uk
website: www.hdra.org.uk

Organic oasis, UK's premier must-visit organic attraction, complete with award-winning shop and restaurant – and much more. Renowned organic display and research gardens and headquarters of HDRA, Europe's largest organic member organisation. Their excellent organic shop sells a comprehensive range of organic foods – fresh, chilled, frozen & ambient – drinks, snacks, wines, gardening sundries, seeds and plants, books, cards and gifts. Operates a local box scheme. Bright and spacious restaurant serves delicious organic food and snacks. Open all week, all year. See also Audley End Walled Organic Kitchen Garden, **Saffron Walden**, Essex (Specialist Providers).

Kim's Cakes

39 Shanklin Drive, **Weddington**,
Nuneaton, CV10 0BA (SA)
T: 02476 351421

Something to celebrate. Kim Bickley bakes over 25 different organic cakes, tea breads, Christmas puddings and cakes, plus homemade seasonal preserves, made with locally produced organic ingredients where possible. Available from local farmers' markets, Down to Earth Organic, **Coventry** (Shops), Elmhurst Farm Shop, **Withybrook** (Farm Shops) on Saturdays and The Naturally Good Food Delivery Service, **Lutterworth** (Leics) (Box Schemes).

WEST MIDLANDS

S. & A. Rossiter

247 Maryvale Rd, **Bournville**,
B30 1PN (SA)
T: 0121 4581598

Traditional family butcher's (90% organic), selling full range of organic beef, pork, lamb and poultry, homemade and organic pickles and preserves, fish, bread, eggs, cheeses, vegetables and cooked meats.

WORCESTERSHIRE

Cridlan and Walker

23 Abbey Road, **Great Malvern**,
WR14 3ET (OF&G)
T: 01684 573008 F: 01684 566017

Traditional butcher's selling 100% organic meat, plus vegetables, dairy and beverages (50% organic). Mail order and home delivery service. Delivery to **Worcester**, **Pershore**, **Ledbury** and **Hereford**.

England West Midlands – Places to Eat and Stay

HEREFORDSHIRE

Dunkertons Cider

Pembridge, nr Leominster,
HR6 9ED (SA)
T: 01544 388653 F: 01544 388654

Well-known cider shop and restaurant which uses organic ingredients where possible. For full entry see p. **270**.

Penrhos Court Restaurant and Hotel

Kington, HR5 3LH (SA)
T: 01544 230720 F: 01544 230754
e-mail: enquiries@penrhos.co.uk
website: www.penrhos.co.uk

Organic heaven on earth. Acclaimed idyllic restored Tudor farmhouse and buildings serving fine organic food by chef, owner, nutritionist and author, Daphne Lambert, who also runs Penrhos School of Health. Their small shop sells organic and eco-friendly products, including organic paints. For full entry see p. **111**.

The Three Crowns Inn

Ullingswick, nr Bromyard, HR1 3JQ
T: 01432 820279 F: 08700 515338
e-mail: info@threecrownsinn.com
website: www.threecrownsinn.com

A find. Seventeenth-century half-timbered, award-winning inn (50% organic) recently voted at www.taste.co.uk one of 10 best pubs. Committed to local and organic foods. Meat is organic or rare breed, including local organic chicken and pork. Local organic farms also supply fruit and vegetables and eggs. Modern classic cuisine, changing menu and fine seasonal cooking. Not residential but will happily get you fixed up with local guest houses.
See also:
Oat Cuisine, **Ross-on-Wye** (Shops)
Lower Bache House, **Kimbolton** (B & B List)

SHROPSHIRE

See: Hopesay Glebe Farm, **Hopesay** (bed and breakfast) (Box Schemes)

WARWICKSHIRE

Glebe Farm House

Stratford Rd, **Loxley**, Stratford-upon-Avon, CV35 9JW
(SA)
T/F: 01789 842501
e-mail: scorpiolimited@msn.com
website: www.glebefarmhouse.com

Organic farm and country guest house, in peaceful landscaped gardens, offering bed and breakfast – see also Glebe Farm House, **Loxley** (B & B List) – and evening meals serving organic ingredients where possible, including their own beef, lamb, homemade sausages, dry cured bacon and eggs.
See also:
Henry Doubleday Research Association, **Ryton-on-Dunsmore** (Specialist Providers)
The Hare on the Park, **Warwick**; Winton House, **Upper Quinton,** Stratford-upon-Avon (B & B List)

WORCESTERSHIRE

The Talbot Inn

Knightwick, Worcester, WR6 5PH
T: 01886 821235 F: 01996 821060
e-mail: admin@the-talbot.co.uk
website: www.the-talbot.co.uk

One of the most remarkable inns in the country. Run by Annie, Wiz and Jean Clift, who have championed local, chemical-free and organic food for 18 years. They hold own farmers' market (2nd Sunday every month), brew own beers and cider and grow own vegetables and salads. Excellent menu (about 20% organic) changes daily, all homemade including bread. One pub everyone should visit. Have 10 guest rooms.
See also:
Beewell, **Pershore** (Shops)
The Mill, **Broadway** (B & B List)

England West Midlands – Farm Gate

HEREFORDSHIRE

Butford Farm

Bowley Lane, **Bodenham**, HR1 3LG (SA)
T: 01568 797195

Recently certified organic producer selling organic eggs and organically raised Oxford Sandy and Black pork from farm gate, plus cider made from local apples (not organic). Please phone first.

Henclose Organic Produce

Little Dewchurch, Hereford, HR2 6PP (SA)
T: 01432 840826

Small organic producer supplying home-produced organic lamb, pork, kid, sausages, goats' milk and eggs. Farm-gate sales. Please phone first.

Hermitage Farm

Canon Pyon, Hereford, HR4 8NN (SA)
T: 01432 760217

Farm-gate sales of apple juice by the case and apples by the box, October to March.

Pardoes

Priors Grove, **Putley**, Ledbury, HR8 2RE (SA)
T: 01531 670511

One of the UK's foremost organic apple producers, growing over 30 varieties ranging from old-fashioned to modern, eaters and cookers; also grows pears and plums. Sells at farm gate in season, but please phone first.

Shortwood Family Farm

Pencombe, Bromyard, HR7 4RP (SA)
T: 01885 400205
e-mail: shortwoodfarm@talk21.com
website: www.shortwoodfarm.co.uk

Farm-gate sales of home-produced organic vegetables and eggs, mainly in summer, plus own organic pork, lamb and Christmas turkeys. Family farm encouraging participation – help feed the animals. Establishing a falconry. Please phone first.

Springfield Poultry

Steen's Bridge, Leominster, HR6 0LU (SA)
T: 01568 760270 F: 01568 760418

Farm-gate sales of home-produced organic and free-range poultry.

SHROPSHIRE

Five Acres

Ford, Shrewsbury, SY5 9LL (SA)
T: 01743 850 832

Old-fashioned varieties of plums and apples and soft fruits available from the farm gate.

Hope Organic Produce

Sandy Lane, **Stoke Heath**, nr Market Drayton, TF9 2LG (SA)
T: 01630 638348

Produces wide range of organic potted herbs and some cut herbs. Summer salad vegetables also available. Visitors welcome, but please phone first. Also available at farmers' markets in **Shropshire** and **Staffordshire**.

Woodfield

Woodfield Church Row, **Clungunford**, Craven Arms, SY7 0PU (SA)
T/F: 01588 660462

A find. Farm-gate sales of home-grown organic soft fruit, vegetables and extensive range of herb plants (culinary/medicinal/natural dyes), including 17 varieties of mint, plus their own organic mutton, slaughtered in local abattoir and butchered to order. Herbs also sold at Bird on the Rock Tea-Rooms in the hamlet of **Abcott**, Clungunford (one of Tea Council's top 100 tea-rooms).

See also:
Hopesay Glebe Farm, **Hopesay** (Box Schemes)
Pimhill Farm, **Harmer Hill** (Specialist Providers)

STAFFORDSHIRE

Staffordshire Organic Cheeses

Newhouse Farm, **Acton**, Newcastle-under-Lyme, ST5 4EE (SA)
T: 01782 680366

Produces well-known organic cow's- and goat's-milk cheeses available from the farm and by mail order along with wide range of other regional cheeses. Phone for availability and price list.

WARWICKSHIRE

Douthwaite & Sons

Townsend Farm, **Radway**, Warwick, CV35 0UN(SA)
T: 01295 670572

Farm-gate sales of home-produced organic beef, lamb and potatoes.

SCOTLAND NORTH

Scotland North – Box Schemes

ABERDEENSHIRE

Croft Organics

Skellarts Croft, Daviot, Inverurie, AB51 0JL (SA)
T: 01467 681717 F: 01467 681718
e-mail: croftorganics@hotmail.com
website: www.croft-organics.co.uk

Local, year-round box scheme supplying mainly home-grown (40%) and local vegetables and fruit (bunch of herbs included free). Also supplies own eggs, organic coffee and wine. Delivery to **Aberdeen** area.

J. W. Fraser

Burnorrachie, **Bridge of Muchalls**, Stonehaven, AB39 3RU (Demeter)
T: 01569 730195

Small, local box scheme. Operates July–May. Supplies home-grown, biodynamic vegetables, salad crops, herbs and soft fruit supplemented with produce from Lembas (see next entry) within 5-mile radius. Also produces beef, available, usually frozen, from farm gate.

Lembas

Lorieneen, **Bridge of Muchalls**, Stonehaven, AB39 3RU (Demeter, SA)
T/F: 01569 731746

Customised box scheme delivering home-grown and local vegetables (one third biodynamic), organic eggs and De Rit Demeter preserves to local pick-up points, or farm-gate pick-up. Growers, distributors and importers of organic and biodynamic produce. Also supply some produce to J. W. Fraser, **Bridge of Muchalls** and Colin Ward, **Newmachar** (Box Schemes) and Newton Dee Store and Bakery, **Bieldside** (Shops).

Lenshaw Organic Produce

Upper Lenshaw Farm, **Rothienorman**, Inverurie, AB51 8XU (SA)
T: 01464 871243 F: 01464 871416
e-mail: jborganics@hotmail.com

Local seasonal vegetable box scheme (100% home-grown) operating August to March. Also produces organic beef, pork, chickens and eggs. Deliveries to **Aberdeenshire**. Meat also available nationwide by overnight courier.

Colin Ward

Bridgefoot, **Newmachar**, AB21 7PE (SA)
T: 01651 862041

Award-winning model local box scheme, 90+% home-grown, other produce from Lembas, **Bridge of Muchalls**, supplying customised vegetable boxes, fruit and eggs to **Aberdeen** area. Emphasis on high quality. Includes unusual varieties.

HIGHLAND

Earthshare

65 Society St, **Nairn**, IV12 4NL
T: 01667 452879
e-mail: earthshare@tiscali.co.uk

Community-supported agricultural scheme supplying 200 families in and around

Moray. In conversion and will be fully organic (SA) by end 2002. Subscribers pick up a weekly box of fruit and vegetables from the farm.

Glendale Salads
19 Upper Fasach, **Glendale**, Isle of Skye
IV55 8WP (SA)
T/F: 01470 511349

Specialist growers of flavoursome organic salads, unusual vegetables, herbs and soft fruit (currants, and red and yellow gooseberries), available March–Oct through their local box scheme on the **Isle of Skye**.

ORKNEY ISLANDS

Wheems
Eastside, **South Ronaldsay**,
KW17 2TJ (SA)
T: 01856 83537

Organic grower and small cheese producer. Operates local home-grown vegetable box scheme, July to February. Delivery to **Orkney**. Also available at farm gate and local farmers' market.

Scotland North – Shops

ABERDEENSHIRE

Newton Dee Store and Bakery
Newton Dee Village, North Deeside Rd,
Bieldside, nr Aberdeen, AB15 9DX
T: 01224 868609 F: 01224 868512

Part of the Camphill Community network with own shop and bakery. Produces breads made with organic flour. Shop (50% organic) sells Loch Arthur, **Beesfield** (D & G) (Farm Shops) cheeses, breads from the bakery, organic fruit and vegetables from Lembas, **Bridge of Muchalls** (Box Schemes), groceries and teas and coffees.

ARGYLL & BUTE

Grapevine
49 Victoria St, **Rothesay**, Isle of Bute,
PA20 0AP
T: 01700 504 414

Healthfood shop, (50% organic), sells organic wholefoods, groceries, and teas and coffees.

Eco Grain Store
50 Hillfoot St, **Dunoon**, Argyll, PA23 7DT
T: 01369 705106

Vegetarian and vegan healthfood store (50% organic) selling wholefoods, groceries, dairy and non-dairy and fruit and vegetables.

MORAY
See:
Phoenix Community Stores, **Findhorn Bay** (Specialist Providers)

Scotland North – Farm Shop

PERTH & KINROSS

Lurgan Farmshop
Drumdewan, by **Aberfeldy**,
PH15 2JQ (SA)
T/F: 01887 829303
e-mail: sally@lurganfarm.demon.co.uk
website: www.lurganfarmshop.co.uk

Attractive farm shop (70% organic) selling organic fruit and vegetables, wholefoods, groceries, dairy, home-produced organic lamb plus locally produced free-range beef and pork and wild venison. Also sells home-baked bread and ready meals with some organic ingredients. Lamb and beef by mail order. Organic teas and coffees and snacks served on outside tables in summer.

Scotland North – Specialist Providers

HIGHLAND

Golspie Mill

Golspie, KW10 6RA (Demeter)
T: 01408 633278

Produces stoneground organic flours and meals in watermill. Mail order only. Products used by Phoenix Community Stores, **Findhorn Bay** (Moray) (Specialist Providers).

Poyntzfield Herb Nursery

Black Isle, By Dingwall,
IV7 8LX (Demeter)
T/F: 01381 610352
e-mail: Info@poyntzfieldherbs.co.uk
website: www.poyntzfieldherbs.co.uk

One of the UK's most remarkable herb farms. Organic grower since 1976. Offers over 400 varieties of culinary, medicinal and aromatic herb plants, including herbs for rock gardens, shade etc. Extensive mail order catalogue (please send 4 x 1st class stamps). Excellent website with online ordering. Nursery open afternoons, March–September. Holds special events. Garden design and advisory service available.

Summer Isles Foods

Achiltibuie, Ullapool, IV26 2YG (OFF)
T: 01854 622353 F: 01854 622335
e-mail: sifsalmo@globalnet.co.uk

Well-known smokery in idyllic location. Sells smoked organic salmon, gravadlax, trout, chicken breasts and cheese. Available by mail order and at shop. Open Easter–October.

MORAY

Findhorn Community

The Park, **Findhorn Bay**, IV36 0TZ (SA)
T: 01309 690311 F: 01309 690933
e-mail: phoenix@findhorn.org
website: www.findhorn.org

Internationally known, environmentally conscious community offering residential courses. Has own organic farm, conference centre and Rudolf Steiner School. Serves vegetarian and vegan meals made with 50% organic ingredients (20% home-grown). Phone for brochure.

Phoenix Community Stores

The Park, **Findhorn Bay**, IV36 0TZ (SA)
T: 01309 690110 F: 01309 692124
e-mail: Phoenix@findhorn.org
website: www.findhorn.org

Part of Findhorn Foundation. Organic fine food shop and separate SA organic bakery. Produces 20 different, excellent organic breads, including rye bread made from local organic rye from Golspie Mill, **Golspie** (Highland) (Specialist Providers)), and around 20 different cakes. Shop also stocks around 2,500 organic products, including foods, drinks, bodycare and clothes. Stall at **Elgin** and **Inverness** farmers' markets.

Wester Lawrenceton Farm Ltd

Forres, IV36 2RH (SA)
T: 01309 676566 F: 01309 676162

Awarded Best Producer 2001, Radio 4's *Food Programme* Awards. Nick and Pam Rodway produce a range of wonderful organic cow's- and goat's-milk cheeses. Not available from the farm direct but sold at **Elgin** and **Inverness** farmers' markets and at nearby Phoenix Community Stores, **Findhorn Bay** – see previous entry. See also SA Farm listing, Scotland.

ORKNEY

The Orkney Salmon Co.
Crowness Point, **Kirkwall**,
KW15 1RG (SA)
T: 01856 876101 F: 01856 873846
e-mail: enquiries@orkneysalmon.co.uk
website: www.orkneysalmon.co.uk

Premier suppliers of Orkney organic salmon from a consortium of independent salmon farmers. Visit the office to buy scallops and organic and non-organic salmon. Available from retailers nationwide.

SHETLAND

Balta Island Sea Fare Ltd
Balta Sound, ZE2 9DX (SA)
T: 01957 711465/711334
e-mail: balta@organic.shetland.co.uk

Produces organic salmon and sea trout sold through Salmac Sales, Aberdeen. If you visit Shetland, knock on door and ask for a fish.

Scotland North – Places to Eat and Stay

ABERDEENSHIRE

Castle of Park
Cornhill, AB45 2AX
T: 01466 751667
e-mail: booking@castleofpark.net
website: www.castleofpark.net

Restaurant and guest house specialising in vegetarian and vegan dishes. All food freshly prepared using as much local and organic produce as possible (40% organic).

ARGYLL & BUTE

Argyll Hotel
Isle of Iona, PA76 6SJ
T: 01681 700334 F: 01681 700510
e-mail:
reservations@argyllhoteliona.co.uk.co.uk
website: www.argyllhoteliona.co.uk

Idyllic and delightful well-known hotel and restaurant (40+% organic) on magical Isle of Iona, with own 20-year-old kitchen garden managed completely organically, which sources the best local and organic produce for their restaurant. Restaurant open to non-residents, offering seasonal menus with daily specials. Strong organic and environmental ethos, including recycling and use of eco-friendly household products. Good website.

HIGHLAND

Old Pines Restaurant with Rooms
Spean Bridge, By Fort William,
Highland, PH34 4EG
T: 01397 712324
e-mail: goodfood@oldpines.co.uk
website: www.oldpines.co.uk

Winner of best small hotel in Britain and restaurant of the year in the *Good Food Guide 2000*. Friendly, personally run restaurant committed to environmental practices, including their own reed bed. Excellent menu changes daily, featuring home-grown vegetables and salads and as many local and organic foods and ingredients as possible (50+% organic).

Three Chimneys Restaurant with Rooms
Colbost, By Dunvegan, Isle of Skye,
IV55 8ZT
T: 01470 511258 F: 01470 511358
e-mail: eatandstay@threechimneys.co.uk

website: www.threechimneys.co.uk

Acclaimed restaurant in restored crofter's cottage. New 5-star-rated guest rooms adjoining restaurant. Uses as much fresh local unadulterated organic and free-range produce as possible, plus organic flour and other ingredients. Fine seasonal cooking, daily changing menu.
See also:
Druimgrianach, **Cuil**; Geddes House, **Nairn**; Lyndale House, **Edinbane,** Isle of Skye (B & B List)

PERTH AND KINROSS
See:
Lurgan Farmshop, **Aberfeldy** (Farm Shops)

STIRLINGSHIRE
See:
Mackeanston House, **Doune**, Trossachs (B & B List)

Scotland North – Farm Gate

ABERDEENSHIRE
See:
J. W. Fraser, **Bridge of Muchalls** (Box Schemes)

SCOTLAND CENTRAL AND SOUTH

Scotland Central and South – Box Schemes

DUMBARTONSHIRE

EPO Growers
Kennels Cottage, **Hardgate**,
G81 5QR (SOPA)
T/F: 01389 875337

Subscription farm producing organic vegetables, soft fruits and herbs, grown on land supplemented with rock dust for extra minerals, as well as composted manures and seaweed. Local delivery and to south side and west end of **Glasgow**. Choice of subscription or box scheme membership (Jul–Dec) – please phone first. Volunteers keen to learn about organic gardening are welcome.

EAST LOTHIAN

East Coast Organic Boxes
24 Boggs Holdings, **Pencaitland**,
EH34 5BD (Demeter)
T/F: 01875 340227
e-mail:
ECOBOX@eastcoastorganics.freeserve.co.uk

Box scheme supplying organic fruit and vegetables and herbs with organic eggs, meat, wholefoods, bread and milk as extras to around 450 households in **Edinburgh** region. Up to 70% home-grown, most of the rest locally supplied.

EDINBURGH

See:
Real Foods (Shops)
Damhead Organically Grown Foods (Farm Shops)

FIFE

Bellfield Organic Nursery
Strathmiglo, Cupar, KY14 7RH (SA)
T/F: 01337 860764

Home delivery and box scheme service, supplying 80% home-grown vegetables, salad crops and herbs, plus organic fruit, Dundee wholefoods, breads and dairy. Delivery within 60–70 mile radius, including to **St Andrews**, **Perth**, **Stirling**, **Edinburgh** and **Glasgow**.
See also:
Pillars of Hercules, **Falkland** (Farm Shops)

SOUTH AYRSHIRE

Stair Organic Growers
11 The Yetts, **Tarbolton**, KA5 5NT (SA)
T: 01292 541369
e-mail: info@organicgrowing.com
website: www.organicgrowing.com

Year-round seasonal selection fruit and vegetable box scheme (35% home-grown) with various customer options, including eggs and dairy. Delivery to **Ayrshire** and south **Glasgow**. Order by phone, email or online.

Scotland Central and South – Shops

DUMFRIES & GALLOWAY

Sunrise Wholefoods

49 King St, **Castle Douglas**, DG7 1AE
T: 01556 504455
e-mail: pstilb@sunrise-wholefo.demon.co.uk

Sells 100% organic fruit and vegetables, plus organic dairy, groceries, chilled foods (30% organic), plus a selection of over 30 organic wines and beers.

DUNDEE

Goodness Me

106 Gray St, **Broughty Ferry**, DD5 2DN
T: 01382 736344

Healthfood shop (70% organic) selling organic wholefoods and groceries including juices and tea and coffees.

EDINBURGH

Henderson's Shop

94 Hanover St, **Edinburgh**, EH2 1DR (SA)
T: 0131 2256694
e-mail: mail@hendersonsofedinburgh.co.uk
website: www.hendersonsofedinburgh.co.uk

Vegetarian shop (70% organic) selling wide range of organic products, including fruit and vegetables, dairy, wholefoods, wines and beers, plus organic wholemeal bread, oatcakes and vegan haggis made in their own bakery. Downstairs is their vegetarian restaurant, The Salad Table, and around the corner their bistro, Henderson's Bistro (Places to Eat and Stay).

New Leaf Health Food Shop

20 Argyle Place, **Marchmont**, Edinburgh, EH9 1JJ (SA)
T: 0131 2288840

Small, busy shop (85% organic). Range includes dairy, bread, wholefoods and gourmet items. Fresh seasonal organic fruit and vegetables delivered to the shop on Mon, Wed and Fri.

Organic Food Shop

45 Broughton St, **Edinburgh**, EH1 3JU
T: 0131 5561722

One hundred per cent organic shop, small and gaily painted, selling everything including organic flower bulbs.

Real Foods Ltd

37 Broughton St, **Edinburgh**, EH1 3JU (SA)
T: 0131 5571911 F: 0131 558 3530

Busy, well-known, large vegetarian healthfood store (30+% organic). Extensive range of organic foods including fruit and vegetables, wholefoods, dairy and frozen foods. Operates customised box scheme to Edinburgh area.

Real Foods Ltd

8 Brougham St, **Tollcross**, Edinburgh, EH3 9DH (SA)
T: 0131 2281201 F: 0131 2211651

Like its larger, sister store (see above) selling same range of organic goods.

GLASGOW

Grassroots

20 Woodlands Rd, Charing Cross, **Glasgow**, G3 6IR (SA)
T: 0141 3533278 F: 0141 3533078
website: www.grassrootsorganic.com

Large, stylish, award-winning, must-visit, friendly vegetarian wholefood shop (50% organic). Sells an impressive range of organic foods and drinks. Have a large deli counter and a crèche for toddlers. Has own café – Café Grassroots (Places to Eat and Stay) – around the corner.

Roots and Fruits Wholefoods and Organics

455 Great Western Rd, **Glasgow**, G12 8UG
T: 0141 339 3077

Organic shop and small delicatessen (80% organic). Stocks comprehensive range of organic foods, including meat, dairy, breads, fresh fruit, groceries and frozen foods. Their fruit and vegetable shop, Roots & Fruits, two doors down (tel: 0141 334 3530) also sells some organic fruit and vegetables.

MIDLOTHIAN

Valleyfield House Partnership

17 High St, **Penicuik**, EH26 8HS
T: 01968 677854

Community scheme, assisting people with learning difficulties. Small shop, (90% organic) selling organic fruit and vegetables, wholefoods, dairy, breads and groceries. Open Sat 10am–12am.

Scotland Central and South – Farm Shops

DUMFRIES & GALLOWAY

Loch Arthur Creamery

Camphill Village Trust, **Beeswing**, DG2 8JQ (Demeter)
T: 01387 760296
e-mail: locharthur@supernet.co.uk

Camphill Village Community with delightful award-winning dairy and creamery. Home-produced organic cheeses and yoghurt, organic bread from their own bakery, beef, pork and lamb. Cheeses available by mail order.
See also:
Cream O'Galloway, **Gatehouse of Fleet** (Specialist Providers)

EDINBURGH

Damhead Organically Grown Foods

32a Damhead, Old Pentland Rd, Lothianburn, **Edinburgh**, EH10 7EA (Demeter)
T: 0131 445 1490 F: 0131 445 5848
e-mail: enquiries@damhead.co.uk
website: www.damhead.co.uk

One hundred per cent organic cornucopia and must-visit, inspirational farm shop, established in 1989, with new picnic and children's playground area. Difficult to praise too highly. Operates a buy-local-first policy and stocks around 2,500 certified organic products, including excellent fruit and vegetable counter featuring home-grown vegetables and herbs throughout summer, local dairy, meat and breads, 4 brands of baby food, wines by the case, plus eco-friendly cleaning products. Home delivery, including fruit and vegetable boxes, to **Central Lowlands**. Extensive organic mail order catalogue, nationwide delivery, featuring 1,500 items, plus excellent online catalogue and website. Order by phone, email or online. Open every day.

FIFE

Jamesfield Farm Shop

Jamesfield Farm, **Newburgh**, KY14 6EW (SOPA)
T: 01738 850498 F: 01738 850741
e-mail: jamesfieldfarm@excite.co.uk
website: www.jamesfieldfarm.co.uk

Well-known organic family farm and meat producers. Organic since 1986, producing Aberdeen Angus beef, lamb, mutton, Christmas turkeys and free-range pork and bacon, butchered and matured on the farm, with their own organic farm shop, open Fri–Sun. Farm shop also sells homemade organic sausages and burgers, home-grown and local organic vegetables, local organic poultry and eggs, fruit and a wide range of organic wholefoods, groceries and eco-friendly household products. Nationwide mail order for their meat (name: Organic Meat and Products Scotland Ltd), including hampers. Online ordering and excellent website.

Pillars of Hercules Farm Shop

Falkland, KY15 7AD (SA)
T: 01337 857749
e-mail: mail@pillars.co.uk
website: www.pillars.co.uk

Established in 1983, inspirational small-scale organic farm, producing lamb, Christmas turkeys, eggs, an extensive range of vegetables, apples and plums, with their own farm shop (90% organic) and box scheme/ home delivery service. Farm shop, open every day, sells organic fruit and vegetables (70% home-grown), their lamb and turkey, Scottish organic beef, pork and poultry, plus organic wholefoods, groceries, dairy, breads and eco-friendly cleaning products. Operates year-round seasonal selection box scheme plus customised home delivery service to **Fife** and **Edinburgh**. Catalogue available. Clear, informative website; order by phone or email. Just opened small café using all organic ingredients.

Scotland Central and South – Specialist Providers

DUMFRIES & GALLOWAY

Cream O'Galloway Dairy

Rainton Farm, **Gatehouse-of-Fleet**, Castle Douglas, DG7 2DR (SA)
T: 01557 814040
e-mail: info@creamogalloway.co.uk
website: www.creamogalloway.co.uk

Tourist attraction, organic farm and dairy (see p. **162**) with children's play area and nature trails. Open daily 11am–6pm from Easter until end October. Shop sells their ice creams and sorbets.
See also:
Loch Arthur Creamery, **Beeswing** (cheese) (Farm Shops)

EDINBURGH

The Engine Shed

Garvald Community Enterprises Ltd, 19 St Leonard's Lane, **Edinburgh**, EH8 9SD (OFF)
T: 0131 6620040 F: 0131 6675319
e-mail: engineshed@aol.com
website: members.xoom.com/Engineshed

Community workshop, small organic bakery, tofu processing unit and vegetarian café serving food made with biodynamic and organic produce.

Iain Mellis
30a Victoria St, **Edinburgh**, EH1 2JW
T: 0131 2266215
Also at:
205 Bruntsfield Place, **Edinburgh**, EH10 4DH
T: 0131 4478889
6 Bakers Place, Stockbridge, **Edinburgh**, EH3 6SY
T: 0131 2256566
492 Great Western Rd, **Glasgow**, G12 8EW
T: 0141 3398998

Scotland's best-known cheesemonger. See p. **154**.

FIFE

ScotMed Herbs
113–115 High St, **Burntisland**, KY3 9AA
T: 01592 872689
e-mail: alan@scotmedherbs.co.uk
website: www.scotmedherbs.co.uk

Shop selling herbal medicines, organic herbal teas, spices, cosmetics, aromatherapy oils, a small selection of organic and fair-traded foods and Rock's organic cordials. Also sells organic herb plants and cut fresh herbs grown at own nursery – see next entry – and dried herbs and spices. Also has therapy centre.

ScotMed Herbs
Garden by the Loch, Craigencalt Farm, **Kinghorn**, KY3 3YG (SA)
T: 01592 874027
e-mail: alan@scotmedherbs.co.uk
website: www.scotmedherbs.co.uk

Located by Loch Kinghorn. Organic herb nursery. Sells extensive range of culinary and medicinal herb plants and seasonal cut herbs, plus. Open April–Sept. Demonstrations and regular herb walks in summer. Advice given plus library for customers to browse. Has shop at Burntisland – see entry above.

GLASGOW
See:
Iain Mellis (cheese), **Edinburgh**

SOUTH AYRSHIRE

Barwinnock Herbs
Barrhill, Girvan, KA26 0RB
T: 01465 821338
e-mail: herbs@barwinnock.com
website: www.barwinnock.com

Herb nursery and garden on the west coast producing over 500 varieties of herb plants, grown to organic standards (not certified organic). Nursery, which features museum of rural life, open April–October. Mail order catalogue. Online ordering on good website.

Scotland Central and South – Places to Eat and Stay

BORDERS
See:
Over Langshaw Farm, **Galashiels** (B & B List)

DUMFRIES & GALLOWAY

Low Craiglemine Farm Holidays
Low Craiglemine, **Whitehorn**, Newton Stewart, DG8 8NE (Demeter)
T: 01988 500730
e-mail: cottage@galloway-timber.co.uk
website: www.kirkmoor.com/lowcraiglemine/cottages

Self-catering cottages on certified organic farm.

Netherfield Farm

Beeswing, DG2 8JE (Demeter)
T/F: 01387 730217

Biodynamic farm and vegetarian organic bed and breakfast guesthouse, plus optional evening meals, 1 mile from Loch Arthur Camphill Community. Dr Hauska massage treatments available for residents and non-residents. Serves only organic and biodynamic foods, including home-grown biodynamic fruit and vegetables and Loch Arthur, **Beesfield** (Farm Shops) dairy products.

The Rossan

Auchencairn, **Castle Douglas**, DG7 1QR
T: 01556 640269 F: 01556 640278
e-mail: bardsley@rossan.freeserve.co.uk
website: www.the-rossan.co.uk

Guesthouse specialising in vegetarian, vegan and special diets (30+% organic). Serves organic muesli, bread, milk, home-grown vegetables and own eggs. Sources as much locally produced food as possible.

EDINBURGH

Henderson's Bistro

25 Thistle St, **Edinburgh**, EH2 1DR
T: 0131 2252131

Same style of food as The Salad Table below but table service. Open for lunch every day, evenings Thur–Sat. Closes 7.30pm Sun.

The Salad Table

94 Hanover St, **Edinburgh**, EH2 1DR
T: 0131 2252131
e-mail: mail@hendersons.co.uk
website: www.hendersonsofedinburgh.co.uk

Located below Henderson's Shop (Shops) and owned and run by the Henderson's. Friendly, busy, licensed vegetarian self-service café (70% organic) serving salads, 5 daily hot dishes, including vegan and gluten-free choice, and desserts, plus their own organic bread, oatcakes and vegan haggis. Use as many organic ingredients as possible, including soya milk. Also offers organic wines, teas and coffees. Wine bar open in evenings with live music.
See also:
The Engine Shed (vegetarian café) (Specialist Providers)

FIFE
See:
Pillars of Hercules, **Falkland** (Farm Shops)

GLASGOW

Air Organic

6 Kelvingrove St, Glasgow G3 7SA
T: 0141 5645200
e-mail: airorganic@emailmsn.com
website: www.travelscotland.co.uk/food/airorganic.htm

Minimalist, stylish café and restaurant. Modern menu serving meals made with 90% organic ingredients.

Café Grassroots

93–97 St Georges Studios, St Georges Rd, Charing Cross, **Glasgow**, G3 6JA
T: 0141 3330534

Friendly, informal vegetarian café, owned by Grassroots shop. Open everyday 10am–10pm. Around 70% food served is made using organic ingredients. All organic wines, beers, teas and coffees.

SOUTH AYRSHIRE

Glendrissaig Guest House

Newton Stewart Rd, **Girvan**, KA26 0HJ
T/F: 01465 714631

Bed and breakfast with en-suite facilities and stunning views. Ground-floor room and secure parking available. Traditional home cooking including vegetarian meals with home-grown organic produce and spring water.

WALES

Wales – Box Schemes

CARDIFF

Green Cuisine

87 Westville Rd, **Cardiff**,
CF23 5DF (OF&G)
T: 02920 498721
e-mail: greencuisine@talk21.com

Home delivery to **Cardiff** and surrounding area. Supplies extensive range of organic products, including fruit and vegetables, meat, poultry, dairy, groceries, spring water from Llanllyr Organic Farm and eco-friendly household products. Uses local organic produce when possible. Phone for list.
See also:
Urban Organics, **Splott** (Shops)

CARMARTHENSHIRE

Organics to Go

Werndolau Farm, **Golden Grove**,
Carmarthen, SA32 8NE (SA)
T/F: 0800 4582524
e-mail: mail@organics2go.co.uk
website: www.organics2go.co.uk

Organic co-operative with their own farm near Swansea, providing year-round flexible box scheme (50% home-grown), serving over 1,000 households in **London**, **Bristol**, **Cardiff** and **Carmarthenshire**.
Various set-price boxes with customer choice, or select from weekly list. Home-grown produce picked and delivered within 24-hours in own van powered by natural gas. Farm being developed as an ecological centre.

Frontline Organics

Pen-y-Lan Farm, Tavernspite Rd,
Whitland, SA34 ONH (SA)
T: 01994 241368 F: 01994 241366
e-mail: frontline.organics@ukgateway.net
website: www.frontlineorganics.co.uk

Organic farm producing vegetables, soft fruit, beef and lamb. Operates home delivery and year-round box scheme, offering set-price or customised orders (90% home-grown in summer) and beef and lamb when available. Delivery to many parts of **South** and **West Wales**.

POWYS

Primrose Organic Centre

Felindre, Brecon, Powys, LD3 0ST (SA)
T: 01497 847636

Local box scheme and farm shop supplying 100% home-grown vegetables, fruit (including 100 different varieties of apples, pears, plums and nuts), salads and herbs. Associated with Primrose Earth Awareness Trust (PEAT:
website: http://www.zyworld.com/peat/home.htm)
See also:
Medhope Organic Growers, **Tintern**, (Farm Shop).
Pencoed Organic Growers, **Pencoed**, (Farm Gate).

Wales – Shops

BRIDGEND

See:
Beanfreaks, Bridgend, under their **Cardiff** entry.

CARDIFF

Beanfreaks

3 St Mary St, **Cardiff**, CF1 2AT
T: 02920 251671

Healthfood shop (70% organic) selling wholefoods and groceries.
Also at:
Beanfreaks, Caradoc Rd, **Cwmbran**, (Torfn)
Beanfreaks, Upper Dock St, **Newport** (Mons)
Beanfreaks, Nolton St, **Bridgend**.

Pulse Wholefoods

171 Kings Rd, Canton, **Cardiff**, CF1 9DE
T: 02920 225873

Sells fruit and vegetables and wines and beers (100% organic) and a wide range of organic wholefoods, dairy and groceries (40% organic).

Urban Organics

32 Splott Rd, **Splott**, Cardiff, Glamorgan, CF24 2DA (SA)
T: 02920 403399
e-mail: sales@urbanorganics.co.uk
website: www.urbanorganics.co.uk

Friendly 100% vegetarian organic shop selling local produce wherever possible. Operates local box delivery to **Cardiff** and surrounding area and has stall in Cardiff's monthly riverside community market.

CAMARTHENSHIRE

Cerdin Produce

The Clock Tower Market, **Newcastle Emlyn**, SA38 9AE
T: 01239 851371

Specialises in local organic produce. Stocks a wide range of Welsh farmhouse cheeses and dairy products (60% organic), their own unpasteurised butter, cream and milk, organic fruit and vegetables, and a wide range of organic wholefoods and groceries.

Eichyd Da

11 Broad St, **Llandovery**, SA20 0AR
T: 01550 720703

Healthfood shop (40% organic) range includes fruit and vegetables (100% organic), wholefoods, groceries, dairy, teas, coffees and juices, breads and babyfood.

CEREDIGION

Go Mango

4–5 Black Lion Mews, High St, **Cardigan**, SA43 1HJ
T: 01239 614727 F: 01239 613653

Wholefood shop (50% organic) selling wholefoods, groceries, dairy and breads plus 100% organic fruit and vegetables.

The Tree House

14 Baker St, **Aberystwyth**, SY23 2LJ (SA)
T: 01970 615 791
e-mail: james@treehouse12.freeserve.co.uk

Bright and friendly organic shop (90% organic) selling organic fruit and vegetables grown in their own market garden, Graig Farm Organics, **Dolau** (Powys) (Farm Shops) meat, fish, dairy, groceries and wholefoods, plus food to go – homemade soups, salads, pâté, quiches, cakes – made with all ingredients. Excellent restaurant serving almost exclusively organic food, at very reasonable prices. Open Mon–Sat daytime plus Thurs–Sat evenings.

GWYNEDD

Dimensions

15 Holyhead Rd, **Bangor**, LL57 2EG
T: 01248 351562

Wholefood shop selling over 2,000 lines (50% organic), including fruit and vegetables, groceries, wholefoods and dairy.

MONMOUTHSHIRE

Irma Fingal Rock

64 Monnow St, **Monmouth**, NP5 3EN
T: 01600 71372
e-mail: irmafinglarock@msn.com
website: www.rockwines.co.uk

Specialist wine and fine food shop stocking a small selection of organic wines and other produce, including local eggs from Little Mill Farm, **Newcastle** (Places to Eat and Stay), fresh vegetables to order every week, flours, olive oil, bread (every day) and cheeses.
See also:
Beanfreaks, **Newport**, under their **Cardiff** entry

PEMBROKESHIRE

Welsh Hook Meat Centre

Woodfield, Withybush Rd,
Haverfordwest, SA62 4BW (SA)
T: 01437 768876 F: 01437 768877
e-mail: ordering@welsh-organic-meat.co.uk
website: www.welsh-organic-meat.co.uk

Award-winning meat supplier. Shop sells all their meats. For full entry see p. **193**.

POWYS

The Quarry Shop

27 Maengwyn St, **Machynlleth**,
SY20 8EB
T: 01654 702339

Wholefood shop (75% organic) selling wholefoods, groceries and dairy. A few doors down from The Quarry Café (Places to Eat and Stay). Both run by Centre for Alternative Technology, **Machynlleth** (Specialist Providers).
Torfaen
See:
Beanfreaks, **Cwmbran**, under their Cardiff entry.

Wales – Farm Shops

CEREDIGION

John Savage

Glynhynod, Ffostrasol, **Llandysul**,
SA44 5JY (SA)
T: 01239 85528

One hundred per cent organic farm shop selling home-produced beef, lamb and pork, butter and dairy.

FLINTSHIRE

The Organic Stores

Brooklyn Farm, Sealand Rd, **Chester**,
CH5 2LQ (SA)
T/F: (shop): 01244 881209
T/F: (office): 01352 740075

Must-visit (though you may need wellies) 100% organic one-stop shop on Welsh border just outside Chester. Sells comprehensive range of organic foods, including fruit and vegetables, wholefoods, groceries, Graig Farm Organics, **Dolau** (Powys) (Farm Shops) meat, dairy, breads, juices, teas and coffees, and wines and beers by the case. Caters for specialist diets. Open Wed, Fri and Sat and at **Ruthin** market Thurs, all 9am– 6pm. Home delivery also.

MONMOUTHSHIRE

Medhope Organic Growers
Tintern, Chepstow, NP16 7NX (SA)
T: 01291 689797

Friendly farm shop and local box scheme (60% home-grown). Supplies either seasonal boxes or customer choice to **Chepstow**. One hundred per cent organic farm shop sells home-grown soft fruits and vegetables, dairy, groceries and homemade organic jams and preserves. Open every day except Mondays, Oct–April.

PEMBROKESHIRE

The Organic Farm Shop
186 Prendergast, **Haverfordwest**, SA61 2PQ (SA)
T: 01437 765040

One hundred per cent organic farm shop selling comprehensive range of organic foods, including home-grown vegetables and salads, fruit, own organic eggs, local organic cheeses, meat and chickens, plus organic groceries, wholefoods, special diet foods, frozen foods, wines and beers and eco-friendly household products.

Pencrugiau Organic Farm Shop
Crymych, SA41 3XH (SA)
T: 01239 881265

Small 100% organic farm shop selling mainly home-grown fruit and vegetables, herbs, and salads, plus locally produced organic eggs. Closed Wed–Sun in summer. Phone first in winter.

Pumpkin Shed Walled Garden
Llanunwas, **Solva**, SA62 6TU (Demeter)
T: 01437 721 949

Small shop selling biodynamic vegetables, herbs and soft fruits from the garden. Organic gardening queries freely answered. Gardening equipment sold.
See also:
Carfai Farm, **St David's** (Places to Eat and Stay)

POWYS

Graig Farm
Dolau, Llandrindod Wells, LD1 5TL (SA)
T: 01597 851655 F: 01597 851991
e-mail: sales@graigfarm.co.uk
website: www.graigfarm.co.uk

Well-stocked farm shop (including locally made organic beauty care products). One of the country's best-known organic meat suppliers and home delivery services (Graig Farm Organics). For full entry see p. **180**.
See also:
Primrose Organic Centre, **Felindre** (Box Schemes)
Presteigne Trout Farm, **Presteigne** (Specialist Providers)

Wales – Specialist Providers

ISLE OF ANGLESEY

Anglesey Sea Salt Co.
Brynsiencyn, LL61 6TQ (SA)
T: 01248 430871 F: 01248 430213
e-mail: enq@seasalt.co.uk
website: www.seasalt.co.uk

Producer of UK's only organic sea salt, Halen Mon. Visitors welcome – they also have a sea zoo. Salt may be purchased at their gift shop. See p. **311** for full entry.

CEREDIGION

Caws Cenarth
Fferm Glyneithinos, Pontseli, **Cenarth**, SA37 0LH (SA)
T: 01239 710432
e-mail: thelma.adams@virgin.net
website: www.cawscenarth.co.uk

Recently converted organic dairy. In 1997 the wonderful Thelma Adams led the revival of farmhouse Caerphilly and now makes three types of cheese from own milk, all suitable for vegetarians: Caerphilly (best Caerphilly at Royal Welsh Show 1998–2000) an award-winning Lancyth and a new, soft, brie-type, Perl Wen (White Pearl). The farm shop just sells own cheeses. Well worth a visit to watch cheese-making.
See also:
Capel Gwnda, **Llandysul** (cheese);
Penbryn Cheese, **Penbryn** (Farm Gate)

DENBIGHSHIRE

Abbey Fisheries
Eglevysen. **Llangollen**, LL20 8DD (SA)
T: 01978 860266

Catch your own organic fish or buy them from the lakeside shop. Also sells small fish to restock customers' organic trout projects.

MONMOUTHSHIRE

G. & P. Roser
Coleford Rd, **Tutshill**, Chepstow, NP6 7BN
T: 01291 622063

Widely acclaimed busy local butcher's (25% organic) selling high-quality meat including locally produced SA organic chickens from Pen-ucha'r-plwyf Farm, nr Usk, reared from slow growing breeds, fed home-grown organic wheat and killed at 14 weeks and also available at farm gate. Also organic beef, lamb and occasional pork.

Wye Valley Plants
The Nurtons, **Tintern**, NP16 7NX (SA)
T: 01291 689253

Organically produced potted plants, herbaceous perennials and herbs. Open all year round.

PEMBROKESHIRE

See:
Caerfai Farm, **St David's** (cheese) (Places to Stay and Eat)

POWYS

Bacheldre Watermill
Churchstoke, Montgomery, SY15 6TE (SA)
T: 01588 620489
e-mail:
jay@bacheldrewatermill.freeserve.co.uk
website: www.go2.co.uk/bacheldrewatermill

Award-winning, stoneground organic and other flours available through their shop and by mail order.

Centre for Alternative Technology
Machynlleth, SY20 9AZ (SA)
T: 01654 702400 F: 01654 702782
e-mail: help@catinfo.demon.co.uk
website: www.cat.org.uk

Internationally renowned environmental centre and tourist attraction. Run residential courses in organic agriculture and alternative technology. Restaurant on site (open to the residents and the public), serving vegetarian and vegan meals made with mostly home-grown organic ingredients. Also run The Quarry Café, **Machynlleth** (Places to Eat and Stay) and The Quarry Shop, **Machynlleth** (Shops)

Presteigne Trout Farm
The Old Leat, Boultingbrooke,
Presteigne, LD8 2BU (SA)
T: 01544 267085

Organic trout available at farm shop.

Wales – Places to Eat and Stay

CARMARTHENSHIRE
See:
Mount Pleasant Farm, **Llanwrda** (B & B List)

CEREDIGION
See:
The Tree House, **Aberystwyth** (Shops)
Broniwan, **Rhydlewis** (B&B list)

DENBIGHSHIRE
See:
Pentre Cerrig Mawr, **Maeshafn** (B&B list)

GWYNEDD

Panteidal Organic Restaurant with Rooms
Aberdyfi, LL35 0RG
T: 01654 767322
e-mail: office@panteidalorganics.co.uk
website: www.panteidalorganics.co.uk

A find. Organic farmhouse-cum-restaurant with rooms with its own spring water, nestling in its own tranquil wooded valley on the Dyfi estuary. Excellent menu for residents only features local organic foods, home-grown vegetables, salads and herbs and their own eggs. Evening meals only.

Pentre Bach
Llwyngwril, nr Dolgellau, LL37 2JU (not cert)
T: 01341 250294
e-mail: ws@pentrebach.com
website: www.pentrebach.com

Self-catering holiday cottages on organically maintained farm in southern Snowdonia. Home-grown fruit and vegetables, grown organically, and own free-range eggs available at farm gate.

Rhosfawr Nurseries
Rhosfawr, **Pwllheli**, LL53 6YA (SA)
T: 01766 8105645

Organic nursery, caravan and camping park. Vegetables from the nursery available on site during high season.

MONMOUTHSHIRE

Little Mill Farm
Newcastle, Monmouth, NP5 4NF (SA)
T: 01600 780449

Wildlife award-winning, organic, 17th-century farm offering bed and breakfast accommodation plus evening meals at weekend. Serves organic food, including home-produced meat, eggs, fruit and vegetables.

PEMBROKESHIRE

Caerfai Farm
St David's, SA62 6QT (SA)
T: 01437 720548
e-mail: wyn.evans@farming.co.uk
website: www.cawscaerfai.co.uk

Organic dairy farm, campsite and attractive, stone-built self-catering holiday cottages. Farm shop (40% organic) open during the high season, sells own organic, unpasteurised Cheddar, Caerphilly and Caerphilly with leeks and garlic cheeses, unpasteurised (green-top) milk and organic new potatoes, plus organic fruit and vegetables and wholefoods. Mail order and farm-gate sales of their cheeses, vacuum-packed if required.

Whitegates Farm

Little Haven, SA62 3LA (OF&G)
T: 01437 781552 F: 01437 781386
e-mail: mailto:welshhaven@aol.com
website: www.welshhaven.com

Situated in the Pembrokeshire National Park, overlooking the sea, well-known poultry producer (see Welsh Haven Products (Farm Gate)) offering organic bed and breakfast accommodation and gastronomic weekends and short breaks. Six pubs and restaurants within walking distance, including one fish restaurant.
See also:
The Old Rectory, **Castlemartin** (B & B List)

POWYS

Pickwick House

St Johns Rd, **Brecon** LD3 9DS
T: 01874 624322 F: 01874 624700
website: www.pickwick-house.brecon.co.uk

No smoking bed and breakfast accommodation serving organic and local foods with homemade bread baked daily. Walker-friendly with unsurpassed access to the Brecon Beacons and the Centre for Alternative Technology.

The Quarry Cafe

13 Maengwyn St, **Machynlleth**, SY20 8EB
T: 01654 702624

Vegetarian and vegan café serving teas and coffees, light meals and snacks using mainly organic ingredients run by Centre for Alternative Technology, **Machynlleth** (Specialist Providers).

WREXHAM

Fraser Cottage

High St, **Bangor-on-Dee**, LL13 0AU
T: 01978 781068

Vegan bed and breakfast serving organic breakfast, ideally situated for exploring the Welsh border towns and countryside.

Wales – Farm Gate

ISLE OF ANGLESEY

Plas Coedana Farm

Llanerchymedd, LL71 8AA (SA)
T: 01248 470378

Newly converted, acclaimed producer of champion, full flavour Welsh Black beef and organic lamb, sold fresh at the farm gate and at **Lancashire** and **Cheshire** farmers' markets.

BRIDGEND

Pencoed Organic Growers

Felindre Nurseries, **Felindre**, Pencoed, CF35 5HU (SA)
T: 01656 861956

Farm-gate sales of home-grown seasonal organic vegetables, salads and herbs, available as set-price boxes or select from a weekly list. Open throughout the year except May. Phone for a price list and for directions.

CARMARTHENSHIRE

Fronun Farm Organic Vegetables

Fronun, **Abergwili**, SA32 7EP (SA)
T: 01267 223979
e-mail: fronun@merlinshill.freeserve.co.uk

Small organic garden growing wide range of organic salads and vegetables available direct from the farm.

Llanboidy Farmhouse Cheesemakers

Cilowen Uchaf Farm, Login, **Whitland**, SA34 0TJ (SA)
T: 01994 448303
e-mail: suejones@llanboidycheesemakers.freeserve.co.uk
website: www.bestofruralwales.co.uk

Makes well-known Llanboidy and new Cilowen organic cheeses from Red Poll cow's milk. Cilowen cheese, softer than Cheddar but harder than Cheshire, has its unique characteristics. Farm-gate sales. Supplied mail order to private customers and direct to wholesalers nationwide. Phone before visiting or for list of stockists.

Maestroydden Fach

Harford, **Llandwda**, SA19 8DU (SA)
T: 01558 650774
website: www.naturalorganicmeats.co.uk

Farm-gate sales of organic Hereford beef and rare breed lamb. Available by the side, or by the cut. Also available nationwide mail order. Phone for brochure.

CEREDIGION

Capel Gwnda

Rhydlewis, **Llandysul**, SA44 5RN
T: 01239 851419
e-mail: cawsceltica@ukonline.co.uk
website: www.cawsceltica cheese.co.uk

Farm-gate sales of own Caws Celtica Lammas and traditional smoked sheep's-milk cheeses. Also available at local farmers' markets. Not certified organic, but sheep raised organically. Phone first.

Garthenor

Llanio Rd, **Tregaron**, SY25 6UR (SA)
T: 01270 493347

Farm-gate sales of home-produced organic eggs, vegetables, wool and lamb to order. Wool from the sheep is sold as uncarded fleece, knitting yarn or knitted into garments to order.

Lluest y Conscience

Trefenter, Aberystwyth, SY23 4HE (SA)
T: 01974 272218

Farm-gate sales of home-grown organic seasonal vegetables, top fruit and eggs. Please phone before visiting.

Penbryn Cheese

Ty Hen Farm, **Penbryn**, Sarnau, Llandysul, SA44 6RD (SA)
T: 01239 810347
e-mail: penbryn.cheese@talk21.com

Much-praised Penbryn unpasteurised, organic cheese, moist, mild and sweet when young, firm, dry and full-flavoured when ripe. Available direct from farm and throughout Wales and elsewhere at specialist cheese, organic and wholefood shops.

DENBIGHSHIRE

See:
Abbey Fisheries, **Llangollen** (Specialist Providers)

MONMOUTHSHIRE

A. D. & C. M. Holt-Wilson

Cefn Maen, **Raglan**, NP15 2HR (SA)
T: 01291 690428

Farm-gate sales of Kelly Bronze(TM) Golden Promise organic turkeys at Christmas. The birds are killed on the farm, dry plucked and hung for a minimum of 7 days to develop texture and flavour. Also available from local butchers.

PEMBROKESHIRE

Bumpylane Organic Rare Breeds

Shortlands Farm, Druidston, **Broad Haven**, SA62 3NE (SA)
T: 01437 781234
e-mail: sales@bumpylane.co.uk
website: www.bumpylane.co.uk

In picturesque location, unique organic meat producers specialising in rearing old British rare breeds, including Longhorn and White Park cattle, pigs and 6 different breeds of sheep. Meat available fresh, ready butchered, at the farm gate, through local farmers' markets and mail order. Limited availability, so please phone first. Small registered caravan and camping park. Good website.

Knock Farm Organics

Knock Farm, **Clarbeston Road**, SA63 4SL (SA)
T: 01437 731342

Registered with the Soil Association since 1987. Produces beef, lamb, pork, dry-air-cured bacon and hams, smoked cooked ham, poultry and eggs, sold at the farm gate. Meat butchered to customer requirements and sides or whole animals available for freezer. Ring to order your meat and arrange a collection date.

Welsh Haven Products

Whitegates Farm, **Little Haven**, SA63 3LA (OF&G)
T: 01437 781552 F: 01437 781386

Farm-gate and mail-order sales of organic chicken, turkey and duck.
See also:
Caerfai Farm, **St David's** (Places to Stay and Eat)

POWYS

Ann & Michael Moorhouse

Cefn Goleu, Pont Robert, **Meifod**, SY22 6JN (SA)
T: 01938 500128
e-mail: cefngoleuturkeys@btclick.com

Bronze and rare breeds organic Christmas turkeys (about 8, and the only UK organic producer to offer all of these), kept to exacting standards and ranging freely over their 15-acre holding, plus organic chicken eggs produced from small flocks, also totally free-ranging. Available at farm gate and in local shops.

Ty'n y Fedw

Hirnant, **Penybont Fawr**, SY10 0HS (SA)
T: 01691 870322
e-mail: martingpeck@gn.apc.org

Small organic farm supplying home-produced lamb and beef, available seasonally, ready butchered, from the farm gate. Limited availability, so please phone first.

Warren Farm
New Radnor, **Presteigne**, LD8 2TN (SA)
T: 01544 350407

Farm-gate sales of home-produced organic beef and lamb, available fresh by the side, ready butchered. Phone first to order and for directions.

VALE OF GLAMORGAN

Multiple Organics
Lake Farm Barns, St Athan Rd, **Cowbridge**, CF71 7HY (SA)
T: 01446 772964
e-mail: multipleorganics@btinternet.com

Specialist organic herb and wild flower growers, plus seeds, composts and plant feeds. Farm-gate sales and mail order.

ALASTAIR SAWDAY'S BED AND BREAKFAST LIST

The following bed and breakfasts have been selected by the editor of *Special Places to Stay: British Bed & Breakfast* (Alastair Sawday Publishing, £13.95). Many also serve dinner and feature on the website **www.specialplacestostay.com** along with many other European bed and breakfasts and hotels.
To buy a copy of *Special Places to Stay: British Bed & Breakfast* at the special price of £11.95 phone 01275 464891.

England East

ESSEX

Little Brockholds Farm
Radwinter, Saffron Walden, CB10 2TF
contacts: Anthony & Anne Wordsworth
T/F: 01799 599458
e-mail: as@brockholds99.freeserve.co.uk

NORFOLK

Highfield Farm
Great Ryburgh, nr Fakenham, NR21 7AL
contact: Elizabeth Savory
T: 01328 829249 F: 01328 829422
See also 'Farm Gate'
Manor Farm Barn, **Tatterford**, nr Fakenham, NR21 7AZ
contacts: Michael & Jane Davidson-Houston
T: 01485 528393

England East Midlands

DERBYSHIRE

Mount Tabor House
Bowns Hill, **Crich**, DE4 5DG
contact: Fay & Steve Whitehead
T: 01773 857008
e-mail: mountabor@email.msn.com

England North East

NORTHUMBERLAND

High Buston Hall
High Buston, Alnmouth, NE66 3QH
contacts: Ian & Therese Atherton
T: 01665 830606 F: 01665 830707
e-mail: highbuston@aol.com

YORKSHIRE NORTH

Potto Grange
Potto, nr Northallerton, DL6 3HH
contacts: Major & Mrs Julian Kynge
T: 01642 700212 F: 01642 700978

England North West

CUMBRIA

Low Fell
Ferney Green,
Bowness-on-Windermere, LA23 3ES
contact: Louise & Steve Broughton
T: 01539 445612 F: 01539 448411
e-mail: lowfell@talk21.com

England South and South East

SUSSEX EAST

Little Orchard House
West St, **Rye**, TN31 7ES
contact: Sara Brinkhurst
T/F: 01797 223831

England South West

CORNWALL

The Old Rectory
Mawgan, Helston, TR12 6AD
contact: Susan Leith
T: 01326 221261 F: 01326 221797
e-mail: leith@euphony.net

Penellick
Pelynt, nr Looe, PL13 2LX
contact: Michael and Ann Macartney
T/F: 01503 272372
e-mail: penellick@hotmail.com

DEVON

Easdon Cottage
Long Lane, **Manaton**, TQ13 9XB
contacts: Liza & Hugh Dagnall
T/F: 01647 221389

Fay Down
Upton, Collompton, EX15 1RA
T/F: 01884 33097
e-mail: stay@manorhill.demon.co.uk

Manor Mill House
Bampton, EX16 9LP
contacts: Chris & Kathy Ayres
T: 01398 332211 F: 01398 332009
e-mail: stay@manormill.demon.co.uk

Mount Tavy Cottage
Tavistock, PL19 9JL
contacts: Mr & Mrs G. H. Moule
T: 01822 614253

Woodhayne Barton
Culmstock, EX15 3JG
contacts: Roger & Charlotte Horne
T: 01884 840708 F: 01884 841479
e-mail:
rogercharlotte@hornewoodhayne.demon.co.uk

The Yeoman's Country House
Collaton, Salcombe, TQ7 3DJ
contact: Mark Andrews
T: 01548 560085 F: 01548 562070
e-mail: yeomanshouse@easicom.com

DORSET

The Old Forge
Fanners Yard, **Compton Abbas**,
Shaftesbury, SP7 0NQ
contact: Tim & Lucy Kerridge
T/F: 01747 811881
e-mail: theoldforge@hotmail.com

GLOUCESTERSHIRE

Grove Farm
Bullo Pill, **Newnham**, GL14 1DZ
contacts: Penny & David Hill
T/F: 01594 516304

SOMERSET

Lower Farm
Shepton Montague, Wincanton, BA9 8JG
contacts: Charles & Susie Dowding
T: 01749 812253
e-mail: susiedowding@netscapeonline.co.uk

Parsonage Farm
Over Stowey, Bridgwater, TA5 1HA
contact: Susan Lilienthal
T: 01278 733237 F: 01278 733511

WILTSHIRE

Bullocks Horn Cottage
Charlton, Malmesbury, SN16 9DZ
contacts: Colin & Liz Legge
T: 01666 577600 F: 01666 577905
e-mail: legge@bullockshorn.clara.co.uk

Ebblesway Courtyard
High Rd, Broadchalke, **Salisbury**, SP5 5EF
contacts: Gail & Peter Smalley
T: 01722 780182 F: 01722 780482
e-mail: enquiries@ebbleswaycourtyard.co.uk

England West Midlands

HEREFORDSHIRE

Lower Bache House
Kimbolton, nr Leominster, HR6 0ER
contacts: Rose & Leslie Wiles
T: 01568 750304
e-mail: leslie.wiles@care4free.net

WARWICKSHIRE

Glebe Farm House
Loxley, Stratford-upon-Avon, CV35 9JW
contact: Ms Kate McGovern
T/F: 01789 842501
e-mail: scorpiolimited@msn.com
See also Glebe Farm House (restaurant), **Loxley** (Places to Eat and Stay).

The Hare on the Park
3 Emscote Rd, **Warwick**, CV34 4PH
contact: Prue Hardwick
T: 01926 491366
e-mail: pruespost@tesco.net

Winton House
The Green, **Upper Quinton**, Stratford-upon-Avon, CV37 8SX
contact: Gail Lyon
T: 01789 720500
T: (mobile): 07831 485483
e-mail: gail@wintonhouse.com
website: www.wintonhouse.com

WORCESTERSHIRE

The Mill
Snowshill Rd, **Broadway**, WR12 7JS
contacts: Hugh & Ann Verney
T: 01386 858298

Scotland

BORDERS

Over Langshaw Farm
Galashiels, TD1 2PE
contacts: Sheila & Martyn Bergius
T: 01896 860244

HIGHLAND

Druimgrianach
Cuil Bay, **Cuil**, Duror, PA38 4DA
contacts: Bridget & Hugh Allen
T: 01631 740286

Geddes House
Nairn, Inverness, IV12 5QX
contacts: Elizabeth & Jamie Mackintosh-Walker
T: 01667 452241 F: 01667 456707
e-mail: elizabeth@geddes55.freeserve.co.uk

Lyndale House
Edinbane, Isle of Skye, IV51 9PX
contact: Mr & Mrs M. F. Ridsdill-Smith
T: 01470 582329
e-mail: linda@lyndale.free-online.co.uk

STIRLINGSHIRE

Mackeanston House
Doune, Trossachs, FK16 6AX
contacts: Fiona & Colin Graham
T: 01786 850213 F: 01786 850414
e-mail: mackean.house@cwcom.net

Wales

CARMARTHENSHIRE

Mount Pleasant Farm
Llanwrda, SA19 8AN
contact: Sue & Nick Thompson
T: 01550 777537/777877 F: 01550 777537
e-mail: rivarevival@aol.com

CEREDIGION

Broniwan
Rhydlewis, Llandysul, SA44 5PF
contacts: Carole & Allen Jacobs
T/F: 01239 851261
e-mail: broniwan@compuserve.com

DENBIGHSHIRE

Pentre Cerrig Mawr
Maeshafn, nr Mold, CH7 5LU
contacts: Charmian & Ted Spencer
T/F: 01352 810607
e-mail: pentre.cerrig@virgin.net

PEMBROKESHIRE

The Old Rectory
Castlemartin, SA71 5HW
contacts: Christopher & Emma Younghusband
T/F: 01646 661677

ACKNOWLEDGEMENTS

Writing this book has been a Herculean task. Once again, it would not have been possible without the help, advice, good will and generosity of many special people, both professional colleagues and some very dear friends.

I should firstly like to thank my publishers Fourth Estate, and my editor Louise Haines and her assistants, Mitzi Angel and Kate Balmforth, for their support, patience and consideration throughout. The burden on them has been considerable, and I am profoundly grateful to them for pulling me through. For Kate's cheerfulness, and for wading through umpteen mountains of paper, my special thanks. For Louise, my love, especially for the pep talks. I owe a special debt of gratitude, too, to my copy editor Sue Phillpott, for her meticulous care and thoroughness, and for taming the beast a second time with such amazingly good grace; and for Carol Anderson for her stalwart work and careful checking of the Directory.

I owe a similar debt of gratitude to my researcher, Jane Faulkes, who worked night and day researching and compiling the Directory. For all her hard work, diligence, unfailing good humour and unstinting co-operation, my most profound thanks: we'll know better next time.

I should secondly like to offer my sincere thanks to various people for providing research material and professional guidance. Dr Elaine Ingham, an authority on soils, inspired me especially and I should like to thank her for allowing me to use much of her own material and for reading through the section on soils. Also Dr Stefan Bergleiter of Naturland, Francis Blake, Dan Bromage, Dennis Overton, Nigel Woodhouse, Marine Stewardship Council (fish); Peter Crofts, UKROFS, Rob Haward, Peter Hall and Lois Philips at Elm Farm Research Centre (pesticides allowed in organic farming); Prof. Jules Pretty (cost of organic farming); Peter Segger (organic food quality, vegetables and fruit); Prof. Tim O'Riordan (organic landscapes); Gundula Meziani (bio-diversity); Richard Young (antibiotics); Robert Kennard (abattoirs); Francis Blake, Alex Starcey-Satton, UKROFS (standards); Catherine Fookes, Sustain (Organic Targets Bill); Craig Sams (organic health, cost of organic food, and most other things organic, too); Compassion in World Farming Trust (animal welfare, nitrogen pollution); Martin

Cunningham (organic statistics); Pat Coleman-Taylor and Carol Charlton (organic catering standards); Sally Bagenal (organic milk); Robert Duxbury, the RSPCA Freedom Foods, NFU (organic chickens); Gill Lowy, Fiona Gately, Clare Marriage, Andrew Whitely (organic bread and flour), Charles Peers (organic eggs); Mark Bosworth (organic sugar); Dom Lane (Organic Food Awards); Steve Christopher (organic beer), Lance Pigott (organic wines); Jim Thomas, Greenpeace (GM foods); Adrian Bebb (GM animal feeds); Paul Behaim (hemp); John and Jan Belleme (miso); Ian Richardson (juicers); Chris Dawson, Eric Vagniez (sea vegetables); Chris Maguire (wheat grass); Green People Company Viridian, Karen Booth at Blackmores UK (superfoods, juice recipes); James Armstrong at Waitrose and Laura Ampoah and Nikki Martin at Sainsbury.

I should thirdly like to pay a very warm tribute to the staff at the Soil Association for their knowledge freely given, and especially for being so willing, whatever the query. For Francis Blake and Rob Haward, for their considerable help, my special thanks.

For allowing me to draw on material previously published for Organic Living, my most sincere gratitude and thanks to Dorling Kindersley. Similarly to YOU magazine and Waitrose Food Illustrated. My thanks also to Peter Beaumont, Jon and Jan Belleme, Joana Blythman (Guardian), Tim Finney, Dr Vyvyan Howard, Dr Jean Munro, Prof. David Pimentel, Rachel Rowlands, Craig Sams, and Andrew Whitley for providing me with additional quotes; the Fairtrade Foundation for their list of fairtrade and organic products; to the Danish Ministry of Agriculture; and to the Soil Association for allowing me to use their material, in particular the Organic Food and Farming report; principles of organic agriculture; bio-diversity benefits of organic farming; and list of permitted additives.

The quote at the beginning of the book came from the New Zealand Wild Honey Company brochure. Two years ago I visited New Zealand. Space did not permit me to acknowledge all those who gave me help then, but I should like to do so now. My thanks, too, to all the various organisations, producers, wholesalers and manufacturers I have talked to who have answered queries and supplied literature; and to Simon Wright and Lizzie Vann for their support. *The Handbook of Organic Food Processing and Production* (2nd edition) published by Blackwell Science, edited by Simon Wright and Diane McCrea (available from www.organic-consultancy.com) has been a valuable resource, as has the Soil Association's own excellent magazine, Living Earth.

For Renée Elliot, a long overdue acknowledgement: my heartfelt thanks (and congratulations) and hope you thought it was worth it. For my agent, Rosemary Scoular, for her common sense, gentle disposition and professional guidance, my affectionate thanks. What on earth did I do without you?

On a personal level, words could never adequately describe my profound gratitude for those who have helped me in so many ways with their kindness. Why they bother, I don't know, but I shall be forever grateful that they did: For Catey, who made the sun shine when all seemed dark and with whom life is always bright; for Joanna, who is always there and one of the best friends a girl could have; for Louise, for her quiet good sense and caring; for Nigel for his sense of humour and everything else; for Christiane, for her love; and for their care and for continuing to work their magic, my respect and most affectionate thanks to Sigyta Hart at the Clinic of Chinese Medicine in Goring, and Fiona Marsden and Jerome Poupel at the House of Good Health in Henley-on-Thames.

Finally, for Rick, who as usual had to suffer the endless squawks and traumas, and who looked after me so nicely when things got extra tough, my very special love. As I keep saying, I really do promise to do better next time.

INDEX